THE CHEMISTRY OF
PLANT GUMS
AND MUCILAGES

AND SOME RELATED POLYSACCHARIDES

F. SMITH

Professor, Institute of Agriculture
University of Minnesota, St. Paul, Minnesota

R. MONTGOMERY

Associate Professor, Department of Biochemistry
State University of Iowa, Iowa City, Iowa

American Chemical Society
Monograph Series

REINHOLD PUBLISHING CORPORATION
NEW YORK

CHAPMAN & HALL, LTD., LONDON

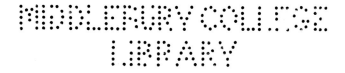

Library of Congress Catalog Card Number: 59-12533

Printed in U.S.A. by
THE GUINN CO., INC.
New York 1, N. Y.

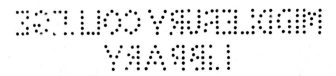

*Videme moderno tempore multos lapides
virtutibus olim sibi attributis deficere.*

*"We now see that many stones lack the
virtues formerly attributed to them."*

PETRUS GARSIAS EPISCOPUS

GENERAL INTRODUCTION

American Chemical Society's Series of Chemical Monographs

By arrangement with the Interallied Conference of Pure and Applied Chemistry, which met in London and Brussels in July, 1919, the American Chemical Society was to undertake the production and publication of Scientific and Technologic Monographs on chemical subjects. At the same time it was agreed that the National Research Council, in cooperation with the American Chemical Society and the American Physical Society, should undertake the production and publication of Critical Tables of Chemical and Physical Constants. The American Chemical Society and the National Research Council mutually agreed to care for these two fields of chemical progress. The American Chemical Society named as Trustees, to make the necessary arrangements of the publication of the Monographs, Charles L. Parsons, secretary of the Society, Washington, D. C.; the late John E. Teeple, then treasurer of the Society, New York; and the late Professor Gellert Alleman of Swarthmore College. The Trustees arranged for the publication of the ACS Series of (a) Scientific and (b) Technological Monographs by the Chemical Catalog Company, Inc. (Reinhold Publishing Corporation, successor) of New York.

The Council of the American Chemical Society, acting through its Committee on National Policy, appointed editors (the present list of whom appears at the close of this sketch) to select authors of competent authority in their respective fields and to consider critically the manuscripts submitted.

The first Monograph of the Series appeared in 1921. After twenty-three years of experience certain modifications of general policy were indicated. In the beginning there still remained from the preceding five decades a distinct though arbitrary differentiation between so-called "pure science" publications and technologic or applied science literature. By 1944 this differentiation was fast becoming nebulous. Research in private enterprise had grown apace and not a little of it was pursued on the frontiers of knowledge. Furthermore, most workers in the sciences were coming to see the artificiality of the separation. The methods of both groups of workers are the same. They employ the same instrumentalities, and frankly recognize that their objectives are common, namely, the search for new knowledge for the service of man. The officers of the Society therefore combined the two editorial Boards in a single Board of twelve representative members.

Also in the beginning of the Series, it seemed expedient to construe rather broadly the definition of a Monograph. Needs of workers had to be recognized. Consequently among the first hundred Monographs appeared works in the form of treatises covering in some instances rather broad areas. Because such necessary works do not now want for publishers, it is considered advisable to hew more strictly to the line of the Monograph character, which means more complete and critical treatment of relatively restricted areas, and, where a broader field needs coverage, to subdivide it into logical subareas. The prodigious expansion of new knowledge makes such a change desirable.

These Monographs are intended to serve two principal purposes: first, to make available to chemists a thorough treatment of a selected area in form usable by persons working in more or less unrelated fields to the end that they may correlate their own work with a larger area of physical science discipline; second, to stimulate further research in the specific field treated. To implement this purpose the authors of Monographs are expected to give extended references to the literature. Where the literature is of such volume that a complete bibliography is impracticable, the authors are expected to append a list of references critically selected on the basis of their relative importance and significance.

PREFACE

Plant gums and mucilages have been known and in use since very early times, reference being made to·them in the Bible; and they seem to have been of commercial value for several thousand years, especially in India, Asia, Africa, Australia, and China. These natural products were later exported to Europe where their use in industry has never ceased to expand. They were used as food by the natives of Africa, Asia, India and Australia as far back as historical records go. The use of the seaweed gums by the natives of the coastal regions of France, Wales, Ireland, Scotland and Scandinavia in food and in medicinal preparations represents an art whose origin cannot be traced.[1]

The word "gum" was probably applied originally to plant exudates, which thickened and hardened on exposure to air. For this reason it had been applied to the water-insoluble resins as well as to the gums proper, which either imbibe or dissolve in water.[2] One of the earliest uses of the word was by Herodotus about 450 B.C., who recorded that the embalmers in Egypt used gum rather than glue for coating the linen in which corpses were clothed. Herodotus uses the word κομμι, from which gum is derived, and it should be noted that this is a foreign and not a native Greek word.

In spite of the tremendous quantity of gums and mucilages employed in industry, a real insight into the chemistry of these substances has been obtained only during the last twenty or thirty years. It is, therefore, not surprising to find even at the present time that the use of gums and mucilages is indeed much more of an art than a science, although certain empirical scientific controls have been employed in the industrial use of gums.

In general, the gums and mucilages were, and still are, used either as they are found in nature or as aqueous extracts of parts of plants. The utilization of these complicated polysaccharide polymers is clearly at the very beginnings of what will eventually come to pass when their chemistry is more fully understood. Modifications and numerous derivatives of gums will be made in ever-increasing numbers in the not too distant future, so that a more extensive and efficient use may be made of these raw materials.

The chemistry of gums and mucilages has been reviewed (2-7) from time to time, but there is no comprehensive treatise on the subject. An attempt is made herein to bring together what is known of the chemistry of plant gums and mucilages, to indicate some of the procedures that may be adopted for studying these and other polysaccharides to stimulate new researches in what can only be described as a fascinating field of organic chemistry, and also to promote new ideas for their industrial application. A brief consideration of the vast petrochemical industry that has arisen from the study of the fundamental chemistry of aliphatic and aromatic compounds will indicate something of the future possibilities of carbohydrate chemistry as it applies to polysaccharide gums and other related carbohydrate polymers. It is hoped that this work will be of some interest to those investigating the chemistry of gums and mucilages and to those engaged in their industrial use.

Acknowledgment. The authors are grateful to Dr. R. S. Tipson of the Bureau of Standards, Washington, D. C. who read the manuscript and offered many valuable suggestions and to Dr. Betty Lewis of the Department of Agricultural Biochemistry, University of Minnesota, for assistance in checking the manuscript and in compiling Appendix II.

1. Chapman, V. J., "Seaweeds and Their Uses," Methuen and Co., Ltd., London, 1950.
2. Robinson, H. H., "On the Present Position of the Chemistry of the Gums," *Rept. Brit. Assoc. for Adv. of Sci.*, 227 (1906).
3. Norman, A. G., "The Biochemistry of Cellulose, the Polyuronides, Lignin, etc." Clarendon Press, Oxford, 1937.
4. Jones, J. K. N., and Smith, F., *Advances in Carbohydrate Chem.*, 4, 243 (1949).
5. Mantell, C. L., "The Water-Soluble Gums," Reinhold Publishing Corp., New York, 1947.
6. Whistler, R. L., and Smart, C. L., "Polysaccharide Chemistry," Academic Press, Inc., New York, 1953.
7. Parry, E. J., "Gums and Resins," Isaac Pitman and Sons, New York, 1918.

F. SMITH
R. MONTGOMERY

St. Paul, Minn.
Iowa City, Iowa
October, 1959

CONTENTS

CHAPTER 1

FUNCTION AND ORIGIN OF GUMS

Gum Exudates

Gum exudates are produced by a surprisingly large number of plants. Exposed to the air and allowed to dry, the exudates form clear, glassy masses which are usually colored from dark brown to pale yellow. It is seldom that colorless exudates are encountered, although some samples of gum tragacanth are almost white. Various parts of the plant may secrete gum. In some cases, the secretion is hardly discernible, but in others, such as the trees producing commercial gums, copious quantities are produced

More than a hundred species of *Acacia* of the *Leguminosae* family produce gums (1), some of them in such large amounts that the supply supports a world-wide industrial market. Gums are also secreted by a number of species of *Astragalus*, which provide the hitherto highly valued gum tragacanth. Likewise, many species of *Prunus* produce gums in large amounts, but they do not seem to be valued as highly as the others mentioned above. Similar gum exudates are produced by the genera *Albizzia, Banhinia, Caesalpinia, Ceratonia,* and *Pithecolobium.* The plant families *Anacardiaceae, Combretaceae, Meliaceae, Rosaceae* and *Rutaceae* are also known for their capacity for producing gums (30).

There is no agreement as to the origin of gum exudates. Some subscribe to the theory (1,2) that they are a product of normal plant metabolism, while others suggest that they arise from a pathological condition. Some evidence favors the latter view, for it has been recognized that healthy *Acacia* trees, grown under favorable conditions of moisture, soil and temperature, do not produce any gum; when grown under the adverse conditions offered by high elevation, heat and lack of moisture, the secretion of gum is favored (3). The gums are thought by others to be formed as a result of an infection of the plant by micro-organisms (4). The plant is believed to synthesize the gum exudates in order to seal off the infected section of the plant and prevent further invasion of the tissue (5–8). It is not yet clear whether the carbohydrate gums are formed at the site of the injury or whether they are generated elsewhere in the plant and then transported to the injured site.

The phenomenon of gum production has also been attributed to fungus growth on the plant with the liberation of fungal enzymes which then proceed to synthesize the complex polysaccharide gums.

It is of interest to note that certain fungi contain enzymes which convert gums into their component sugars. For example, the parasite *Stereum purpureum*, which causes a disease (lead disease), induces plum trees to produce a considerable amount of gum at the place where the parasite grows (6). Lutz (9,10) has proceeded from this observation and claims that the *Stereum purpureum* fungus has a slow but definite hydrolytic action on cherry gum and that the component sugars are generated. The fungus *Asterula gummipara* Vuill., isolated from the trunks of *Acacia verek*, completely liquefied cherry gum in three months. Other fungi, such as, *Xanthochrous hispidus*, *Polyporus sulfureus*, and *Coriolus versicolor* had no effect on cherry gum.

In this connection it is to be noted that an enzyme extracted from *Turbo cornutus* is capable of hydrolyzing the seaweed gum obtained from *Chondrus ocellatus*, while agar and carrageenin are hydrolyzed by the organism *Bacillus gelaticus* found in sea water. Similarly, the mucilage found in the root of *Hydrangea paniculata* is cleaved by *Bacillus mesentericus vulgatus*. An organism growing on rotting agar has recently been shown to secrete an enzyme which hydrolyzes agar to give a disaccharide, neoagarobiose.

In certain cases, gum formation by *Acacia* trees has been attributed to the action of bacteria (3,11). However, no one appears to have succeeded beyond doubt in stimulating gum formation in *Acacia* trees by inoculation, although it has been reported that inoculation of peach trees with *Bacterium acaciae* isolated from the exudate of *A. binervata* trees produced gummosis (12). Such an achievement as this would be important not only scientifically, but also from a commercial standpoint; this possibility should be examined. The gums are evidently produced in greatest quantity by injured trees, growing under unfavorable conditions, namely, at elevated, hot and dry locations. The theory that gum exudation is caused by infection of the trees is not supported by the observation that *Acacia* trees continue to survive and indeed propagate, even though they are supposed to be diseased and are growing under unfavorable climatic conditions. More recently it has been reported (31) that gum formation can be produced by the injection of ascorbic acid into the culms of *Arundo donax* and *Phalaris tuberosa*.

The most likely function of gum formation is that the tree produces the gum in order to seal off the injured parts, not so much to prevent infection, but to prevent loss of moisture (13–16). Some support for this is forthcoming from the fact that gum tragacanth is produced by what can only be assumed to be healthy trees immediately after mechanical injury.

Whatever the exact origin and mode of formation of the gums may be, it is reasonable to believe that gum exudates are formed by some type of enzymic polymerization and not by direct chemical polymerization. If this is so, it is quite likely that the gums would contain entrapped enzymes that have escaped inactivation, since they are in close contact with the product elaborated and, under suitable conditions, these stranded enzymes would be capable of hydrolyzing the gums originally synthesized. There are numerous analogous examples which support this contention. For example, the enzymes which synthesize starch have been found in plants in contact with the synthetic polymer (starch) and after isolation they have been shown to be capable of reversing the synthetic polymerization and converting starch into α-D-glucosyl-phosphate in the presence of excess inorganic phosphate (17).

It was claimed long ago that cherry gum will undergo slow autolysis to give a mixture of reducing sugars (18) and that the enzyme present in cherry gum will hydrolyze plum gum but not gum arabic.

In refuting an earlier claim by Kosman (19) that an enzyme present in foxglove leaves was capable of hydrolyzing gum arabic, Reinitzer stated (20) that an enzyme capable of fermenting gum arabic was present only in gum arabic itself, cherry gum, a few of the rarer gums, and various stone fruits. Other investigators (21) disagreed, but relatively recently Lutz (22) has expressed the view that plant gums contain an enzyme which is capable of effecting autolysis under aseptic conditions. This is a point of considerable interest and should be investigated further.

A more recent viewpoint is that the stability of gum solutions to autolysis may be due to the presence of peroxidases which inactivate the degrading enzymes (23).

Another interesting feature, perhaps fortuitous, is that the gum exudates, such as those produced by the *Acacia* and mesquite trees, are chemically and structurally related to the pneumococcus polysaccharides which encapsulate and protect the pneumococcus organisms. These capsular polysaccharides are known to offer protection to the pneumococcus organisms and it is not unlikely that the injured trees produce gum, which acts in much the same manner as the capsular polysaccharide.

Gums and mucilages are said by some to arise from starch (25,26) while others suggest that they are produced at the expense of cellulose or hydrocellulose (27). The finding of traces of pentose oligosaccharides in certain gums has been taken to indicate their function as intermediate enzymic substrates in the synthesis of the gums (23). There seems to be no evidence which will enable this question to be decided at the present time. Perhaps some progress could be made if investigations were carried out into the relationship between the composition and structure of the gum and of the simple carbohydrates and carbohydrate polymers in various parts of the tree.

It is claimed that a histochemical examination of the gum exudations of the cherry (*Prunus cerasus*) tree indicates that the material first formed is composed entirely of hexoses. Afterwards the outer surfaces of the gum granule show the presence of uronic acid and pentoses. In none of these stages of exudation were the cell walls implicated in the gum formation which was claimed to be a "deviation" from normal metabolism (32).

Another interesting observation made recently in this connection (24) is that all the neutral sugars in plum gum are indeed present in the tissue of the tree in the free state. The D-glucuronic acid appears in the fruit just before gummosis occurs. It was further noted that the concentration of glucuronic acid in the mesocarp tissue was higher near the site of gummosis than at places farther removed from the site of gum formation. One other significant fact emerged, namely, that D-glucuronolactone is a good substrate for tissue regeneration and that its metabolism does not result in the formation of xylose; from this it has been tentatively deduced that pentoses do not arise from uronic acids by a process of decarboxylation.

The origin of the gum exudates represents a fascinating and challenging problem. The solution to it, coupled with the determination of the relationship between the various gum polysaccharides and the pneumococcus capsular polysaccharide would be of great value scientifically and might lead to the development of a synthetic vaccine for combatting pneumonia (28).

Plant Mucilages

What we have said thus far has been concerned with the gum exudates produced by trees that have not been intentionally injured, although they have been cultivated under unfavorable conditions. The so-called vegetable mucilages, which appear to have a much less complicated structure, are derived from the bark, roots, leaves, seeds, and in some cases, the flowers of the plants (7). They are products of normal plant metabolism and may serve as food reserves (14,29) in much the same manner as starch in many plants and glycogen in animals. The mucilages may arise from starch (25,26) and, in certain plants at least, they seem to act, as do the polysaccharides in succulent plants, (*Aloe, Euphorbiaceae*), as agents for holding water (13–15).

Gum tragacanth is exuded from the stems and roots of the *Astragalus* trees immediately after incisions are made. This highly valued commercial gum is generated within the plant (13) at certain times of the year and, as it exudes, water is absorbed from the surrounding tissues. The gum eventually congeals and blocks the incision in much the same way that coagulated blood seals off a wound.

The fact that gum tragacanth is generated immediately after incisions are made in the bark of the tree leads to the view that the gum is already present in the tree, but in spite of this it does not appear to have been proved by sectioning and extracting to see what part of the tree generates the gum. Unlike the *Acacia* gums, gum tragacanth usually contains starch granules that were present in the plant cellular material.

An excellent source of mucilages composed of neutral sugar residues are the seeds of many *Leguminosae* such as the locust bean or carob bean (*Ceratonia siliqua* L.), guar (*Cyamopsis tetragonolobus*), Kentucky coffee bean *Gymnocladus dioica*), honey locust (*Gleditsia tricanthos*), and many others (see Tables II and III). Palm seeds also provide a neutral mucilaginous polysaccharide.

The seeds, especially those of the *Leguminosae*, are usually hard and some, for example the carob and Kentucky coffee beans, require considerable force to break them. The gum or mucilage is found as a hard vitreous layer on the inside of the seed coat. It can be removed either by a milling process, as is the case with the guar seed, or more efficiently but slowly, as in the case of the Kentucky coffee bean, by soaking the broken seeds in water to allow the mucilaginous material to swell, after which it can be mechanically removed.

Carob seed or locust bean gum is a valuable commercial gum in the food, textile, printing and ore-refining industries. Guar gum, another excellent seed mucilage, is also becoming an important commercial commodity and like carob gum, it can be used in place of the more expensive, though usually superior, gum tragacanth. The popularity of tamarind seed (*Tamarindus indica*) gum for industrial use is also growing. The consumption of these readily accessible, easily harvested, and cheaper gums is likely to continue to increase at the expense of gum tragacanth, except for specialized items.

Root Mucilages

The roots of certain plants such as Iles mannan (*Amorphophallus oncophyllus*) and konjak mannan (*A. konjak*), contain a polysaccharide which may be extracted with hot water or dilute alkali to give excellent mucilages that are useful in the paper and rubber latex industries. They are likewise normal metabolic products as is the mucilage extracted

Figure 1. Map showing the origin of the more important vegetable gums (1). 1. Gum arabic (*Acacia senegal* Willd.) 2. Other *Acacia* gums 3. Gum tragacanth (*Astragalus* Sp.) 4. Karaya gum or Indian tragacanth (*Sterculia urens* Roxb.) 5. Carob (locust) bean (*Ceratonia siliqua* L.) gum 6. Kutira (*Cochlospermum gossypium* DC) gum 7. Ghatti (*Anogeissus latifolia* Wall.) gum 8. Angico (*Piptadenia* Sp.) gum 9. Mesquite (*Prosopis juliflora* DC) gum 10. Guar (*Cyamopsis tetragonolobus*) gum 11. Iles mannan (from *Amorphophallus oncophyllus*) 12. Seaweed gums (Agar, carrageenin, algin, etc.) 13. Konjak mannan (from *Amorphophallus konjak*) Adopted from "Vegetable Gums and Resins," by F. N. Howes, published by Chronica Botanica Company, Waltham, Mass., 1949.

from asparagus roots which is reported to be of superior quality as far as viscosity is concerned.

Seaweed Gums or Mucilages

Although these substances have long been in use by people of the coastal areas of the world, only agar, a complex polysaccharide mixture produced almost exclusively by the Japanese from a variety of sea weeds by a somewhat lengthy and not well-understood extraction process, has occupied a permanent position as a commercial product of world-wide significance. In recent years, however, other sea-weeds have been examined and as a result two additional products, algin, a polygulurono-mannuronic acid and carrageenin, a polyanhydrogalactosylgalactose sulfate, are being produced in quantity in Europe and North America for use in the food, textile, metallurgical, and other industries. The uses of these two products are expanding rapidly.

It is of some interest to note the origin of the more important commercial vegetable gums (see Figure 1) (1). The greatest production of gums which have to be collected by hand is to be found in those regions where labor is cheap. Even where hand labor is expensive, commercial development of certain gums becomes possible when mechanical devices can be used for harvesting the plants or plant products. Thus, sea-weed gums are being extracted in Europe and North America and guar gum is being produced on a small scale from beans grown in the United States where the seeds can be mechanically harvested and milled.

REFERENCES

1. Howes, F. N., "Vegetable Gums and Resins," Chronica Botanica Co., Waltham, Mass. (1949).
2. Malcolm, D. W., "Report on Gum and Gum Arabic" (Dar es Salaam, Gov. Printer) 1936.
3. Blunt, H. S., "Gum Arabic with Special Reference to its Production in the Sudan," London, Oxford Univ. Press (1926).
4. Thaysen, A. C., and Bunker, H. J., "The Microbiology of Cellulose, Hemicellulose, Pectin and Gums." London, Oxford Univ. Press (1927).
5. Frank, H. B., Ann. Agronom., 11, 86 (1885); Brit. Chem. Abstracts, 48, 684 (1885).
6. Brooks, F. T., New Phytologist, 27, 85 (1928).
7. Jones, J. K. N., and Smith, F., "Advances in Carbohydrate Chem.," 4, 243 (1949).
8. Swarbrick, T., J. Pomology Hort. Sci., 6, 137 (1927).
9. Lutz, L., Ann. pharm. franc., 3, 58 (1945).
10. Lutz, L., Compt. rend., 218, 766 (1944).
11. Greig-Smith, R., Proc. Linn. Soc., N. S. Wales, 27, 383 (1902); 28, 541 (1903); 29, 217 (1904).
12. Greig-Smith, R., Proc. Linn. Soc., N. S. Wales, 28, 114 (1903).

13. Stewart, E. G., *Bull Torrey Botan. Club*, **46**, No. 5, 157 (1919); *Expt. Sta. Record*, **43**, 226; *Chem. Abstracts*, **15**, 2898 (1921).
14. Montemartini, L., *Lavori ist. botan. Palermo*, **5**, 45 (1934).
15. McNair, J. B., *Am. J. Botany*, **19**, 168 (1932).
16. Rae, J., *Pharm. J.*, **151**, 241 (1943).
17. Barker, S. A., and Bourne, E. J., *Quart. Rev. (London)*, **7**, 56 (1953).
18. Garros, F., *J. Pharm.*, [5], **26**, 535 (1893); *Brit. Chem. Abstracts*, **64**, 180 (1893).
19. Kosmann, C., *Bull. soc. chim.*, **27**, 246 (1877); *Brit. Chem. Abstracts*, **32**, 876 (1877).
20. Reinitzer, F., *Z. physiol. Chem.*, **14**, 453 (1890); *Brit. Chem. Abstracts*, **58**, 998 (1896).
21. Fowler, G. J., and Malandkar, M. A., *J. Indian Instit. Sci.*, **8A**, 221 (1925).
22. Lutz, L., *Bull. sci. pharmacol.*, **47**, 12 (1940).
23. Pridham, J. B., Abstracts 128th A C. S., Meeting, Minneapolis (1955), 17D.
24. Hough, L., and Pridham, J. B., *Arch. Biochem. Biophys.*, **59**, 17 (1955).
25. Jaretzky, R., and Ulbrich, H., *Arch. Pharm.*, **272**, 796 (1934).
26. Jaretzky, R., and Bereck, E., *Arch. Pharm.*, **276**, 17 (1938).
27. Lloyd, F. E., *Am. J. Botany*, **6**, 156 (1919).
28. Horsfall, F. L., Jr., and McCarthy, M., *J. Exptl., Med.*, **85**, 623 (1947).
29. Ravenna, C., and Zamorani, M., *Atti-R. Accad. Lincei*, **19**, 247 (1910); *Chem. Abstracts*, **5**, 1632 (1911).
30. Greenway, P. J., *East African Agric. J.*, **6**, 241 (1941).
31. Vittoria, A., *Boll. soc. ital. biol. sper.*, **32**, 935 (1956); *Chem. Abs.*, **51**, 11493 (1957).
32. Ceruti, A., and Scurti, J., *Annuar. ist. sper. chim. agrar. Torino*, **18**, 249 (1952–54); *Chem. Abs.*, **51**, 7510 (1957).

CHAPTER 2

CLASSIFICATION OF GUMS AND MUCILAGES

Vegetable gums and mucilages exhibit such a wide spectrum of physical and chemical properties that it is difficult to devise a means of classification without considering a large number of exceptions. The formerly accepted classifications were generally based upon physical properties such as solubility, viscosity, feel and adhesiveness, which controlled the industrial uses to which the gums could be applied.

Vegetable gums may be distinguished from the so-called gum resins by their behavior with water. The former may also be distinguished from the latter group by the fact that they are insoluble in organic solvents such as alcohol, benzene, ether and chloroform, whereas the gum resins dissolve in such organic solvents. In many cases this is true, but certain gums, such as gum myrrh consist of two components one being soluble in organic solvents and the other soluble in water.

The early work on gums led to the hypothesis that these substances, recognized as carbohydrates by Gay-Lussac and Thénard (11), could be assigned to a relatively few classes designated by the terms bassorin, cerasin and arabin. Although this view soon proved to be inadequate it is of interest to note the origin of it. Vauquelin in 1811 (12) reported on gum Bassora, so named because it was exported in those days from Bassora in Turkey; Pelletier who was also investigating the plant gums proposed (17) the name bassorine for this particular gum. It was pointed out (13) that "gum Bassura," or gum Bassora, probably gum tragacanth, was an article of commerce in London in 1906. In 1812 John published (14) a paper on several *Prunus* (plum and cherry) gums and to these polysaccharides he assigned the name *prunin* or *cerasin* from *Prunus cerasus.* In 1833 Chevreul reported (18) on the work of Guerin (15) on gum arabic and gum Senegal and referred to them by the name *arabine.* Generally speaking, the early investigators classified the gums into those soluble in cold water, the *arabin* group, and those insoluble in cold water, the *cerasin* or *bassorin* group; O'Sullivan (16), who later worked on a number of gums including Geddah gum, gum arabic, and gum tragacanth, also used the term "bassorin."

Until quite recently gums were classified, as recommended by the early investigators, according to their behavior when treated with water (19). There was one group, including gum arabic, mesquite, damson and cherry gum, the natural gum exudates, which dissolve completely in water; the so-called "Persian insoluble gum," said to be derived from a species of *Prunus* growing in Persia, belonged to the second group of partially soluble gums. These members of the second group generally swell to form thick jellies or jelly-like mucilages and give translucent viscous solutions. At equal concentrations, those in the first, or gum arabic group, form much less viscous solutions than those in the second or tragacanth group. This type of classification has proved useful, especially in industry, but it can be shown to be dependent upon such minor variations of pH or inorganic or protein impurity that as a classification, in spite of its convenience, it can only be regarded as a very rough one. Thus locust (carob) bean gum has been said to belong to the tragacanth or mucilage group, as it eventually came to be known, since it is only partially soluble in water. In point of fact, the carbohydrate fraction of the insoluble portion of this gum is chemically identical with that of the soluble portion. The insolubility is due to protein (1) and were it not present, the gum would fall into the first, or water-soluble, group. Similarly, chagual gum, from a species of *Puya*, is only partially soluble in water, but after metal ions are removed, either by dialysis or cation exchange resins, the gum becomes completely soluble in water (2). It can also be demonstrated that purified or completely water-soluble gums of the galactomannan group (see later) form mucilaginous solutions when their aqueous solutions are treated with small amounts of borax (3). The solubility in water of the seaweed gum, algin, which is composed of D-mannuronic and L-guluronic acid units varies with the pH thus displaying properties of either a gum or a mucilage (4). The same is true of carrageenin extracted from Irish moss (5,6). *Consequently, in the light of present knowledge, there is no clear line of demarcation between gums and mucilages and, as we shall see later, there is no chemical basis to support such a classification.*

Recognizing this defect in the classification of gums and mucilages, an attempt was made to introduce some measure of order by pointing out that while many of the gums in the Acacia group differ in the nature of the neutral sugar building units, they invariably contain D-glucuronic acid as the acid building unit. From an inspection of the composition of such mucilages as tragacanth, linseed, and slippery elm, it can be seen that the common feature is that the acid building unit is D-galacturonic acid (7). This classification was useful in a limited sort of way, but it does not take into consideration those gums and mucilages that are composed only of neutral sugar building units or those seaweed polysaccharide mucilages, such as agar, which contain sulfate groups.

Another difficulty with the hitherto adopted classifications is their failure to accommodate such synthetic gums as O-(2-hydroxyethyl) starch and partially methylated cellulose. Moreover the classification is now of little value since certain gums, for example Khaya gum, contain both D-glucuronic and D-galacturonic acid (8).

It will be shown in a later section that the physical properties of gums, mucilages, and related polysaccharides depend not so much on the actual building units, although this is an important consideration, as upon the over-all molecular architecture of the complex polysaccharides. Polysaccharides in general constitute a whole spectrum of polyhydroxy compounds whose physical properties, such as solubility and viscosity, depend largely on whether the polysaccharide has a linear or a branched structure. At one end of the spectrum of compounds there are such carbohydrate polymers as cellulose and the amylose component of starch which have essentially a linear structure. At the opposite end of the spectrum of compounds are the so-called true plant gums exemplified by gum arabic or mesquite gum, which have a highly branched and complex structure both from the point of view of type of linkage and component building units; such compounds as these dissolve in water to give clear solutions with adhesive properties. Introduction of partial irregularity into linear compounds by changing some of the sugar building units (Iles glucomannan) or by changing some of the linkages (barley β-D-glucan, oat lichenin or β-D-glucan) or by partial alkylation (mono-O-methyl cellulose, Methocel) or by replacing —CH_2OH by —CO OH (alginic acid) or by adding a D-galactose side chain to linear chains of D-mannose units (guar gum, or locust bean gum and other galactomannans), has a marked effect on this solubility in water. These changes bring about a gradual modification of the truly linear molecule. It appears that if the side chains or modifications introduced occupy regularly spaced positions, mucilage-like bodies result whereas irregular substitutions or modifications lead to the manifestation of gum-like properties. The more regular is the branching, the better the chance of a three dimensional structural network being set up, which gives rise to thick mucilage or gel. The more irregular the branching the less likelihood will there be for association of parts of molecular chains; hence a three-dimensional network cannot be formed and the substance will behave like the natural gum exudates and give a true solution in water. Sometimes the presence of carboxyl groups, regularly distributed as in alginic acid, aids the development of a three-dimensional network and gives rise to mucilage or gel-like properties. On the other hand irregularly spaced carboxyl groups, found in the true gums or the synthetic gums such as O-(carboxymethyl)-starch or O-(carboxymethyl)-cellulose, prevent the formation of net-like structures; such substances as these form true gums that give viscous, non-gelling solutions.

This concept of the structure of gums and mucilages attempts to correlate gum- or mucilage-like properties with the whole molecular structure rather than with the detailed composition of the types of building units and linkages present in the polysaccharide.

Worth noting here are the studies on synthetic organic ion-exchange resins in which the presence of sulfate or basic groups in linear polymers renders them soluble and that insolubility is conferred on such derivatives of linear polymers by cross-linkages (9,10).

For the purposes of this, book, therefore, it is proposed to dispense with the old classifications which tried to distinguish gums and mucilages largely because such a differentiation had grown up in the gum harvesting areas and in commerce. Purely for the sake of order and simplicity, gums and mucilages, whether they are naturally occurring or synthetic, will be divided into two groups, I and II, as shown in Table I; group I contains the acid gums and mucilages while II comprises the neutral compounds.

TABLE I. CLASSIFICATION OF GUMS AND MUCILAGES

Group I		Group II
Acidic Gums and Mucilages containing:		Neutral Gums and Mucilages containing:
Acid components	Neutral components	
L-guluronic acid		
D-glucuronic acid	Hexoses	Hexoses
D-galacturonic acid	Pentoses	6-Deoxyhexoses
Sulfate groups	6-Deoxyhexoses	Pentoses
Phosphate groups	Sugar alcohols	Sugar alcohols
Ethers of all of the above	Ethers of all of the above	Ethers of all of the above

The above classification will accommodate all the natural gums and mucilages. Although no basic gums or mucilages have been encountered thus far in Nature, synthetic gums containing basic groups will most certainly be synthesized and hence provision should be made for the compounds in a third group.

Group III

Basic Gums and Mucilages containing

Basic components	Neutral components
Amino sugars	Hexoses
Amino alkyl ethers	Pentoses
Amino acids, polypeptides or proteins	6-Deoxyhexoses
O- and N-Alkyl derivatives of all of the above	Sugar alcohols
	Ethers of all of the above

REFERENCES

1. Cuendet, L. S., and Smith, F., unpublished.
2. Hamilton, J. K., Smith, F., and Spriestersbach, D., *J. Am. Chem. Soc.*, **79**, 443 (1957).
3. Mantell, C. L., "The Water-Soluble Gums," Reinhold Pub. Corp., New York (1947).
4. Steiner, A. B., and McNeely, W. H., "Advances in Chem. Series," **11**, 68 (1954).
5. Stoloff, L., "Advances in Chem. Series," **11**, 92 (1954).
6. Smith, D. B., and Cook, W. H., *Arch. Biochem. Biophys.*, **45**, 232 (1953).
7. Jones, J. K. N., and Smith, F., "Advances in Carbohydrate Chem.," **4**, 243 (1949).
8. Aspinall, G. O., Hirst, E. L., and Matheson, N. K., *J. Chem. Soc.*, 989 (1956).
9. Griessbach, R., *Angew. Chem., Beihefte*, No. 31 (1939).
10. Samuelson, O., "Ion Exchangers in Analytical Chemistry," John Wiley and Sons, Inc., New York, (1953) p. 12.
11. Gay-Lussac, L. J., and Thénard, L. J., *Ann. Chem.*, **74**, 47 (1810).
12. Vauquelin, *Bull. de Pharmacie*, **3**, 49 (1811).
13. Robinson, H. H., *Brit. Assoc. Advance. Sci. Rep.*, 227 (1906).
14. John, D., *Schweiggers Journal für Chemie und Physik.*, **6**, 374 (1812).
15. Guérin, R. T., *Ann. Chem.*, **49**, 248 (1832).
16. O'Sullivan, C., *J. Chem. Soc.*, **45**, 41 (1884); **57**, 59 (1890); **59**, 1029 (1891); **79**, 1164 (1901); *Proceedings Chem. Soc.* (London), **5**, 166 (1889); **7**, 131 (1891); **17**, 156 (1901).
17. Pelletier, *Bull. de. Pharmacie*, **3**, 556 (1811).
18. Chevreul, *Nouvelles Annales du Museum d'Histoire Naturelle*, **2**, 126 (1833).
19. Jacobs, M. B., "The Chemistry and Technology of Food and Food Products," Interscience, New York, Vol. 1 (1944), p. 819.

CHAPTER 3

OCCURRENCE AND ISOLATION OF SOME OF THE MORE IMPORTANT GUMS AND MUCILAGES

Isolation of Gum Exudates

Gum Arabic and Other Acacia Gums. Although many species of Acacia are known, the commercial gum, coming largely from the Sudan region of N. Africa, is produced essentially from one species, *Acacia senegal*, which is synonymous with *Acacia verek*. Collection of gum from only one species of *Acacia* has led to a more uniform product and adulteration is reduced. *Acacia senegal* is said to be the characteristic species growing from Senegal to the Red Sea and further east to India (1,2,5). The trees grow on sandy soil. Many trees grow wild, but in certain regions they are cultivated. The largest pure stands of *Acacia senegal* are found in the Kordofan province of Africa, hence the name Kordofan gum. In the Sudan, the dominant species is *A. mellifera*, whereas to the south of the Sudan, *A. seyal* becomes more common (1,3).

The *Acacia* tree usually grows to a height of 15 or 20 feet. Under very unfavorable conditions, it remains stunted and bush like. The trunk may be about a foot in diameter; the bark is usually light in color and quite thin, while the cambium layer is bright green (4). The tree has feathery leaves and along the branches are hooked thorns, arranged in groups of three. The tree bears broad, flat, membranous seed pods which remain on the trees after the seeds have ripened, in the manner of the pods of the honey locust in North America. The tree lives for 20-30 years during which time it is attacked by many insects, including white ants, which eventually kill the tree; the foliage and branches are eaten by goats and camels (5).

Acacia seyal is the source of the Sudan gums such as, gum Takl, Talea, Talha, Talki or Snakim. The tree is widely distributed in the Sudan, growing to a height of 30 feet and having long spines and a rust-colored, powdery bark. The tree bears curved seed pods (1,6). As with all *Acacia* trees, the seeds are hard and germinate slowly. It is reported that tapping does not reduce gum exudation in this particular species of *Acacia.*

In addition to the above two species of *Acacia*, the following have been recognized in the Sudan region: *A. abyssinica, A. albida, A. arabica, A. camplyacantha, A. thunbengiana, A. drepanolobium, A. farnesiana, A. flava, A. kirkii, A. lacta, A. orfota, A. sieberiana, A. spinocarpa,* and *A. stenocarpa* (1).

In the early days, all of the gum collection was derived from spontaneous exudation. Tapping of *Acacia* trees began about 50 years ago and is carried out by driving an axe underneath the bark which is pulled back until it breaks horizontally to give two broken ends. The ends are pulled and a vertical strip of bark about 1 to 2 inches wide is torn off the tree. At each gum season, a new strip of bark is torn from a different part of the trunk. Gum forms slowly in places along the length of the wounded trunk. Gum formation is favored by dry and retarded by cold or wet weather. A first collection of gum may be made 3 weeks after tapping and thereafter at intervals of about two weeks. Apparently only one strip wound is made each season, for gum continues to exude from the one wound. The gum is formed only in the dry season just after the leaves wither and die. In the rainy season, when the trees are in full leaf, tapping does not produce any gum. In experimental plantations the yield of gum might be 60 pounds per acre, some trees yielding about 1 pound of gum each. Trees will exude gum when 6 to 7 years old. Earlier tapping may eventually kill the trees. As they grow older, the yield of gum decreases until, at an age of 25 to 30 years, the trees yield no gum.

After the gum has been collected, it is hand sorted to remove fragments of bark and other impurities and then spread out in the sun for several weeks to dry, when it assumes the well-known frosted appearance. Some bleaching goes on during the exposure of the gum to the bright sun and intense heat. Strangely enough, its quality is judged largely on appearance!

The *Acacia senegal* gum from French West Africa differs little from that collected in the Sudan, although the former has been reported to give solutions of greater viscosity and less adhesiveness (7). Natural exudates of the gum are collected and little tapping is practiced, even though it is said to be as effective as in the Sudan. Accounts of the Senegal gum trade have been recorded by DeCordemay (8) and the gum industry by Chevalier (9).

Acacia gums are produced to a lesser extent in Nigeria, being known there by such names as Falli, Marrua, and Mumuye. *Acacia lacta* has been reported to produce a gum which, unlike other *Acacia* gums, forms mucilaginous solutions even at low concentrations. It would be of interest to ascertain how the structure of this particular gum compares with those already known for other *Acacia* gums which do not give mucilaginous solutions. Other species of *Acacia* occurring in Nigeria are *A. campylacantha, A. sieberiana,* and *A. albida.* Species belonging to such genera as *Albizzia, Anogeissus, Combretum, Isoberlinia, Khaya, Odina,* and *Sclerocarya* have also been used as sources of gum (1).

Smaller amounts of *Acacia* gums are collected in East Africa in the regions from Somaliland to Natal. In Tanganyika, gum collection is organized and a fairly uniform product is collected, but in other areas the gums are collected from a variety of *Acacia* trees, among which about 20 have been recognized, for example, *A. fistula, A. fischeri, A. stenocarpa, A. spinocarpa, A. stuhlmannii, A. kirkii, A. senegal, A. seyal, A. malacocephala, A. sieberiana, A. benthami, A. orfota, A. usambarensis, A. mellifera, A. arabica, A. albida,* and *A. xanthophloea* (1,10).

In Tanganyika, most of the gum is collected as a natural exudate from *Acacia drepanolobium* in the dry season. Grass fires are said to stimulate the exudation of gums from these trees which grow only about ten feet high. The gum is not exposed to the sun for bleaching, but is exported directly, much of it to India and hence it gets the name of "East Indian Gum Arabic." It is of relatively poor quality but, as a result of expert sorting and mixing with native Indian *Acacia* gums, it can be much improved.

Gums derived from species of *Acacia* are collected in regions of the North African continent other than the Sudan. Gum harvested in Morocco from natural exudation of *A. gummifera, A. spinocarpa* and *A. arabica,* and often called Morocco, Mogodor, or Brown Barbary gum, is inferior to the Kordofan gum from the Sudan.

In the North East African continent, e.g. Somaliland and Abyssinia, *Acacia* gums that go by the name of Adad, Talefan, Hobloho and Nugal are collected from natural exudations, although gum secretion is sometimes encouraged by bruising of the bark. The gum from these regions is a mixture, being derived from *A. senegal, A. abyssinia, A. glaucophylla,* and probably from *A. bussei* and *A. mellifera.*

The so-called Cape gum of South Africa, which is collected from *Acacia karroo* (syn. *A. horrida*), is not as good as gum Kordofan, but it is said to produce a good adhesive mucilage. There is no great trade in this gum, though some used to be exported to Europe. It is used locally as an adhesive and, having a sweet taste, it is sometimes eaten. In former times, it was used as a medicinal.

India also produces *Acacia* gums, but usually they are from mixed species of trees, such as *A. farnesiana, A. jacquemontii, A. leucophloea* and *A. ferruginea,* and hence less valued than the Kordofan or Senegal gum of Egypt. The conditions in certain parts of India are more favorable for growth and some of the *A. arabica* trees grow to a height of one hundred feet and produce as much as two pounds of gum each. Unlike those in the Sudan, the older trees are reported to produce more gum than younger ones, although the gum contains more color. No tapping is practiced, but some of the trees are bruised in order to promote gum exudation. To distinguish native gum from that produced in Africa and sorted in India called East Indian gum arabic, it is called Indian gum arabic.

In Ceylon *Acacia catechu* is the source of the local gum supply while in the Punjab region the large trees of *Acacia modesta* provide the gum. The gums of India are known by a variety of names, e.g. bavul, gundar, durk, kher, maklai, ghati, katira, deshi, etc., which depend on the local dialect.

There are a large number of *Acacia* trees growing in Australia that produce gums; the quality varies and seldom approaches that of the Sudan or Kordofan gums (11). The best known is perhaps the Black Wattle gum secreted by the black wattle *Acacia decurrens*, Var. *mollis* (syn. *A. mollisima*.). Unfortunately, it has a dark reddish brown color and only one quarter of it dissolves in water (12). The gums from *A. homalophylla*, *A. pendula* and *A. sentis* are soluble in water and of better quality than the wattle gum from *A. decurrens*. Many other varieties of Australian *Acacia* trees that produce gum have been classified, such as *A. pendulata*, *A. binervata*, *A. dealbata*, *A. elata*, *A. glaucescens*, *A. penninervis*, *A. bakeri*, *A. cunninghamii*, *A. harphphylla*, *A. leiophylla*, *A. maidenni*, *A. oswoldi*, *A. pycnantha*, *A. retinoides*, *A. salicina*, and *A. verniciflua*. A number of gums from these trees have been examined (13).

Gum Tragacanth. This gum is obtained from plants of the genus *Astragalus* in which there are 1600 or more species; not all of these produce gum and only testing by making an incision will tell which are the gum producers. The plants, which grow three or four feet high, are shrublike in appearance and thrive in dry locations in the mountainous regions from Asia Minor to Iran. The shrubs are widely distributed (see Table 2). The gum is exuded naturally in some species, but the best gum is produced by artificial stimulation (143).

The gum may be exuded from the stems of plants that are damaged, but the best gum is obtained by slitting the roots with a knife and wedging the cut open. The gum exudes as thin, ribbon-shaped flakes which dry in a day or two when they are collected. Rapid drying in calm weather gives the almost colorless, well-known, ribbon tragacanth. Dust storms and rain contaminate the exuding gum with soil and sand, and such gums are considered inferior. In some areas, gum exudation after tapping is accelerated by burning the tops of the shrubs. *Vermicelli* gum tragacanth

TABLE 2. GEOGRAPHICAL DISTRIBUTION OF SOME OF THE MORE
IMPORTANT ASTRAGALUS SPECIES (1,14)

Species	Distribution
A. gummifer	N. Kurdistan, Armenia, Asia Minor and Syria
A. kurdicus	S. Kurdistan to Asia Minor and Syria
A. brachycalyx	Iranian Kurdistan and Luristan
A. eriostylus	Luristan
A. pycnocladus	Kermanshab
A. verus	W. Iran
A. leiocladus	W. and Central Iran
A. adscendens	S. W. and S. Iran
A. strobiliferus	E. Iran
A. heratensis	Khorasan to Afghanistan

is produced by puncturing the stems of the plants which reach the gum producing stage when two years old. The *Astragalus* plant, which has a life span of about five to seven years, is said to produce gum every other year.

Gum tragacanth is perhaps the most valuable of all gums being used extensively in pharmaceutical products. This gum has the advantage of giving highly viscous aqueos solutions at relatively low concentrations, a property common to few natural gums or mucilages. Gum tragacanth is evidently generated by the plant in an attempt to seal off the injured part, but it remains to be seen whether by extracting various parts of the plant the gum is a preformed metabolic product.

Reports from an examination of plants growing in Iran, on and near the eastern slopes of the Zagros mountains, indicate that there are two types of *Astragalus* plants, all of them bush-like and said to resemble a turtle in appearance. The plant has very small leaves and thorns. The variety which yields the ribbon type of gum can be distinguished from those that secrete the flake type of gum. The ribbon type is harvested the day after tapping whereas the flake type is collected about twenty days after tapping. The gathering of the ribbon gum is said to begin in May and lasts until October, while the flake type is harvested from July until October. The harvesting of the gum is complicated by the fact that beside the two gum producing plants, there are other varieties of *Astragalus* plants growing in the same area which do not produce any gum, and moreover, the gum producing plants are outnumbered by five or six to one. When one also considers the transportation problem and the fact that a plant yields a maximum of about 25 grams of gum per tapping, it is not surprising that the gum is expensive. By this hand producing method, Iran was able to export about 3300 tons of gum tragacanth (all grades) for the year 1950–1951.

Karaya Gum. This gum, which is often called Indian gum tragacanth since it is frequently used as a substitute for the true gum tragacanth is produced from *Sterculia urens*, a large deciduous tree growing in the dry, elevated areas of North and Central India. Karaya gum exudes naturally but most of it is produced by artificial stimulation through a special tapping procedure, involving the removal of a foot square of bark. The gum is produced rapidly, most of it in about a day, and after its removal, further gum formation is induced by scraping the wound to expose fresh surface. Tapping, or blazing as it is sometimes called, is carried out with care. Only well-established trees that have reached a girth of about three feet are tapped and only two taps, on opposite sides of the trunk, are made in each tree. Excessive tapping eventually kills the tree.

The gum is now replacing gum tragacanth and the demand, especially in the United States (7), continues to grow since it is cheaper and also because it is said to be superior to gum tragacanth in some industries.

There are many species of *Sterculia* besides the one from which karaya gum is produced and some of them, such as *S. campanulata, S. foetida, S. guttata, S. ornata, S. villosa,* all found in India, and *S. barteri, S. cinerea, S. setigera, S. tragacantha,* found in Africa, and *S. acerifolia, S. diversifolia, S. plantanifolia, S. quadrifica, S. rupestris,* from Australia, *S. hypochroa, S. thorelii,* from Indochina, and *S. scaphigera* from China and Indochina, produce gums. Although some are valuable they are not available in commercial amounts.

All the above trees, except one, produce gum by exudation from the trunk. The exception is *Sterculia scaphigera,* growing in Indochina, in which case the gum is extracted from the fruits by maceration with water. This indicates that karaya gum is a normal metabolic product.

One other interesting gum, resembling karaya gum, is that produced from the black kurrajong tree (*Brachychiton diversifolium*) of Australia. It is said that as much as a "pail" of gum may be obtained from a single tree!

Kutira Gum. This is an exudate of the tree *Cochlospermum gossypium,* resembling karaya gum, and is of some value and importance. Like karaya, with which it is often confused, it smells of acetic acid and swells up when moistened with water. Many gums related to karaya are known and for a discussion of their origin, the reader is recommended to read Howes (1).

Another gum of some commercial value is gum "ghati" produced freely in the dry seasons from trees (*Anogeissus latifolia*) growing in the dry deciduous forests of India and Ceylon. It is said to be readily distinguished from other gums because it forms highly viscous solutions in water. At equal concentration it has twice the viscosity of gum arabic.

Mesquite Gum. This is the only gum of the North American Continent that is of any commercial significance. It is collected by hand from small leguminous mesquite trees or shrubs (*Prosopis julifora* D.C.) growing in Southwestern United States and Mexico. Since mesquite gum is little used it is presumably inferior to good quality gum arabic. A close relative of the American mesquite tree, *Prosopis spicigera*, grows in Northern India.

Some Gums of South America. In South America, leguminous trees of the genera *Caesalpinia* and *Piptadenia* produce gums which are as yet of little or no commercial importance though at times, when supplies of gum arabic were cut off, the gum from *Piptadenia macrocarpa* was collected and exported to Europe under the name Brazilian gum arabic. *Anacardium humile*, *A. occidentale*, and *A. nanum* provide Cashew or Acajou gum sometimes in uncommonly huge tears. This gum is not only a reasonably good adhesive but it also contains small amounts of cashew oil which acts as an insect repellent.

In Central America, there are produced a number of cactus (*Cactaceae*) gums which await evaluation and investigation. The woody cactus, *Opuntia*, but not the fleshy members of the *Cactaceae*, produce gum exudates which form excellent mucilages.

Gums and Mucilages Isolated from Seeds.

Locust or Carob Seed Gum. This gum is produced from the hard seeds of the locust or carob bean, *Ceratonia siliqua* L., an evergreen tree that grows in the coastal regions of the Mediterranean. The tree is large and may produce half a ton per year of the well-known brown beans which have been eaten by man and beast since earliest times. These beans are probably the "locusts" that St. John ate while in the wilderness They have a pleasant sweet taste due to the presence of about 50% sugar. The extremely hard seeds, once thought to be valueless, now provide the highly important industrial gum that has been called carob gum, locust bean gum, gum tragon, tragasol, St. John's Bread gum, etc. The gum, present as an inner vitreous coating of the seeds, is isolated by a special milling process and then powdered. This material, without further purification, can be used in place of the most expensive gums, including tragacanth and karaya. Its use is likely to expand in the future.

Guar Gum. Guar gum is obtained from seeds of the leguminous plant, *Cyamopsis tetragonolobus* or *C. psoraloides*, the gum being found as a vitreous layer on the inner side of the seed coat. The guar bean plant, which grows about two feet high, is suited to large scale cultivation. It is grown extensively in Pakistan as a forage crop and on a small scale in the south western regions of the United States. The seed coat containing the gum is separated from the protein portion by a mechanical milling operation which splits the seed into two parts. The milling may or may not be preceded by a preliminary treatment of the seed to remove the brown outer layer. The vitreous parts of the seed, or "splits" as they are sometimes called, are then ground to a suitable mesh size and used in industry without further purification, except that the material may be treated to inactivate the enzymes. Unlike the gum exudates discussed previously, this gum, which is a neutral substance, belongs to the class of galactomannan polysaccharides. Since it produces highly viscous solutions at low concentrations, it can be used as a substitute for gum tragacanth in some applications.

Other Galactomannan Gums and Mucilages. The reduction of the importation of gums and mucilages into the United States from the middle and far East during the war of 1939–45, led to an investigation of the seeds of a number of leguminous plants that grow in North and South America. In addition to the locust bean (*Ceratonia siliqua*) and the guar bean (*Cyamopsis* Sp.) those listed in Table 3 were found to contain polymers composed of D-galactose and D-mannose (15,16,17).

TABLE 3. SOME PLANTS PRODUCING SEEDS CONTAINING
GALACTOMANNAN GUMS

Honey locust (*Gleditsia tricanthos*)
Flame tree (*Delonix regia*)
Kentucky coffee bean (*Gymnocladus dioica*)
Palo verde (*Cercidium torreyandum*)
Tara (*Caesalpinia spinosa*)
Huizache (*Caesalpinia cacalaco*)
Japanese pagoda tree (*Sophora japonica*)
Lucerne, alfalfa (*Medicago sativa*)
Clover (*Trifolium* Sp.)

The seeds of the ivory nut contain two mannans, designated A and B (18), extractable with alkali (20) which form an excellent source of the sugar D-mannose (19), they do not have any useful gum-like properties.

Gums and Mucilages Extracted from Roots

A polymer called konjak mannan, composed of D-glucose and D-mannose, is extracted from the corms of *Amorphophallus konjak* by superheated water or by the action of a pancreatic enzyme preparation on the ground konjak tubers. A similar extraction of Javanese tubers (*Amorphophallus oncophyllus*) provides a glucomannan, sometimes called Iles mannan, which is used in the creaming of rubber latex. The linear structural characteristics of these two glucomannans makes them valuable beater additives for augmenting the strength of paper sheets.

A mucilage composed of D-mannose residues, salep mannan, extracted with water from the powdered tubers of *Orchidaceae*, does not appear to be of any industrial significance.

Of less interest from an industrial point of view, are the neutral mucilaginous polysaccharides extracted from such parts of plants as the flowers, stems, leaves and shoots (Table 4).

TABLE 4. THE SOURCE AND COMPONENT SUGARS OF CERTAIN
NEUTRAL MUCILAGES

Source of Mucilage	Sugars present	Reference
Sterculia plantanifolia (Young shoots)	L-arabinose, D-galactose	107
Colocasia antiquorum (Tuberous roots)	D-glucose	107
Vitis pentaphylla (Stems and leaves)	D-galactose	107
Opuntia Sp. (Fleshy stems)	D-galactose	107
Opuntia vulgaris	D-galactose, L-arabinose	108
Oenothera jaquinii (Stems and leaves)	D-galactose, L-arabinose	107
Kadsura japonica (Stems and leaves)	D-galactose, L-arabinose	107
Hydrangea paniculata (Sieb) (Bark)	D-galactose, L-arabinose, 6-deoxyhexose	111
Anagyris foetida (Seeds)	D-galactose, L-arabinose	112
Polygonatum officinale All. (Rhizome)	D-glucose, L-arabinose, D-fructose	113
Actinidia callosa Lindl. var. rufa makino (Bark)	D-galactose, L-arabinose	114
Abelmoschus manihot (Root)	D-arabinose, D-galactose, L-rhamnose	109
Capsicum (Seeds)	L-arabinose, D-galactose	110
Viola flowers	—	115

There are also a large number of mucilages containing sugar acid building units in addition to neutral sugar residues referred to previously. They appear to have a much more complicated structure than the neutral mucilages such as the galactomannans from the seeds of the *Leguminosae* and they resemble more closely the natural gum exudates (see Table 5).

TABLE 5. SOURCE AND COMPONENT SUGARS OF CERTAIN MUCILAGES
THAT CONTAIN URONIC ACID RESIDUES

Source of Mucilage	Sugars Present	Reference
Linum usitatissimum Flax (Seed)	D-xylose, L-galactose, L-rhamnose, D-galacturonic acid	116–123
Brassica alba White mustard (Seed)	D-xylose, L-arabinose, 6-deoxyhexose (rhamnose), D-glucuronic acid, D- galacturonic acid	124
Lepidium sativum Cress (Seed)	L-arabinose, D-galactose, L-rhamnose, D-xylose, D-galacturonic acid	125
Kadsura Japonica. Dun. (Stem)	D-xylose, D-glucuronic acid	126,127
Scaphium affine Pierre (Fruit)	L-arabinose, D-galacturonic acid, (acetic acid)	128
Brasenia schreberi Gmel. (Leaves)	D-galactose, D-mannose, L-arabinose, D-glucuronic acid	129
Plantago psyllium (Seed)	L-arabinose, D-xylose, D-galacturonic acid	130,131
Plantago fastigiata (Seed)	L-arabinose, D-xylose, D-galacturonic acid	132
Plantago lanceolata (Seed)	D-galactose, D-xylose, D-galacturonic acid	133
Plantago arenaria (Seed)	D-xylose, L-arabinose, D-galactose, D-galacturonic acid	134
Ulmus fulva Slippery elm (Bark)	L-rhamnose, D-galactose, D-galacturonic acid	135–137
Pachyra affina	—	138

Seaweed Gums and Mucilages

Isolation of Irish Moss Mucilage, Carrageenin. The industrial development of the isolation and use of the polysaccharides from seaweeds
resulted in large part from the fact that World War II cut off European
supplies of agar, gum tragacanth, gum arabic, etc. Attention was turned
to Irish moss extract, or carrageenin, and the algin polysaccharides for
substitutes. Fortunately, the impetus supplied by the war has continued
and, at the present time, a number of companies are engaged in processing seaweed polysaccharides.

Irish moss provides carrageenin, a mucilaginous carbohydrate polymer
long used by the French, Irish, Scandinavians, Scots and Welsh in foods
and pharmaceutical remedies. The polysaccharide is extracted from salt-
water plants variously called Irish moss, or carrageen (rock) moss. It is
designated more exactly as *Chondrus crispus* (L) Stackh. of the family
Gigartinaceae in the class *Rhodophyceae* or red algae. Carrageenin may
also be extracted from *Gigartina stellata.* *Chondrus crispus* grows from

a disc-like root which attaches itself to rocks in relatively shallow coastal waters; in some places this seaweed has been found growing at depths up to forty feet. The plants are about eight inches long and although normally colored a reddish-purple, in certain locations they are green, being entirely free of the red pigment.

On the North American coast, the plants are harvested with long-handled rakes. Harvesting must be carried out at the correct time of year, since there is a seasonal variation in the polysaccharide gum content (36–38). The plants are not uprooted; they break off and the holdfast or root remains firmly attached to the rock surface. New shoots form from the old holdfast and hence cropping may be repeated. Natural reproduction from spores takes about two months for germination and development of the root or holdfast, and another ten or twelve months are required before the plants can be harvested. Harvesting by hand is done in calm weather, but during storms, the moss is torn away from the rocks and collects on shore at low tide. At present, harvesting requires good drying weather unless artificial drying can be supplied. The freshly harvested moss is spread out in the sun to dry; on drying it assumes a dark color from the concentrated red pigment in the fronds. In this process, there is an 80% loss in weight. Further refinement is effected by treating the moss with limited amounts of fresh water to leach out the red and green pigments. Excessive amounts of water must be avoided because in the absence of salt the required polysaccharide dissolves. The ancient process of pigment removal depended on dew and light rains. The washing removes not only color, but also salt and as a result subsequent processing is greatly facilitated. After removal of pigment and salt the dried moss has a pale-yellow color.

The purified moss is given a final washing in cold water and is then extracted with hot water to remove the required carrageenin polysaccharide. The extract, if not too viscous, can be clarified by filtration, centrifugation, and by treatment with charcoal, after which it is freed from water by evaporators and finally by drum drying. Produced in this manner, the carrageenin or seaweed gum, as it sometimes is called, is a fine, buff-colored powder which readily disperses in water to give a viscous solution. The yield of carrageenin may vary from 60 to 80 per cent of the dry weight of the plants (21).

In addition to the seaweeds mentioned above that are of industrial value, those listed in Table 6 have also been examined, though not in great detail. Quite a number of them are sulfate esters, while others contain the relatively rare sugar L-fucose. A simplified version of a classification published previously (22) is given in Table 7.

TABLE 6. SOURCE AND COMPOSITION OF SOME SEAWEED MUCILAGES

Source	Components	Reference
Chondrus elatus	L-arabinose, D-galactose, "Floridose"	58–60
Gloiopeltis furcata var. *coliformis*	L-arabinose, L-fucose, D-galactose	58–60
Iridaea laminarioides var. *cornucopiae*	L-arabinose, D-galactose, "Floridose," -SO_4	58–60
Cladophora rupestris	L-arabinose, L-galactose, D-xylose, L-rhamnose	142
Chondrus crispus *Ceramium rubrum* *Delesseria sanguinea* *Delesseria elata* *Polysiphonia fastigiata* *Plumaria elegans*	D-galactose, D-glucose, -SO_4	61,62
Ascophyllum nodosum	L-fucose, D-mannose	63
Laminaria flexicaulis	D-galactose, D-glucose	64
Gelidium pacificum Okam.	D-galactose	65
Chondrus ocellatus Holmes *Fucus typicus, Fucus giganteus* Okam. *Iridaea laminarioides*	D-galactose, 6-deoxyhexose (fucose), 2-ketohexonic acid (probably 3,6-anhydro-D-galactose), D- and L-erythrose, -SO_4	66–71
Laminaria and *Fucus* sp.	L-fucose, -SO_4	72
Fucus evanescens	L-fucose, -SO_4	73
Eisenia bicyclis *Laminaria japonica*	glucose, fucose, -SO_4	73
Macrocystis pyrifera	L-fucose, -SO_4	74,75
Chondrus crispus (carrageenin)	3,6-anhydro-D-galactose, D-galactose, -SO_4	61,76–81
Dilsea edulis	D-galactose, -SO_4	82,83
Gigartina stellata	D-galactose, -SO_4	84
Gigartina tenella	galactose, (?) -SO_4	73
Rhodymenia palmata	D-xylose	83
Laminaria cloustoni	D-glucose, D-mannitol	85,86
Laminaria digitata	D-glucose, D-mannitol	86–88
Gelidium latifolium *Gelidium crinale* *Gracilaria confervoides* (Agar)	D-galactose, L-galactose, 3,6-anhydro-L-galactose and -SO_4	89–106
Porphyra capensis	D-galactose, L-galactose, 6-O-methyl-D-galactose, 3,6-anhydro-L-galactose	140

A more recent arrangement (146) of the seaweeds of the red algae type according to whether they contain an agar-like (non-electrolyte) or a car-

TABLE 7. SOURCE OF SOME SEAWEED POLYSACCHARIDES

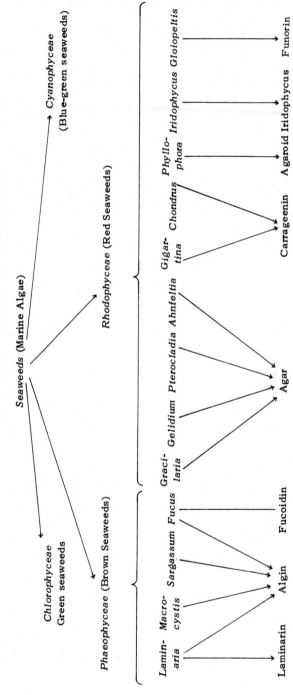

rageenin-like (electrolyte) material as the major polysaccharide is given in Table 8. Included also are six species under the subheading, carrageenin-like. The physical properties of the polysaccharides extracted from these six plants are similar to those of carrageenin, but unlike the latter they do not give a specific agglomeration reaction with milk protein.

TABLE 8. SEA PLANT GENERA AND SPECIES LISTED ACCORDING TO DOMINANT TYPE OF WATER-EXTRACTABLE POLYSACCHARIDE

Agars

Acanthopeltis japonica
Ahnfeltia plicata
Camphylaephora hypnaeoides (Syn. Ceramium hypnaeoides)
Ceramium boydenii
Corallopsis salicornia
Digenea simplex
Endocladia muricata
Gelidiella acerosa (Syn. Gelidium rigidum)
Gelidium amansii
G. arborescens
G. arbuscula
G. attenuatum
G. cartilagineum
G. corneum
G. crinale
G. japonicum
G. latifolium
G. nudifrons
G. pacificum
G. pristoides
G. pulchellum
G. pulvinatum
G. pusillum
G. sesquipedale
G. subcostatum
Gracilaria armata
G. blodgettii
G. caudata
G. cornea
G. henriquesiana
G. lichenoides
G. multipartita
G. taenioides
G. verrucosa (Syn. G. confervoides)
Phyllophora nervosa
Phyllophora rubens
Pterocladia lucida
P. pinnata (Syn. P. capillacea)

Carrageenins

Aeodes orbitosa
Chondrus canaliculatus
C. crispus
C. ocellatus
Eucheuma cottonii
E. edule
E. muricatum (Syn. E. spinosum, E. denticulatum)
Gigartina acicularis
G. asperifolia
G. canaliculata
G. decipiens
G. pistillata
G. radula
G. stellata (Syn. G. mamillosa)
Gloiopeltis coliformis
G. furcata
G. tenax
Gymnogongrus norvegicus
G. patens
Iridaea laminarioides
I. capensis (Syn. Iridophycus capensis)
I. flaccida

Carrageenin-like

Agardhiella tenera
Furcellaria fastigiata
Hypnea cervicornis
H. musciformis
H. spicifera
Suhria vittata

It was pointed out that all species of the same genus have the same type of water-extractable polysaccharide, but it was also apparent that discrepancies appeared when the genera were considered from a phylogenetic point of view. For example, agar is found in *Endocladia* and carrageenin in *Gloiopeltis*, both of which belong to the Endocladiaceae. Also, with the Phyllophoraceae, agar is present in *Phyllophora* and *Ahnfeltia*, carrageenin in *Gymnogongrus*; and within the *Gelidiaccae*, agar occurs in *Gelidium*, *Gelidiella*, *Pterocladia*, and *Acanthopeltis*, whereas a carrageenin-like polysaccharide is found in *Suhria*.

Further investigation of these substances will no doubt show that many of them can be utilized in industry. For the distribution of marine algae reference should be made to Chapman (144).

Some idea of the tremendous quantities of marine algae and of the possible sources of industrial material can be discerned from what Sir Joseph Hooker had to say in his "Botany of the Antarctic Voyage of 1839–1843" (quoted in Chapman 144) about the genus *Lessonia* which grows around the coast of South America. He says "they are truly wonderful Algae, whether seen in the water or on the beach; for they are arborescent branched trees, with the branches pendulous and again divided into sprays from which hang leaves 1–3 feet long. The trunks usually are about 5–10 feet long, as thick as the human thigh.... The plants...form a miniature forest...thousands of these trees are flung ashore by the waves, and with the *Macrocystis* and *Durvillea* form along the beach continued masses of vegetable rejectamanta, miles in extent, some yards broad, and three feet in depth.... The ignorant observer at once takes the trunks of *Lessonia* thus washed up for pieces of driftwood...."

The giant kelp *Macrocystis pyrifera* growing off the coast of California may grow to a length of 150 feet with the leafy parts of the plant floating on the surface of the water.

Isolation of Agar. The large-scale isolation of this particular seaweed gum is carried out almost solely by the Japanese. Most of the material is manufactured for export to Europe and America. Many kinds of seaweed are used for the preparation of agar and it seems that the correct amounts and combinations of plants to be employed has been worked out over many years by trial and error. Each plant yields a certain gum and the same plant may give a gum whose properties and yield may differ according to the harvesting season.

The most important plants for producing agar-agar are *Gelidium amansii* and *G. pacificum* which grow in considerable quantity along the coast of Japan. The plants are harvested by a raking method in shallow water and by divers in deep water areas. The plants growing in deep water are said to be more desirable. The early harvest season is from April to June and a second crop is gathered between July and September. The plants are spread on racks where they undergo some bleaching from the sun and rain. When the plants are dry they are stacked in covered barns until processing time. Apparently, dried plants do not decompose.

The species of plants given in Table 9 represent those most commonly employed in the manufacture of agar by the Japanese. There are two general types of plants one designated "hard," which releases its polysaccharides slowly upon extraction with hot water, and the other "soft," from which the gum is readily extracted with boiling water.

TABLE 9. SEAWEEDS USED IN THE MANUFACTURE
OF AGAR IN JAPAN (23)

Species of Plant

A. *Hard type*[a]
    (a) *Gelidium amansii* Lmx.
       G. pacificum Okam.
       G. divaricatum Martens
       G. crinale (Turn) Lmx.
       G. liatulum Okam.
       G. pusillum (Stckl) Je. Jol.
       G. subfastigiatum Okam.
       G. vagum Okam.
       Pterocladia capillacea (Gmel.) Born et Thur.
       P. tenuis Okam.
       P. densa Okam.
       P. nana Okam.
       Gelidiella acerosa Feldm. et Hamel.
    (b) *Gelidium japonicum* (Harv.) Okam.
    (c) *Acanthopeltis japonica* Okam.
    (d) *Gelidium subcostatum* Okam.
       G. tenue Okam.
       G. planuisculum Okam.

B. *Soft type*
    (e) *Ceramium hypnaeoides* (J. Ag.) Okam.
    (f) *Gracilaria confervoides* (L.) Grev.
       G. gigao Harv.
       G. chorda Holm
       G. compressa (Ag.) Grev.
       G. blodgetti Harv.
       G. lichenoides (L.) Harv.
    (g) *Gelidium linoides* Kutz
       Ceramium rubrum J. Ag.
       C. boydenii Gepp.
       C. crassum Okam.

TABLE 9. (*Continued*)

Species of Plant

C.[b] *Eucheuma muricatum* (Gm.) Web. V. B.
     E. gelatinosa (Esp.) J. Ag.
     E. amakusaensis Okam.
     E. crustae forme Web. V. Bos.
     Ahnfeltia plicata (Huds) Fr. Scan (Var. *Tobuchiensis kanno*).

[a]For explanation of "hard" and "soft" types see above.
[b]Those listed in section C. of Table 9, found only in the sea off Formosa and Karofuto, are seldom used in the Japanese industry.

The art of agar production is so well developed that the proportion of the seven groups of seaweeds to be used has been worked out to give a gum with the correct physical properties (see Table 10.).

TABLE 10. PROPORTIONS OF VARIOUS GROUPS OF SEAWEED USED FOR MAKING AGAR

Proportion (%)	Group
45	(a)
10	(b)
5	(c)
10	(e)
15	(f)
5	(g)
10	(d)

Extraction of Agar. The plants are soaked in fresh cold water in direct sunlight in order to effect softening and bleaching of the dried material. The so-called hard weeds require about 24 hours and the soft weeds about 12 hours. During this time the plants are agitated and subjected to some type of pressing to accelerate the softening process and also to dislodge foreign material. When the softening process is complete the weeds are thoroughly washed and then set aside to drain. The correct proportions of hard and soft weeds are introduced into about 3500 liters of boiling water in batches of about 500 pounds. The "hard" weeds are added first and when the water resumes boiling, about 750 g. of sulfuric acid is added, the pH then being about 6.3 to 7.0. After the boiling has gone on for 1 to 5 hours, the soft weeds are added and the boiling is continued for 15 minutes, and finally, at this point, the softest weed (*Ceramium hypnaeoides*) used is then added. The vigorous boiling operation is arrested and the entire batch is simmered with stirring for 12 more hours.

The liquid is decanted and the residue is given a second extraction for 10 hours with boiling water. The first and second extracts are combined and filtered through cloth. Before the agar solution has completely set the upper layer is drawn off, more impurities having settled out, and placed in shallow trays for the final process of dehydration. The agar gel is cut into suitable sizes and placed in open trays. During the night the gel freezes and ice crystals form; the following day the ice melts taking with it soluble impurities which are drained off. Freezing and thawing, which occur under natural conditions where the processing plants are located, are allowed to go on for about two weeks until no more water can be removed. By this process, the yield of agar amounts to about 20–25% of the weight of the dried plants. The annual output before World War II approached 2000–3000 tons.

The agar produced in Japan is characterized by its ability to form firm gels at low concentrations (0.5 to 1.0% in water). The gel changes to a sol at about 39°, giving a clear mobile solution; for this reason it serves as an excellent medium for bacteriological plating studies.

Many seaweeds growing in other parts of the world beside Japan are reported to contain agar-like polysaccharides (see Tables 11 and 12) (24), but they have not yet become the source of any large amounts of agar. The confusion that exists about the term ''agar'' and possible sources of this substance among the many species of Gelidiaceae and Rhodophyceae families, clearly indicates that the three common seaweed polysaccharides, agar, algin, and carrageenin, to say nothing of the others, such as fucoidin, and laminarin have not always been distinguishable. The confusion will undoubtedly disappear when a more detailed knowledge of the chemistry of these polysaccharides is accumulated (24,26,28,145).

There have been numerous attempts to find a substitute for the Japanese agar product, but the main point that seems to have been overlooked is that the Japanese agar is a composite of seaweed polysaccharides, the properties of which will depend in no small measure on the proportion of the various polysaccharides present in the mixture. It can easily be shown that the physical properties of a mixture of two polysaccharide gums cannot be predicted from a knowledge of the properties of the separate polysaccharides, especially when interaction occurs.

Isolation of Algin. The isolation of this seaweed polymer was first recorded in 1881 (27), and it is reported that the modern methods of isolation (28,29) are variants of these early investigations which used brown marine algae as the starting material. The procedure involves washing the algin containing seaweed with water or acid to remove soluble constituents after which digestion with dilute sodium carbonate is

TABLE 11. SPECIES AND LOCATION OF SEAWEEDS REPORTED TO
CONTAIN AGAR-LIKE POLYSACCHARIDES (24)

Seaweed	Location
Ahnfeltia plicata	Russia (Maritime Coast and White Sea area)
Camphylaephora hypneoides	China
Endocladia muricata	California
Eucheuma spinosum	China
E. isiforme	China
E. denticulatum	China
Gelidium amansii	California, China
G. cartilagineum	California, China, S. Africa
G. corneum	China, California
G. australe	California
G. pristoides	S. Africa
Gigartina asperifolia	California
G. canaliculata	California
G. serrata	California
Gloiopeltis	California
Gracilaria confervoides	China, Australia, S. Africa, California
G. lichenoides	China, Australia
Phyllophora nervosa	Russia, Black Sea
P. rubens	Russia, Black Sea
Pterocladia lucida	Australia
P. capillaceae	Brazil
Suhria vittata	S. Africa

TABLE 12. SEAWEEDS OF THE ATLANTIC COAST REPORTED TO
CONTAIN AGAR-LIKE POLYSACCHARIDES (24)

Seaweed	Location
Ahnfeltia plicata	North East Coast
Eucheuma isiforme	Florida
Gracilaria confervoides	East Coast of N. America
G. multipartita	East Coast of N. America

applied. This provides a solution of sodium alginate which is filtered to remove insoluble plant debris and acidified to precipitate alginic acid. The latter is then washed, pressed and dried (21). On the Pacific Coast of America, the giant kelp, *Macrocystis pyrifera*, is used and the alginate isolated as the aqueous insoluble calcium salt following one or other of a number of methods (30–34).

On the North American Atlantic Coast, the alginate is extracted from *Laminaria digitata* with dilute sodium carbonate after the seaweed has been washed with calcium chloride solution (35). The procedure recommended in Britain for isolating algin from *Ascophyllum nodosum* and from *Laminaria digitata* is to wash the plants with water and then treat them with 0.2*N* mineral acid under controlled conditions at 50–65°. Thereafter, the alginate is extracted from the plants with dilute sodium carbonate and precipitated with an acidified calcium chloride solution (29). The quality or "grade" of material and the yield are governed by (a) the temperature and duration of the water and/or acid wash stages and (b) the method for precipitating the calcium alginate (29). The insoluble character of the calcium alginate forms the basis of the analysis for alginic acid (29).

Alginic acid has been extracted from *Ascophyllum nodosum*, *Fucus spiralis*, *F. vesiculosus*, *F. serratus*, *Laminaria cloustoni*, *L. saccharina*, *L. digitata*, and *Pelvetia canaliculata*. Fresh seaweeds give the best grade of product, as judged by viscosity and predrying of the weeds is deleterious unless carried out at room temperature or below. Treatment of the product with hypochlorite or hydrogen peroxide improves the color, but degradation occurs (35).

On the Scottish coast, the alginic acid content of the common species of *Laminariaceae* and *Fucaceae* was found to vary with the season of the year and the depth of immersion (36–38).

The Canadian brown seaweeds, arranged in decreasing order of their alginic acid content, are *Laminaria digitata*, *Nereocystis luetkeana*, *Macrocystis integrifolia*, *Ascophyllum nodosum* and *Fucus vesiculosus* (39).

Mucilaginous polysaccharides have been isolated from eighteen species of green algae, *Cheamydomonas*, found in soil and fresh water. All but one were reported to contain galactose and arabinose as the main sugar components; in the other case, glucose and xylose were the predominant sugars. Associated with the two main sugars were fucose, rhamnose, mannose, uronic acids and other unidentified components. Comment is made on the role played by these algae in determining the character of soil and their possible chelating or sequestering action for metals.

Gums from Cereal Grains

Recent studies have shown that the common cereal grains, such as wheat, barley, rye, oats and maize, contain carbohydrate polymers which are gum-like in character. They have, as yet, not been considered as vegetable gums, but they fall within the definition adopted in this book and a brief account will be given of them. They are in effect seed gums and hence analogous to such galactomannans as guar and locust bean gum; they may well serve a similar purpose in nature.

These cereal gums have not been isolated so far on a large scale and as yet there are no industrial operations making use of them, though the crude extracts have good protective colloidal properties. The gum or mucin (40) of rye flour is said to form solutions more viscous (41) than those of starch, egg albumin or gelatin. The cereal gums are difficult to obtain in the pure state because they occur in the grains in the presence of much larger amounts of starch, and extraction by hot water should be avoided. The problem is further complicated by the fact that the cereal gums, which are of a pentosan-like character, seem to be closely associated with protein and simple aqueous extraction provides a product containing both carbohydrate and protein.

In the maize kernel, however, the gum-like body is located in the pericarp and it is a relatively simple matter to isolate the gum free from contaminating starch and protein.

To obtain the gum from wheat and rye, the grains are ground to a powder (flour), boiled with 80–90% aqueous ethyl alcohol to inactivate the enzymes, and then extracted with water, either at room temperature or below the gelatinization point of the starch (42,43). A purer product may be obtained by adding ammonium sulfate to the extract to precipitate the protein impurities (44).

Extraction of oat flour gives a mucilage-like material which contains both protein and polysaccharide; the highly viscous character of this mucilage is apparently due to the two components. This material is used as an anti-oxidant and it is said to be of some value in the treatment of skin diseases (45).

The cereal gums can be purified by fractional precipitation from aqueous solution with alcohol and by acetylation (50,51).

It may be pointed out that just as the properties of gum exudates or seaweed gums may depend to a great extent on the mutual effect of two or more gums upon each other, these cereal gums derive their viscous character from the presence of a mixture of polysaccharides (139) and proteins.

When barley grain flour is extracted with water, after inactivation of enzymes, a polysaccharide gum is obtained which consists of a mixture of a pentosan and a hexosan (52–55). The viscous character of aqueous solutions of this product is mainly due to the hexosan, a β-D-glucan, which can be preferentially separated from the pentosan by fractional precipitation from aqueous solution with ammonium sulfate at a concentration of 20 to 30 per cent (52).

The maize pentosan gum is best isolated by aqueous alkaline extraction of the hulls obtained as a by-product in the wet milling of the whole corn kernel (56). The viscous alkaline extract is neutralized with acetic acid and the polysaccharide gum precipitated with alcohol. This material has excellent gum-like properties and, being obtained from a waste product, it is relatively cheap to produce. It appears to be well worth examination for possible industrial applications.

Isolation of a Lichenin-like Product from Oats. The ground grain is extracted at room temperature with water containing a small amount of iodine. The extracts are centrifuged and filtered through celite to remove starch. Proteins were removed with lead acetate and the polysaccharide gum precipitated as the lead complex by adding ammonium hydroxide. Removal of lead as the carbonate with carbon dioxide followed by heating to coagulate protein gave a solution of the required gum. Acidification with acetic acid and subsequent addition of ethanol precipitated the crude lichenin-like polysaccharide. Purification by extraction with 50 per cent acetic acid and precipitation with ethanol gave the gum which showed $[\alpha]_D + 8°$ in $2N$ sodium hydroxide (46,47).

It is not certain whether this so-called oat lichenin is the same as the lichenin isolated (48) from Iceland moss (*Cetraria islandica*) which is also a glucan, but it is worth noting that lichenen of Iceland moss is soluble in water (49) while the oat gum is not.

REFERENCES

1. Howes, F. N., "Vegetable Gums and Resins," Chronica Botanica Co., Waltham, Mass. U.S.A. (1949).
2. Weir, A. H. W., "Report on gum Arabic in Bornu Province, Nigeria" (Lagos, Gov. Printer).
3. Malcolm, D. W., "Report on Gum and Gum Arabic" (Dar-es-Salaam, Gov. Printer, 1936).
4. Lely, H. V., "The Useful Trees of Northern Nigeria" (London, Crown agent for the Colonies (1925).
5. Blunt, H. S., "Gum Arabic with Special Reference to its Production in the Sudan," Oxford University Press, London (1926).
6. Dalziel, J. M., "The Useful Plants of West Tropical Africa" (London, Crown Agents for the Colonies) (1937).
7. Mantell, C. L., "The Water-Soluble Gums" Reinhold Pub. Corp., New York (1947).
8. DeCordemoy, H. J., *Les Plantes à gommes et à Rèsins*, Octave Dom et Fils Paris (1911).
9. Chevalier, A., *Rev. Bot. Appl.*, **11**, 438 (1932).
10. Greenway, P. J., *East African Agric. Journal*, **6**, 241 (1941).
11. Maiden, J. H., *Pharm. J.*, **20**, (3), 869, 980 (1890).
12. van Royen, M. J., *Beriehten van de Afdeeling Handelsmuseum van de Kon. Vereeniging Koloniaal Inst.*, No. 40, (1929).
13. Maiden, J. H., *Jour. and Proc. Roy. Soc., N. S. Wales*, **35**, 161 (1901).
14. Trease, O. E., *Pharm. J.*, **137**, 206 (1936); *Chem. Abstracts*, 31, 7603 (1937).
15. Wise, L. E., and Appling, J. W., *Ind. Eng. Chem., Anal. Ed.*, **16**, 28 (1944).
16. Anderson, E., *Ind. Eng. Chem.*, **41**, 2887 (1949).
17. May, F., and Schulz, A. S., *Z. Biol.*, **97**, 201 (1936); *Chem. Abstracts*, **30**, 8254 (1936).

18. Klages, F., and Niemann, R., *Ann.*, **523**, 224 (1936).
19. Hudson, C. S., *Organic Synthesis, Coll. Vol.* **III**, 541 (1955).
20. Lüdtke, M., *Ann.*, **456**, 201 (1927).
21. Idson, B., "*Chemical Week*," **79**, No. 3, 57 (1956).
22. Tseng, C. K., *Science*, **101**, 597 (1945).
23. *Fishery Leaflet* 263, U. S. Dept. of Interior, Sept. 1947.
24. *Fishery Leaflet 173*, U. S. Dept. of Interior, March 1946.
25. Black, W. A. P., and Woodward, F. N., *Advances in Chem. Series*, **11**, 83 (1954).
26. Marshall, S. M., and Orr, A. P., *Advances in Chem. Series*, **11**, 101 (1954).
27. Stanford, E. C. C., *Chem. News*, **47**, 254 (1883); *J. Soc. Arts*, **32**, 717 (1884); *J. Soc. Chem. Ind.*, **3**, 297 (1884); **4**, 518 (1885); **5**, 218 (1886); Brit. Pat., 142 (1881); Brit. Pat., 13, 433 (1884).
28. Steiner, A. B., and McNeeley, W. H., *Advances in Chem. Series*, **11**, 68 (1954).
29. Bashford, L. A., Thomas, R. S., and Woodward, F. N., *J. Soc. Chem. Ind.*, **69**, 337 (1950).
30. Green, H. C., U. S. Pat. 2,036,934 (1936).
31. Thornley, F. C., Tapping, F. F., and Reynard, O., U. S. Pat. 1,509,035 (1924).
32. Thornley, F. C., and Walsh, M. J., U. S. Pat. 1,814,981 (1931).
33. Thornley, F. C., Tapping, F. F., and Reynard, O., Brit. Pat. 211,174 (1922); *Chem. Abstracts*, **18**, 2062 (1924).
34. Reynard, O., U. S. Pat., 1,778, 688 (1930); Brit. Pat., 316,119 (1928).
35. Black, W. A. P., Cornhill, W. J., and Dewar, E. T., *J. Sci. Food Agr.*, **3**, 542 (1952).
36. Black, W. A. P., *J. Soc. Chem. Ind.*, **67**, 165, 169, 172 (1948); **67**, 355 (1948).
37. Black, W. A. P., *J. Soc. Chem. Ind.*, **68**, 183 (1949); **69**, 161 (1950).
38. Black, W. A. P., *J. Mar. biol. Ass., (United Kingdom)*, **29**, 45 (1950).
39. Rose, R. C., *Can. J. Technol.*, **29**, 19 (1951).
40. Rotsch, A., *Mühlenlab.*, 11, 1 (1941); *Chem. Zentr.*, I, 2051 (1941), *Chem. Abstracts* **37**, 4483 (1943).
41. Kretovitch, V. L., and Petrova, I. S., *Biokhimya*, **12**, 97 (1947); *Chem. Abstracts* **41**, 4861 (1947).
42. Montgomery, R., and Smith, F., *J. Am. Chem. Soc.*, **77**, 3325 (1955).
43. Montgomery, R., and Smith, F., *J. Agr. and Food Chem.*, **4**, 716 (1956).
44. Freeman, M. E., and Gortner, R. A., *Cereal Chem.*, **9**, 506 (1932).
45. Musher, S., U. S. Pat., 2,436,818 (1948).
46. Morris, D. L., *J. Biol. Chem.*, **142**, 881 (1942).
47. Letzig, E., *Z. Lebensm. Untersuch. u. Forsch.*, **92**, 170 (1951).
48. Hess, K., and Lauridsen, L. W., *Ber.*, **73B**, 115 (1940).
49. Drake, B., *Biochem. Z.*, **313**, 388 (1943).
50. Perlin, A. S., *Cereal Chem.*, **28**, 382 (1951).
51. Montgomery, R., and Smith, F., *J. Am. Chem. Soc.*, **77**, 2834 (1955).
52. Preece, I. A., and Mackenzie, K. G., *J. Inst. Brewing*, **58**, 353 (1952).
53. Preece, I. A., and Hobkirk, R., *J. Inst. Brewing*, **59**, 385 (1953).
54. Gilles, K. A., Meredith, W. O. S., and Smith, F., *Cereal Chem.*, **29**, 314 (1952).
55. Aspinall, G. O., and Telfer, R. G. J., *J. Chem. Soc.*, 3519 (1954).

56. Wolf, M. J., MacMasters, M. M., Cannon, J. A., Rosewall, E. C., and Rist, C. E., *Cereal Chem.*, **30**, 451 (1953).
57. Acker, L., Diemair, W., and Samhammer, E., *Z. Lebensm. Untersuch. u.- Forsch.*, **100**, 180 (1955).
58. Takahashi, E., *J. Coll. Agr. Hokkaido Imp. Univ.*, **8**, 183 (1920); *Chem. Abstracts* **15**, 249 (1921).
59. Tadakoro, T., and Saito, T., *J. Soc. Chem. Ind. Japan*, **38**, (suppl. binding) 270 (1935); *Chem. Abstracts*, **29**, 6388 (1935).
60. Hassid, W. Z., *J. Am. Chem. Soc.*, **55**, 4163 (1933); **57**, 2046 (1935).
61. Haas, P., *Biochem. J.*, **15**, 469 (1921).
62. Haas, P., and Russell-Wells, Barbara, *Biochem. J.*, **23**, 425 (1929).
63. Manske, R. H. F., *J. Biol. Chem.*, **86**, 571 (1930).
64. Gruzewska, Z., *Compt. rend.*, **173**, 52 (1921).
65. Uyeda, Y., *J. Soc. Chem. Ind. Japan*, **32**, 568 (1929); suppl. binding, **32**, 175B (1929); *Chem. Abstracts*, **23**: 4968 (1929).
66. Mori, T., and Tsuchiya, Y., *J. Agr. Chem. Soc. Japan*, **14**, 609, 616 (1938); *Chem. Abstracts*, **32**, 9175, 9176 (1938).
67. Mori, T., *J. Agr. Chem. Soc. Japan*, **15**, 1070 (1939); *Chem. Abstracts*, **34**, 3285 (1940).
68. Mori, T., Tutiya, Y., *J. Agr. Chem. Soc. Japan*, **15**, 1065 (1939); *Chem. Abstracts*, **34**, 3313 (1940).
69. Yanagigawa, T., and Yosida, T., *Repts. Impt. Ind. Research Inst., Osaka, Japan*, **17**, No. 5 (1936); **20**, No. 5 (1939); *Chem. Abstracts*, **34**, 4418 (1940).
70. Tadokoro, T., and Yoshimura, K., *J. Chem. Soc. Japan*, **56**, 655 (1935); *Chem. Abstracts* 29, 7390 (1933).
71. Tadakoro, T., Yoshimura, K., and Yanase, M., *J. Chem. Soc. Japan*, **56**, 188 (1935); *Chem. Abstracts*, **29**, 4406 (1935).
72. Kylin, H., *Z. physiol. Chem.*, **83**, 171 (1913).
73. Miwa, T., *Japan J. Botany*, **11**, 41 (1940); *Chem. Abstracts*, **35**, 7466 (1941).
74. Hoagland, D. R., and Lieb, L. L., *J. Biol. Chem.*, **23**, 287 (1915).
75. Nelson, W. L., and Cretcher, L. H., *J. Biol. Chem.*, **94**, 147 (1931).
76. Dillon, T., and McGuinness, A., *Sci. Proc. Roy. Dublin Soc.*, **20**, 129 (1931).
77. Haas, P., and Hill, T. G., *Ann. Appl. Biol.*, **7**, 352 (1921).
78. Butler, Margaret, R., *Biochem. J.*, **28**, 759 (1934).
79. Dillon, T., and O'Colla, P., *Nature*, **145**, 749 (1940).
80. Lunde, G., Lunde, S., and Jakobson, A., *Fiskeridirector, Skrifter Ser. Havundersøk (Rept. Norweg. Fishery Marine Investigation)*, **5**, No. 5, (1938); *Chem. Abstracts*, **34**, 7482 (1940).
81. Percival, E. G. V., and Buchanan, J., *Nature*, **145**, 1020 (1940).
82. Barry, V. C., and Dillon, T., *Proc. Roy. Irish. Acad.*, **50B**, 349 (1945).
83. Barry, V. C., and Dillon, T., *Nature*, **146**, 620 (1940).
84. Dewar, E. T., and Percival, E. G. V., *Nature*, **156**, 633 (1945).
85. Barry, V. C., *Sci. Proc. Roy. Dublin Soc.*, **21**, 615 (1938).
86. Peat, S., Whelan, W. J., and Lawley, H. G., *Chemistry and Industry*, 35 (1955).
87. Barry, V. C., *Sci. Proc. Roy. Dublin Soc.*, **22**, 59 (1939).
88. Barry, V. C., *Sci. Proc. Roy. Dublin Soc.*, **22**, 423 (1941).
89. Araki, C., and Arai, K., *Bull. Chem. Soc. Japan*, **29**, 339 (1956).

90. O'Neill, A. N., and Stewart, D. K. R., *Can. J. Chem.*, **34**, 1700 (1956).
91. Neuberg, C., and Ohle, H., *Biochem. Z.*, **125**, 311 (1921).
92. Fairbrother, F., and Mastin, H., *J. Chem. Soc.*, **123**, 1412 (1923).
93. Hoffman, W. F., and Gortner, R. A., *J. Biol. Chem.*, **65**, 371 (1925).
94. Lüdtke, M., *Biochem. Z.*, **212**, 419 (1929).
95. Nanji, D. R., Patton, F. J., and Ling, A. R., *J. Soc. Chem. Ind.*, **44**, 253T. (1925).
96. Pirie, N. W., *Biochem. J.*, **30**, 369 (1936).
97. Percival, E. G. V., Munro, J., and Somerville, J. C., *Nature*, **139**, 512 (1937).
98. Hands, S., and Peat, S., *Chemistry and Industry*, 937 (1938).
99. Hands, S., and Peat, S., *Nature*, **142**, 797 (1938).
100. Percival, E. G. V., Somerville, J. C., and Forbes, I. A., *Nature*, **142**, 797 (1938).
101. Forbes, I. A., and Percival, E. G. V., *J. Chem. Soc.*, 1844 (1939).
102. Percival, E. G. V., and Soutar, T. H., *J. Chem. Soc.*, 1475 (1940).
103. Duff, R. B., and Percival, E. G. V., *J. Chem. Soc.*, 830 (1941).
104. Jones, W. G. M., and Peat, S., *J. Chem. Soc.*, 225 (1942).
105. Isaac, W. E., Finlayson, M. H., and Simone, M. G., *Nature*, **151**, 532 (1943).
106. Percival, E. G. V., and Somerville, J. C., *J. Chem. Soc.*, 1615 (1937).
107. Yoshimura, K., *Bull. Coll. Agric. Imp. Univ. Tokyo.*, **2**, 207 (1895); *Chem. Centralbl.*, **67**, I, 46 (1886).
108. Harlay, V., *J. Pharm. chim.*, [VI], **16**, 193 (1902).
109. Ozawa, T., *J. Chem. Ind.*, (*Japan*), **25**, 389 (1922); *Chem. Abstracts*, **16**, 4086 (1922).
110. Bittó, B. V., *Landw. Versuchs. Stat.*, **46**, 307 (1895).
111. Komatsu, S., and Ueda, H., *Mem. Coll. Sci., Kyoto, Imp. Univ.*, **8**, 51 (1925); *Chem. Abstracts*, **19**, 3481 (1925).
112. Condorelli, P., *Ann. chim. applicata*, **15**, 426 (1925) [*Chem. Abstracts*, **20**, 1095 (1926)]; *ibid.*, **18**, 313 (1928) [*Chem. Abstracts*, **23**, 930 (1929)].
113. Gaal, B., *Ber. ungar. pharm. Ges.*, **3**, 133 (1927); *Chem. Abstracts*, **23**, 1929 (1929).
114. Kihara, Y., *J. Agr. Chem. Soc. Japan*, **14**, 733 (1938); *Chem. Abstracts*, **32**, 9176 (1938).
115. Balavoine, P., *Pharm. Acta Helv.*, **21**, 19 (1946); *Chem. Abstracts*, **40**, 4768 (1946).
116. Hilger, A., *Ber.*, **36**, 3197 (1903).
117. Pringsheim, H., and Liss, G., *Ann.*, **460**, 32 (1928); *Chem. Abstracts*, **22**, 1575 (1928).
118. Kinoshita, Y., *Bull. Coll. Agric. Imp. Univ. Tokyo*, **2**, 205 (1895).
119. Neville, K., *J. Agric. Sci.*, **5**, 113 (1913); *Chem. Abstracts*, **7**, 2445 (1913).
120. Tipson, R. S., Christman, C. C., and Levene, P. A., *J. Biol. Chem.*, **128**, 609 (1939).
121. Anderson, E., and Crowder, J. A., *J. Am. Chem. Soc.*, **52**, 3711 (1930).
122. Anderson, E., *J. Biol. Chem.*, **100**, 249 (1933).
123. Anderson, E., and Lowe, H. J., *J. Biol. Chem.*, **168**, 289 (1947).
124. Bailey, K., and Norris, F. W., *Biochem. J.*, **26**, 1609 (1932).
125. Bailey, K., *Biochem. J.*, **29**, 2477 (1935).
126. Nishida, K., Hashima H., and Fukamizu, T., *J. Agr. Chem. Soc. Japan*, **10**, 1001 (1934); *Chem. Abstracts*, **29**, 952 (1935).

127. Nishida, K., and Hashima, H., *J. Agr. Chem. Soc. Japan*, 11, 261 (1935); *Chem. Abstracts*, 29, 6574 (1935).
128. Nakahara, H., *J. Agr. Chem. Soc. Japan*, 11, 310 (1935); *Chem. Abstracts*, 9, 6623 (1935).
129. Nakahara, H., J. *Agr. Chem. Soc. Japan*, 16, 876 (1940); *Bull Agr. Chem. Soc. Japan*, 16, 140 (1940); *Chem. Abstracts*, 35, 4416 (1941).
130. Anderson, E., and Fireman, M., *J. Biol. Chem.*, 109, 437 (1935).
131. Youngken, H. W., *Am. J. Pharm.*, 106, 157 (1934).
132. Anderson, E., Gillette, L. A., and Seeley, M. G., *J. Biol. Chem.*, 140, 569 (1941).
133. Mullan, J., and Percival, E. G. V., *J. Chem. Soc.*, 1501 (1940).
134. Nelson, W. A. G., and Percival, E. G. V., *J. Chem. Soc.*, 58 (1942).
135. Gill, R. E., Hirst, E. L., and Jones, J. K. N., *J. Chem. Soc.*, 1469 (1939).
136. Anderson, E., *J. Biol. Chem.*, 104, 163 (1934).
137. Gill, R. E., Hirst, E. L., and Jones, J. K. N., *J. Chem. Soc.*, 1025 (1946).
138. Meyer, T. M., and van Dalfsen, J. W., *Arch. Rubbercultuur*, 23, 172 (1939); *Chem. Abstracts*, 34, 3943 (1940).
139. Deuel, H., Solms, J., and Neukom, H., *Chimia*, 8, 64 (1954); *Chem. Abstracts*, 48, 6150 (1954).
140. Nunn, J. R., and von Holdt, Mrs. M. M., *Chemistry and Industry*, 467 (1956).
141. Lewin, R. A., *Can. J. Microbiol.*, 2, 665 (1956).
142. Fisher, I. S., and Percival, Elizabeth E., *J. Chem. Soc.*, 2666 (1957).
143. Gentry, H. S., *Econ. Botany*, 11, 40 (1957).
144. Chapman, V. J., "Seaweeds and Their Uses," Methuen and Co. Ltd., London (1950).
145. Stoloff, L., *Advances in Chem. Series*, 11, 92 (1954).
146. Stoloff, L., and Silva, P., *Econ. Botany*, 11, 327 (1957); cf. Sauvageau, C., *Bull. Sta. Biol. d'Arcachon (Soc. Sci. d'Ar.)*. 1921.

CHAPTER 4

DETECTION AND IDENTIFICATION
OF GUMS AND MUCILAGES

The identification of a specimen of a gum or mucilage may be relatively simple if full use is made of the present knowledge of these substances and the available analytical techniques. However, it is sometimes found to be more convenient in industry, for one reason or another, to use a mixture of two or more gums or even to add some other carbohydrate compound, such as lactose, sucrose, starch, or starch dextrin, in which case the problem of identification is more difficult.

If in the native state, single specimens of gums may sometimes be recognized by their physical appearance (size, shape, color, brittleness, appearance on fracture, etc.). The tough, opaque, whitish flakes of gum tragacanth are readily identified and never confused with the clear, pale yellow or brownish appearance of the "tears" of gum arabic which fracture readily. Similarly, the yellowish brown or light brown tears of mesquite gum having a rough surface can be distinguished from the large, almost colorless, vitreous tears of chagual gum. Commercial samples of gums cannot be recognized in this way since most of them are used in the powdered form.

Some gums can be recognized by the way they dissolve or disperse in water. Thus gum arabic dissolves easily in water (2) and can readily be distinguished from gum tragacanth, karaya, chagual and khaya gums, which partially dissolve in water. Moreover dispensions of these last named gums are much more viscous than that of a solution of gum arabic of equal concentration. In general, the natural gum exudates, such as arabic, mesquite, cherry, plum, and damson gums dissolve more readily and completely, and give less viscous solutions than the root and seed mucilages. Gum tragacanth, Iles mannan, konjak mannan, the various galactomannans extracted from seeds of the legumes, and flax seed mucilage, form viscous, and in certain cases, stringy, mucilaginous dispersions.

The physical appearance and the rate of settling of precipitates, formed when aqueous solutions of the gums are treated with alcohol, may also be used as a preliminary test for the identification of gums (2,24). Thus, O'Sullivan observed (3) that gum arabic, having a highly branched, spherical structure, separated as a curdy precipitate which readily settled, whereas gum tragacanth, with a relatively linear structure, produced a stringy, mucilaginous precipitate (4). In applying this technique for the identification of commercial gums in food products, it has been stated (24) that locust or carob bean gum gives a stringy, opaque, non-adherent precipitate, while gum tragacanth gives a long, stringy, adherent precipitate. Karaya gum yields fine filamentous, non-adherent particles, while agar gives rise to a heavy flocculent precipitate which readily settles.

The preliminary tests should also include measurement of the specific optical rotation in either water or dilute alkali. The specific rotation of a suitable derivative of the gum, such as the acetate, is also useful for identification purposes.

The more modern technique of infra-red analysis should also prove to be useful since the various component sugars and glycosidic linkages can often be distinguished (5). The technique of differential thermal analysis (21) formerly used for inorganic substances may well prove to be a valuable analytical method in the study of gums and mucilages since the initial results indicate that carbohydrate polymers as well as oligosaccharides, having different glycosidic linkages, may be differentiated (21–23).

With a mixture of gums or other polymers of gum-like character, it is useful to take advantage of certain specific reactions that gums and mucilages undergo with a series of selected coagulating reagents. The behavior of a number of gums when they are treated with various reagents is recorded in Table 13 (6). In this Table are given the amounts of a particular reagent in milliequivalents per gram of polysaccharide or synthetic polymer necessary to produce coagulation. Many of the gums show a specific behavior which facilitates their identification (see also ref. 28).

Identification of gums may be effected in certain cases by the way they react with dyes (7,8). Of some interest are the following so-called specific reactions for certain gums used in industry (24), which should be considered in conjunction with those quoted in Table 13 (cf. ref. 27) and those in Table 13A taken from a more recent study (30).

Gum arabic. With one drop of Millon reagent, a white precipitate forms slowly. No precipitate is formed with an excess of the reagent.

Locust bean gum. Iodine solution added to a solution of the gum produces a purplish coloration and with sodium tetraborate a solution of the gum gels. This is not specific for locust bean gum, but it is specific for

TABLE 13. COAGULATION OF WATER SOLUBLE POLYSACCHARIDES AND OTHER HIGH POLYMERS BY ELECTROLYTES (6)

Polymer	Reagent[a]	Hydrochloric Acid	Trichloroacetic Acid	Picric Acid	Tannic Acid	Potassium Hydroxide	Potassium Chloride	Methylene Blue
Starch	1%	—	50	—	0.85	—	—	—
Dextrin	1%	—	—	—	1.70	—	—	—
Lichenin	0.5%	—	—	—	3.40	—	—	—
Lupine seed galactan	0.5%	—	100	10.0	1.70	—	—	—
Inulin	0.5%	—	—	—	—	—	—	—
Yeast mannan	1%	—	—	—	—	—	—	—
Salep mannan	0.5%	—	—	—	1.17	—	—	—
Locust bean gum	0.5%	—	—	—	1.70	—	—	—
Fenugreek seed mucilage	0.5%	—	—	—	1.70	—	—	—
Konjak glucomannan	0.5%	—	—	—	1.70	—	—	—
Tamarind seed mucilage	0.5%	—	—	—	1.70	—	—	—
Malva mucilage	0.5%	—	—	—	—	—	—	—
Althaea leaf mucilage	0.5%	—	—	—	—	—	—	1.00
Althaea root mucilage	0.5%	—	—	—	—	—	—	1.00
Cherry gum	0.5%	—	—	—	—	—	—	—
Gum tragacanth	0.5%	—	—	—	—	—	—	—
Gum arabic	1%	—	—	—	—	—	—	—
Quince seed mucilage	0.1%	10.0	10.0	10.0	85.0	—	—	0.50
Plantago ovata mucilage	0.1%	—	—	—	85.0	—	—	—
Plantago psyllium mucilage	0.1%	—	—	—	8.50	—	—	—
Plantago arenaria mucilage	1%	—	—	—	0.85	—	—	—
Flax seed mucilage	0.1%	—	—	—	—	—	—	—
Agar	0.1%	—	—	—	1.70	—	—	—
Carrageenin	0.5%	—	—	—	—	200	40.0	1.00
Na alginate	0.5%	20.0	10.0	—	—	—	—	10.0
Na pectate	0.5%	20.0	10.0	—	—	200	200	2.00
Na pectinate	0.5%	—	—	—	—	200	—	—
Gelatin	0.1%	—	—	10.0	0.009	—	—	—
Casein	0.5%	—	20.0	2.00	0.017	—	—	—
Poly(ethylene) oxide	0.5%	—	—	—	0.003	—	—	—
Poly(vinyl) alcohol	1%	—	—	—	0.17	—	—	—
O-Methylcellulose	0.5%	—	—	—	0.17	—	—	—
O-(Carboxymethyl)-cellulose	0.5%	200	—	—	3.40	—	—	1.00
Oxycellulose (Na salt)	0.5%	20.0	—	—	—	—	—	10.0
Na poly(acrylate)	0.5%	—	—	—	—	—	—	1.00
Na poly(methacrylate)	0.5%	20.0	10.0	—	—	—	—	10.0

[a] Milliequivalents of reagent per gram of polysaccharide.

TABLE 13. (CONTINUED)

Desogen Geigy	Sulfuric Acid	Beryllium Nitrate	Magnesium Chloride	Calcium Chloride	Copper Sulfate	Fehling Solution	Barium Chloride	Lead Acetate	Borax	Mercuric Nitrate
–	–	–	–	–	–	–	–	–	–	–
–	–	–	–	–	–	–	–	–	–	–
20.0	800	400	–	–	2.00	–	–	2.00	–	4.00
–	–	–	–	–	–	–	0.80	2.00	–	–
–	–	–	–	–	–	5.60	–	–	–	–
–	–	–	–	–	–	0.56	–	20.0	–	–
–	–	–	–	–	–	0.112	–	20.0	50.0	–
2.00	–	–	–	–	–	5.60	–	–	–	40.0
–	–	–	–	–	–	5.60	–	–	–	–
–	–	–	–	–	–	0.112	–	–	–	–
0.20	–	–	–	–	–	–	400	200	–	–
0.02	–	–	–	–	20.0	–	400	2.00	–	0.40
0.40	–	–	–	–	–	–	–	–	–	–
0.20	–	–	–	–	–	–	–	2.00	–	–
0.04	–	–	–	–	4.00	–	–	2.00	–	–
1.00	–	–	–	–	–	–	–	–	–	–
0.10	0.80	200	–	–	10.0	–	–	10.0	–	0.002
100	–	–	–	–	–	–	–	–	–	–
100	–	–	–	–	–	–	–	–	–	–
0.10	–	–	–	–	–	–	–	–	–	–
20.0	–	–	–	–	–	–	–	200	–	–
–	–	–	–	–	–	–	–	–	–	–
0.04	–	–	–	–	–	–	400	–	–	–
0.20	16.0	8.00	–	4.00	2.00	–	4.00	2.00	–	0.80
0.20	16.0	0.80	20.0	2.00	2.00	56.0	4.00	200	–	0.40
0.40	–	–	–	–	0.20	56.0	4.00	0.20	–	0.40
–	–	–	–	–	–	–	–	–	–	–
0.04	800	0.40	–	–	0.40	–	–	–	–	0.04
–	–	–	–	–	–	–	–	–	–	–
–	–	–	–	–	–	28.0	–	–	–	–
–	–	–	–	–	–	–	0.40	4.00	–	–
0.02	16.0	–	–	–	0.20	–	40.0	0.02	–	0.04
0.20	80.0	–	–	–	4.00	–	4.00	4.00	–	0.40
0.20	80.0	–	20.0	4.0	20.0	–	8.00	2.00	–	0.80
0.40	8.00	8.00	200	40.0	4.00	–	40.0	4.00	–	0.80

TABLE 13. (CONTINUED)

Polymer	Benzidine Hydrochloride	Ferric Chloride	Phosphotungstic Acid	Ruthenium Red	Thorium Nitrate	Hexol Nitrate	Iodine + KI	Casein
Starch	−	−	−	−	−	−	1.26	−
Dextrin	−	−	−	−	−	−	−	+
Lichenin	−	−	0.44	−	−	−	−	−
Lupine seed galactan	3.60	−	0.004	1.20	−	−	−	−
Inulin	−	−	−	−	−	−	−	−
Yeast mannan	−	−	−	−	−	−	−	−
Salep mannan	−	−	0.044	−	−	−	−	−
Locust bean gum	−	−	0.44	−	−	−	−	−
Fenugreek seed mucilage	−	−	0.44	−	−	−	−	−
Konjak glucomannan	−	−	0.088	−	−	−	2.52	−
Tamarind seed mucilage	−	−	0.44	−	−	−	0.54	−
Malva mucilage	−	−	−	6.00	200	−	−	+
Althaea leaf mucilage	−	12.0	−	1.20	0.40	0.019	−	−
Althaea root mucilage	3.60	−	4.44	6.00	20.0	1.90	−	−
Cherry gum	−	−	4.44	6.00	−	1.90	−	−
Gum tragacanth	−	−	0.88	6.00	−	0.038	−	−
Gum arabic	−	−	−	3.00	−	0.95	−	−
Quince seed mucilage	18.0	1.20	0.044	30.0	0.01	0.095	−	−
Plantago ovata mucilage	−	−	−	−	−	−	−	−
Plantago psyllium mucilage	−	−	22.2	−	−	−	−	−
Plantago arenaria mucilage	−	−	2.22	−	−	−	−	+
Flax seed mucilage	−	−	22.2	−	−	−	−	+
Agar	−	−	2.22	−	−	−	−	−
Carrageenin	3.60	2.40	4.44	0.60	2.00	1.90	−	−
Na alginate	3.60	2.40	0.44	6.00	2.00	0.38	−	+
Na pectate	0.04	1.20	0.44	6.00	2.00	1.90	−	−
Na pectinate	−	2.40	0.44	6.00	2.00	0.19	−	+
Gelatin	−	−	0.44	−	−	−	−	−
Casein	0.72	−	0.0004	6.00	−	−	−	−
Poly(ethylene) oxide	−	−	0.44	−	−	−	0.025	−
Poly(vinyl) alcohol	−	−	2.22	−	−	−	−	−
O-Methylcellulose	3.60	−	0.44	−	−	−	−	−
O-(Carboxymethyl)-cellulose	−	0.024	0.088	6.00	0.20	0.19	−	−
Oxycellulose (Na salt)	3.60	12.0	0.08	6.00	2.00	1.90	−	−
Na poly(acrylate)	3.60	12.0	0.04	−	0.40	0.19	−	−
Na poly(methacrylate)	−	2.40	−	−	0.20	1.90	−	−

TABLE 13A. PRECIPITATION REACTIONS OF POLYSACCHARIDE GUMS AND GELATIN (30)

Gum	1 Vol. 1% Solution of Cationic Soap[a]	0.5 Vol. Saturated Ammonium Sulfate	Diluted[b] Stokes's Acid Mercuric Nitrate Added Dropwise	1 Vol. 2% Papain[c]	1 Vol. 2% Gelatin[c]	4 Vol. 95% C_2H_5OH + 2 to 3 Drops Saturated NaCl
De-esterified pectin	Fine opaque precipitate	Gelatinous translucent precipitate	Gels (almost opaque). Insoluble in excess reagent	Precipitate	Precipitate	Gelatinous precipitate, gels (1 vol.)
Alginate	Fine opaque precipitate	Nil	Gels (almost opaque). Insoluble in excess reagent	Precipitate	Precipitate	Gelatinous precipitate (1 vol.) becomes stringy with 4 vol. alcohol
Pectin	Flocculent precipitate	Nil	Forms almost opaque gel which dissolves in excess reagent	Cloudy	No definite effect	Transparent gelatinous precipitate. Gels (1 vol.)
Irish moss	Stringy or flocculent precipitate	Gelatinous precipitate or gel	Transparent gel. Re-dispersed by excess reagent	Precipitate	Precipitate	Stringy precipitate.
Agar	Gelatinous precipitate	Flocculent precipitate	Turbid or cloudy	Cloudy	Precipitate	Fine flocculent precipitate
Tragacanth	Fine opaque precipitate	Nil	Flocculent precipitate. Dissolves in excess reagent	Precipitate	Precipitate	Voluminous precipitate, jellylike
O-Methylcellulose	Nil	Precipitate	Nil	Nil	Nil	Nil
Starch	Nil	Precipitate	Nil	Nil	Nil	Opaque flocculent precipitate
O-Carboxymethyl-cellulose	Gelatinous clotted precipitate	Gelatinous precipitate	Precipitate dissolves in excess reagent	Precipitate	Precipitate	Voluminous clotted precipitate
Locust	Nil	Precipitate (voluminous)	No pronounced effect	No pronounced effect	Nil	Voluminous opaque stringy precipitate, forms clot

TABLE 13A. (CONTINUED)

Gum	1 Vol. 1% Solution of Cationic Soap[a]	0.5 Vol. Saturated Ammonium Sulfate	Diluted[b] Stokes's Acid Mercuric Nitrate Added Dropwise	1 Vol. 2% Papain[c]	1 Vol. 2% Gelatin[c]	4 Vol. 95% C_2H_5OH + 2 to 3 Drops Saturated NaCl
Karaya	Flocculent precipitate	Nil	Flocculent precipitate dissolves in excess reagent	Precipitate	Precipitate	Flocculent precipitate, discrete particles
Arabic (acacia)	Precipitate (very fine)	Nil	Flocculent precipitate dissolves in excess reagent	Precipitate	Precipitate	Fine opaque non-settling precipitate
Ghatti	Fine precipitate	Nil	Nil	Nil	Precipitate	Fine precipitate, non-settling (2 to 3 vol.)
Gelatin	Precipitate in alkaline medium	Precipitate	Nil	Nil	Nil	Finely flocculent pre-cipitate, coagulates

(a) Rodalon (alkyl dimethyl benzyl ammonium chloride).
(b) Mercury dissolved in twice its weight of concentrated nitric acid and diluted to 100 times its volume with distilled water.
(c) Precipitates with papain and gelatin are observed only in weakly acidic medium and most exhibit properties of coacervates rather than true precipitates.

the galactomannan types of gums isolated from the seeds of leguminous plants (25).

Gum Tragacanth. When a solution of the gum is boiled with a few drops of 10 per cent aqueous ferric chloride solution a deep yellow stringy precipitate is formed. A stringy precipitate is formed on heating the gum solution with Schweitzer reagent (made by dissolving freshly precipitated copper oxide in concentrated ammonium hydroxide) (24).

Karaya gum. Upon adding one drop of 10 per cent aqueous potassium hydroxide to a solution of the gum, a white precipitate is formed which settles in 4 to 5 minutes. Other gums form precipitates which are said to take much longer to settle. The gum gives a pink color when boiled either with concentrated phosphoric acid or concentrated hydrochloric acid.

Agar. A solution of this gum gives a violet red color with iodine solution (26). This gum should not be confused with certain starch dextrins which also give reddish colors with iodine.

Irish Moss, Carrageenin. With 10 per cent ferric chloride solution this gum immediately forms a light-colored, opaque precipitate and gives a stringy, opaque precipitate with 10 per cent thorium nitrate (cf Table 13). Pectin also gives a positive test but the precipitate is firm and transparent.

Algin and Alginates. These give a pink color changing to cherry red and finally deep purple when treated with a solution made by dissolving ferric oxide in concentrated sulfuric acid.

Prior to the above work (6,24), a method of group analysis was recommended (2) for the identification of certain gums in commercial use.

TABLE 14. BEHAVIOR OF GUMS WHEN TREATED WITH WATER

Gum	Form of gum	Test solution (%)	Manner of solution in water
Arabic	powder or lump	1	Dissolves readily and gives clear solution
Tragacanth	powder	1	Swells and forms translucent, viscous solution becoming ropy on standing
Agar	ribbon	0.5	Dissolves on warming. Gels on cooling.
Karaya	powder or lump	1	Not very soluble. Particles swell
Algin	seaweed	0.5	Translucent, viscous, yellowish solution
Quince	seed	1	Opalescent solution becoming stringy on keeping
Locust bean	powder	1	Partially soluble, giving viscous cous solution. Insoluble fraction settles

TABLE 15. REAGENT TESTS WITH CERTAIN GUMS (24)

Gum	Millon Reagent	Neutral Lead Acetate (20%)	Basic Lead Acetate	Potassium Hydroxide (10%)	Ferric Chloride (5%)
Gum arabic	White fine, opaque ppt., sol in excess reagent	No ppt.	White, curdy ppt. insol in excess	Faint yellow tinge	Ppt. sol in excess
Gum tragacanth	Voluminous, translucent ppt.	Voluminous ppt. gels	Voluminous ppt. gels.	Bright-yellow, stringy precipitate	Gels
Agar	Gels	Flocculent ppt. gels	Voluminous ppt.	Clarifies solution	Gelatinizes, with excess and heat ppt.
Gum karaya	White, curdy ppt. settles rapidly	No ppt.	Stringy ppt. settles rapidly	No reaction	Ppt. coagulates on heating
Carrageenin	Gels	Flocculent ppt. gels	Voluminous, flocculent ppt., gels	Gels	Voluminous, stringy ppt., gels
Quince seed mucilage	Voluminous, yellowish ppt.	Yellowish, flocculent ppt., gels	Yellowish, voluminous ppt., gels	Stringy ppt.	Stringy ppt.
Locust bean gum	Gels	Voluminous ppt. gels.	Gels.	Slight flocculent ppt.	Stringy ppt.
Cashew gum (29)	. . .	No ppt.	Cloudy solution	Yellow, becomes dark on heating	No reaction

Table 14 shows the behavior of some of these gums upon treatment with water (2).

The behavior of the gums with eleven reagents is shown on Table 15. It is claimed (24, cf. 30) that by the application of these tests the individual gums may be identified. Millon reagent is recommended since by its use it is possible to divide the gums into four groups and the members of each group may be further identified by a group specific reagent. Hence by the use of two reagents the individual gum listed may be differentiated although in the case of agar and Irish moss a third reagent is advisable.

TABLE 15. (CONTINUED)

Alcohol Precipitate	Borax (4%)	Schweitzer Reagent	Iodine Solution	Tannic Acid (10%)	Sulphuric acid conc.
Very fine floc. non-adherent; with 40 ml. point of definite pptn.	No reaction	No reaction	No reaction	No reaction	No reaction
Coagulates, long and stringy adherent, 10 ml.	No reaction	Stringy ppt. on heating	Blue color	No reaction	Stringy ppt. on heating
Heavy floc. adherent to beaker, 20 ml.	No reaction	No reaction	No reaction	No reaction	Clarifies solution
Fine filamentous particles nonadherent, 15–20 ml.	No reaction	No reaction	No reaction	Ppt.	Ppt.
Coagulated, translucent, stringy adherent, 20 ml.	No reaction	No reaction	No reaction	No reaction	...
Coagulates, short, stringy nonadherent 25 ml.	No reaction	Stringy ppt. on heating	No reaction	Ppt.	Stringy ppt.
Stringy, clotty, opaque, non-adherent; start 2 ml; complete 15 ml.	Gels	No reaction	No reaction	Ppt.	Ppt.
...	Gels	...	...	Opalescent	No reaction

The reactions given appear to be reasonably sound for the eight gums listed, but all the tests are empirical so that the method may not be generally applicable.

A more recent method (30) of group analysis is given in Table 15A. This method, also based on a series of precipitation reactions, can only be applied after the gum has been separated from other substances. In order to complete the identification it is then necessary to determine the physical properties and composition of the gum as described in Chapter 7.

TABLE 15A. PRECIPITATION REACTIONS USED AS BASIS OF PROPOSED PROCEDURE FOR IDENTIFICATION OF GUMS (30)

(Reactions used as identification tests within heavy lines)

Gum	$\frac{1}{5}$ Vol. 2.5% CaCl$_2$	$\frac{1}{5}$ Vol. 2.5% CaCl$_2$ + $\frac{1}{5}$ Vol. 3N NH$_4$OH	1 Vol. 3N NaOH	$\frac{1}{10}$ Vol. Saturated Ba(OH)$_2$ Cold	$\frac{1}{10}$ Vol. Saturated Ba(OH)$_2$ Heated	1 Vol. Saturated Ba(OH)$_2$	$\frac{1}{5}$ Vol. Basic Lead Acetate	Basic Lead Acetate + $\frac{1}{5}$ Vol. 3N NH$_4$OH	Confirmatory Tests
De-esterified pectin	Gelatinous ppt. or gel		Gelatinous or flocculent ppt., yellow color on heating	Gel or gelatinous ppt.	Ppt. and soln. turn yellow	As for $\frac{1}{10}$ vol.	Gels	As for lead acetate alone	Gelatinous ppt. when acidified with mineral acids
Alginate	Gelatinous ppt. or gel		Clear yellow soln. on heating	Gel or gelatinous ppt.	Ppt. and soln. turn yellow	As for $\frac{1}{10}$ vol.	Gels	As for lead acetate alone	Gelatinous ppt. when acidified with mineral acids
Pectin		Gelatinous ppt. forms slowly	Gelatinous or flocculent ppt., yellow color on heating	Gel or gelatinous ppt.	Ppt. and soln. turn yellow	As for $\frac{1}{10}$ vol.	Translucent gel	As for lead acetate alone	
Irish moss	Some samples may give flocculent ppt.			Gelatinous ppt. or gel, almost opaque	Ppt. may flocculate with prolonged heating	Gelatinous ppt. or gel	Gelatinous ppt. or gel	As for lead acetate alone	Forms blue fibrous ppt. with aqueous methylene blue
Tragacanth				May be small amount of ppt.	Lemon yellow color	Flocculent ppt.	Flocculent ppt.	As for lead acetate alone	
Agar				Nil	Becomes yellow then green and gray	Nil	Flocculent ppt.	Gels	Gives blue or black stain with tincture of iodine
O-Methylcellulose				Nil	Becomes turbid or forms gel; becomes clear on cooling	Nil	Nil	Gels	Aqueous dispersions are not precipitated by alcohol, but form gel or become cloudy when heated

Starch	Opaque flocculent ppt.	May redisperse	Flocculent ppt.	Flocculent ppt.	Very heavy flocculent or gelatinous ppt.	Blue stain with I2-KI reagent
O-Carboxy-methyl-cellulose	Ppt. dissolves on shaking	Nil	Flocculent ppt.	Gels	As for lead acetate alone	Forms clotted ppt. with CuSO4
Locust[a]			Clotted opaque ppt.	Opaque gel	As for lead acetate alone	Gels with 1/3 vol. 4% borax
Karaya			Flocculent ppt., forms slowly	Flocculent ppt.	As for lead acetate alone	Swells and stains pink with ruthenium red test solution
Arabic (acacia)				Voluminous opaque ppt.	As for lead acetate alone	Readily soluble in water at room temperature
Ghatti				May be small amount of flocculent ppt.	Voluminous opaque ppt.	Fine ppt. with 4 vol. of alcohol. Arabic also gives fine ppt.
Gelatin						Gives fine yellow ppt. when added to saturated picric acid.

[a] Locust bean gum and guar gum give identical reactions and cannot be distinguished on basis of these tests.

Infrared Spectra and X-ray Crystallographic Data of Gums

Recently, infrared measurements have been applied to simple sugars and glycosides (9,10) and the various types of glycosidic bonds characterized (5). Extension of these studies to polysaccharides indicates that the major glycosidic bonds may be identified. When enough data has been accumulated it is very likely that this approach will prove valuable for the identification of gums and mucilages.

X-ray crystallographic examinations have been applied very effectively to a few polysaccharides, such as starch (11–13) and cellulose (14–16) and in the field of gums and mucilages to alginic acid (17–19) and guar gum (20). For those carbohydrate polymers possessing a high degree of linearity the method might well prove valuable as it has in the case of alginic acid and guar gum; for the irregularly branched gums and mucilages this method is of limited value.

Identification by Differential Thermal Analysis. It has long been known that the way in which inorganic compounds undergo decomposition enables them to be classified and in certain cases identified. This has recently been extended to simple sugars and oligosaccharides (21,22) and, in a few cases, to polysaccharides (21–23). It appears that the decomposition is dependent to some extent on the nature of the glycosidic bonds, for starch and cellulose, like maltose and cellobiose, behave differently. It is too early to predict the outcome of the application of this technique to gums and mucilages, but it is clear that the results so far are encouraging enough to merit further study.

In the final analysis (1) of a suspected gum confirmation should be obtained by identifying the sugars produced upon hydrolysis by paper chromatography as described later. If possible the rate and perhaps the order in which the particular sugars are liberated should be ascertained at the same time since certain gums may be differentiated by their stability towards acidic reagents (1).

While many of the above tests have been developed empirically for identifying gums and related water-soluble polysaccharides, a consideration of them will reveal that the above tests could probably be put to good use for the purification of these polymers.

REFERENCES

1. Hirst, E. L., and Jones, J. K. N., "Modern Methods of Plant Analysis," Ed. K. Paech and M. V. Tracey, II, Springer-Verlag Berlin (1955), 275.
2. Jacobs, M. B., and Jaffe, L., *Ind. Eng. Chem. Anal. Ed.*, **3**, 210 (1931).
3. O'Sullivan, C., *J. Chem. Soc.*, **45**, 41 (1884).
4. O'Sullivan, C., *J. Chem. Soc.*, **79**, 1164 (1901).

5. Barker, S. A., Bourne, E. J., and Whiffen, D. H., *Methods of Biochemical Analysis*, 3, Ed. D. Glick, Interscience (1956), 213.
6. Deuel, H., and Neukom, H., *Advances in Chem. Series*, 11, 51 (1954).
7. Lloyd, F. E., *Trans. Roy. Soc. Canada*, 14, Sect. V, 23 (1920).
8. Bungenberg de Jong, H. G., and Kok, B., *Proc. Acad. Sci., Amsterdam*, 43, 728 (1940); *Chem. Abstracts*, 36, 6873 (1942).
9. Kuhn, L. P., *Anal. Chem.*, 22, 276 (1950).
10. Whistler, R. L., and House, L. R., *Anal. Chem.*, 25, 1463 (1953).
11. French, D., in "*Chemistry and Industry of Starch*" 2nd Ed., Academic Press, New York (1950) 157.
12. Katz, J. R., and Derksen, J. C., *Z. physik Chem.*, A165, 228 (1933).
13. Rundle, R. E., *J. Am. Chem. Soc.*, 69, 1769 (1947).
14. Meyer, K. H., and Misch, L., *Helv. Chim. Acta*, 20, 232 (1937).
15. Peirce, F. T., *Nature*, 153, 586 (1944).
16. Hermans, P. H., *Kolloid Z.*, 102, 169 (1943).
17. Astbury, W. T., *Nature*, 155, 667 (1945).
18. Palmer, K. J., *J. Appl. Phys.*, 17, 405 (1946).
19. Palmer, K. J., and Hartzog, M. B., *J. Am. Chem. Soc.*, 67, 1865 (1945).
20. Palmer, K. J., and Ballantyne, M., *J. Am. Chem. Soc.*, 72, 736 (1950).
21. Morita, H., and Rice, H. M., *Anal. Chem.*, 27, 336 (1955).
22. Morita, H., *Anal. Chem.*, 28, 64 (1956).
23. Morita, H., *J. Am. Chem. Soc.*, 78, 1397 (1956).
24. Bundesen, H. N., and Martinek, M. J., *Milk and Food Technol.*, 17, 79 (1954).
25. Anderson, E., *Ind. Eng. Chem.*, 41, 2887 (1949).
26. *Pharmacopoeia of the United States of America*, 14th ed. (1950).
27. Hart, F. L., *J. Assoc. Off. Agr. Chem.*, 20, 527 (1937).
28. Deuel, H., Solms, J., and Denzler, A., *Helv. Chim. Acta*, 36, 1671 (1953).
29. Tiomno, F. R., *Rev. quím ind. (Rio de Janeiro)*, 15, No. 168, 23; No. 172, 19 (1946).
30. Ewart, M. H., and Chapman, R. A., *Anal. Chem.*, 24, 1460 (1952).

CHAPTER 5

SEPARATION OF MIXTURES OF POLYSACCHARIDES

The methods that have been developed for studying the fine structure of polysaccharides have reached such a degree of precision that the purity of the starting products becomes of great importance. Thus, for example, it is possible to separate and identify components in the hydrolyzate of polysaccharides and their methyl derivatives that are present to the extent of 0.5 per cent, or even less. Whether or not these small amounts are of structural significance depends largely upon the purity of the original polysaccharide. They may arise from the polysaccharide and thus be structurally significant, but they may be derived from a polysaccharide impurity. If such components, present in small or large amounts, arise from a mixture of polysaccharides then structural deductions made from them will obviously be incorrect. It is therefore of the utmost importance to establish the homogeneity of the starting materials (1).

There are many indications that like the proteins many naturally occurring polysaccharides are by no means homogeneous when judged by a variety of techniques. Thus, starch has been shown to consist of the two components, amylose, the so-called "linear fraction" and amylopectin, the "branched fraction" (cf. 171). It is worth bearing in mind that, in spite of the vast difference in structure and molecular weight of these two components of starch, their complete separation is far from being a simple task, and although pure amylose is relatively easy to obtain (cf. 156), since it crystallizes as a complex with certain organic molecules, considerable difficulty is encountered is isolating pure amylopectin. This is not too surprising when consideration is given to the difficulty involved in separating two relatively simple organic molecules by precipitation techniques. It may well be that homogeneous polysaccharides are the exception rather than the rule.

In addition to the example of heterogeneity of starch mentioned above, reference should be made to the fact that the so-called pure forms of cellulose, prepared from plant sources, always contain small amounts of other sugars such as arabinose, xylose and mannose (5). Whether or not

54

these sugars form an integral part of the cellulose molecule is not yet clear, but it is known that they cannot be removed completely by any physical method without degrading the cellulose. Similarly gum tragacanth has been shown to consist of a mixture of a polyglycosiduronic acid and a galactoaraban (2), while esparto grass xylan has been resolved into an araban and a xylan (3). Likewise, Iles mannan consists of a mixture of a glucomannan and a glucan resembling amylose (4). Similarly, the heterogeneity of the cereal gums is shown by the fact that barley gum contains at least three carbohydrate components, an α-D-glucan, a β-D-glucan (barley lichenin) and an arabo-glucurono-xylan. Certain mucilages, such as those from *Linum usitatissimum*, *Plantago ovata*, and *Plantago indica*, appear to be heterogeneous from fractionation studies using copper acetate and alcohol (6).

These preliminary findings have been derived mainly from results of fractional precipitation methods. At any rate, heterogeneity in polysaccharides is more common than hitherto believed and it is appropriate to consider methods available for the purification of polysaccharides. This is not only an important issue as far as polysaccharide gums and mucilages are concerned, but it is a major problem in the field of polysaccharide chemistry.

Fractional Precipitation

By "Crystallization" or Precipitation from Water. Certain polysaccharides can be purified by dissolution in water and allowing the solution to cool when the polymer precipitates. Inulin (7), agar (unless free from cations) (8,9), the lichenins (10) from Iceland moss and oat flour (11), the xylans from birchwood (12) and barley straw (12–15) and ivory nut mannan (12,16) have been purified in this manner.

With Alcohol or other Organic Liquids. This has been the main method of purifying polysaccharide gums and mucilages as well as their acetate, nitrate, and methylated derivatives. The technique consists of dissolving the polysaccharide in water, for example, and adding ethanol gradually to effect precipitation. Although there is a tendency for co-precipitation, this disadvantage can be overcome to some extent by repeated fractional precipitation. However, unless the solubility of the components being separated is quite different, this method at best can only produce a rough separation. The arabans (17) and fructans (18,23, 24) have been found to respond particularly well to this type of fractionation. Fructans may also be purified by precipitation from pyridine with acetone (19). More recently, dimethyl sulfoxide has shown promise as a solvent for preferential extraction and precipitation (20,21) of polysaccharides.

The success of the fractionation, and hence the inhomogeneity of the polysaccharide, may be ascertained by measurement of the specific rotation, molecular weight (by the elevation in boiling point (23,24), depression or melting point (27), or the Barger vapor pressure method (25,26), usually on a derivative) viscosity, sedimentation, light scattering, osmotic pressure (22), and by the determination of the nature and percentage of the component sugars in each fraction.

Acetic acid has been found useful for the precipitation of starch (28) and glycogen (108) from aqueous solutions, the former being precipitated at a concentration of 66 per cent acetic acid and the latter at about 80 per cent acetic acid (28). These properties have enabled glycogen and starch to be separated from the carbohydrates of sweet corn (Zea mays) and from each other (28,29,31). The method is also useful for the separation of pentosans and hexosans (67). The so-called lichenin of oat flour has been purified by reason of its insolubility in 50 per cent acetic acid (30). This technique, first noted in studies on glycogen (104), could be more extensively employed in the purification of gums provided that care is taken to see that degradation is avoided.

Fractional Precipitation with Salts. Polysaccharides can be fractionated by precipitation from aqueous solution with salts in a manner analogous to the fractionation of proteins. Thus barley β-D-glucan (barley lichenin) can be separated from an α-D-glucan and a pentosan present in the aqueous extract of barley flour (barley gum) by the addition of ammonium sulfate (32 cf. 33). The barley lichenin is precipitated in a fairly pure condition with 20 per cent ammonium sulfate and the pentosan is precipitated with 30 per cent ammonium sulfate. An arabo-xylan can be obtained from the aqueous extract of wheat flour in a similar way (34,36), and corn hull hemicellulose may also be precipitated with ammonium sulfate (36).

Controlled addition of ammonium, potassium, rubidium or cesium salts also serves to separate the two components (K and λ) of carrageenin (35), the polysaccharide extracted from Chondrus crispus and Gigartina stellata. One of these components, K-carrageenin, composed of about one part of 3,6-anhydro-D-galactose and 2 parts of D-galactose 4-sulfate, is capable of being precipitated with potassium, ammonium, rubidium, and cesium ions (35), whereas λ-carrageenin, which is a poly-D-galactose 4-sulfate, is not affected by potassium ions (37). This sensitivity of K-carrageenin to potassium and other ions of similar size and not to such ions as sodium or lithium suggests that the phenomenon is due to the size of the hydrated ions. By reason of the attraction between the potassium ions and the sulfate ions of the K-carrageenin, the molecules of the latter may be sufficiently close to each other to produce aggregation and ultimately precipitation. X-ray diffraction studies have shown (37) that the sulfate groups in the K-carrageenin are 6.3Å apart and hence can accommodate the hydrated potassium ions which have a diameter of 2.5 to 4.0Å (38,39).

In λ-carrageenin the X-ray studies showed that the sulfate groups are only 4.2Å apart and it is believed that this distance is too small to enable the univalent potassium ions to effect aggregation.

The specificity of this reaction shows that even large molecules are capable of fairly precise orientation even in solution.

This technique of using salts for the fractionation of polysaccharides seems to offer certain advantages over many of the other precipitation methods, especially those employing solvents, in that the tendency for co-precipitation is much less since salts have the effect of reducing hydrogen bonding. Since the method has been used in the relatively simple problem of effecting a gross separation of amylose and amylopectin (170), it would appear to be worthy of wider application.

Acidic polysaccharides such as alginic acid and pectic acid can be separated almost quantitatively from neutral polysaccharides as their insoluble calcium (40) or barium salts (41); the technique has been recommended for the determination of alginic acid in seaweed gums (40). In a somewhat similar way, quaternary ammonium salts, such as cetyl trimethylammonium bromide (42) and cetylpyridinium chloride (44) have been employed for the purification of acidic polysaccharides. More recently cetyltrimethylammonium bromide has been used in conjunction with borate complex formation to separate certain neutral polysaccharides (43).

Fructans of the inulin type, with a fairly high molecular weight, can be purified as stated above by "crystallization" from water, whereas those of lower molecular weight, present in cereal grains and in bulbs like the onion, can be separated from other polysaccharides by precipitation with barium hydroxide or alcoholic alkali (45).

Some polysaccharides containing a large proportion of uronic acid units, among which may be mentioned alginic acid, pectic acid and tragacanthic acid, can be purified by precipitation with dilute mineral acid.

Fractional Precipitation with Complexing Agents

(1) **With organic molecules.** The classical example is the separation of amylose from amylopectin by complexing the former with such polar organic molecules as 1-butanol or Pentasol (46,47). A wide variety of other agents besides alcohols may be used for this purpose including

fatty acids, nitro-paraffins, ketones, esters, phenols and aromatic nitro-compounds (48,49). Thus far, this technique does not appear to have been used for the purification of gums and mucilages.

(2) **With copper salts.** Fehling solution has been widely employed for purifying polysaccharides, especially those containing a relatively high proportion of mannopyranose units joined by $1 \longrightarrow 4$-β-D-glycosidic bonds (4,50,51,53,54). Pentosans of the xylan type may also be purified in this way (3,52). In addition to Fehling solution, cupric chloride (55), cupric sulfate (56), cupric acetate (6,57), and cupriethylenediamine (52–54) have been employed for the same purpose. Based upon this phenomenon an interesting diagnostic test for the identity of certain glucosans has also been devised (29). The glucomannan of Iles mannan (from *Amorphophallus oncophyllus*) has been separated from a starch-like, polysaccharide impurity (4) and the glucomannan (61) of konjak flour (from *Amorphophallus konjak*) has been purified in the same way. The two components of Iceland moss (*Cetraria islandica*), lichenin (62) and isolichenin (63–65), have likewise been purified by making use of the ability of these polysaccharides to form copper complexes.

Most, if not all, the galactomannan gums extracted from seeds of the *Leguminosae* (see Table 29 page 106) give copper complexes with Fehling solution and this offers a means for their purification and identification.

The polysaccharide xylan found in ramie (esparto) grass, composed only of D-xylose units, may be separated from an araban by reason of the fact that only the former is precipitated with Fehling solution (3,66–68). Certain glucans, for example, the dextrans synthesized by some *Leuconostoc* organisms can be fractionated by copper complex formation (70).

A closer examination (69) of this reaction between copper solutions and polysaccharides shows that neutral copper sulfate solutions containing the cation, $Cu(OH_2)_4^{++}$, precipitate only yeast mannan and the galactan of *Lupinus albus*. With Fehling solution the following polysaccharides at concentrations as low as 0.5 per cent are also precipitated: the mannan of *Orchis morio*, the galactomannans of *Ceratonia siliqua* and *Gleditsia tricanthos*, and the mucilage, tamarind gum, from *Tamarindus indica* seeds. Alkaline copper sulfate solutions, which contain the anion, $Cu(OH)_4^{--}$, form precipitates with lichenin, gum arabic, cherry gum, gum tragacanth, and the mucilages from *Plantago psyllium* and *Linum usitatissimum*; no precipitates are formed under these conditions with carrageenin, agar, and gum karaya.

The fact that certain polysaccharides composed of sugar residues having *cis* adjacent hydroxyl groups at C_2 and C_3, form stable complexes with cuprammonium solution, recognized by major changes in optical rotation, has been used to ascertain the type of linkage present in poly-saccharides. In the case of 1,4 linked glucans there is a strong negative shift whereas 1,2 linked glucans exhibit a large positive optical rotatory shift (71). Lichenin, the glucan from *Phytomonas tumefaciens*, starch, glycogen and some mannan polysaccharides have been investigated by this method, but its value in the field of gums and mucilages still awaits investigation. Although it has been reported that a mannan can be sepa-rated from a xylan by dissolving the mixture in cuprammonium solution and adding sodium hydroxide to a concentration of 0.2N (72), there is as yet little or no evidence to indicate that this is a general method for the separation of polysaccharides.

With borates. In spite of the fact that almost all galactomannans form gelatinous complexes with sodium tetraborate (borax) (73,74) and that the reaction is used for classification and identification purposes (75, 76) (see Chapter 4), it does not appear to have been used for the purifi-cation of polysaccharides.

The structural requirements for forming borate complexes are the same as those for forming copper complexes, namely, adjacent cis hydroxyl groups are required. Cross linkages may be formed if the borate ion, $B(OH)_4^-$, complexes two adjacent molecular chains. This leads to the formation of a three dimensional network which in turn may result in gel formation (76–78).

Complex formation with borax has been shown by viscosity measure-ments to be dependent upon the amount of borax added (see Table 16). The complexes are stable only in the presence of the borate for borax gels liquefy when dialyzed against water (77).

TABLE 16. EFFECT OF CONCENTRATION ON THE VISCOSITY OF SOLUTIONS OF LOCUST BEAN GUM (77)

Concentration of Locust Bean Gum

	0.15%		0.175%		0.20%
Borax (%)	Specific viscosity	Borax (%)	Specific viscosity	Borax (%)	Specific viscosity
0.00	2.0	0.00	2.5	0.00	4.0
0.05	2.2	0.05	2.7	0.025	4.5
0.10	2.5	0.10	3.1	0.050	5.3
0.20	2.7	0.20	3.7	0.075	6.5
0.35	2.8	0.35	4.2	0.100	7.3
0.50	2.7	0.50	4.4	0.5	gels
0.75	2.5	0.75	4.5		
1.00	1.4	1.0	3.9		
		2.5	1.8		

Borate complexes with gums are also influenced by pH. Table 17 shows the effect of pH on the complex between borate (0.35%) and locust bean gum (0.15%).

TABLE 17. EFFECT OF pH ON THE VISCOSITY OF BORATE-LOCUST BEAN GUM SOLUTIONS (77)

pH	3.4	7.1	7.6	8.1	8.6	8.7	8.8	9.0	10.0
Specific viscosity	1.9	2.0	2.3	2.8	2.9	3.0	2.8	2.7	1.8

Just as one polysaccharide is influenced by another, so simple polyhydroxy compounds and sugars will affect the complexes formed between polysaccharides and borax. Presumably part of the borax is diverted from complexing with the polymer (see Table 18).

TABLE 18. EFFECT OF SMALL MOLECULAR WEIGHT POLYALCOHOLS ON THE BORATE LOCUST BEAN GUM COMPLEX—(BORAX 0.35%; LOCUST BEAN GUM 0.15%)

Fructose (%)	Specific viscosity	Glycerol (%)	Specific viscosity	Sucrose	Specific viscosity
0.0	2.8	0.0	2.8	0.0	2.8
0.025	2.1	0.5	2.4	2.0	2.6
0.125	2.0	5.0	2.0	5.0	2.7

It has long been known that boric acid combines with simple polyhydroxy compounds only when hydroxyl groups are available on adjacent carbon atoms, cis-hydroxyl groups forming a complex more readily than trans-hydroxyl groups (79–84). The product formed has a cyclic structure. In other cases, boric acid forms monobasic borospirans (85). In the case of polysaccharides, both types of complexes are probably present.

Boric acid does not behave like borax, as may be shown by the fact that dextrins and starches do not react with boric acid whereas they form a gel with borax.

In order to develop the three dimensional gel structure between boric acid or borax and a polysaccharide, each molecule must be joined to others in at least two positions. The higher the molecular weight the more effective will be the boric acid or borate on the increase in molecular weight of the complex. Thus, a polysaccharide of molecular weight 50,000 may be joined to another to give a complex molecule of molecular weight 100,000, whereas one with a molecular weight of 5,000 under the influence of the same amount of boric acid or borate will form a complex of 10,000 and to form a complex molecule with a molecular weight of 100,000 would require ten times the amount of complexing reagent. On this basis it is possible to bring about with boric acid the fractionation of polyhydroxy compounds of like structure but of different molecular weight with boric acid. Although the method has been applied to synthetic poly(vinyl)acetals, it has not yet been used for the fractionation of natural polyhydroxy compounds like the gums and mucilages. Some use has been made of the fractional extraction of polysaccharides with alkaline borate solution (144) rather than with alkali alone, which has been extensively applied in attempts to effect fractional extraction of the so-called hemicelluloses of wood and straw (145-149). There is little evidence to show that fractional extraction is anything more than a crude method (150,151) at best, mainly because the polysaccharides in the native state are not all equally accessible to the reagent. Once the polymers have been extracted the chances of fractionation by acidification are much better. The precision of the borate complexing reaction could probably be extended by making use of the fact that borate complexes can be dissociated with 1,2-glycols, such as glycerol or mannitol.

With Aluminum Hydroxide. Since aluminum hydroxide has been used (156) to separate the linear and branched chain components of starch, this and other polyvalent inorganic substances should be considered in connection with the resolution of mixtures of polysaccharides.

With Other Polysaccharides. The observation that polysaccharides having similar structures are difficult to separate, suggests that one polysaccharide can be used to purify another, providing that the new polysaccharide complex formed can be split either by chemical or enzymic means. An example of this technique is the use of cellulose to form a complex with amylose whereby it is separated from amylopectin (86-88).

The observation that galactomannans, such as guar gum, locust bean gum and the glucomannans, Iles mannan, and konjak mannan, form good beater additives (89,90) indicates that cellulose could probably be used to purify such glycomannans as well as other polysaccharides having structures with a certain amount of linear character. Clearly this method is capable of much wider application.

With Proteins. This is perhaps the most selective method presently available and holds out considerable promise for the preparation of pure polysaccharides.

Polysaccharides and especially the gums, like gum arabic, containing uronic acid groups, form complexes with proteins such as gelatin (91); since only the free gum acid shows this property, the reaction is due largely to salt formation. Whereas this might be useful for separating acid polysaccharides from neutral ones, its use is somewhat restricted and the more specific reactions between carbohydrates and proteins appear to offer greater promise for polysaccharide purification. Polygalacturonic acids have also been shown to react with polyethyleneimine (169).

Certain polysaccharides having a particular molecular configuration may be precipitated with the protein, concanavalin-A (92), extracted from Jackbean meal. This protein will precipitate yeast gum (yeast mannan) and glycogen completely from aqueous solution (93,94) and certain dextran-like glucans (95) can be precipitated, whereas many other polysaccharides including the starches are not affected by it.

In analogous experiments, it has been shown that antipneumococcus horse sera will precipitate certain polysaccharides which are structurally related to the antipneumococcus polysaccharides. The use of these immunological reactions is illustrated by the fact that they have enabled gum arabic to be separated into two components which differ in their rhamnose content (96–98).

Chromatographic Separation

Only the smaller molecular weight oligosaccharides can be separated by the usual methods of paper chromatography either directly or in the form of derivatives, such as the N-glycosides. However, displacement chromatography using a charcoal column (99) may sometimes be used, as in the case of yeast mannan, which can be purified by this technique using 15 to 20 per cent alcohol as the eluting solvent (100). Hyaluronic acid may be similarly purified.

This method, in conjunction with suitable solvents, should prove to be valuable for the separation of some of the lower molecular weight gums and mucilages.

There are already indications that methylated polysaccharide gums can be separated on alumina (101) in a similar manner.

Separation by Means of Enzymes

Mixtures of polysaccharides can be resolved by destroying the undesirable components with specific enzymes. Thus the wheat pentosan gum has been freed from starch by amylolysis (102) and yeast gum has been separated from glycogen in a similar manner by autolysis (103). Similarly, the glucomannan in Iles mannan can be freed from the amyloselike impurity by preferential decomposition of the latter with α or β-amylase.

The polysaccharides can be freed from protein in a number of ways, e.g., by denaturation with heat, by decomposition of the protein with alkali (104), denaturation by shaking with alcohols such as butanol

(166) or chloroform-amyl alcohol (105,106), precipitation with trichloro-acetic acid (107,108), uranyl acetate (109) or stannic chloride (110). Proteins may also be removed by preferential absorption on calcium phosphate gel (111), bentonite (103), or charcoal and certain of them may be removed with powdered cellulose.

Fractional Precipitation of Derivatives

Polysaccharides that are difficult to separate by complex formation or by fractional precipitation from aqueous solutions with alcohol, because of very close similarity of structure or association by hydrogen bonding, can sometimes be fractionated after acetylation, for by this means the hydroxyl character is obliterated and there is much less tendency for molecular association. Thus, for example, cereal gum pentosan can readily be separated from contaminating glucans such as starch, since the pentosan acetates are much less soluble than the hexosan acetates (113,114). After resolution of the polysaccharides in this way, the acetyl groups can readily be saponified and the polysaccharides recovered unchanged.

Polysaccharides may also be separated by fractional precipitation of the methyl derivatives from acetone or chloroform solution with ether of petroleum ether. It is a valuable technique to apply during methylation studies, but it suffers from the disadvantage that demethylation cannot be effected to give the unmethylated polysaccharide.

Minor variations in the fractionation techniques are worth noting inasmuch as improved fractionation may thereby be effected. When a solution of a polysaccharide derivative is treated with a solvent in which the derivative is insoluble, considerable care must be exercised to avoid co-precipitation. This can be avoided by adding the precipitant slowly with stirring to avoid local concentrations of it and hence premature precipitation, or the mixture can be warmed to redissolve the precipitate and then cooled slowly to regenerate it (115). Another device is to add the precipitant to incipient turbidity after which slow cooling will bring about reasonably good fractionation (4). Still another method (121) that has proved useful in fractionating cellulose nitrate employs slow evaporation of solvent from aqueous organic solvent solution; the technique is worthy of wider application. Fractional extraction can also be applied if the physical conditions of the derivative are suitable (116–120).

Separation of Polysaccharides by Electrophoresis and Ionophoresis

The separation of polysaccharides using the Tiseleus apparatus has only been partially successful. A pentosan constituent of pear cell walls has been purified in this manner (122), but application of the method to other quite divergent groups of polysaccharides (123) met with little success. More recently, however, using a borate buffer, some progress has been made in the separation of glycogen, starch and yeast mannan (124) and there is good evidence to show that gum arabic is heterogeneous (125).

The best results so far obtained from a preparative point of view have been achieved with the aid of some inert supporting medium. Using a simple but ingeneous apparatus, continuous electrophoretic fractionation or relatively high molecular weight carbohydrate polymers in more than micro quantities has been achieved (127,128) with the glucans derived enzymatically from amylose. These substances were separated as iodine-iodide complexes under the influence of a potential drop of 350 volts in an acetate buffer (pH, 4.8) containing $0.001M$ I_2 and $0.002M$ KI, the current flow was about 250 mA. There seems no reason why the same type of electrophoretic separation should not be applied equally well to other polysaccharides, provided they can be induced to assume an electric charge in a suitable buffer so that differential movement in an electric field can be effected (126,167). Using the same principles, small amounts of polysaccharide may be separated by electro-kinetic ultrafiltration in a collodion membrane (129).

Electrophoresis (ionophoresis, zone electrophoresis) (135–140,142, 143) using filter paper and a borate buffer has provided some indications that certain polysaccharides can be separated and distinguished (130–132). This method, however, is severely handicapped by the fact that the technique used, which is similar to that used for the separation of readily detectable sugars and their derivatives, requires specific color reactions for detecting the polysaccharides that are not interfered with by the cellulose paper. In order to overcome this difficulty, paper made from glass-fiber has been recommended (132). With this inert support (133,134), any polysaccharide can be detected for there is no restriction on the type or vigor of chemical test that has to be applied to locate the polysaccharides. Two reagents that have proved useful are the Molisch 1-naphthol reagent and alkaline permanganate (132). Using this technique and $2N$ sodium hydroxide as the electrolyte (132) it has been established that quite a large number of polysaccharides, purified by the methods discussed above, are still heterogeneous. Gum tragacanth, gum arabic, gum ghatti, the dextrans, a number of galacto- and glucomannans and almost all pentosans, except those that are crystalline (12,13), appear to be heterogeneous. By using thick glass paper or powdered glass (134) there is every reason to believe that this technique will form the basis for the preparation of enough material for quite extensive studies.

Advantage has not yet been taken of the fact that certain polysaccharide gums, which form complexes with cuprammonium ions, might be separated electrophoretically either in solution or on some suitable inert support. The feasibility of this is illustrated by the fact that, using a solution of cupriethylene diamine, acid modified cellulose can be shown to be heterogeneous (141).

Additional proof of the homogeneity of polysaccharides should be sought and it is perhaps possible that infrared studies (152) and differential thermal analysis (153–155) could be applied.

Separation by Ultrafiltration

The method of ultrafiltration, using membranes or filters of controlled porous size was developed (157–160) for the separation of large particles such as viruses. The technique has been shown to be applicable to such cellulose derivatives as the nitrate (161,162) and the acetate (168) but because of the coiling of linear chains, it has been suggested that the method is not suitable for linear polymers (163,164).

By means of a series of bacteriological filters and a Zsigmondy-Sartorius apparatus (165), dextran has been separated into fractions of different molecular weight. It was also observed that these fractions could be differentiated by electrophoresis on glass paper (132) but that the differences did not correspond to a difference in molecular weight.

The ultrafiltration technique has not been applied to any natural gums or mucilages but it is clearly worthy of consideration especially for those polymers whose molecules, such as gum arabic, have a more or less spherical shape.

With purified polysaccharides, prepared by the above methods or combinations of them, the time spent in applying the many highly refined chemical and biochemical methods available for structural investigations will be amply rewarded by the greater constitutional significance of the findings. What effect this approach will have on the present concepts of the structure of gums and mucilages and indeed all polysaccharides, cannot be judged until the structural significance of the heterogeneity is ascertained.

REFERENCES

1. Smith, F., and Montgomery, R., *Annual Reviews Biochem.*, **21**, 79 (1952).
2. James, Sybil, P., and Smith, F., *J. Chem. Soc.*, 739 (1945).
3. Chanda, S. K., Hirst, E. L., Jones, J. K. N., and Percival, E. G. V., *J. Chem. Soc.*, 1289 (1950).
4. Rebers, P. A., and Smith, F., *J. Am. Chem. Soc.*, **76**, 6097 (1954).
5. Adams, G. A., and Bishop, C. T., *Tappi*, **38**, 672 (1955).

6. Erskine, A. J., and Jones, J. K. N., *Can. J. Chem.*, **34**, 821 (1956).
7. Kiliani, H., *Ann.*, **205**, 145 (1880).
8. Payen, M., *Compt. rend.*, **49**, 521 (1859).
9. Bauer, R. W., *J. prakt. Chem.*, [2], **30**, 367 (1884).
10. Berzelius, J., *Sweiggers Journal*, **7**, 317 (1813).
11. Acker, L., and Diemair, W., and Samhammer, E., *Z. für Lebensm. Untersuch. u Forsch.*, **100**, 180 (1955).
12. Yundt, A. P., *J. Am. Chem. Soc.*, **71**, 757 (1949).
13. Bishop, C. T., *Can. J. Chem.*, **31**, 793 (1953).
14. Yundt, A. P., *Tappi*, **34**, 91 (1951).
15. Yundt, A. P., *Tappi*, **34**, 89 (1951).
16. Yundt, A. P., *Tappi*, **34**, 94 (1951).
17. Hirst, E. L., and Jones, J. K. N., *Advances in Carbohydrate Chem.*, **2**, 235 (1946).
18. McDonald, Emma J., *Advances in Carbohydrate Chem.*, **2**, 253 (1946).
19. Boggs, L. A., and Smith, F., *J. Am. Chem. Soc.*, **78**, 1880 (1946).
20. Smith, F., unpublished.
21. Höaglund, E., Lindberg, B., and McPherson, J., *Acta Chem. Scand.*, **10**, 1160 (1956).
22. Senti, F. R., Hellman, N. N., Ludwig, N. H., Babcock, G. E., Tobin, R., Glass, C. A., and Lamberts, B. L., *J. Polymer Sci.*, **17**, 527 (1955).
23. Schlubach, H. H., and Koenig, K., *Ann.*, **514**, 182 (1934).
24. Schlubach, H. H., and Lubbers, H., *Ann.*, **598**, 225 (1956).
25. Arni, P. C., and Percival, E. G. V., *J. Chem. Soc.*, 1822 (1951).
26. Caesar, G. V., and Gruenhut, N. S., and Cushing, M. L., *J. Am. Chem. Soc.* **69**, 617 (1947).
27. Haworth, W. N., and Streight, H. R. L., *Helv. Chim. Acta*, **15**, 609 (1932).
28. Hassid, W. Z., and McCready, R. M., *J. Am. Chem. Soc.*, **63**, 1632 (1941).
29. Morris, D. L., and Morris, Carol T., *J. Biol. Chem.*, **130**, 535 (1939).
30. Morris, D. L., *J. Biol. Chem.*, **142**, 881 (1942).
31. Sumner, J. B., and Somers, G. F., *Arch. Biochem.*, **4**, 7 (1944).
32. Preece, I. A., and Mackenzie, K. G., *J. Inst. Brewing*, **58**, 353 (1952).
33. Barry, V. C., Halsall, T. G., Hirst, E. L., and Jones, J. K. N., *J. Chem. Soc.* 1468 (1949).
34. Freeman, M. E., and Gortner, R. A., *Cereal Chem.*, **9**, 506 (1932).
35. Smith, D. B., and Cook, W. H., *Arch. Biochem. Biophys.*, **45**, 232 (1953).
36. Montgomery, R., and Smith, F., *J. Am. Chem. Soc.*, **79**, 695 (1957).
37. Bayley, S. T., *Biochim. et Biophys. Acta*, **17**, 194 (1955).
38. Gorin, M. H., *J. Chem. Phys.*, **7**, 405 (1939).
39. Moelwyn-Hughes, E. A., *Physical Chemistry*, Cambridge (1944), p. 39–49.
40. Black, W. A. P., and Woodward, F. N., *Advances in Chem. Series*, **11**, 83 (1954).
41. Bailey, K., *Biochem. J.*, **29**, 2477 (1935).
42. Jones, A. S., *Biochim. et Biophys. Acta*, **10**, 607 (1953).
43. Barker, S. A., Stacey, M., and Zweifel, G., *Chemistry and Industry* 330 (1957).
44. Scott, J. E., *Biochem. J.*, **62**, 31p (1956).
45. Tillmans, J., *Z. für Unters. d. Lebensm.*, **56**, 26 (1928).
46. Schoch, T. J., *Cereal Chem.*, **18**, 121 (1941).
47. Schoch, T. J., *J. Am. Chem. Soc.*, **64**, 2957 (1942).
48. Pigman, W. W., and Goepp, R. M., "*Chemistry of the Carbohydrates*," Academic Press, New York (1948), p. 564.

49. Whistler, R. L., and Smart, C. L., *Polysaccharide Chemistry*, Academic Press, New York (1953) p. 42.
50. Salkowski, E., *Ber.*, **27**, 497 (1894).
51. Haworth, W. N., Hirst, E. L., and Isherwood, F. A., *J. Chem. Soc.*, 784 (1937).
52. Aspinall, G. O., Hirst, E. L., Moody, R. W., and Percival, E. G. V., *J. Chem. Soc.*, 1631 (1953).
53. Andrews, P., Hough, L., and Jones, J. K. N., *J. Chem. Soc.*, 2744 (1952).
54. Smith, F., and Srivastava, H. C., *J. Am. Chem. Soc.*, **81**, 1715 (1959).
55. Amin, El. S., *J. Chem. Soc.*, 282 (1955).
56. Hirst, E. L., and Dunstan, Sonia, *J. Chem. Soc.*, 2332 (1953).
57. Easterby, D. G., and Jones, J. K. N., *Nature*, **165**, 614 (1950).
58. Bishop, C. T., Adams, G. A., and Hughes, E. O., *Can. J. Chem.*, **32**, 999 (1954).
59. Harwood, V. D., *Can. J. Chem.*, **29**, 974 (1951).
60. Mueller, W. A., and Rogers, L. N., *Ind. Eng. Chem.*, **45**, 2522 (1953).
61. Nishida, K., and Hashima, H., *J. Dept. Agr. Kyushu Imp. Univ.*, **2**, 277 (1930); *Chem. Abstracts*, **25**, 498 (1931).
62. Hess, K., and Friese, H., *Ann.*, **455**, 180 (1927).
63. Meyer, K., and Gürtler, P., *Helv. Chim. Acta*, **30**, 761 (1947).
64. Meyer, K., and Gürtler, P., *Helv. Chim. Acta*, **31**, 100 (1948).
65. Karrer, P., and Joos, B., *Z. physiol. Chem.*, **141**, 311 (1924).
66. Salkowski, E., *Z. physiol Chem.*, **34**, 162 (1901).
67. Norris, F. W., and Preece, I. A., *Biochem. J.*, **24**, 59 (1930).
68. Angell, S., and Norris, F. W., *Biochem. J.*, **30**, 2155 (1936).
69. Deuel, H., and Neukom, H., *Makromol. Chem.*, **4**, 97 (1950).
70. Srivastava, H. C., Lewis, Bertha A., and Smith, F., unpublished.
71. Reeves, R. E., *Advances in Carbohydrate Chem.*, **6**, 107 (1951).
72. Hess, K., and Lüdtke, M., *Ann.*, **466**, 18 (1928).
73. Williams, A. L., *Analyst*, **53**, 411 (1928).
74. Hart, R., *Ind. Eng. Chem., Anal. Ed.*, **2**, 329 (1930).
75. Mantell, C. L., *The Water-Soluble Gums*, Reinhold Pub. Corp., New York (1947).
76. Deuel, H., and Neukom, H., *Advances in Chem. Series*, **11**, 51 (1954).
77. Deuel, H., and Neukom, H., *Makromol. Chem.*, **3**, 13 (1949).
78. Deuel, H., Neukom, H., and Weber, F., *Nature*, **161**, 96 (1949).
79. Magnanini, G., *Z. physikalisch. Chem.*, **6**, 58 (1890).
80. Ageno, F., and Valla, Elena, *Gazz. chim. ital.*, **43**, (2), 163 (1913).
81. Boeseken, J., *Rec. trav. chim.*, **39**, 178 (1920); **40**, 553 (1921).
82. Boeseken, J., and Shoof, G., *Proc. Acad. Sci.*, Amsterdam, **37**, 584 (1934).
83. Boeseken, J., *Bull soc. chim.*, **53**, 1332 (1933).
84. Hermans, P. H., *Proc. Acad. Sci.*, Amsterdam, **26**, 32 (1923); *Z. physik. chem.*, **113**, 337 (1924); *Chem. Abstracts*, **17**, 2867 (1923); **19**, 970 (1925).
85. Boeseken, J., and Vermaas, N., *Rec. trav. chim.*, **54**, 853 (1935).
86. Tanret, C., *Compt. rend.*, **158**, 1353 (1914).
87. Pacsu, E., and Mullen, J. W., *J. Am. Chem. Soc.*, **63**, 1168 (1941).
88. Samec, M., *Ber.*, **73**, 85 (1940).
89. Rowland, B. W., *Chemurgic Digest*, **4**, 369 (1945); *Chem. Abstracts*, **40**, 1655 (1946).
90. Wise, L. E., Green, J. W., and Rittenouse, Ruth C., *Tappi*, **32**, 335 (1949).
91. Graham, T., *J. Chem. Soc.*, **15**, 266 (1862).
92. Sumner, J. B., and Howell, S. F., *J. Biol. Chem.*, **115**, 583 (1936).

93. Cifonelli, J. A., and Smith, F., *Anal. Chem.*, **27**, 1639 (1955).
94. Cifonelli, J. A., Montgomery, R., and Smith, F., *J. Am. Chem. Soc.*, **78**, 2485 (1956).
95. Cifonelli, J. A., and Smith, F., *J. Am. Chem. Soc.*, **79**, 5055 (1957).
96. Heidelberger, M., and Adams, J., *J. Exptl. Med.*, **103**, 189 (1956).
97. Beiser, S. B., Kabat, E. A., and Schor, J. M., *J. Immunol.*, **69**, 297 (1952).
98. Heidelberger, M., Adams, J., and Dische, Z., *J. Am. Chem. Soc.*, **78**, 2853 (1956).
99. Whistler, R. L., and Durso, D. F., *J. Am. Chem. Soc.*, **72**, 677 (1950).
100. Cifonelli, J. A., and Smith, F., *J. Am. Chem. Soc.*, **77**, 5682 (1955).
101. Jones, J. K. N., *J. Chem. Soc.*, 333 (1944).
102. Simpson, F. J., *Can. J. Microbiol.*, **1**, 131 (1954).
103. Adams, Mildred, Richtmyer, N. K., and Hudson, C. S., *J. Am. Chem. Soc.*, **65**, 1369 (1943).
104. Levene, P. A., and Mori, T., *J. Biol. Chem.*, **84**, 49 (1929).
105. Sevag, M. G., *Biochem. Z.*, **273**, 419 (1934).
106. Sevag, M. G., Lockman, D. B., and Smolens, J., *J. Biol. Chem.* **124**, 425 (1938).
107. Abdel-Akher, M., and Smith, F., *J. Am. Chem. Soc.*, **73**, 994 (1951).
108. Bell, D. J., and Young, F. C., *Biochem. J.*, **28**, 882 (1934).
109. Steiner, E. T., and Guthrie, J. D., *Ind. Eng. Chem., Anal. Ed.*, **16**, 736 (1944).
110. Clendenning, K. A., *Can. J. Res.*, **20C**, 403 (1942).
111. Sumner, J. B., and O'Kane, D. J., *Enzymol.*, **12**, 251 (1948).
112. Bernard, C., *Leçons sur le diabète* (Bailliere, Paris) (1877) p. 303.
113. Perlin, A. S., *Cereal. Chem.*, **28**, 370 (1951).
114. Montgomery, R., and Smith, F., *J. Am. Chem. Soc.*, **77**, 2834, 3325 (1955).
115. Hodge, J. E., Karjala, S. A., and Hilbert, G. E., *J. Am. Chem. Soc.*, **73**, 3312 (1951).
116. Laidlaw, R. A., and Percival, E. G. V., *J. Chem. Soc.*, 528 (1950).
117. Hirst, E. L., Percival, E. G. V., and Wylam, Claire B., *J. Chem. Soc.*, 189 (1950).
118. Mullan, J., and Percival, E. G. V., *J. Chem. Soc.*, 1501 (1940).
119. Percival, E. G. V., and Willox, I. C., *J. Chem. Soc.*, 1608 (1949).
120. Percival, E. G. V., and Nelson, W. A. G., *J. Chem. Soc.*, 58 (1942).
121. Timell, T. E., and Snyder, J. L., *Textile Research J.*, **25**, 870 (1955).
122. Isherwood, F. A., and Jermyn, M. A., *Chem. Constit. of Cell Wall Polysacc. 1st Int'l. Congr. of Biochem.*, Cambridge (1949) *Abst. No.* 339/11.
123. Colvin, J. R., Cook, W. H., and Adams, G. A., *Can. J. Chem.*, **30**, 603 (1952).
124. Northcote, D. H., *Biochem. J.*, **58**, 353 (1954).
125. Joubert, F. J., *J. South African Chem. Instit.*, **7**, [2], 107 (1954).
126. Grassmann, W., and Harmig, K., *Naturwissenschaften*, **37**, 397 (1950).
127. Mould, D. L., and Synge, R. L. M., *Biochem. J.*, **58**, 585 (1954).
128. Norberg, Ethelda, and French, D., *J. Am. Chem. Soc.*, **72**, 1202 (1950).
129. Mould, D. L., and Synge, R. L. M., *Biochem. J.*, **58**, 571 (1954).
130. Foster, A. B., Newton-Hearn, Miss P. A., and Stacey, M., *J. Chem. Soc.*, 30 (1956).
131. Preece, I. A., and Hobkirk, R., *Chemistry and Industry*, 257 (1955).
132. Briggs, D. R., Garner, E. F., and Smith, F., *Nature*, **178**, 154 (1956).
133. Fuller, K. W., and Northcote, D. H., *Biochem. J.*, **64**, 657 (1956).
134. Hocevar, B. J., and Northcote, D. H., *Nature*, **179**, 488 (1957).

135. Geldmacher-Mallinckrodt, M., and Weinland, H., Z. physiol. Chem., 292, 65 (1953).
136. Gardell, S., Arkiv. für Kemi, 4, 449 (1952).
137. Macheboeuf, M., Rebeyrotte, P., and Brunerie, M., Bull. soc. chim. biol., 33, 1543 (1951).
138. Durrum, E. L., J. Am. Chem. Soc., 72, 2943 (1950).
139. Wieland, T., Angew. Chem., 60, 313 (1948).
140. Cremer, H. D., and Tiselius, A., Biochem. Z., 320, 273 (1950).
141. Adams, Mabelle, E., Karon, M. L., and Reeves, R. E., J. Am. Chem. Soc., 73, 2350 (1951).
142. Kunkel, H. G., and Tiselius, A., J. Gen. Physiol., 35, 89 (1951).
143. Schneider, G., and Wallenius, G., Scand. J. Clin. and Lab. Inv., 3, 145 (1951).
144. Wise, L. E., Jones, J. K. N., Jappi, Josephine P., Tappi, 39, 139 (1956).
145. O'Dwyer, Margaret H., Biochem. J., 20, 656 (1926).
146. O'Dwyer, Margaret H., Biochem. J., 33, 713 (1939); 34, 149 (1940).
147. Sands, Lila, and Gary, W. Y., J. Biol. Chem., 101, 573 (1933).
148. Sands, Lila, and Nutter, Pauline, J. Biol. Chem., 110, 17 (1935).
149. Schulze, E., Ber., 22, 1192 (1889); 24, 2277 (1891).
150. Preece, I. A., Biochem. J., 34, 251 (1940); 35, 659 (1941).
151. Falconer, E. L., and Adams, G. A., Can. J. Chem., 34, 338 (1956).
152. Barker, S. A., Bourne, E. J., and Whiffen, D. H., Methods of Biochemical Analysis, III, ed D. Glick, Interscience, New York, (1956) p. 213.
153. Morita, H., and Rice, H. M., Anal. Chem., 27, 336 (1955).
154. Morita, H., Anal. Chem., 28, 64 (1956).
155. Morita, H., J. Am. Chem. Soc., 78, 1397 (1956).
156. Bourne, E. J., Donnison, G. H., Peat, S., and Whelan, W. J., J. Chem. Soc., 1 (1949).
157. Zsigmondy, R., Angew. Chem., 39, 398 (1926).
158. Bechhold, H., Kolloid Z., 66, 329 (1934); 67, 66 (1934).
159. Erbe, F., Kolloid Z., 59, 32, 195 (1932); 63, 277 (1933).
160. Elford, W. J., Trans. Faraday Soc., 33, 1094 (1937).
161. Kumichel, W., Kolloidchem. Beihefte, 26, 161 (1928).
162. Duclaux, J., and Nodzu, R., Rev. gen. colloïdes, 7, 241 (1929); Chem. Abstracts, 24, 721 (1930).
163. Meyer, K. H., High Polymers, Vol. 4, Natural and Synthetic High Polymers, 2nd Ed., Interscience, New York (1950) p. 25.
164. Cragg, L. H., and Hammerschlag, H., Chem. Reviews, 39, 79 (1946).
165. Wilkie, K. C. B., Jones, J. K. N., Excell, Barbara J., and Semple, R. E., Can. J. Chem., 35, 795 (1957).
166. Lewis, Bertha A., and Smith, F., unpublished.
167. Houldsworth, E. S., Biochem. J., 55, (Proceedings) XIV (1953).
168. Caille, A., Chemie et industrie, 25, 276 (1931).
169. Deuel, H., Solms, J., and Denzler, A., Helv. Chim. Acta, 36, 1671 (1953).
170. Dutch Pat., 78,328 (1955).
171. Frey-Wyssling, A., "Macromolecules in Cell Structure" Harvard University Press, Cambridge, Mass. (1957) p. 4.

CHAPTER 6

MOLECULAR WEIGHT OF POLYSACCHARIDES

Chemical and physical methods have been employed in determining the molecular weight of gums and mucilages. The chemical methods are usually based on reactions of the terminal reducing group which is assumed to be present. For some polysaccharides, such an assumption may be valid even though it has seldom been proved (see below). For others it is demonstrably incorrect. In many fructans, the hitherto assumed reducing end has been shown by chemical (1–7) and enzymic (8–13) methods to be blocked by a glucopyranose unit in a sucrose-type linkage. Laminarin also falls partly into this nonreducing polysaccharide group because, although it does reduce Fehling solution (14,15), a portion of the polysaccharide complex has been shown to possess a terminal D-mannitol residue which thus blocks the reducing end of the β-D-1 $\rightarrow$ 3 linked linear glucose polymer (16,17).

In spite of the doubtful nature of the so-called reducing end in carbohydrate polymers many polysaccharides have been subjected to evaluation on the assumption that a reducing group is indeed present and that all the molecules possess such a reducing end. The evidence cited above (16,17) casts some doubt on this assumption as do the results of studies on the electrophoretic inhomogeneity of polysaccharides (see Chapter 5).

When the polysaccharides possess a reducing group a chemical determination of molecular weight can be applied. Several reagents, including sodium hypoiodite (18), cupric salt solutions (19), and ferricyanide (20), have been suggested for this determination and while they may not give absolute results, since the reactions involved are not stoichiometric, they have their uses for comparing one polysaccharide fraction with another of related structure (21).

A colorimetric method using 3,5-dinitrosalicylic acid has also been used on the basis that it is specific for the reducing group (22). More recently, however, this method has been found to be of limited value, since the reaction is influenced by atmospheric oxygen which has the effect of oxidizing the reducing end and thus giving high values for the molecular weight. Contrary to expectation simple reducing methylated sugars, such as 2,3-di- and 2,3,6-tri-*O*-methyl-D-glucose do not react (23). Presumably, therefore, any polymers possessing a reducing residue linked through C2 and C3 or C2, C3 and C6 would not display the expected reducing properties and would be reported to have either a very high or an infinite molecular weight.

The determination of the ammonia liberated upon hydrolysis of a polysaccharide cyanohydrin has also proved of some value (24,25). This reaction is best applied to those reducing polysaccharides that react quickly with cyanide so that the concomitant hydrolysis of the cyanide to an ammonium ion can either be ignored or corrected for by a blank determination. If, however, the cyanide condensation proceeds slowly and hydrolysis of the inorganic cyanide cannot be ignored, it is necessary to isolate the polysaccharide cyanohydrin before hydrolysis (25). Another attractive and highly sensitive method involves replacement of the sodium cyanide in the above reaction by $NaC^{14}N$ (19,26).

If only the terminal units of the polysaccharide give rise to formic acid upon oxidation with periodate the molecular weight of linear polymers, and branched polymers, if the amount of branching is known, could be ascertained from the amount of formic acid produced by periodate oxidation.

A simple alternative method is to reduce the carbohydrate polymer with sodium borohydride (15) and the product, without isolation is oxidized with periodate whereby the reduced end of the molecule will provide an amount of formaldehyde according to the type of linkage by which it is bound to the rest of the molecule (21). If the reducing unit of the polysaccharide is an aldohexose joined by a $1 \rightarrow 6$ glycosidic bond as in (I), it will give rise to the polysaccharide alcohol (II) which, upon periodate oxidation will give one molecular proportion of formaldehyde. If the

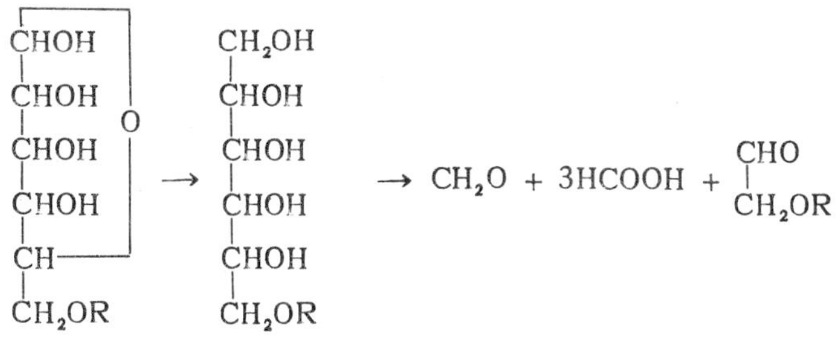

terminal reducing hexose unit is joined by a $1 \rightarrow 5$ or a $1 \rightarrow 2$-linkage, the reduced polymer in both cases will give rise to one molecular proportion of formaldehyde, whereas in the case of a 1 → 3- or 1 → 4 linked terminal unit, periodate oxidation will furnish two molecular proportions of formaldehyde. The reaction applied to the 1 → 3 linked hexopyranose unit (III) proceeds *via* IV as follows:

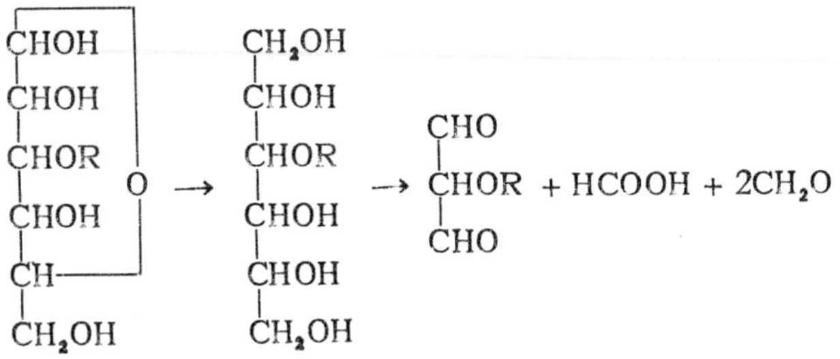

$$
\begin{array}{ccccc}
\begin{array}{l}
CHOH \\
CHOH \\
CHOR \\
CHOH \\
CH \\
CH_2OH
\end{array} O &\to&
\begin{array}{l}
CH_2OH \\
CHOH \\
CHOR \\
CHOH \\
CHOH \\
CH_2OH
\end{array}
&\to&
\begin{array}{l}
CHO \\
CHOR + HCOOH + 2CH_2O \\
CHO
\end{array}
\\
\\
III && IV &&
\end{array}
$$

In the course of the periodate oxidation of the polysaccharide alcohol other building units may be cleaved by the periodate, but the molecule as a whole will remain intact.

When the degree of polymerization, D.P., of the polymer is fairly low (< 100), the amount of formaldehyde generated is relatively high and may be determined directly by the chromotropic acid method in the presence of the residual oxidized polysaccharide (29). As the DP increases and the amount of polysaccharide has to be increased in order to furnish enough formaldehyde for reliable results, the oxidized polysaccharide interferes with the colorimetric procedure (27). In such cases it is necessary to separate the formaldehyde by dialysis (28) before the determination is carried out.

The preliminary results of the application of this method to amylose (28) and laminarin indicate that it may prove to be a valuable tool. Inspection of other possible structures will reveal that the method should be applicable equally well to carbohydrate polymers that have a pentose sugar for the terminal reducing group.

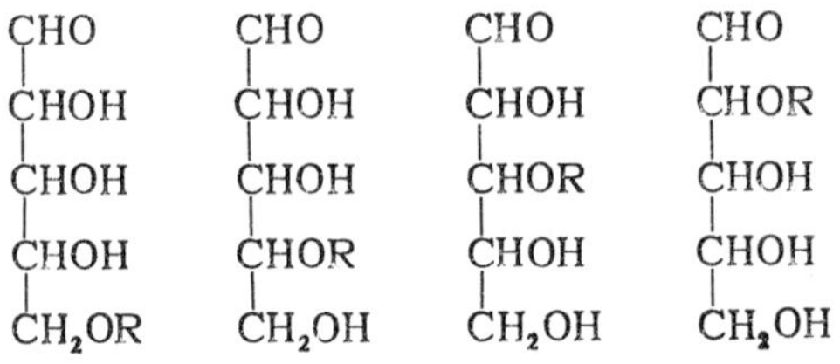

$$
\begin{array}{cccc}
\begin{array}{l}
CHO \\
CHOH \\
CHOH \\
CHOH \\
CH_2OR
\end{array}
&
\begin{array}{l}
CHO \\
CHOH \\
CHOH \\
CHOR \\
CH_2OH
\end{array}
&
\begin{array}{l}
CHO \\
CHOH \\
CHOR \\
CHOH \\
CH_2OH
\end{array}
&
\begin{array}{l}
CHO \\
CHOR \\
CHOH \\
CHOH \\
CH_2OH
\end{array}
\\
\\
V & VI & VII & VIII
\end{array}
$$

All the possible structures for the terminal systems are shown in formulae V to VIII. Each would yield formaldehyde upon reduction followed by periodate oxidation and in the case of the 1 → 3-linked terminal unit (VII) the oxidation of the polysaccharide alcohol will give two molecular proportions of formaldehyde.

Yet another method of ascertaining the chemical molecular weight involves oxidation of the reducing group to a carboxyl group and titration of the polysaccharide acid with alkali (30), or determination of the ash content of the potassium salt (31,32). This method has its limitations especially with those carbohydrate polymers that contain a large amount of uronic acid.

For molecules of the linear type, the usual methylation studies will provide results for the amount of terminal nonreducing residue and thus enable the molecular weight to be calculated. If the molecules are branched, the amount of end group determined by this method will give a value for the size of the average repeating unit and in order to calculate the true molecular weight the number of branches in the molecule has to be determined. Thus far, there are no methods for doing this.

From the discussion on the use of periodate oxidation of gums (see page 194) it will also be apparent that in certain selected cases the amount of glycerol formed by periodate oxidation, reduction, and hydrolysis, will furnish results from which the molecular weight of the polysaccharide can be calculated. This may be illustrated (15) by reference to the seaweed polysaccharide, laminarin (IX), which has been reported (14, cf. 38) to be composed of about twenty β-D-glucopyranose units joined by 1 → 3 glycosidic bonds.

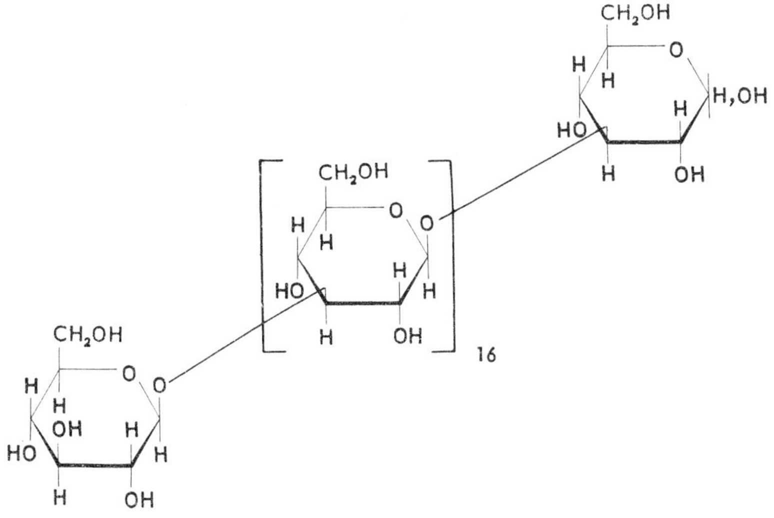

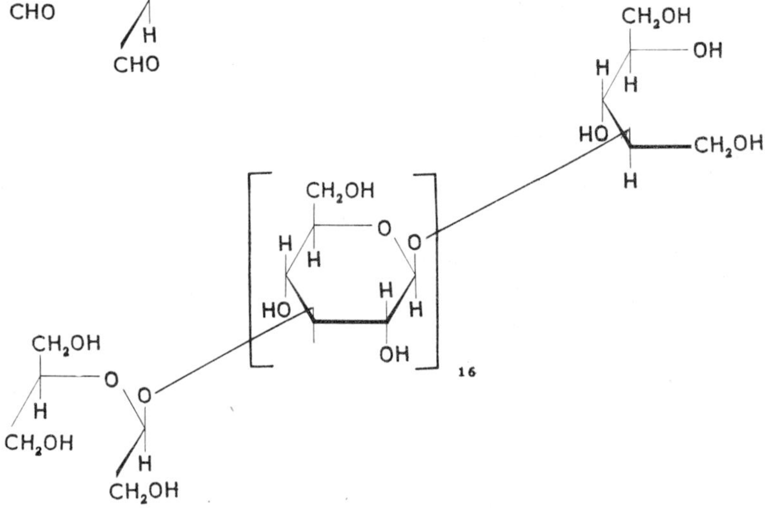

By oxidizing the laminarin (IX) with periodic acid in the cold (0–5°)
the terminal reducing group is cleaved only between C1 and C2, the
formyl group formed from C1 preventing further oxidation (34). The nonreducing end, however, is cleaved as shown in X. Reduction with sodium
borohydride (15,33) affords the corresponding polyalcohol (XI) and hydrolysis of this provides glycerol, D-glucose and D-arabitol. Equimolecular amounts of glycerol and D-arabitol should be produced if the
molecule is linear and the molecular ratio of D-glucose to glycerol (or
D-arabitol) should give the number, less two, of glucose units in the
molecule of laminarin (35).

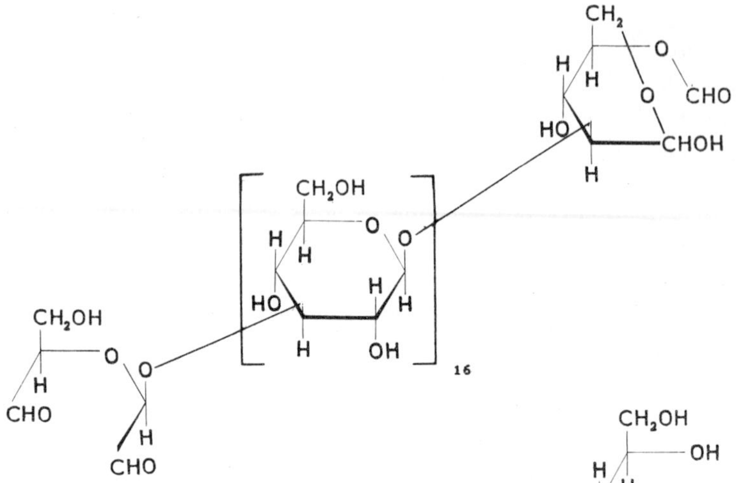

It will be apparent that if a molecule such as laminarin, has a single
branch then the ratio of glycerol to D-arabitol would be 2:1 and if there
were n branches the ratio would be $(n + 1):1$.

This method is capable of wide application, but certain structural features relating to the types of linkage present in the polysaccharides should first be ascertained.

The characteristic reaction of the reducing sugars with thioalcohols to give dialkyl thioacetals (36,37) thus: $R—CHO + 2R_1SH \rightarrow RCH(SR_1)_2$, might also prove useful for ascertaining the molecular weight of those polysaccharides having a reducing group, provided that the reaction goes to completion and that degradation does not take place.

Physical methods utilizing osmotic pressure, viscosity, light scattering, and sedimentation should also be taken into consideration when molecular weight determinations have to be carried out and the reader is referred to standard treatises on these subjects for further details.

REFERENCES

1. Arni, P. C., and Percival, E. G. V., *J. Chem. Soc.*, 1822 (1951).
2. Laidlaw, R. A., and Reid, S. G., *J. Chem. Soc.*, 1830 (1951).
3. Bell, D. J., and Palmer, Anne, *J. Chem. Soc.*, 3763 (1952).
4. Dedonder, R., *Bull. soc. chim. biol.*, **34**, 144 (1952).
5. Aspinall, G. O., Hirst, E. L., Percival, E. G. V., and Telfer, R. G. J., *J. Chem. Soc.*, 337 (1953).
6. Aspinall, G. O., and Telfer, R. G. J., *J. Chem. Soc.*, 1106 (1955).
7. Hirst, E. L., McGilvray, D. I., and Percival, E. G. V., *J. Chem. Soc.*, 1297 (1950).
8. Dedonder, R., *Compt. rend.*, **232**, 1442 (1951).
9. Dedonder, R., *Bull. soc., chim. biol.*, **34**, 157, 171 (1952).
10. Palmer, Anne, *Biochem. J.*, **48**, 389 (1951).
11. Edelman, J., and Bacon, J. S. D., *Biochem. J.*, **49**, 446, 529 (1951).
12. Grandchamp-Chaudun, A. de, *Compt. rend.*, **231**, 1082 (1950).
13. Schlubach, H. H., and Holzer, K., *Ann.*, **578**, 207, 213 (1952).
14. Connell, J. J., Hirst, E. L., and Percival, E. G. V., *J. Chem. Soc.*, 3494 (1950).
15. Abdel-Akher, M., Hamilton, J. K., and Smith, F., *J. Am. Chem. Soc.*, **73**, 4691 (1951).
16. Peat, S., Whelan, W. J., and Lawley, H. G., *Chemistry and Industry*, 35 (1955).
17. Whelan, W. J., Lawley, H. G., and Evans, J. M., *Biochem. J.*, **61**, X (1955).
18. Chanda, S. K., Hirst, E. L., Jones, J. K. N., and Percival, E. G. V., *J. Chem. Soc.*, 1289 (1950).
19. Isbell, H. S., Snyder, C. F., Holt, N. B., and Dryden, M. R., *J. Res. Natl. Bur. Standards*, **50**, 81 (1953).
20. Nussenbaum, S., and Hassid, W. Z., *Anal. Chem.*, **24**, 501 (1952).
21. Smith, F., and Montgomery, R., Methods of Biochemical Analysis, *Vol. 3*, Ed. D. Glick, Interscience (1956) p. 153.
22. Meyer, K. H., Noelting, G., and Bernfeld, P., *Helv. Chim. Acta*, **31**, 103 (1948).
23. Bell, D. J., Manners, D. J., and Palmer, Anne, J. *Chem. Soc.*, 3760 (1952).
24. Frampton, V. L., Foley, Lucia P., Smith, L. L., and Malone, Jane G., *Anal. Chem.*, **23**, 1244 (1951).

25. Scheurer, P. G., and Smith, F., *Anal. Chem.*, **27**, 1616 (1955).
26. Isbell, H. S., *Science*, **113**, 532 (1951).
27. Lambert, Marguerite, and Neish, A. C., *Can. J. Res.*, **B28**, 83 (1950).
28. Unrau, A. M., and Smith, F., *Chemistry* and *Industry*, 330 (1957).
29. Hough, L., and Perry, M. B., *Chemistry* and *Industry*, 768 (1956).
30. Barry, V. C., *J. Chem. Soc.*, 578 (1942).
31. French, D., Levine, M. L., and Pazur, J. H., *J. Am. Chem. Soc.*, **71**, 356 (1949).
32. Levine, M., Foster, J. F., and Hixon, R. M., *J. Am. Chem. Soc.*, **64**, 2331 (1942).
33. Abdel-Akher, M., Hamilton, J. K., Montgomery, R., and Smith, F., *J. Am. Chem. Soc.*, **74**, 4970 (1952).
34. Huffman, G. W., Lewis, Bertha A., Smith, F., and Spriestersbach, D. R., *J. Am. Chem. Soc.*, **77**, 4346 (1955).
35. Hamilton, J. K., and Smith, F., *J. Am. Chem. Soc.*, **78**, 5907 (1956).
36. Wolfrom, M. L., and Sowden, J. C., *J. Am. Chem. Soc.*, **60**, 3009 (1938).
37. Wolfrom, M. L., Myers, D. R., and Lassettre, E. N., *J. Am. Chem. Soc.*, **61**, 2172 (1939).
38. Goldstein, I. J., Smith, F., and Unrau, A. M., *Chemistry and Industry*, 124 (1959).

CHAPTER 7

ANALYTICAL PROCEDURES

Determination of Composition

The polysaccharide material for analysis is first purified by extraction with water. Dissolution may be accelerated by using dilute acids or alkalis. If either dilute acid or water is employed heat should be avoided since partial hydrolysis (1,2) may occur in the case of gums which contain labile sugar residues, such as arabofuranose. That structural changes in gums and mucilages do indeed occur when their aqueous solutions are heated is shown by the fact that the viscosity of the solutions decrease and reducing sugars are eventually generated.

Gums found in the seeds of leguminous plants, such as guar and locust bean and certain cell-wall hemicellulose gums, are more readily dissolved in dilute sodium hydroxide. Application of too much heat is inadvisable during alkaline extractions, for although undesirable protein is thereby eliminated, decomposition of the uronic acid building units may occur. An example of this is the depolymerization of pectin-like compounds by glycosidic splitting in alkaline solutions (8). This type of decomposition occurs with polymers containing esterified uronic acid units, as in the case of the esters of pectic acid, but it does not take place with those substances containing free uronic acid groups. Certain polysaccharides such as seaweed gums and mucilages can only be efficiently extracted with hot water, and in other cases even alkali fails (9).

The solution of the gum or mucilage is filtered to remove insoluble impurities and the polysaccharide recovered by precipitation with alcohol. Repeated precipitation from acidified aqueous solution with ethanol serves to remove inorganic ions and proteinaceous impurity. Elimination of inorganic ions may also be effected by electrodialysis or by passing an aqueous solution of the material through a cation exchange resin (3,4). Certain polysaccharides can be purified by precipitation from aqueous or acidified aqueous solution with acetic acid (5) while others containing a large percentage of uronic acid are best precipitated from aqueous solution with dilute mineral acid.

The gums or mucilages may be further purified by fractional precipitation from aqueous solution with ethanol a procedure adopted many years ago by O'Sullivan in his studies on gum arabic (6), gum tragacanth (7) and cereal gums (370).

The purified products thus obtained are dried prior to analysis by solvent exchange, azeotropic distillation of the water with benzene-ethanol, or by freeze-drying. Such a procedure usually provides light amorphous white powders. When gums which contain moisture are dried by methods other than freeze-drying they often form hard, horny masses that are difficult to manipulate. It is advisable not to dry these polysaccharides by heating for certain undesirable changes in solubility may develop and, in the case of those gums containing acidic groups, hydrolysis and decomposition may occur. It is also of interest to note that when the purified glucomannan, present in the Iles mannan extracted from *Amorphophallus oncophyllus*, is purified and dried, it will no longer disperse in water, nor will it dissolve in alkalis, and recourse was had to the use of a strong solution of sodium xylenesulfonate, followed by alkali (10). Such examples as this are rare and, generally speaking, gums and mucilages can be dissolved almost completely or partially in water, especially if metallic ions are removed.

When gums contain considerable amounts of protein, precipitation of the polysaccharide with ammonium sulfate or acetic acid may be advantageous. This procedure retains the protein in solution (11,12). Gums may also be freed from protein by acetylation after which the polysaccharide acetate may be precipitated with water, thus leaving the protein in solution. The acetylation may be carried out by dissolving the gum in formamide and adding pyridine and acetic anhydride (13,14). Since urea is also capable of eliminating hydrogen bonding and dissolving polysaccharides (cf 16), it might also prove useful in acetylations. Dimethyl formamide and ammonium salts are worthy of consideration for this purpose, since they have proved useful for the acetylation of cellulose (16). Dimethyl sulfoxide, a good solvent for many polysaccharides (15), has not yet been examined as a reaction medium.

The gum acetates may be purified by precipitation from acetone or chloroform solution with diethyl ether or petroleum ether and the polysaccharide regenerated by deacetylation with sodium hydroxide or potassium hydroxide (400).

For a further discussion of the purification of polysaccharides see Chapter 5.

General Quantitative Analysis

The purified gum is characterized by the determination of the specific optical rotation either in water or dilute alkali, the methoxyl content, and if necessary, the gum or mucilage can be analyzed for nitrogen. The equivalent weight of an acid containing polysaccharide should also be ascertained by titration, and account taken of any acetyl groups that may be present by their separate determination (28).

The uronic acid content of an acid gum or mucilage, provided no acetyl groups are present, can be determined by titration with standard alkali. Thus, damson gum has been shown to have a neutral equivalent of 1110 (1), while arabic acid has an equivalent of 1300 (2,17). The equivalent weight of 1110 for damson gum acid corresponds to an anhydrouronic acid content of 16 per cent. By distilling with hydrochloric acid the uronic acid units undergo decarboxylation and the evolved carbon dioxide (collected in standard alkali and titrated or absorbed and weighed) is a measure of the uronic acid content (22, 25, 26). For damson gum, the carbon dioxide evolved corresponded to a anhydrouronic acid content of 16.4 per cent. Colorimetric methods using phenol (24), anthrone (23), naphthoresorcinol (18) or carbazole (19–21) may also be employed.

Acetyl groups present in a gum, for example karaya, may be determined by steam distillation in the presence of p-toluenesulfonic acid and titration of the acetic acid in the distillate (27,28).

The amount of pentosan (xylose and arabinose) in gums can be ascertained from the amount of furfural produced when the gum is boiled with 12 per cent hydrochloric acid. The furfural may be determined by titration with bromate (29), by precipitation with phloroglucinol (30,31), 2,4-dinitrophenylhydrazine (32), thiobarbituric acid (33) or by spectrophotometric measurements either directly (34,35) or after combination with a chromophoric group (24,36).

The disadvantage of these methods is that they are not too accurate and corrections must be made for the presence of uronic acid which also provides furfural when heated with hydrochloric acid. 5-Methylfuraldehyde from the 6-deoxyhexoses and 5-(hydroxymethyl)-2-furaldehyde from the hexoses also interfere.

The hexose content of hexosans can be determined by the anthrone colorimetric method (38–40) and by the phenol-sulfuric acid reagent (24,37). Pentosans interfere to some extent (41).

Pentoses and hexoses in the presence of each other can be determined colorimetrically reasonably well by the orcinol reaction (42-44) while the galactan content can be ascertained by nitric acid oxidation to galactaric acid (45).

The micro-methods in conjunction with paper chromotography are much more reliable for analyzing the mixtures of sugars produced from gums and mucilages (see later). The components are separated and each one is determined independently.

Hydrolysis of Gums and Mucilages and Determination of the Component Sugars.

Qualitative analysis. Plant gums, such as gum arabic, containing labile furanose sugar residues, undergo partial hydrolysis when heated with 0.01 to 0.1N sulfuric acid. In fact, such gums are so sensitive to acid that the free polysaccharide gum acids will undergo autohydrolysis when their aqueous solutions are heated (1,2); 6-deoxyhexoses if present, may also be liberated. This mild method of hydrolysis may furnish oligosaccharides that are valuable in establishing the constitution of complex polysaccharide gums (2,46).

The more stable gums and mucilages or those portions of polysaccharides remaining after autohydrolysis, may be hydrolyzed by heating at 95-100° with 1 to 2 N sulfuric acid. Interruption of this more vigorous hydrolytic treatment will often provide aldobiouronic acids or oligosaccharides whose structures are of constitutional importance.

The more stable polysaccharide gums and mucilages can sometimes be hydrolyzed with boiling concentrated formic acid. Thus, alginic acid gives D-mannuronic acid in fairly good yield (47). The method suffers from the disadvantage that some formylation may occur (48), but if the problem under examination concerns the characterization of sugars or sugar acids which readily form crystalline glycosides, the gum hydrolyzate, produced by means of formic acid, can be directly treated with methanolic hydrogen chloride (49). In this process, glycoside formation is accompanied by deformylation. One pronounced advantage of the formic acid method of hydrolysis is that the excess acid can be removed by distillation *in vacuo* thus eliminating the time consuming step of neutralization that is necessary when mineral acid is used for hydrolysis. An example of the use of the formic acid method is the characterization of D-mannose in the hydrolyzate of such gums as guar, locust bean, and Kentucky coffee bean, as the crystalline methyl α-D-mannopyranoside. In fact, application of the formic acid method to locust bean gum (52) or to guar gum (50) provides a cheap and readily accessible source of D-mannose (cf. 51).

Hydrolysis accompanied by acetylation (acetolysis) has long been used to degrade cellulose to cellobiose octaacetate (53,54), but apart from its application to the glucomannan of konjac meal (55) it has been used very little in the study of gums and mucilages. Some recent experiments with Iles glucomannan show that the method is capable of providing oligosaccharides of structural value (56).

Bearing in mind the ease with which many sugars form dithioacetals when treated with thioalcohols in the presence of concentrated hydrochloric acid (57,58), it seems reasonable to believe that those gums and mucilages, which would undergo hydrolysis with relative ease and without excessive decomposition, could be induced to yield certain crystalline sugar dithioacetals. Some success has attended the application of this method to agar (59,62) and carrageenin (60,61).

Although enzymic techniques have been found useful industrially in certain textile finishing operations, the value of enzymes in the study of the composition and structure of gums and mucilages still remains to be fully exploited. It was applied a number of years ago to carob (locust) bean gum (63,64), but it is only recently that the value of a method, used so extensively in the case of starch and glycogen, has been utilized to any extent in the study of gums, such as guar (65–68) and agar (69,70). Some idea of the value of enzymes for bringing about hydrolysis is illustrated by the degradation of agar (69) to a disaccharide, neo-agarobiose. Information has also been obtained concerning the structure of hemicelluloses by the use of a hemicellulase isolated from the organism *Myrothecium verrucaria* (71,72). This enzyme should prove to be quite effective for hydrolyzing gums and mucilages whose structures are based on a xylan framework.

Prior to the discovery of partition chromatographic analysis (see later) much of the qualitative and not a little of the quantitative analysis of gums, and mucilages, and polysaccharides in general, depended upon the classical techniques of organic chemistry, namely, isolation of characteristic crystalline derivatives (73,74), especially hydrazones and osazones. This technique is still as important as it ever was for the characterization of sugars and sugar derivatives, but it is employed much less at the present time as a quantitative tool.

In Table 19 are found some of the simple derivatives that may be used for characterizing the sugars and sugar acids.

In many cases where only minute amounts of sugars are available methods using a microscope for the recognition of characteristic crystalline derivatives, such as the hydrazones and osazones, may eventually be developed along the lines already worked out for D-mannose (388), D-lyxose (388), L-arabinose (389), L-fucose (389), and D-fructose (390).

TABLE 19. IDENTIFICATION OF SUGARS COMMONLY FOUND IN GUMS AND MUCILAGES (AND CERTAIN OTHER POLYSACCHARIDES)[a]

Sugar	Identify As	Reference
L-Arabinose	Free sugar	
	methyl β-pyranoside,	
	benzylphenylhydrazone,	73,76
	diphenylhydrazone,	73
	N-(p-nitrophenyl)glycosylamine	78
	L-arabitol.	

TABLE 19. (CONTINUED)

Sugar	Identify As	Reference
D-Xylose	Free sugar, di-*o*-benzylidine-dimethylacetal, phenylosazone.	77 73
D-Galactose	Free sugar, α-methylphenylhydrazone, galactaric acid, galactitol hexaacetate.	73,76
D-Glucose	Free sugar, phenylosazone, phenylosatriazole, *N*-(*p*-nitrophenyl)glycosylamine glucaric acid (K acid salt).	73 79 78
D-Mannose	Free sugar, phenylhydrazone, *N*-(*p*-nitrophenyl)glycosylamine methyl α-pyranoside, mannitol hexaacetate, *N*-phenylglycosylamine	73 78 397,398
3,6-Anhydro-D-galactose	2,4,5-tri-*p*-nitrobenzoate-dimethyl acetal, diethyldithioacetal phenylosazone.	80 60,61,62,81 80
3,6-Anhydro-L-galactose	As for the D-compound.	62
D-Glucuronic acid	D-Glucuronolactone *N*-(*p*-nitrophenyl)glycosylamine	4
4-*O*-Methyl-D-Glucuronic acid	Amide methyl glycoside (α and β forms)	82,83
D-Galacturonic acid	Free acid (monohydrate), Methyl α-glycoside methyl ester α-glycoside (monohydrate), galactaric acid (mucic acid).	89 88 90,91 93
D-Mannuronic acid	D-Mannuronolactone (dimorphous)	47,84,85,86
L-Rhamnose	Free sugar (monohydrate), 2,3-*O*-isopropylidene acetal, β-naphthylhydrazone, *p*-nitrophenylhydrazone, *p*-tolyhydrazone.	87 73 73 73
L-Fucose	Free sugar, *p*-bromphenylhydrazone, α-methylphenylhydrazone, *p*-sulfonylhydrazone.	73 73 75

TABLE 19. (CONTINUED)

Sugar	Identify As	Reference
D-Fructose	p-nitrophenylhydrazone,	73
	1,2; 4,5-di-O-isopropylidine	92,543
	diacetal.	

[a]References 543 and 545 should also be consulted.

The quantitative analysis of the sugars formed by hydrolysis of gums and mucilages was formerly based upon the preparation of some sparingly soluble derivative. Although these methods were, at best only semi-quantitative, and have since been replaced by chromatographic procedures, a brief account of the derivatives will be given here, since some of them still serve to identify the sugars and should be considered in conjunction with the data in Table 19.

L-Arabinose forms a well-defined benzylphenylhydrazone (73), a sparingly soluble benzoylhydrazone (73,94) and it may also be converted into a crystalline diphenylhydrazone (73) and a p-nitrophenylhydrazone (73).

D-Xylose has been recognized in the past by the shape of the crystals of the double salt of cadmium xylonate and cadmium bromide, $(C_5H_9O_6)_2 \cdot Cd \cdot CdBr_2 \cdot 2H_2O$; this method leaves something to be desired since the preparation is lengthy and requires considerable material. The di-O-benzylidene dimethyl acetal derivative (77) serves the purpose much better. It is said to form a p-nitroaniline drivative (78) but this is not easily prepared.

L-Fucose may be separated as the p-bromophenylhydrazone (73) and as the α-methylphenylhydrazone, and L-rhamnose gives a crystalline phenylhydrazone (73), p-nitrophenylhydrazone (73) and a p-nitroaniline derivative (78).

D-Galactose readily forms a crystalline α-methylphenylhydrazone (94) and upon oxidation with nitric acid it gives galactaric acid which is best characterized as the n-butyl ester (95), a derivative that shows a well-defined melting point; the L-isomer may be identified in the same manner.

D-Glucose forms a crystalline p-nitrophenylhydrazone (73), but for small amounts the p-nitroaniline derivative (78) is recommended. Oxidation with nitric acid and formation of the potassium acid salt of D-glucaric acid can be used if plenty of material is available.

D-Mannose has long been characterized as its sparingly soluble phenylhydrazone (73). This derivative is not readily recrystallized, although formamide is a fairly good solvent, and hence conversion to the anhydro-hydrazone tetraacetate (96,97) should be adopted. It can also be identified as its p-nitroaniline derivative (78) and, after reduction with sodium borohydride (98,99) followed by acetylation, as mannitol hexaacetate (99).

Most of the above sugars may also be characterized as their sulfonyl-hydrazones (100), 2,5-dichlorophenylhydrazones (101), or thiosemicar-bazones (102). After oxidation of aldoses with sodium hypoiodite the derived aldonic acids readily react with o-phenylenediamine to give good yields of the corresponding crystalline imidazoles (364,365). More recently, it has been shown that reducing sugars, including certain of the disaccharides, react smoothly with long chain fatty amines to give good yields of products that crystallize with ease (366). This reaction might prove useful for the identification of certain reducing methylated sugars.

On occasions in the past, selective fermentation has proved to be useful for the identification of sugars in a mixture (403); the chromatographic technique however, is to be preferred (see below).

Isolation Of Simple Sugars And Derivatives

Studies of the composition of polysaccharide gums and mucilages and their behavior when treated with varying concentrations of acids have provided simple methods for the isolation of some of the more expensive sugars and their derivatives in useable amounts. The source of some of them is given in Table 20.

TABLE 20. ISOLATION OF SUGARS AND THEIR DERIVATIVES
FROM GUMS AND MUCILAGES

Sugar or Derivative	Source	Reference
L-Arabinose	Mesquite gum	103–106,359
	Gum arabic	2,107
D-Xylose[a]	Chagual gum	4
	(Flax seed mucilage)	109
L-Fucose	Fucoidin	110,111
	(from *Ascophyllum nodosum*)	
D-Galactose	Chagual gum	4
	Carrageenin	
	(from *Gracilaria confervoides*)	112,113
	Galactomannans	
	(St. Ignatius Bean, *Nux Vomica*)	424,425
L-Galactose	Flaxseed mucilage	114
3,6-Anhydro-L-galactose	Agar	62,115–117
3,6-Anhydro-D-galactose	Carrageenin	60,61,81
D-Mannose	Guar gum	52
	Locust bean gum	
D-Mannuronic acid	Alginic acid	47
(D-mannuronolactone)		

TABLE 20. (CONTINUED)

Sugar or Derivative	Source	Reference
L-Guluronic acid	Alginic acid	399
4-O-Methyl-D-glucuronic acid	Mesquite gum	82,83

(a)Many hemicelluloses containing a high percentage of xylan, can be used for making D-xylose; sapote gum (108,311) and tamarind gum (354) should be a good source of this sugar.

Paper and Column Chromatography. Paper partition chromatography, introduced in 1944 for the separation and determination of amino acids (118), has been highly successful for the separation of sugars and probably even more successful for their quantitative determination. It was demonstrated (119,120) that closely related sugars could be separated from each other provided a suitable solvent or combination of solvents could be selected.

The apparatus required for this type of analysis is inexpensive and simple to construct. The technique is surprisingly simple and separation of a sugar mixture is usually clear cut and quantitative (121–124). The method involves placing a small amount (0.5 mg. or less) of the mixture of sugars on a narrow strip or a wide sheet of filter paper, depending upon the number of sugars in the mixture and the number of accompanying standard sugars that have to be applied as reference compounds. The material is applied as a small drop of a solution and the solvent allowed to evaporate. One end of the paper is then immersed in a trough made of glass, or stainless steel, or some other suitable inert material, containing the selected solvent. The solvent is drawn up from the trough by capillary attraction and flows past the spot containing the mixture of sugars, eventually dripping off the bottom of the paper.

The separation of the sugars depends upon the relative ease with which they can pass from the solid or static phase (cellulose saturated with water) to the moving phase (the developing solvent). The exact mechanism of this phenomenon is not understood, but certain factors such as temperature, type of cellulose paper and nature of solvent have a profound effect upon the movement of the sugars. The asymmetric nature of the cellulose paper coupled with the difference in the mutual association of the polyhydroxy sugar compounds with the cellulose polymer evidently play an important role in chromatographic separations (121). The presence of acidic groups, such as carboxyl and sulfonic acid groups, introduced during the liberation of the cellulose from wood by pulping processes, may also exert some effect (406). Under a given set of conditions of temperature, solvent, type of paper, and pH (118,226,

383,384), the rate of movement of a particular sugar will be fairly constant. This rate of movement relative to the movement of the solvent is called the R_F value, a measurement which now assumes in organic chemistry almost as much importance as the boiling point or the melting point. The 6-deoxyhexoses, such as L-rhamnose and L-fucose, move more rapidly than the pentoses, D-xylose and L-arabinose, and these in turn move more rapidly than the hexoses, D-glucose, D-galactose, and D-mannose. On the other hand, the uronic acids, D-glucuronic acid, D-galacturonic acid, and D-mannuronic acid move even more slowly than the hexoses. The pentoses may be separated from each other and mixtures of the hexoses can also be resolved into their components with suitable irrigating solvents. One solvent or mixture of solvents may not be capable of resolving all sugars, but by carrying out two or three chromatographic analyses using a different solvent each time, the identity of all the components in a mixture can usually be decided with little difficulty.

Since 1944 many modifications in technique have been devised. Thus, instead of allowing the solvent to move down the paper strip (descending technique) from an upper solvent reservoir (118–120,385), the paper may be dipped in a trough and the solvent allowed to travel up the paper (ascending technique) (125). Alternatively the paper may be held in a horizontal position and the solvent moves along it from a trough into which one end of the paper dips (126,130). A simple modification of the horizontal technique has been developed for circular filter papers and is sometimes referred to as circular chromatography (127–129). In addition an electric potential may be applied to the paper in a direction at right angles to the flow of the solvent. This modification and that making use of paper ionophoresis alone are especially valuable for separating basic or acidic sugar derivatives and for substances that are difficult to separate by the normal solvent partition procedures. Sometimes, in the separation of uronic acids it is an advantage to impregnate the paper with an acidic insoluble polymer such as alginic acid, O-(carboxymethyl)cellulose (431), or cation exchange resins (431) which prevent ionization; this modification (131) enables sugar acids to be separated with a wide variety of solvents without incorporating such acids as formic (134) or acetic acid (119,120) to suppress ionization, as formerly recommended (119,120,132,133,135,136).

Modification of the cellulose filter paper has also been effected by the introduction of alkyl, acyl (387), and aryl groups (137). This produces paper having hydrophobic properties which is useful for separating acetyl derivatives of sugars as well as many other organic compounds, including amino acids and fatty acids (137). Carboxyl paper (378), papers modified with aluminum oxide (379–381), cellulose acetate (412), or silica gel (382), and glass paper impregnated with silicic acid (413), may sometimes be of considerable value in chromatography of sugar derivatives. Cellulose derivatives of anionic character, prepared by introducing 2-(diethylamino)ethyl-(417,418), triethylaminoethyl-(419), sulfomethyl or sulfoethyl (419) groups, which have proved to be effective for separating proteins (417,419) and other ionic compounds might also be useful for the resolution of mixtures of carbohydrates.

A wide variety of solvents has been used for separating sugars; all of them contain water which is absorbed on the cellulose to serve as the static phase. Table 21 gives a few of the more useful solvents. To avoid extensive trial experiments to ascertain the best porportions for any given solvent mixture, a method has been devised (394) that seems quite helpful. By the use of these techniques the sugars usually encountered in the hydrolyzate of a gum or mucilage can readily be separated. This may be seen from an inspection of the R_F values of the sugars commonly occurring in carbohydrate polymers (121–123).

TABLE 21. SOME SOLVENTS FOR SEPARATING SUGARS AND SUGAR ACIDS BY PAPER CHROMATOGRAPHY[a]

Solvents for Sugars	Proportions (by vol.)	Reference
Phenol: water	phenol saturated with water	119,120
Butanone: water	azeotrope	120,139
1-Propanol: water	azeotrope	56
2-Propanol: water	9:1	140
1-Butanol: ethanol: water	4:1:5	120
1-Butanol: pyridine: water	6:4:3	141,142
2-Propanol: pyridine: acetic acid: water	8:8:1:4	363
Ethyl acetate: acetic acid: water	3:1:3	135
Ethyl acetate: pyridine: water	2:1:2	135
Solvents for Sugar Acids[b]		
1-Butanol: acetic acid: water	4:1:5	120
1-Butanol: formic acid: water	12:1:7	143
1-Pentanol: 5N formic acid	1:1	134,136
Tert-Amyl alcohol: 1-propanol: water	4:1:5	144
2-Propanol: pyridine: acetic acid: water	8:8:1:4	363
Pyridine: ethyl acetate: acetic acid: water	5:5:3:1	386

(a)For other solvents see references 121–123,138.

(b)Using paper impregnated with alginic acid or O-(carboxymethyl)cellulose, any suitable solvent without a "swamping" acid may be used.

The sugars are located on the dried papers by various color reactions. The reagents selected make use of the reducing property of the sugar or sugar derivative, glycol cleavage with lead tetraacetate or periodate, or acid degradation to a furfural derivative. Other color reactions depend on the presence of certain groups such as the —NH$_2$ group in amino sugars for which the ninhydrin reaction may be applied, and the ester or lactone groups which may be determined by the hydroxamic acid test (146). The chromatograms are sprayed with, or dipped into, a suitable reagent that gives a color with trace amounts of the sugars upon standing or after heating to a suitable temperature (100 to 150°). In other cases the sugars are detected by spraying and examining the chromatograms in ultraviolet light.

Some of the more useful spray reagents are listed in Table 22. One of the best methods of detection in the art of chromatography involves drawing the papers through an acetone solution of silver nitrate after which they are sprayed with aqueous alcoholic sodium hydroxide. The position of the sugars is indicated by black spots appearing on the almost white paper chromatogram (145). The Tollen reagent formerly used consisted of a mixture of equal parts of $0.1N$ silver nitrate and $5N$ ammonium hydroxide with which the paper chromatogram was sprayed and then heated for 2 to 5 minutes at 100–110° (120). By using a reagent prepared by adding strong ammonium hydroxide to $2N$ silver nitrate, sugars can be detected by keeping the sprayed chromatograms at room temperature in the dark. This avoids the darkening of the whole paper that occurs when it is heated. A sensitive reagent for use at room temperature may be made by dissolving silver oxide in ammonium hydroxide. This reagent should not be kept since explosive silver fulminate is generated. Paper chromatograms sprayed with this reagent turn completely black almost at once. After 10 to 15 minutes the papers are dipped into dilute ammonium hydroxide or thiosulfate solution when the location of sugars is revealed by the appearance of black spots on a white background (139).

TABLE 22. REAGENTS FOR DETECTING SUGARS AND THEIR
DERIVATIVES ON PAPER CHROMATOGRAMS

Reagent[a]	Sugars or derivatives detected	Reference
Alkaline silver nitrate	Aldoses, ketoses, uronic acids, alcohols, reducing and nonreducing oligosaccharides	120,139, 145,150
Alkaline 3,5-dinitrosalicylic acid	Reducing sugars and uronic acids	142
Alkaline picric acid[b]	Reducing sugars, sugar phosphates	367

TABLE 22. (CONTINUED)

Reagent[a]	Sugars or derivatives detected	Reference
O-Aminophenol (with H_3PO_4)	Reducing sugars	407
Aniline hydrogen phthalate	Reducing sugars and uronic acids	120,124
Aniline phosphate	Aldoses (no color with ketoses)	151
Aniline oxalate	Aldoses and uronic acids	124
2-Amino-biphenylamine	Aldoses and ketoses and uronic acids	363
4-Amino-biphenylamine	Aldoses and uronic acids	237
p-Anisidine (hydrochloride, tri-chloroacetate, phosphate)	Aldoses, ketoses, uronic acids	141,152
N,N-Dimethyl-p-aminoaniline (hydrochloride, formate, tri-chloroacetate)	Aldoses, ketoses, uronic acids	139
N-(1-Naphthyl)ethylenediamine	Aldoses, ketoses, uronic acids	139,363
m-Phenylenediamine	Aldoses, ketoses (detected in U. V. light)	369
Naphthoresorcinol or other phenolic compounds	Pentoses, ketoses, uronic acids	120,368
Fehling solution followed by phosphomolybdic acid	Reducing sugars	542
1-Naphthol and phosphoric acid	Ketoses	154
Urea hydrochloride, urea oxalate	Ketoses	156
Anthrone	Ketoses	153
Alkaline phenyltetrazolium chloride	Reducing sugars and uronic acids	145,155
Acid permanganate	Reducing sugars and glycosides	156
Alkaline permanganate	Sugars and glycosides	147
Periodate and Schiff reagent	Sugars, glycosides, lactones and alcohols	132
Basic lead acetate	Galacturonic acid	387
Periodate-benzidine	Reducing sugars, glycosides, acids, lactones, alcohols	116,363
Periodate-benzidine	Reducing sugars	435

[a]For other reagents consult references 121–124,138,363.

[b]Picric acid can be incorporated in the irrigating solvent and the chromatogram developed by spraying with alcoholic alkali.

Many aromatic amines in the presence of an acid react with sugars on being heated to about 130°, to give brown, red, or pink colors. In this manner, pentoses, hexoses, ketoses and uronic acids may be differentiated (139,141). Ketoses may be detected with a reagent containing acidified naphthoresorcinol (120) and also by the anthrone reagent (153).

Carbohydrate esters or lactones may be detected by the hydroxamic acid test (146). Sugar glycosides and other nonreducing carbohydrate compounds containing hydroxyl groups may be detected directly by an alkaline permanganate reagent (147), but this method suffers from the disadvantage that the spots produced last only a short time since the paper is also attacked. Chromic oxide followed by diphenylcarbazide is said to be useful for detecting nonvicinal hydroxyl groups (401).

When glycosides or lactones are being located, the use of periodate spray reagents has been recommended in combination with an additional reagent applied afterwards to detect either the oxidation product (132) of the carbohydrate compound or the reduction product (144) of the periodate. Lead tetraacetate may also be used for detecting 1,2 glycol groupings (132).

While uronic acids are readily detected they are difficult to separate from each other although recently a reasonably good separation has been effected with a mixture of pyridine: ethyl acetate: acetic acid: water (386,387). Alternatively, the ester glycosides of the uronic acids can be reduced with sodium or potassium borohydride or lithium aluminum hydride to the corresponding sugar glycosides after which they are hydrolyzed and the sugars so formed identified in the usual way (402). Chromatographic analysis combined with micro-fermentation constitutes a powerful technique for the identification of sugars as well as for structural studies on oligosaccharides (351,404,405).

Some of the more useful reagents for detecting sugars and their derivatives on paper chromatograms are given in Table 22 and the R_F values of certain sugars are recorded in Table 23.

Another procedure for identifying carbohydrates that are susceptible to periodate oxidation involves spraying the chromatograms with dilute sodium periodate after which a potassium permanganate spray is applied in order to oxidize further the organic compounds already partially oxidized by the metaperiodate. This results in the deposition of manganese dioxide on the paper where the oxidizable carbohydrate compounds are lo-

TABLE 23. R_F VALUES OF SOME SIMPLE SUGARS AND URONIC ACIDS

	Solvent[a]				
	Phenol saturated with water	Ethyl Acetate (3) Acetic Acid (1) Water (3)	Ethyl Acetate (2) Pyridine (1) Water (2)	1-Butanol (4) Ethanol (1) Water (5)	Butanone- Water Azeotrope
Reference	(120)	(135)	(135)	(120,157)	(158, cf 120)
Compound					
L-Arabinose	1.54	1.22	0.33	0.12	0.036
D-xylose	0.44	0.26	0.38	0.15	0.046
D-Galactose	0.44	0.14	0.23	0.07	0.011
D-Glucose	0.39	0.17	0.28	0.09	0.013

TABLE 23. (CONTINUED)

Solvent[a]

Compound	Phenol saturated with water	Ethyl Acetate (3) Acetic Acid (1) Water (3)	Ethyl Acetate (2) Pyridine (1) Water (2)	1-Butanol (4) Ethanol (1) Water (5)	Butanone- Water Azeotrope
Reference	(120)	(135)	(135)	(120,157)	(158, cf120)
D-Mannose	0.45	0.19	0.32	0.11	0.023
D-Fructose	0.54		0.32	0.12	0.027
L-Sorbose	0.42				0.023
D-Glucuronic acid	0.12				0.04
D-Glucurono- lactone	0.60				0.31
D-Mannurono- lactone	0.62				
D-Galacturonic acid	0.13	0.13	0.025		0.03
L-Rhamnose	0.59	0.34	0.49	0.30	0.086
L-Fucose	0.63			0.21	0.046

[a]Figures in parentheses are parts by volume.

TABLE 23. (CONTINUED)

Compound	1-Butanol (4) Acetic acid (1) Water (5)	Sym-Collidine saturated with water	Ethyl Acetate (5) Acetic Acid (1) Pyridine (5) Water (3)
Reference	(120)	(120)	(386,387)[b]
L-Arabinose	0.21	0.43	
D-Xylose	0.28	0.50	
D-Galactose	0.16	0.34	
D-Glucose	0.18	0.39	
D-Mannose	0.20	0.46	
D-Fructose	0.23	0.42	
D-Glucuronic acid	0.12	0.16	1.16
D-Glucuronolactone	0.32	0.72	3.39
D-Mannuronic acid			1.45
D-Mannuronolactone			2.98
D-Galacturonic acid	0.14	0.14	1.00
L-Rhamnose	0.37	0.59	
L-Fucose	0.27	0.44	

[b]R(galacturonic acid) Value.

TABLE 23. (CONTINUED)

	Tert-Pentanol (4) 2-propanol (1) Water (1.5)	Tert-Pentanol (4) 2-propanol (1) Water (1)	1-Butanol (4) 1-Ethanol (1) Water (5)
Reference	(144)	(144)	
Compound			
L-Arabono-γ-lactone		0.39 0.59[c]	
D-Xylono-γ-lactone			0.41
D-Galactono-γ-lactone			0.35
D-Glucono-γ-lactone		0.56	0.32
D-Glucono-δ-lactone			0.22
D-Mannono-γ-lactone		0.39	0.25
L-Rhamnono-γ-lactone		0.37 0.63[c]	
D-Glucose	0.42	0.39	
Methyl-α-D-glucoside	0.58		
Methyl-β-D-glucoside	0.63		
Methyl-α-D-galactoside	0.54		
Methyl-β-D-galactoside	0.51		
Methyl-α-D-mannoside	0.68		
Methyl-α-D-mannofuranoside	0.74		
Methyl-α-L-arabinoside	0.60	0.65	
Methyl-β-D-arabinoside	0.68		
Methyl-α-L-fucoside ✔	0.76		
Methyl-α-L-rhamnoside	0.86	0.87	
Methyl-α-D-Xyloside	0.75	0.76	

[c]The lower figure is due to the aldonic acid

TABLE 23. (CONTINUED)

	1-Butanol (4) Water (5) Malonic acid (1)	1-Butanol (4) Water (5) Propionic acid (1)
Reference	(159)	(159)
Compound		
L-Arabinose	0.22	0.17
D-Xylose	0.25	0.19
D-Galactose	0.14	0.09
D-Glucose	0.15	0.11
D-Mannose	0.19	0.15
D-Fructose	0.15	0.11
L-Sorbose	0.19	0.13
D-Glucuronic acid	0.14	0.04
D-Glucuronolactone	0.33	0.26
D-Mannuronolactone	0.22	0.20
D-Galacturonic acid	0.12	0.05
L-Rhamnose	0.38	0.33
L-Fucose	0.33	0.26

cated. After washing out the excess of the periodate the deposits of manganese dioxide and hence the carbohydrates are detected by a benzidine spray which gives a dark blue color (148). This procedure is said to be rather more sensitive than a previous one (149).

For most research purposes three reagents are usually sufficient. First, the ammoniacal silver nitrate reagent, suitably modified (145), is capable of detecting reducing sugars, nonreducing sugars, sugar alcohols, and in general all polyhydroxy compounds containing two or more adjacent hydroxyl groups. Second, a reagent containing an acid together with an aromatic amine, such as aniline (120,124,151), p-anisidine (141, 152), p-phenetidine, or N,N-dimethyl-p-aminoaniline (139) is suitable for detecting reducing sugars or sugar derivatives that undergo hydrolysis with acid; this reagent does not detect sugar alcohols or sugar acids. Third, a general reagent, such as one utilizing periodate, which is capable of detecting adjacent hydroxyl groups (144,363) and, when suitably modified (148,149), any oxidizable carbohydrate compound.

Not only has paper partition chromatography provided a means for the preliminary identification of the sugars, but by using thicker or larger sheets of paper it is possible to separate the components of the hydrolyzate from a gum or mucilage in sufficient amounts to enable the components to be characterized, either by direct crystallization or transformation into a crystalline derivative.

In conjunction with paper chromatography, it is sometimes advisable to take advantage of paper electrophoresis (ionophoresis) (160–165,395, 396). The method is rapid and in certain instances, it is possible to separate sugars or their derivatives that are not resolved by paper chromatography. Although a variety of techniques have been devised, one of the simpler methods involves placing a small amount of the component or mixture of components at the center of a strip of paper, both ends of which are soaked in a suitable buffer, such as a 0.1M sodium tetraborate, almost up to the starting line where the substances have been placed. The paper is then placed on a suitable insulating framework (163) or clamped between sheets of glass, preferably using a foam-rubber sheet to equalize the pressure on the paper, and the ends of the paper are allowed to dip into separate vessels containing the buffer solution. When the two boundaries of the buffer solution have coalesced so as to complete the electrical circuit, a potential of 300 to 1000 volts is applied for 0.5 to 3 hours by inserting electrodes into the vessels containing the buffer solutions. A simple device for impregnating the paper with buffer solution is to put the paper on a perforated Lucite plate that forms the top of a rectangular Lucite box which can be evacuated. Buffer solution is poured on to the paper and the excess removed by suction. While suction is maintained the paper is lifted off the plate, placed on a suitable supporting framework of glass rods and the sugars applied in the usual manner. When separation is judged to be complete, the paper is removed, dried, and the sugar components located in the usual manner by one of the many reagents mentioned above.

The results for the simple sugars given in Tables 24 and 25 are expressed as migration or M_g values, which is the ratio of the distance travelled by the substance to the distance travelled by D-glucose.

More recently, ionophoresis of the benzylamine derivatives of the sugars in an acid electrolyte (formic acid and sodium hydroxide, pH 1.8) has been recommended for the identification of the reducing aldose sugars of a homologous series (357). Paper electrophoresis of the bisulfite addition compounds of sugars by using a bisulfite buffer offers certain advantages (409) since mobility bears a relationship, though not a direct one, to molecular weight. The sugars may also be distinguished by this technique after conversion to their cyanohydrins (410).

For many purposes and especially when the sugar compounds are difficult to detect the filter paper may be replaced by one made from glass fibers (166). This modification permits the most vigorous chemical reac-

TABLE 24. ELECTROPHORETIC SEPARATION OF SIMPLE SUGARS ON FILTER PAPER

Substances	M_g Values (Borate buffer)[a]	
	0.2M, pH 10	0.1M, pH 9.2
L-Arabinose	0.96	1.00
D-Lyxose		0.84
D-Ribose	0.77	0.87
D-Xylose	1.00	1.06
L-Fucose	0.89	0.97
L-Rhamnose	0.52	0.73
D-Galactose	0.93	0.92
D-Glucose	1.00	1.00
D-Mannose	0.72	0.85
D-Fructose	0.90	0.90
L-Sorbose	0.95	0.92
D-Glucuronic acid	1.20	1.08
D-Galacturonic acid		1.06
D-Mannuronic acid		1.01
L-Arabitol	0.90	0.89
Galactitol	0.98	0.89
D-Glucitol	0.89	0.89
D-Mannitol	0.90	0.84

$$^{(a)}M_g = \frac{\text{Migration of Substance}}{\text{Migration of D-Glucose}} \text{ (414)}$$

TABLE 25. MOBILITIES OF SUGARS (cm.^{2}/v. sec. X10^5) AT 20° IN
BORATE AT VARIOUS pH VALUES ON WHATMAN NO. 1 PAPER

Sugar	pH				
	7.0	8.0	8.6	9.2	9.7
D-Fructose	8.2	9.7	11.4	12.5	13.1
L-Sorbose	8.7	10.4	12.2	14.1	14.3
D-Glucose	2.4	6.5	11.4	14.5	14.6
D-Galactose	2.8	5.8	9.6	13.0	13.1
D-Mannose	2.6	4.9	7.8	9.8	10.0
D-Ribose	7.0	9.1	10.2	10.9	11.0
L-Arabinose	3.2	6.5	10.3	13.3	13.9
L-Rhamnose	1.3	2.4	4.4	7.1	7.8
Cellobiose	0.5	0.5	1.5	3.2	4.5
Raffinose	0.5	0.9	1.7	3.6	4.8

tions to be applied (165). Moreover, interference by the cellulose with the complex between the compound to be separated and the borate is avoided (165,414).

Some use may be made of the complex formation between certain sugars and the borate ion in paper chromatography by adding boric acid to the irrigating solvent as shown by the fact that the separation of glucose from mannose can be brought about more readily in the presence of boric acid than in its absence (167).

Column Chromatography of Gum Hydrolyzates. If it is necessary to determine the composition of a mixture of sugars and at the same time identify them, the filter paper method of partition chromatography may be replaced by the technique of column chromatography using cellulose (168,169) or a mixture of cellulose and hydrocellulose (170).

In these methods the eluate from the column is collected in fractions, the amount of liquid collected in each fraction being controlled by one of a number of automatic devices for changing the receiver (133,168,169, 171-177), upon which various commercial models have been fashioned. It is advisable to maintain the column at a constant temperature by circulating water through a jacket surrounding the column (169).

By suitable tests such as those used in detecting sugars on paper chromatograms (see above) or a modified Molisch test using 1-naphtholsulfonate (179) or phenol (24), the fractions containing the required component sugars are located and freed from solvent. The sugars are obtained in almost quantitative yield and invariably they crystallize directly. Small amounts of impurity extracted from the cellulose of the column can be eliminated by a suitable solvent extraction process. Failing this, or if the amount of the component is small, a suitable derivative of the sugar is made (see above).

Partition chromatographic analysis has been employed to study the composition and structure of a number of gums and mucilages, among which are the following: gum arabic (46), cherry gum (180), cholla gum (181), almond tree gum (182), *Sterculia setigera* gum (183), flaxseed mucilage (193), slippery elm mucilage (184,192,193), gum myrrh (184), peach gum (185), black wattle gum (186), Iles glucomannan (56), corn hull hemicellulose (187,188,190), chagual gum (4), and the gums from cereal grains (191).

The value of this method of analysis is demonstrated by the fact that it has revealed a number of hitherto unsuspected components of certain polysaccharides. For example, 3-O-methyl-D-galactose was shown to be present in slippery elm (*Ulmus fulva*) mucilage (192,193) and D-mannitol has been found in laminarin (194,195); this appears to be the first time that a sugar alcohol has been found to be present in a naturally occurring polysaccharide. Paper chromatography has also revealed the presence of 3,6-anhydro-D-galactose in *Chondrus ocellatus* mucilage (426).

Although the column method of chromatographic analysis is a rather lengthy operation and seldom used solely for determining the composition of polysaccharides, it serves the vital purpose of providing relatively large amounts of the components of polysaccharide hydrolyzates in a pure state (196). As a preliminary step to such a separation on a cellulose column, it is an advantage to resolve the hydrolyzate into mono-, di, trisaccharides etc. This may be accomplished by means of charcoal, alone or in admixture with an inert solid (197–200). The latter is added to increase the solvent flow rate, a result that may also be achieved by applying pressure to the top or, less satisfactorily, by suction at the bottom of the column. The charcoal should be freed from mineral impurities by extraction with hydrochloric acid or cirtic acid (199) and, if necessary, deactivated by adding stearic acid (201). Charcoal column separations of sugars make use of displacement chromatography or desorption; the fundamental observations on which charcoal, displacement chromatography depends were made by Hayashi (202), who demonstrated that sugars are adsorbed on charcoal to different extents, the disaccharides being adsorbed more readily than the monosaccharides (see Table 26) (cf 197). The desorption of the sugars by aqueous alcohol was also observed and the conditions necessary for the separation of glucose and sucrose were established (see Table 26).

The monosaccharides are usually displaced with water and the higher saccharides by increasing concentrations of aqueous alcohol (197). It is better, however, to dispense with the initial water washing and begin the displacement of the sugars with 2 to 3 per cent aqueous ethanol (56,

203). This avoids "bleeding" and overlapping of the fractions, a phenomenon that may be deduced from the results of Table 27.

TABLE 26. INHIBITORY ACTION OF ETHANOL ON ADSORPTION OF VARIOUS SUGARS ON CHARCOAL (202)

(0.5 g. sugar in 50 ml of aqueous ethanol, 1.0 g. charcoal)

Sugar	Adsorption of Sugars by 1.0g of charcoal in absence of ethanol (mg.)	Concentration of Ethanol	
		0.1M; 0.46% Adsorption (mg.)	0.5M; 2.3% Adsorption (mg.)
L-Arabinose	109.4	87.0	38.0
D-Glucose	171.6	142.2	72.6
Lactose	390.2	369.1	302.0
Sucrose	481.7	465.3	437.9

TABLE 27. ADSORPTION OF D-GLUCOSE AND SUCROSE (202)

(50 ml. sugar solution, 1 g. charcoal)

Adsorption of Sugar (%)

Sugar	0.01M Sugar Solution	0.001M Sugar Solution				
			Concentration of Ethanol in Water			
	Water	Water	0.1M (0.46%)	0.5M (2.3%)	1.0M (4.6%)	2.0M (9.2%)
Glucose	59.6	77.0	46.6	14.8		
Sucrose	98.7	100.0	100.0	100.0		
Glucose	33.9	73.1	45.4	13.1	3.8	0
Sucrose	95.7	100	100	97.9	76.0	24.8

Separations of mono- and oligosaccharides can also be effected on columns of charcoal by elution with solvents containing borate (204) or molybdate (205). The effect of borate on the separation of carbohydrates on paper (167) and on columns of anion exchange resins (206,207) has also been noted.

Separation of oligosaccharides containing uronic acid units may be accomplished with the aid of anion exchange resins. Thus, mixtures of oligosaccharides of the glucuronosyl-glucosamine series are absorbed on a Dowex resin in the formate form and resolved by elution with increasing concentrations of formic acid, the progress of separation being ascertained colorimetrically on aliquots of the eluate (210).

In a similar manner mono-, di-, tri-, and tetra-D-galacturonic acids have been separated by displacement from a column of Dowex 3 (formate form) with formic acid, the mono being eluted with $0.1N$ formic acid, the di- with $0.5N$, the tri- with $1.0N$ and the tetra-D-galacturonic acid with $2.5N$ formic acid (212).

The method has been applied to the separation of the aldobio- and aldotriouronic acids obtained by acid hydrolysis of *Khaya grandifolia* gum. In this case the acids were displaced with increasing concentrations of acetic acid from "Amberlite 1RA-400" anion exchange resin in the acetate form (213,214).

Quantitative Analysis of Sugars

The composition of gums and mucilages is best determined by paper chromatography in conjunction with a micro-volumetric or better still perhaps a colorimetric method of sugar analysis. The analytical procedure may be outlined as follows. A small sample (10–20 mg.) of the purified gum or mucilage is hydrolyzed by heating in a sealed tube with dilute sulfuric acid (or hydrochloric acid) in a boiling water bath. [Cation exchange resins may also be used to effect hydrolysis (3,215) since the sugars appear to be stable after liberation (216). Refluxing with concentrated (90 to 95%) formic acid may also be used (47).] When the hydrolysis is complete, the solution is neutralized with barium carbonate, if the original polysaccharide contains sugar acid components, and then passed through a cation exchange resin (H form), such as "Amberlite IR-120"; this gives a solution containing a mixture of neutral sugars and sugar acid derivatives. If the original polysaccharide is composed only of neutral sugar residues, the hydrolysis solution may be neutralized by passing it through such anion-exchange resins as Duolite A4 or Amberlite IR-4B. Strong basic anion resins such as Amberlite IRA-400 should be avoided since they absorb sugars (217–220) and also bring about Lobry de Bruyn transformation (221–223).

The aqueous solution containing the components of the gum is concentrated in *vacuo* if necessary and examined by paper chromatography as described above using two and preferably three different solvent systems for the identification of the components to be determined. When acidic components are present, modified papers (131,137,431) or a swamping acid (120,134–136) should be employed to suppress ionization which causes trailing of the acid components.

For the quantitative analysis a small amount of an aqueous solution (it is advisable to dissolve the dry sirupy mixture of sugars in 20 per cent aqueous ethanol to avoid growth of organisms with loss of the components) is accurately transferred to the starting line of a chromatogram by means of a micropipet, the pipet being guided by a ruler, if necessary, during the transfer. The amount of the mixture of sugars added should contain not less than about 50 μg of the minor component so that after separation and extraction from the paper with water, the extract will contain 5 to 50 μg per 2 ml. If necessary, two or more applications of the solution containing the hydrolyzate can be made with the micropipet, allowing the paper to dry between each application. The separations are conveniently carried out on pieces of Whatman No. 1 or other suitable filter paper, 8 inches by 22 inches. Some recommend washing the paper before use, but since all soluble carbohydrate material cannot be removed (224) there is little advantage in doing this. The starting line is ruled 4 inches from one of the narrow ends of the paper and marginal sections are ruled off 1.5 inches from each side of the paper. The solution to be analyzed is put on the section of the starting line that is confined to the inner portion of the chromatogram. In the center of the starting line of the outer marginal strips is placed a drop or two of the solution being analyzed.

The paper is left until the solvent has evaporated and then placed in the chromatographic vessel for irrigation in the usual way, the time required for separation of the components having been estimated from preliminary qualitative chromatographic analysis. The paper is removed and allowed to dry in the air. The outer marginal strips are cut off, sprayed with a suitable reagent, (see Table 22) and the components located as described previously. The chromatogram is then reassembled and the areas on the unsprayed central portion of the chromatogram containing the individual components cut out and measured. The strips of paper are cut into pieces of about 2 to 3 sq. cms. and placed in a closed container with water, the volume of the solution being adjusted so that the extract will contain about 5 to 50 μg of sugar or sugar derivative per 2 ml. The papers are gently swirled in the water to facilitate extraction of the sugar which takes place rapidly and is complete in a minute or two. Disintegration of the filter paper with a glass rod or by other means such as vigorous agitation is unnecessary and should be avoided since it promotes extraction of carbohydrate impurity from the cellulose fibers and this interferes with the analysis. Other more complicated methods of extraction have been used (225–229), but the simple procedure is recommended (24,230). For further details see reference 198.

The extracts containing the separate components are filtered through a plug of glass wool to remove cellulose fibers and a 2 ml. aliquot is placed in a colorimeter tube with 0.1 ml. of 80 per cent aqueous phenol; concentrated sulfuric acid (5 ml.) is then added rapidly and the mixture is shaken and allowed to cool to room temperature. The absorbance of the characteristic yellow-orange color is measured at 490 mμ by means of a suitable colorimeter; the best results are obtained with the Beckman DU instrument, but for most purposes a Coleman Junior, and Evelyn colorimeter, or other suitable instrument can be used (24).

To correct for the small amount of hemicellulose-like compound extracted from the filter paper (224), a blank determination is carried out on a piece of paper of known area cut from a sheet of paper irrigated with solvent in the same manner as the chromatogram and the appropriate deduction made from the absorbance given by each of the extracts containing sugar. The amount of sugar in the extracts is determined by reference to a standard curve, relating concentration of sugar to absorbance, prepared for each of the sugars being analyzed (24).

The advantages of this particular method are that it is simple, the intensity of the color reaches a maximum quickly and remains constant over long periods and no special precautions, such as control of temperature and time of heating, are necessary in developing the color. Moreover, the method is applicable to pentoses, hexoses, ketohexoses, uronic acids and their derivatives including the methyl ethers. In the event that a sugar alcohol is encountered as the constituent of a gum or mucilage, as is the case with laminarin (194,195), the determination could be carried out by a modification (232,233) of the chromotropic acid method (234).

The phenol-sulfuric acid method is also useful for the determination of total carbohydrate in a wide variety of natural products, including gums and mucilages, since protein does not interfere with color development (427).

Another method for the micro-colorimetric determination of aldoses in gums and mucilages makes use of the color formed with aniline phthalate. The sugars are separated as described above, the strips, containing each component sugar, are cut from the chromatogram and extracted with methanol. To the extract is added a 2.5 per cent solution of aniline phthalate (1 ml.) after which the solvent is removed under reduced pressure and the residue heated at 60 $\pm$ 1° for 25 minutes for the aldopentoses and at 100 $\pm$ 1° for 15 minutes for the aldohexoses. The colored compound formed in this manner is then dissolved in methanol (5 ml.) and the color intensity determined after 15 minutes (235,236). A similar method using benzidine has been devised (411). Ketoses cannot be determined by these procedures since they produce little color.

A somewhat similar though less involved method for determining aldoses employs the color developed when the sugars, separated chromatographically, are heated with p-aminodiphenylamine. The paper does not interfere with this procedure, but long periods of heating are required to develop maximum color (237).

More recently, it has been shown that aldose sugars separated on chromatograms can be determined by spraying with a p-anisidine hydrochloride reagent and after heating the paper in an oven at 130° the colors so formed are extracted with aqueous methanol (containing stannous chloride to stabilize the color) and determined spectrophotometrically (238). The method, with which the paper does not interfere, has been successfully used for aldohexoses, aldopentoses, hexuronic acids and 6-deoxyaldohexoses. Since the color formed for the aldopentoses and hexuronic acids shows a selective absorption band at 510 mμ, aldohexoses one at 400 mμ and 6-deoxyaldohexoses a band at 385 mμ, it might be possible to analyze mixtures of these classes of compounds, particularly those containing pentoses or hexuronic acids and hexoses or 6-deoxyaldohexoses, without separation.

A procedure using the anthrone reaction (38) has been developed for the determination of sugars separated on chromatograms. To an aliquot (3 ml.) of the filtered aqueous extract of each component sugar (9 to 90 μg) cooled to 15° is added a layer of the anthrone reagent, (6 ml., prepared by dissolving anthrone (0.2g) in concentrated sulfuric acid (100 ml.)). The reactants are then mixed and heated for exactly 10 minutes on a boiling water bath. The colored solution is cooled immediately and the absorbance determined at 620 mμ (239).

A less sensitive colorimetric method (requiring 0.1 to 0.5 mg. of sugar) utilizes the brownish color formed when reducing sugars react with alkaline solutions of 3,5-dinitrosalicylic acid (240). Direct measurement by a reflectance method, without elution, of the color produced on the chromatograms when the sugars are treated with aniline phthalate (241) or ammoniacal silver nitrate (242,243), has formed the basis of other procedures for the determination of sugars.

Micro-volumetric methods have been devised (228,244) which make use of a copper reagent (245), the alkaline-hypoiodite reagent of Willstätter and Schudel (157,246), the sodium metaperiodate reagent (229) of Malaparade (247) or the ferricyanide reagent (428) of Hagedorn-Jensen (429). Compared with the micro-colorimetric methods discussed above, these volumetric procedures are rather less sensitive and, in the case of the copper reduction methods, very careful control of the conditions is necessary.

Another interesting device which is of rather doubtful value for the chromatographic analysis of sugars, involves directing the moving component sugars through a narrow "bottle neck" cut in the paper. Irriga-

(text cont'd on p. 117)

TABLE 28. COMPOSITION OF NEUTRAL GUMS AND MUCILAGES

Source	Sugars (%)					Other Sugars	Reference
	D-Galactose	D-Mannose	D-Glucose	L-Arabinose	D-Xylose		
Iles mannan (Amorphophallus oncophyllus)		67	23				10
Orchid (Cremastra variabilis)		+	+				250
Orchid (Bletilla striata)		+	+				250
Eremuran (Eremurius regelii)		+	+				436
Konjak mannan (Amorphophallus konjak (rivieri))		67	23				55
Konjak flour (unknown source)		+	+				251
Iris (Iris ochroleuca)	3	40	60				252
Iris (Iris sibirica)	3	48	48				252
Iris (Iris pseudacorus) (I. germanica) (I. foetidissima)		82		18			376,377
Tragacanth, neutral fraction (Order of Astragalus)	+			+			255
Cashew (Anacardium occidentale)	+			+			259
Neem (Azadirachta indica)	+			+			260
Sterculia plantanifolia	+			+			261
Oenothera jaquinnii	+			+			261

							Reference
Lily bulbs (*Lilium umbellatum*)		67	33				361
Lily bulbs (*Lilium henryii*)		67	33				361
Kadzura japonica	+			+			261
Prickly Pear (*Opuntia vulgaris*)	+			+			262
Capsicum seed	+			+			263
Bean trefoil (*Anagyris foetida*)	+			+			264
Actinidia callosa Lindl. var. rufa Makino	+			+			265
Abelmoschus manihot	+			+		L-rhamnose	266
Polygonatum ofcinale All.				+		D-fructose	267
Bassora (*Cochlospermum gossypium*)	+		+		+		268
Flaxseed (*Linum usitatissimum*)				9	25	L-galactose (8)	183
Tamarind (*Tamarindus indica L.*)	17		53		30	L-rhamnose (13)	269,270,354
Xylan component					100		420
Salai tree (*Boswellia serrata*)	+			+	+		271
Khaya tree (*Khaya madagascariensis*)	+			+			272
Almond (Order of *Amygdalus*)	+			?	?		273
Colocasia antiquorum			+				261
Vitis pentaphylla	+						261
Prickley Pear (*Opuntia genus*)	+						261
Plantago seeds (*Plantago ovata Forsk*)	+ (trace)			14	80		275,276

TABLE 28. (CONTINUED)

Source	D-Galactose	D-Mannose	D-Glucose	L-Arabinose	D-Xylose	Other Sugars	Reference
			Sugars (%)				
Brown algae (Ascophyllum nodosum)	?9					L-fucose (2) (SO₃H)	277
Kentucky coffee nut (Gymnocladus canadensis)			+	+			278
Barbados aloes (Aloe vera)		49	49			uronic acid (2)	279
Salep mannan (Genus of Orchis)		100					280,281
Barley flour β-D-glucan			100				370–373
Oat flour β-D-glucan			100				374,375
Rye flour araboxylan			5	29	60		539,544

TABLE 29. COMPOSITION OF GALACTOMANNANS

Source	Sugars (%)		Reference
	D-Galactose	D-Mannose	
Tara	26	71	282
(*Caesalpinia spinosa*)			
Huizache	28	69	282
(*Caesalpinia cacalaco*)			
Carob, locust bean ⎤	20–14	80–86	282
(*Ceratonia siliqua L.*) ⎬	17	83	283
⎦	20–25	75–80	284
Paloverde	22	73	282
(*Cercidium terreyanum*)			
Flame tree	19	79	282
(*Delonix regia*)			
Guar ⎤	33	67	285
(*Cyamopsis tetragonolobus*) ⎦	36	64	282
Honey locust	26	71	282
(*Gleditsia tricanthos*)			
Gleditsia amorphoides	26	59	408
(seed pods)			
Gum garrofin	30	70	408
(*Gleditsia amorphoides*)			
Kentucky coffee bean	20	80	286
(*Gymnocladus dioica*)	26	71	282
Japanese pagoda	16	81	282
(*Sophora japonica*)			
Prairie-mimosa	26	70	282
(*Desmanthus illinoiensis*)			
Indigo	23	72	282
(*Indigofera hirsuta*)			
Senna	21	65	282
(*Cassia leptocarpa*)			
Rattlebox	28	64	282
(*Crotalaria intermedia*)			
Lucerne	67	23	287
(*Medicago sativa*)			
Clover	44	56	287
(*Trifolium pratense*)			
Fenugreek seeds	45	55	288
(*Trigonella foenum-graecum*)			
Soy bean hulls	40	60	541
(*Glycine soja*)			

TABLE 30. COMPOSITION OF GUMS AND MUCILAGES CONTAINING D-GLUCURONIC ACID

Source	Sugars %							Reference
	D-Glucuronic acid	D-Galactose	D-Mannose	D-Glucose	L-Arabinose	D-Xylose	Other Sugars	
Konjak mannan (*Amorphophallus konjak*)	+		+	+				289
Iles Mannan (*Amorphophallus oncophyllus*)	4		41	49			Pentoses (2)	290
Asparagus (*Asparagus filicinus*)	5		45	40			D-Fructose (10)	291
Acacia karroo (Hayne)	12	50			36		L-Rhamnose (2)	355
Acacia catechu	+	+			+		L-Rhamnose	437
Gum Arabic (*Acacia verek*)	16	52			19		L-Rhamnose (14)	6,107, 292–297
Black Wattle gum (*Acacia mollissima*, Willd)	9	42			42		L-Rhamnose (7)	186
Mesquite gum (*Prosopis juliflora* DC)		31			51		4-O-Methyl-D-glucuronic acid (18)	83,103,106, 298–300
Cherry gum (*Prunus cerasus*)	12	21	10		55		L-Rhamnose (trace)	301
Cherry gum (*Prunus virginiana* L.)	9	26	13		29		L-Rhamnose (23)	302

Source						Other constituents (%)	References
Egg plum gum (*Prunus domestica*)	15	40		34	11		303,304
Acacia cyanophylla	24	49		7		L-Rhamnose (20)	356
Acacia pycnantha	5	65		27		L-Rhamnose (1–2)	46
Damson gum (*Prunus insitia*)	16	30	15	38	trace		1,305,345
Almond tree gum (Order of *Amygdalus*)	10	30		40	20		182,306
Peach tree gum (*Prunus persica*)	7	36		43	14	L-Rhamnose (trace)	185
Fagara xanthoxyloides		61		21		4-O-methyl-D-glucuronic acid (17)	441
Lemon gum (*Citrus limonia*)	22	55		22		4-O-Methyl-D-glucuronic acid, 6-deoxy-hexose	307–309,423
Grapefruit gum (*Citrus maxima*)	31	53		16			307
New Zealand Flax Phormium gum (*Phormium tenax*)	+				+		310
Myrrh gum (*Commiphora myrrha*)		50		12		4-O-Methyl-D-glucuronic acid (38)	184
Gum asafetida (*Ferula* sp. roots)	+	+		+		Rhamnose	442

TABLE 30. (CONTINUED)

Source	D-Glucuronic acid	D-Galactose	D-Mannose	D-Glucose	L-Arabinose	D-Xylose	Other Sugars	Reference
				Sugars %				
Sapote gum (Sapota achras)	16				30(?)	54		108,311,346
Asparagus (Asparagus adscendens)	25			25		50		312
	50			25		25		312
Silk oak gum (Grevillea robusta)	+	+			+			313
Anogeissus schimperi	+	+			+			314
Gum Ghatti (Anogeissus latifolia, Wall)	12	27	8		41		3-O-Methyl pentose (trace)	320,358
Water shield (Brasenia schreberi, Gmel. (leaves)	+	+	+		+			315
Green seaweed (Ulva lactuca)	+			+		+	L-Rhamnose	316
Prunus serrulata	6 to 8	36				92–94		317
Chagual gum (Species of Puya)	15				7	43		4,318
Corn hull gum (Zea mays)	7 to 12	7			35	48		187,188,190 319,348–353
Curculigo orchioides	42		23	35				360
Ketha gum (Feronia elephantum)	Aldobio-uronic acid	+			+	+	L-Rhamnose (trace)	342
Hakea acicularis	8	58	7		19	8		421

Virgilia oroboides	?+	+	+	L-Rhamnose 430
V. divaricata	?+	+	+	L-Rhamnose 430
Combretum verticillatum (water soluble fraction)	+	15	38	438
Mimosa pudica (seed mucilage)	21		trace	79 439
Brachychiton diversifolium gum (*Sterculia caudata*)	50	25		L-Rhamnose 538 (25)

TABLE 31. COMPOSITION OF GUMS AND MUCILAGES CONTAINING D-GALACTURONIC ACID

Source	Sugars (%)						Reference
	D-Galacturonic acid	D-Galactose	L-Arabinose	D-Xylose	L-Rhamnose	Other Sugars	
Tragacanth, acid fraction (Order of *Astralagus*)	+			+		L-Fucose	254
Tragacanth (whole gum)	+	+	+	+		L-Fucose	7,256–258
Cholla gum (*Opuntia fulgida*)	8	25	50	16	trace		181,321,322
Karaya gum (*Sterculia urens*)	43	14			15	Keto-hexose	324
	36	33			32	(trace)	440
	35	40			24		440
Cacao (*Sterculia setigera*)	50	28			22	D-Tagatose	325,326
Joel (*Lannea grandis*)	+	+	+				327
Flaxseed (*linum usitatissimum*)	+		12	27	29 (?)	L-Galactose (12) L-Fucose or D-Ribose	183
Plantago seeds (*Plantago arenaria*)	7	6	16	65	6		328
(*Plantago psyllium*)	+		+	+			329,330
(*Plantago fastigiata*)	+		+	+			331
(*Plantago ovata Forsk*)	+		+	+	+		275
(*Plantago lanceolata*)	15	+		72	(?)11		332
Nori-utsugi (*Hydrangea paniculata,* Sieb.)	+	+	+		+		253,393

Source						Reference	Component
Slippery elm (*Ulmus fulva*)	33	+			33	193,333	3-*O*-Methyl-D-galactose, glucose, fucose
Quince seed (*Cydonia oblonga*)	?		+	+		334	*O*-Methyl hexuronic acid
White mustard seed (*Brassica alba*)	+		+	+	?	335	Glucuronic acid
Cress seed (*Lepidum sativum*)	+		+	+	+	336	
Okra (*Hibiscus esculentus*)	+				+	337	
Okra (*Bamia fellahi* or *H. esculentus*)	6	80	3		10	422	
Lupine (*Lupinus termis*)	8	79	14			540	
Asparagus (*Asparagus racemosus*)	+					338,339	D-Glucose
Honey locust gum (*Gleditsia tricanthos*)	(?) 22	34	44		+	340	
Khaya gum (*Khaya grandifolia*)	+	+	?		+	213,314	4-*O*-Methyl-D-glucuronic acid
Khaya gum (*Khaya senegalensis*)	+	+	?		+	213	4-*O*-Methyl-D-glucuronic
Tororo-aoi (*Abelmoschus manihot*)	+		+	+	+	341,347	D-Glucose

TABLE 31. (CONTINUED)

Source	Sugars (%)						Reference
	D-Galacturonic acid	D-Galactose	L-Arabinose	D-Xylose	L-Rhamnose	Other Sugars	
Ketha gum (*Feronia elephantum*)	(?)	+	+	+	+		342
Scaphium affine, Pierre	+		+				343
Grapes (*Vitis vinifera L.*)	16	34	16		12	Mannose (20)	362
Indian gum (*Cochlospermum gossypium*)	+	+			+		324

TABLE 32. COMPOSITION OF ALGAL POLYSACCHARIDES

Polysaccharides or Source	Component	Reference
Acanthopeltis japonica	3,6-anhydro-L-galactose	115,116
	L-galactose	492,493,503
Anabaena cylindrica	arabinose (1 mole)	189
	galactose (1 mole)	
	glucose (5 moles)	
	glucuronic acid (4 moles)	
	rhamnose (1 mole)	
	xylose (4 moles)	
Ascophyllum nodosum	L-fucose	458
	mannose	
Ceramium hypnaeoides	3,6-anhydro-L-galactose	492
	galactose	
Ceremium rubrum	D-galactose	456
	D-glucose	
	sulfate	
Cetraria islandica (lichenin)	D-glucose	532–535
Chondrus crispus	D-galactose	60,81,456,
	D-glucose	465,500,501
	3,6-anhydro-D-galactose	
	sulfate	
Chondrus elatus	L-arabinose	452
	D-galactose	
	"floridose"	
Chondrus ocellatus	6-deoxyhexose	426,445
	D- and L-erythrose	497,498
	D-galactose	
	L-galactose	
	3,6-anhydro-D-galactose	
	2-ketohexonic acid (probably	
	3,6-anhydrogalactose)	
	sulfate	
Cladophora rupestris	arabinose (3.7 moles)	434
	galactose (2.8 moles)	
	rhamnose (0.4 mole)	
	xylose (1 mole)	
Calothrix scopulorum	D-glucose	520
(Cyanophycean starch)		522–525
Delesseria elata	D-galactose	456
D. sanguinea	D-glucose	
	sulfate	

TABLE 32. (CONTINUED)

Polysaccharides or Source	Component	Reference
Dilsea edulis	D-galactose uronic acid; sulfate	470,471 530
Dilsea edulis (Floridean starch)	D-glucose	517
Dumontia incrassata	galactose uronic acid; sulfate	504
Eisenia bicyclis (Laminarin)	D-glucose	495

Fucus typicus and
F. giganteus Okam.
	6-deoxyhexose
	D-galactose
	2-keto-hexonic acid
	    (probably 3,6-anhydro
	    galactose).
	D- and L-erythrose
	sulfate
		445

Fucus vesiculosus	L-fucose D-galactose D-glucose D-glucose D-xylose; sulfate	432
Furcellaria fastigiata (Floridean starch).	D-glucose	518
Gelidium amansii	D-galactose L-galactose 3,6-anhydro-L-galactose	115,116 491–493 503
Gelidium crinale G. latifolium	D-galactose 3,6-anhydro-L-galactose sulfate	62,115,117 211,477–491
Gelidium pacificum Okam.	D-galactose	460
Gelidium subcostatum	L-galactose 3,6-anhydro-L-galactose	115,116 492,493 503
Gigartina stellata	D-galactose L-galactose sulfate	442 472 499
Gloiopeltis furcata (var. coliformis)	L-arabinose L-fucose D-galactose 3,6-anhydro-L-galactose (31%) D-galactose (46,6%) L-galactose (3.9%) sulfate (18.5%)	452 433

TABLE 32. (CONTINUED)

Polysaccharides or Source	Component	Reference
Himanthalea lorea (fucoidin)	L-fucose (57%) D-galactose (4%) uronic acid (3%) D-xylose (1.5%) sulfate (38%)	444
Iridaea laminarioides (var. conucopiae)	L-arabinose D-galactose "floridose" sulfate	452
Iridaea laminarioides	3,6-anhydrogalactose D- and L-erythrose D-galactose 6-deoxyhexose 2-keto-hexonic acid sulfate	445
Laminaria cloustoni (laminarin)	D-glucose D-mannitol	194,195 473,505–507
Laminaria flexicaulis	D-galactose D-glucose	459,494
Laminaria digitata (laminarin)	D-glucose D-mannitol	194,195 461,474–476 494,505 506,508
Lemania nodosa (Floridean starch)	D-glucose	519
Laminaria digitata (fucoidin)	L-fucose sulfate	496
Laminaria and *Fucus* sp. (fucoidin)	L-fucose sulfate	461,462
Macrocystis pyrifera	L-fucose sulfate	463
Nitella sp.	D-glucose	537
Nostoc sp.	galactose glucose galacturonic acid glucuronic acid rhamnose (6%) xylose (15%)	537
Oscillatoria sp.	D-glucose	537

TABLE 32. (CONTINUED)

Polysaccharides or Source	Component	Reference
Plumaria elegans	D-galactose D-glucose sulfate	456
Polysiphonia fastigiata	D-galactose D-glucose sulfate	456
Porphyra capensis *P. laciniata*	3,6-anhydro-L-galactose D-galactose L-galactose 6-O-methyl-D-galactose DL-galactose	249,484 521
Rhodymenia palmata (xylan)	D-xylose	471,515 516
Umbilicaria pustulata *U. hirsuta* (pustulin)	D-glucose ,,	536 533
Alginic acid from: *Ascophylum nodosum* *Fucus serratus* *Laminaria cloustoni* *Laminaria digitata* *Macrocystis pyrifera*	 D-mannuronic acid ,, ,, L-guluronic acid ,,	 47 526–529 531 399
Cellulose from: Brown algae Green algae *Fucus vesiculosus* *Gelidium amansii* *Iridaea laminarioides* *Laminariae* *Laminaria cloustoni* *L. digitata*	 D-glucose ,, ,, ,, ,, ,, ,, ,,	 461,509 510 514 513 449,512 511 514 514

TABLE 33. THE PERCENTAGE OF D-MANNURONIC AND L-GULURONIC ACID IN PHAEOPHYCEEN[a] (399)

	"Anhydrouronic Acid" (%) in Algae	
	D-Mannuronic acid	L-Guluronic Acid
Colpomenia sinuosa	1.6	2.1
Chorda filum	6.3	5.2
Laminaria digitata	10.6	4.6
Padina pavonia	2.2	1.8
Dictyopteris polypodioides	2.6	3.0
Ascophyllum nodosum	13.0	4.3
Fucus vesiculosus	3.6	3.0
Fucus spiralis L. var. platycarpa	6.3	2.8
Himanthalia lorea	10.2	3.7
Cytoseira mediterranea	5.5	4.1
Sargassum linifolium	4.7	5.3

[a]Many of these seaweeds also contained glucuronic acid, but it is not believed to be an integral part of the alginic acid molecule.

tion is arrested while the sugar component to be analyzed is still in the bottle neck. The concentration of the sugar is then a function of the length of the spot in the "bottle neck" as revealed by a suitable spray reagent (248).

The above methods of sugar analysis making use of paper chromatography have completely superseded those which were based on the preparation of a so-called "insoluble" derivative, such as the determination of D-galactose by oxidation to galactaric acid or D-mannose as its phenylhydrazone and so on.

The following have been found as components of various gums and mucilages (see Tables 28 to 33).

Aldopentoses:	L-arabinose, D-xylose
Aldohexoses:	3,6-anhydro-D-galactose, 3,6-anhydro-L-galactose, D-galactose, L-galactose, 3-O-methyl-D-galactose, 6-O-methyl-D-galactose D-galactose 4-sulfate, D-glucose, D-mannose
Ketohexoses:	D-fructose, D-tagatose
6-Deoxyhexoses:	L-fucose, L-rhamnose
Uronic acids:	D-galacturonic acid, D-glucuronic acid, 4-O-methyl-D-glucuronic acid, L-guluronic acid, D-mannuronic acid
Hexitols:	D-mannitol

The compositions of a number of gums and mucilages are recorded in Tables 28 and 29 and the compositions of acidic gums and mucilages appears in Tables 30 and 31, and that of seaweed polymers in Tables 32, and 33.

It is likely that homologs of the above mentioned sugars and their derivatives will eventually be found in gums and mucilages.

REFERENCES

1. Hirst, E. L., and Jones, J. K. N., *J. Chem. Soc.*, 1174 (1938).
2. Smith, F., *J. Chem. Soc.*, 744 (1939).
3. Wadman, H. W., *J. Chem. Soc.*, 3051 (1952).
4. Hamilton, J. K., Smith, F., and Spriestersbach, D. R., *J. Am. Chem. Soc.*, **79**, 443 (1957).
5. Bell, D. J., and Young, F. G., *Biochem. J.*, **28**, 882 (1934).
6. O'Sullivan, C., *J. Chem. Soc.*, **45**, 41 (1884).
7. O'Sullivan, C., *J. Chem. Soc.*, **79**, 1164 (1901).
8. Vollmert, B., *Makromol. Chem.*, **5**, 110 (1950).
9. Torigata, H., *J. Chem. Soc. Japan, Pure Chem. Sect.*, **72**, 373 (1951); *Chem. Abstracts*, **46**, 3009 (1952).
10. Rebers, P. A., and Smith, F., *J. Am. Chem. Soc.*, **76**, 6097 (1954).
11. Preece, I. A., and Mackenzie, H. G., *J. Inst. Brewing*, **58**, 353 (1952).
12. Freeman, M. E., and Gortner, R. A., *Cereal Chem.*, **9**, 506 (1932).
13. Carson, J. F., and Maclay, W. D., *J. Am. Chem. Soc.*, **68**, 1015 (1946).
14. Smith, F., *J. Am. Chem. Soc.*, **70**, 3249 (1948).
15. Smith, F., unpublished.
16. Thomas, J. C., *J. Am. Chem. Soc.*, **75**, 5346 (1953).
17. Briggs, D. R., *J. Phys. Chem.*, **38**, 867 (1934).
18. Kopp, Eleanor M., *J. Biol. Chem.*, **134**, 143 (1940).
19. Percival, E. G. V., and Ross, A. G., *J. Soc. Chem. Ind.*, **67**, 420 (1948).
20. McComb, Elizabeth A., and McCready, R. M., *Anal. Chem.*, **24**, 1630 (1952).
21. Dische, Z., *J. Biol. Chem.*, **183**, 489 (1950).
22. Johanson, A., Lindberg, B., and Theander, O., *Svensk Papperstidning*, **57**, 41 (1954).
23. Helbert, J. R., and Brown, K. D., *Anal. Chem.*, **28**, 1098 (1956); **27**, 1791 (1955).
24. Dubois, M., Gilles, K. A., Hamilton, J. K., Rebers, P. A., and Smith, F., *Anal. Chem.*, **28**, 350 (1956).
25. Dickson, A. D., Otterson, H., and Link, K. P., *J. Am. Chem. Soc.*, **52**, 775 (1930).
26. Maher, G. C., *Anal. Chem.*, **21**, 1142 (1949).
27. Kuhn, R., and Roth, H., *Ber.*, **66**, 1274 (1933).
28. Chaney, A., and Wolfrom, M. L., *Anal. Chem.*, **28**, 1614 (1956).
29. Launer, H. F., and Wilson, W. K., *J. Research Natl. Bur. Standards*, **22**, 471 (1939).
30. Kröber, E., *J. für Landw.*, **48**, 357 (1900); **49**, 7 (1901).
31. Mann, F., Krüger, M., and Tollens, B., *Angew. Chemie*, 33 (1896).
32. Brissaud, L., Roudier, A., Lhoste, P., and Eberhard, L., *Mém., services chim., état (Paris)* **35**, 57 (1950); *Chem. Abstracts*, **45**, 10139 (1951).
33. Bailey, A. J., *Ind. Eng. Chem. Anal. Ed.*, **8**, 389 (1936).
34. Dunstan, S., and Gillam, A. E., *J. Chem. Soc.*, S140 (1949).

35. Miller, G. L., Golden, R. H., and Miller, Elizabeth, E., *Anal. Chem.* **23**, 903 (1951).
36. Johansson, A., *Svensk Papperstidning*, **55**, 820 (1952).
37. Dubois, M., Gilles, K. A., Hamilton, J. K., Rebers, P. A., and Smith, F., *Nature*, **168**, 167 (1951).
38. Dreywood, R., *Ind. Eng. Chem., Anal. Ed.*, **18**, 499 (1946).
39. Fairbairn, N. J., *Chemistry and Industry*, 86 (1953).
40. Loewus, F. A., *Anal. Chem.*, **24**, 219 (1952).
41. Johanson, R., *Nature*, **171**, 176 (1953).
42. Albaum, H. G., and Umbreit, W. W., *J. Biol. Chem.*, **167**, 369 (1947).
43. Drury, H. F., *Arch. Biochem.*, **19**, 455 (1948).
44. Kawamura, S., Koboyashi, T., Osima, M., and Mino, M., *Bull. Agr. Chem. Soc. Japan*, **19**, No. 1, 69 (1955).
45. Klein, G., "*Pflanzenanalyse*," Spezielle Analyse, **I**, Julius Springer Verlag., Wien, (1932) 831.
46. Hirst, E. L., and Perlin, A. S., *J. Chem. Soc.*, 2622 (1954).
47. Spoehr, H. A., *Arch. Biochem.*, **14**, 153 (1947).
48. Jones, J. K. N., *J. Chem. Soc.*, 3292 (1950).
49. Chanda, S. K., Hirst, E. L., Jones, J. K. N., and Percival, E. G. V., *J. Chem. Soc.*, 1289 (1950).
50. Smith, F., unpublished.
51. Hudson, C. S., *Org. Syntheses, Coll. Vol. 1*, John Wiley and Sons, Inc., New York, 371.
52. Smith, F., *J. Chem. Soc.*, 1989 (1948).
53. Franchimont, A. P. N., *Ber.*, **12**, 1938 (1879).
54. Brown, G., *Org. Syntheses*, **17**, 34, 36 (1937).
55. Nishida, K., and Hashima, H., *J. Dept. Agr. Kyushu Imp. Univ.*, **2**, 277 (1930); *Chem. Abstracts*, **25**, 498 (1931).
56. Smith, F., and Srivastava, H. C., *J. Am. Chem. Soc.*, **78**, 1404 (1956).
57. Fischer, E., *Ber.*, **27**, 673 (1894).
58. Lawrence, W. T., *Ber.*, **29**, 547 (1896).
59. Hirase, S., and Araki, C., *Bull. chem. soc. Japan*, **27**, 105 (1954).
60. O'Neill, A. N., *J. Am. Chem. Soc.*, **77**, 6324 (1955).
61. O'Neill, A. N., *J. Am. Chem. Soc.*, **77**, 2837 (1955).
62. Araki, C., and Hirase, S., *Bull. Chem. Soc. Japan*, **26**, 463 (1953).
63. Effront, J., *Compt. rend.*, **125**, 116 (1897).
64. Bourquelot, E., and Herissey, H., *Compt. rend.*, **129**, 614 (1899).
65. Whistler, R. L., and Eoff, E. W., and Doty, D. M., *J. Am. Chem. Soc.*, **72**, 4938 (1950).
66. Whistler, R. L., and Stein, Joan Z., *J. Am. Chem. Soc.*, **73**, 4187 (1951).
67. Whistler, R. L., and Durso, D. F., *J. Am. Chem. Soc.*, **73**, 4189 (1951).
68. Whistler, R. L., and Smith, C. G., *J. Am. Chem. Soc.*, **74**, 3795 (1952).
69. Araki, C., and Arai, K., *Bull. Chem. Soc. Japan*, **29**, 339 (1956).
70. Ishimatsu, K., Kibesaki, Y., and Maitani, S., *Science and Industry*, (Japan), **28**, 100 (1954); *Chem. Abstracts*, **49**, 14070 (1955).
71. Bishop, C. T., *J. Am. Chem. Soc.*, **78**, 2840 (1956).
72. Whitaker, D. R., *Arch. Biochem. Biophys.*, **43**, 253 (1954).
73. Van der Haar, A. W., *Anleitung zum Nachweis, zur Trennung und Bestimmung der Monosaccharide und Aldehydsaüren*, Gebrüder Borntraeger, Berlin (1920).

74. Micheel, F., *Chemie der Zucker und Polysaccharide*, Akademische Verlagsgesellschaft m.b.H., Leipzig (1939).
75. Aspinall, G. O., Jamieson, R. S. P., and Wilkinson, J. F., *J. Chem. Soc.*, 3483 (1956).
76. Van Ekenstein, A., and Lobry du Bruyn, C. A., *Rec. trav. chim.*, **15**, 97, 225 (1896).
77. Breddy, L. J., and Jones, J. K. N., *J. Chem. Soc.*, 738 (1945).
78. Weygand, F., Perkow, W., and Kuhner, P., *Ber.*, **84**, 594 (1951).
79. Hann, R. M., and Hudson, C. S., *J. Am. Chem. Soc.*, **66**, 735 (1944).
80. Haworth, W. N., Jackson, J., and Smith, F., *J. Chem. Soc.*, 620 (1940).
81. Percival, Elizabeth E., *Chemistry and Industry*, 1487 (1954).
82. Smith, F., *J. Chem. Soc.*, 2646 (1951).
83. White, E. V., *J. Am. Chem. Soc.*, **70**, 367 (1948).
84. Ault, R. G., Haworth, W. N., and Hirst, E. L., *J. Chem. Soc.*, 517 (1935).
85. Stacey, M., and Wilson, P. I., *J. Chem. Soc.*, 587 (1944).
86. Spriestersbach, D. R., and Smith, F., unpublished.
87. Fischer, E., *Ber.*, **28**, 1145 (1895).
88. Morell, S., and Link, K. P., *J. Biol. Chem.*, **100**, 385 (1933).
89. Link, K. P., and Nedden, R., *J. Biol. Chem.*, **94**, 307 (1931).
90. Levene, P. A., and Kreider, L. C., *J. Biol. Chem.*, **120**, 597 (1937).
91. Morell, S., and Link, K. P., *J. Biol. Chem.*, **100**, 385 (1933).
92. Cadotte, J. E., Smith, F., and Spriestersbach, D., *J. Am. Chem. Soc.*, **74**, 1501 (1952).
93. Kent, W. H., and Tollens, B., *Ann.*, **227**, 221 (1885).
94. Hirst, E. L., Jones, J. K. N., and Woods, E. A., *J. Chem. Soc.*, 1048 (1947).
95. Abdel Akher, M., and Smith, F., unpublished.
96. Wolfrom, M. L., and Blair, Mary G., *J. Am. Chem. Soc.*, **68**, 2110 (1946).
97. Stepanenko, B. N., and Ignatyuk-Maistrenko, V. A., *Doklady Akad. Nauk. S.S.S.R.*, **73**, 1251 (1959); *Chem. Abstracts*, **45**, 2877 (1951).
98. Wolfrom, M. L., and Wood, H. B., *J. Am. Chem. Soc.*, **73**, 2933 (1951).
99. Abdel-Akher, M., Hamilton, J. K., and Smith, F., *J. Am. Chem. Soc.*, **73**, 4691 (1951).
100. Westphal, O., Feier, H., Lüderitz, O., and Fromme, I., *Biochem. Z.*, **326**, 139 (1954).
101. Mandl, Ines, and Neubert, C., *Arch. Biochem. Biophys.*, **35**, 326 (1952).
102. Gardner, T. S., Smith, F. A., Wenis, E., and Lee, J., *J. Am. Chem. Soc.*, **74**, 2106 (1952).
103. Anderson, E. and Sands, Lila, *J. Am. Chem. Soc.*, **48**, 3172 (1926).
104. Anderson, E., and Sands, Lila, *Org. Syntheses, Coll. Vol. I*, 2nd Ed. 67 (1946).
105. Anderson, E., and Sands, Lila, *Ind. Eng. Chem.*, **17**, 1257 (1925).
106. White, E. V., *J. Am. Chem. Soc.*, **69**, 715 (1947).
107. Carrington, H. C., Haworth, W. N., and Hirst, E. L., *J. Chem. Soc.*, 1653 (1934).
108. Anderson, E., and Ledbetter, H. D., *J. Am. Pharm. Assoc.*, **40**, 623 (1951).
109. Anderson, E., *J. Biol. Chem.*, **100**, 249 (1933).
110. Black, W. A. P., Cornhill, W. J., Dewar, E. T., and Woodward, F. N., *J. Sci. Food Agric.*, **4**, 85 (1953).
111. Black, W. A. P., Dewar, E. T., and Woodward, F. N., *J. Sci. Food Agric.*, **3**, 122 (1952).

112. Mizuguchi, J., Suzuki, S., and Misono, S., *J. Agric. Chem. Soc. Japan*, **26**, 461 (1952); *Chem. Abstracts*, **47**, 6687 (1953).
113. Black, W. A. P., and Cornhill, W. J., *Chemistry and Industry*, 514 (1954).
114. Anderson, E., and Lowe, H. J., *J. Biol. Chem.*, **168**, 289 (1947).
115. Forbes, I. A., and Percival, E. G. V., *J. Chem. Soc.*, 1844 (1939).
116. Percival, E. G. V., Somerville, J. C., and Forbes, I. A., *Nature*, **142**, 797 (1938).
117. Hands, S., and Peat, S., *Nature*, **142**, 797 (1938).
118. Consden, R., Gordon, A. H., Martin, A. J. P., *Biochem. J.*, **38**, 224 (1944).
119. Partridge, S. M., *Nature*, **158**, 270 (1946).
120. Partridge, S. M., and Westall, R. G., *Biochem. J.*, **42**, 238 (1948).
121. Kowkabany, G. N., *Advances in Carbohydrate Chem.*, **9**, 303 (1954).
122. Cramer, F., *Papier Chromatographie*, 2nd ed., Verlag Chemie, Weinheim (1953).
123. Lederer, E., and Lederer, M., "Chromatography, a Review of Principles and Applications," Elsevier, New York (1953).
124. Partridge, S. M., "Partition Chromatography," *Biochem. Soc. Symposia*, **3**, Cambridge University Press (Cambridge), (1950) 52.
125. Williams, R. J., and Kirby, Helen, *Science*, **107**, 481 (1948).
126. Rutter, L., *Nature*, **161**, 435 (1948); *Analyst*, **75**, 37 (1950).
127. Giri, K. V., and Rao, N. A. N., *J. Indian Inst. Sci.*, **34**, 95 (1952).
128. Bersin, T., and Müller, A., *Helv. Chim. Acta*, **35**, 475 (1952).
129. Lüderitz, O., and Westphal, O., *Z. Naturforsch.*, **7b**, 136 (1952).
130. Cuendet, L. S., Montgomery, R., and Smith, F., *J. Am. Chem. Soc.*, **75**, 2764 (1953).
131. Smith, F., and Spriestersbach, D., *Nature*, **174**, 466 (1954).
132. Buchanan, J. G., Dekker, C. A., and Long, A. G., *J. Chem. Soc.*, 3162 (1950).
133. Howard, G. A., and Martin, A. J. P., *Biochem. J.*, **46**, 532 (1950).
134. Lugg, J. W. H., and Overell, B. T., *Aust. J. Sci. Res. Phys. Sci.*, **1**, 98 (1948); *Chem. Abstracts*, **43**, 6946 (1949).
135. Jermyn, M. A., and Isherwood, F. A., *Biochem. J.*, **44**, 402 (1949).
136. Buch, M. L., Montgomery, R., and Porter, W. L., *Anal. Chem.*, **24**, 489 (1952).
137. Micheel, F., and Albers, P., *Ber.*, **89**, 140 (1956).
138. Hough, L., *Methods of Biochemical Analysis, Vol.* **1**, Interscience Publishers, New York (1954) 205.
139. Boggs, L., Cuendet, L. S., Ehrenthal, I, Koch, R., and Smith, F., *Nature*, **166**, 520 (1950).
140. Horecker, B. L., Smyrniotis, P. Z., and Seegmiller, *J. Biol. Chem.*, **193**, 383 (1951).
141. Hough, L., Jones, J. K. N., and Wadman, W. H., *J. Chem. Soc.*, 1702 (1950).
142. Jeanes, Allene, Wise, C. S., Dimler, R. J., *Anal. Chem.*, **23**, 415 (1951).
143. Wiggins, L. F., and Williams, J. H., *Nature*, **170**, 279 (1952).
144. Cifonelli, J. A., and Smith, F., *Anal. Chem.*, **26**, 1132 (1954).
145. Trevelyan, W. E., Procter, D. P., and Harrison, J. S., *Nature*, **166**, 444 (1950).
146. Abdel-Akher, M. A., and Smith, F., *J. Am. Chem. Soc.*, **73**, 5859 (1951).
147. Pacsu, E., Mora, T. P., and Kent, P. W., *Science*, **110**, 446 (1949).
148. Wolfrom, M. L., and Miller, J. B., *Anal. Chem.*, **28**, 1037 (1956).
149. Lemieux, R. V., and Bauer, H. F., *Anal. Chem.*, **26**, 920 (1954).
150. Hough, L., *Nature*, **165**, 400 (1950).

151. Bryson, J. L., and Mitchell, T. J., *Nature*, **167**, 864 (1951).
152. Mukherjee, L., and Srivastava, H. C., *Nature*, **169**, 330 (1952).
153. Johanson, R., *Nature*, **172**, 956 (1953).
154. Albon, N., and Gross, D., *Analyst*, **75**, 454 (1950); **77**, 406 (1952).
155. Wallenfels, K. W., *Naturwissenschaften*, **37**, 491 (1950).
156. Prochazka, Z., *Chem. Listy*, **44**, 43 (1950); *Chem. Abstracts*, **45**, 5561 (1951).
157. Hirst, E. L., Hough, L., and Jones, J. K. N., *J. Chem. Soc.*, 928 (1949).
158. Lewis, Bertha A., and Smith, F., unpublished.
159. Koch, R., and Smith, F., unpublished.
160. Consden, R., and Stanier, Winifred M., *Nature*, **169**, 783 (1952).
161. Foster, A. B., and Stacey, M., *J. Appl. Chem.*, **3**, 19 (1953).
162. Foster, A. B., *Chemistry and Industry*, 1050 (1952).
163. Kunkel, G. G., "*Methods of Biochemical Analysis*" Ed. by D. Glick *Vol.* 1, Interscience Publishers, New York (1954) 141.
164. Briggs, D. R., Garner, E. F., Montgomery, R., and Smith, F., *Anal. Chem.*, **28**, 1333 (1956).
165. Briggs, D. R., Garner, E. F., and Smith, F., *Nature*, **178**, 154 (1956).
166. O'Leary, M. J., Hobbs, R. B., Missimer, J. K., and Erving, J. J., *Tappi*, **37**, 446 (1954); *Chem. Abstracts*, **49**, 615 (1955).
167. Williams, K. T., and Bevenue, A., *J. Assoc. Offic. Agr. Chemists.*, **36**, 969 (1953).
168. Hough, L., Jones, J. K. N., and Wadman, W. H., *J. Chem. Soc.*, 2511 (1949).
169. Boggs, L. A., Cuendet, L. S., Dubois, M., and Smith, F., *Anal. Chem.*, **24**, 1148 (1952).
170. Geerdes, J. D., Lewis, Bertha A., Montgomery, R., and Smith, F., *Anal. Chem.*, **26**, 264 (1954).
171. Moore, S., and Stein, W. H., *J. Biol. Chem.*, **176**, 367 (1948).
172. Stein, W. H., and Moore, S., *J. Biol. Chem.*, **176**, 337 (1948).
173. Grant, R. A., and Stitch, S. P., *Chemistry and Industry*, 230 (1951).
174. Cuckow, F. W., Harris, R. J. C., and Speed, F. E., *J. Soc. Chem. Ind.*, **68**, 208 (1949).
175. Gilson, A. R., *Chemistry and Industry*, 185 (1951).
176. Phillips, D. M. P., *Nature*, **164**, 545 (1949).
177. Randall, L. L., and Martin, A. J. P., *Biochem. J.* **44**, Proc., XI (1949).
178. Delmon, P. J., *Nature*, **174**, 755 (1954).
179. Devor, A. W., *J. Am. Chem. Soc.*, **72**, 2008 (1950).
180. Jones, J. K. N., *J. Chem. Soc.*, 3141 (1949).
181. Brown, F., Hirst, E. L., and Jones, J. K. N., *J. Chem. Soc.*, 1761 (1949).
182. Brown, F., Hirst, E. L., and Jones, J. K. N., *J. Chem. Soc.*, 1677 (1948).
183. Easterby, D. G., and Jones, J. K. N., *Nature*, **165**, 614 (1950).
184. Hough, L., Jones, J. K. N., and Wadman, W. H., *J. Chem. Soc.*, 796 (1952).
185. Jones, J. K. N., *J. Chem. Soc.*, 534 (1950).
186. Stephen, A. M., *J. Chem. Soc.*, 646 (1951).
187. Whistler, R. L., and Corbett, W. M., *J. Am. Chem. Soc.*, **77**, 6328 (1955).
188. Montgomery, R., Smith, F., and Srivastava, H. C., *J. Am. Chem. Soc.*, **79**, 698 (1957).
189. Bishop, C. T., Adams, G. A., and Hughes, E. O., *Can. J. Chem.*, **32**, 999 (1954).
190. Srivastava, H. C., and Smith, F., *J. Am. Chem. Soc.*, **79**, 982 (1957).
191. Montgomery, R., and Smith, F., *J. Agr. Food Chem.*, **4**, 716 (1956).

192. Gill, R. E., Hirst, E. L., Jones, J. K. N., *J. Chem. Soc.*, 1025 (1946).
193. Hirst, E. L., Hough, L., and Jones, J. K. N., *J. Chem. Soc.*, 323 (1951).
194. Peat, S., Whelan, W. J., and Lawley, H. G., *Chemistry and Industry*, 35 (1955).
195. Whelan, W. J., and Lawley, H. G., and Evans, J. M., *Biochem. J.*, 61, Proc. [1], x (1955).
196. Scott, T. A., and Senti, F. R., *J. Am. Chem. Soc.*, 77, 3816 (1955).
197. Whistler, R. L., and Durso, D. F., *J. Am. Chem. Soc.*, 72, 677 (1950).
198. Andrews, P., Hough, L., and Powell, D. B., *Chemistry and Industry*, 658 (1956).
199. Whelan, W. J., Bailey, J. M., and Roberts, P. J. P., *J. Chem. Soc.*, 1293 (1953).
200. Whistler, R. L., and Chen Chuan Tu, *J. Am. Chem. Soc.*, 74, 3609 (1952).
201. Synge, R. L. M., and Tiselius, A., *Acta Chem. Scand.*, 3, 231 (1949).
202. Hayashi, F., *J. Biochem. (Japan)*, 16, 1 (1932).
203. Jeanes, Allene, Wilham, C. A., Jones, R. W., Tsuchiya, H. M., and Rist, C. E., *J. Am. Chem. Soc.*, 75, 5911 (1953).
204. Barker, S. A., Bourne, E. J., and Theander, O., *J. Chem. Soc.*, 4276 (1955).
205. Barker, S. A., Bourne, E. J., Foster, A. B., and Ward, R. B., *Nature*, 179, 262 (1957).
206. Khym, J. X., and Zill, L. P., *J. Am. Chem. Soc.*, 74, 2090 (1952).
207. Zill, L. P., Khym, J. X., Cheniae, G. M., *J. Am. Chem. Soc.*, 75, 1339 (1953).
208. Mowery, D. F., *J. Am. Chem. Soc.*, 73, 5049 (1951).
209. Lemieux, R. V., Bishop, C. T., and Pelletier, G. E., *Can. J. Chem.*, 34, 1365 (1956).
210. Weissmann, B., Meyer, K., Sampson, Phyllis, and Linker, A., *J. Biol. Chem.*, 208, 417 (1954).
211. Butler, Margaret R., *Biochem. J.*, 28, 759 (1934).
212. Derungs, R., and Deuel, H., *Helv. Chim. Acta*, 37, 657 (1954).
213. Aspinall, G. O., Hirst, E. L., and Matheson, N. K., *J. Chem. Soc.*, 989 (1956).
214. Khym, J. X., and Doherty, D. G., *J. Am. Chem. Soc.*, 74, 3199 (1952).
215. Glegg, R. E., and Eidinger, D., *Anal. Chem.*, 26, 1365 (1954).
216. Glegg, R. E., *Anal. Chem.*, 28, 532 (1956).
217. Hulme, A. C., *Nature*, 171, 610 (1953).
218. Phillips, J. D., and Pollard, A., *Nature*, 171, 41 (1953).
219. Rosewan, S., Abeles, R. H., and Dorfman, A., *Arch. Biochem. Biophys.*, 36, 232 (1952).
220. Yorston, F. H., *Pulp and Paper Mag. Can.*, 50, No. 12, 108 (1949).
221. Rebenfeld, L., and Pacsu, E., *J. Am. Chem. Soc.*, 75, 4370 (1953).
222. Sowden, J. C., *J. Am. Chem. Soc.*, 76, 4487 (1954).
223. Blair, Mary G., and Sowden, J. C., *J. Am. Chem. Soc.*, 77, 3323 (1955).
224. Huffman, G. W., Rebers, P. A., Spriestersbach, D. P., and Smith, F., *Nature*, 175, 990 (1955).
225. Dent, C. E., *Biochem. J.*, 41, 240 (1947).
226. Dent, C. E., *Biochem. J.*, 43, 169 (1948).
227. Laidlaw, R. A., and Reid, S. G., *Nature*, 166, 476 (1950).
228. Flood, A. E., Hirst, E. L., and Jones, J. K. N., *J. Chem. Soc.*, 1679 (1948).
229. Hirst, E. L., and Jones, J. K. N., *J. Chem. Soc.*, 1659 (1949).

230. Drake, B., *Nature*, **160**, 602 (1947).
231. Jermyn, M. A., *Modern Methods of Plant Analysis*, **2**; Ed. K. Paech and M. V. Tracey, Springer-Verlag, Berlin (1955) 209.
232. Hamilton, J. K., and Smith, F., *J. Am. Chem. Soc.*, **78**, 5910 (1956).
233. Unrau, A., and Smith, F., *Chemistry and Industry*, 330 (1957).
234. Lambert, Marguerite, and Neish, A. C., *Can. J. Research*, **28B**, 83 (1950).
235. Blass, Judith, Macheboeuf, M., and Nunez, C., *Bull. soc. chim. biol.*, **32**, 130 (1950).
236. Bartlett, J. K., Hough, L., and Jones, J. K. N., *Chemistry and Industry*, 76 (1951).
237. Timell, T. E., Glaudemans, C. P. J., and Currie, A. L., *Anal. Chem.*, **28**, 1916 (1956).
238. Pridham, J. B., *Anal. Chem.*, **28**, 1967 (1956).
239. Dimler, R. J., Schaefer, W. C., Wise, C. S., and Rist, C. E., *Anal. Chem.*, **24**, 1411 (1952).
240. Borel, E., Hostettler, F., and Deuel, H., *Helv. Chim. Acta*, **35**, 115 (1952).
241. Gustafson, C., Sundman, J., and Lindl, T., *Paper and Timber (Finland)*, **B33**, 1 (1951); *Chem. Abstracts*, **45**, 4175 (1951).
242. McFarren, E. F., Brand, Kathleen, and Rutkowski, H. R., *Anal. Chem.*, **23**, 1146 (1951).
243. McCready, R. M., and McComb, E. A., *Anal. Chem.*, **26**, 1645 (1954).
244. Shallenberger, R. S., and Moores, R. G., *Anal. Chem.*, **29**, 27 (1957).
245. Somogyi, M., *J. Biol. Chem.*, **160**, 61 (1945).
246. Hawthorne, J. R., *Nature*, **160**, 714 (1947).
247. Malaprade, L., *Bull. soc. chim.*, **43**, 683 (1928); *Compt. rend.*, **186**, 382 (1928).
248. Mori, L., *Science*, **119**, 653 (1954).
249. Oshima, K., and Tollens, B., *Ber.*, **34**, 1422 (1901).
250. Otsuki, T., *Acta Phytochim. (Japan)*, **10**, 1 (1937); *Chem. Abstracts*, **31**, 8610 (1937).
251. Smith, F., and Srivastava, H. C., *J. Am. Chem. Soc.*, **81**, 1715 (1959).
252. Andrews, P., Hough, L., and Jones, J. K. N., *J. Chem. Soc.*, 1186 (1953).
253. Komatsu, S., and Ueda, H., *Mem. Coll. Sci. Kyoto Imp. Univ.*, **8**, 51 (1925); *Chem. Abstracts*, **19**, 3481 (1925).
254. James, Sybil P., and Smith, F., *J. Chem. Soc.*, 739 (1945).
255. James, Sybil P., and Smith, F., *J. Chem. Soc.*, 749 (1945).
256. Widtsoe, J. A., and Tollens, B., *Ber.*, **33**, 132 (1900).
257. Hilger, A., and Dreyfus, W. E., *Ber.*, **33**, 1178 (1900).
258. Selby, K., *J. Chem. Soc.*, 2504 (1953).
259. Tiomno, F. R., *Rev. quím ind, Rio de Janeiro*, **15**, No. 168, 23; No. 172, 19 (1946); *Chem. Abstracts*, **41**, 2921 (1947).
260. Mukherjee, S., and Srivastava, H. C., *Current Sci., (India)*, **20**, 127 (1951).
261. Yoshimura, K., *Bull. Coll. Agric. Imp. Univ. (Tokyo)*, **2**, 207 (1895); *Chem. Centralbl.*, **67**, I, 46 (1886).
262. Harlay, V., *J. pharm. chim.*, [VI], **16**, 193 (1902); *Chem. Centralbl.*, **2**, 1264 (1902).
263. Bittó, B. V., *Landw. Versuchs. Stat.*, **46**, 307 (1895).
264. Condorelli, P., and Chindemi, A., *Ann. chim. applicata*, **18**, 313 (1928); Condorelli, P., *ibid.*, **15**, 426 (1925).
265. Kihara, Y., *J. Agr. Chem. Soc. (Japan)*, **14**, 733 (1938); *Chem. Abstracts*, **32**, 9176 (1938).

266. Ozawa, T., J. Chem. Ind. (Japan), 25, 389 (1922); Chem. Abstracts, 16, 4086 (1922).
267. Gaal, B., Ber. Ungar. pharm. Ges., 3, 133 (1927); Chem. Abstracts, 23, 1929 (1929).
268. Robinson, H. H., J. Chem. Soc., 89, 1496 (1906).
269. Savar, G. R., and Sreenivasan, A., J. Biol. Chem., 172, 501 (1948).
270. Rao, P. S., and Beri, R. M., Proc. Indian Acad. Sci., 35a, 1 (1952); Chem. Abstracts, 47, 6875 (1953).
271. Malandkar, M. A., J. Ind. Inst. Sci., 8A, 240 (1925); Chem. Abstracts, 20, 837 (1926).
272. Gerard, A., Bull. sci. pharmacolog., 18, 148 (1912); Chem. Abstracts, 6, 307 (1912).
273. Huerre, R., J. pharm. chim., ⌊6⌋, 27, 561 (1908); Chem. Abstracts, 2, 2970 (1908).
274. Balavorne, P., Pharm. Acta Helv., 21, 19 (1946).
275. Laidlaw, R. A., and Percival, E. G. V., J. Chem. Soc., 1600 (1949).
276. Laidlaw, R. A., and Percival, E. G. V., J. Chem. Soc., 528 (1950).
277. Dillon, T., Kristensen, K., and O'hEochdha, C., Proc. Roy Irish Acad., 55b, 189 (1953).
278. Stone, W. E., and Test, W. H., Am. Chem. J., 15, 660 (1893).
279. Roboz, Elizabeth, and Haagen-Smith, A. J., J. Am. Chem. Soc., 70, 3248 (1948).
280. Hilger, A., Ber., 36, 3197 (1903).
281. Pringsheim, H., and Liss, G., Ann., 460, 32 (1928).
282. Anderson, E., Ind. Eng. Chem., 41, 2887 (1949).
283. Swanson, J. W., J. Am. Chem. Soc., 71, 1510 (1949).
284. Hirst, E. L., and Jones, J. K. N., J. Chem. Soc., 1278 (1948).
285. Rafique, C. M., and Smith, F., J. Am. Chem. Soc., 72, 4634 (1950).
286. Larson, E. B., and Smith, F., J. Am. Chem. Soc., 77, 429 (1955).
287. Andrews, P., Hough, L., and Jones, J. K. N., J. Am. Chem. Soc., 74, 4029 (1952).
288. Andrews, P., Hough, L., and Jones, J. K. N., J. Chem. Soc., 2744 (1952).
289. Torigata, H., J. Chem. Soc. (Japan), 73, 533 (1952); Chem. Abstracts, 46, 10652 (1952).
290. Wise, L. E., Arch. Biochem., 23, 127 (1949).
291. Rao, P. S., and Roydon, O. N., Proc. Indian Acad. Sci., 31A, 441 (1950); 32A, 264 (1950).
292. Smith, F., J. Chem. Soc., 1035 (1940).
293. Scheibler, C., Ber., 6, 612 (1873).
294. Butler, C. L., and Cretcher, L. H., J. Am. Chem. Soc., 51, 1519 (1929).
295. Kiliani, H., Ber., 13, 2304 (1880); 15, 34 (1882).
296. Claësson, P., Ber., 14, 1270 (1881).
297. Weinmann, F., Biochem. Z., 236, 87 (1931).
298. White, E. V., J. Am. Chem. Soc., 68, 272 (1946).
299. Anderson, E., and Otis, Louise, J. Am. Chem. Soc., 52, 4461 (1930).
300. White, E. V., J. Am. Chem. Soc., 69, 2264 (1947).
301. Jones, J. K. N., J. Chem. Soc., 558 (1939).
302. Butler, C. L., and Cretcher, L. H., J. Am. Chem. Soc., 53, 4160 (1931).
303. Hirst, E. L., and Jones, J. K. N., J. Chem. Soc., 1064 (1947).
304. Hirst, E. L., and Jones, J. K. N., J. Chem. Soc., 120 (1948).
305. Hirst, E. L., and Jones, J. K. N., J. Chem. Soc., 506 (1946).

306. Hirst, E. L., *J. Chem. Soc.*, 70 (1942).
307. Connell, J. J., Hainsworth, Ruth M., Hirst, E. L., and Jones, J. K. N., *J. Chem. Soc.*, 1696 (1950).
308. Anderson, E., Russell, F. H., and Seigle, L. W., *J. Biol. Chem.*, 113, 683 (1936).
309. Parisi, E., *Ann. chim. applicata*, 25, 230 (1935); *Chem. Abstracts*, 29, 6790 (1935).
310. McIlroy, R. J., *J. Chem. Soc.*, 1372 (1951).
311. White, E. V., *J. Am. Chem. Soc.*, 75, 257 (1953).
312. Rao, P. S., and Gakhar, K. L., *Proc. Indian Acad. Sci.*, 35A, 310 (1952); *Chem. Abstracts*, 47, 8663 (1953).
313. Anderson, E., and Harris, L., *J. Am. Pharm. Assoc.*, 41, 529 (1952).
314. McIlroy, R. J., *J. Chem. Soc.*, 1918 (1952).
315. Nakahara, H., *J. Agr. Chem. Soc. (Japan)*, 16, 876 (1940); *Bull. Agr. Chem. Soc. Japan*, 16, 140 (1940); *Chem. Abstracts*, 35, 4416 (1941).
316. Brading, Joyce, W. E., Georg-Plant, Millicent M. T., and Hardy, Doreen, M., *J. Chem. Soc.*, 319 (1954).
317. Tachi, I., and Yamamori, N., *Mokuzai Kenkyu*, 4, 11 (1950); *Chem. Abstracts*, 45, 9856 (1951).
318. Winterstein, E., *Ber.*, 31, 1571 (1898).
319. Wolf, M. J., MacMasters, Majel M., Cannon, J. A., Rosewall, E. C., and Rist, C. E., *Cereal. Chem.*, 30, 451 (1953).
320. Hanna, D., and Shaw, E. H., Jr., *Proc. S. Dakota Acad. Sci.*, 21, 78 (1941).
321. Anderson, E., Sands, Lila, and Sturgis, N., *Am. J. Pharm.*, 97, 589 (1925).
322. Sands, Lila, and Klaas, Rosalind, *J. Am. Chem. Soc.*, 51, 3441 (1929).
323. Beauquesne, L., *Compt. rend.*, 222, 1056 (1946).
324. Hirst, E. L., and Dunstan, Sonia, *J. Chem. Soc.*, 2332 (1953).
325. Hirst, E. L., Hough, L., and Jones, J. K. N., *J. Chem. Soc.*, 3145 (1949).
326. Hough, L., and Jones, J. K. N., *J. Chem. Soc.*, 1199 (1950).
327. Mukherjee, S. N., and Banerjee, G., *J. Indian Chem. Soc.*, 25, 59, 63 (1948).
328. Hirst, E. L., Percival, E. G. V., and Wylam, Clare B., *J. Chem. Soc.*, 189 (1954).
329. Anderson, E., and Fireman, M., *J. Biol. Chem.*, 109, 437 (1935).
330. Youngken, H. W., *Am. J. Pharm.*, 106, 157 (1934).
331. Anderson, E., Gillette, L. A., and Seeley, M. G., *J. Biol. Chem.*, 140, 569 (1941).
332. Mullan, J., and Percival, E. G. V., *J. Chem. Soc.*, 1501 (1940).
333. Gill, R. E., Hirst, E. L., and Jones, J. K. N., *J. Chem. Soc.*, 1025 (1946).
334. Renfrew, Alice G., and Cretcher, L. H., *J. Biol. Chem.* 97, 503 (1932).
335. Bailey, K., and Norris, F. W., *Biochem. J.*, 26, 1609 (1932).
336. Bailey, K., *Biochem. J.*, 29, 2477 (1935).
337. Whistler, R. L., and Smart, C. L., *Polysaccharide Chemistry*, Academic Press, New York (1953) 333.
338. Rao, P. S., and Gakhar, K. L., *Proc. Indian Acad. Sci.*, 36A, 70 (1952); *Chem. Abstracts*, 47, 11361 (1953).
339. Rao, P. S., Beri, R. M., Budhiraja, R. P., *J. Sci. Ind. Research (India)*, 10B, 261 (1951); *Chem. Abstracts*, 47, 10882 (1953).
340. Anderson, E., and Blake, B. B., *J. Am. Pharm. Assoc.*, 42, 662 (1953).
341. Machida, S., and Uchino, N., *J. Chem. Soc. (Japan)*, Pure Chem. Sect., 72, 917 (1951); *Chem. Abstracts*, 46, 7351 (1952).

342. Mathur, G. P., and Mukherjee, S., *J. Sci. Ind. Research (India)*, 11B, 544 (1952); *Chem. Abstracts*, 47, 10881 (1953).
343. Nakahara, H., *J. Agr. Chem. Soc., Japan*, 11, 310 (1935); *Chem. Abstracts*, 29, 6623 (1935).
344. Meyer, T. M., and van Dalfsen, J. W., *Arch. Rubbercultuur*, 23, 172 (1939); *Chem. Abstracts*, 34, 3943 (1940).
345. Hirst, E. L., and Jones, J. K. N., *J. Chem. Soc.*, 1482 (1939).
346. White, E. V., *J. Am. Chem. Soc.*, 75, 4692 (1953).
347. Machida, S., and Uchino, N., *J. Chem. Soc. (Japan)*, 74, 183 (1953); *Chem. Abstracts*, 47, 11782 (1953).
348. Whistler, R. L., and Be Miller, J. N., *J. Am. Chem. Soc.*, 78, 1163 (1956).
349. Whistler, R. L., and Corbett, W. M., *J. Org. Chem.*, 21, 694 (1956).
350. Montgomery, R., Smith, F., and Srivastava, H. C., *J. Am. Chem. Soc.*, 78, 2837 (1956).
351. Montgomery, R., Smith, F., and Srivastava, H. C., *J. Am. Chem. Soc.*, 78, 6169 (1956).
352. Goldstein, L. J., Montgomery, R., Smith, F., and Srivastava, H. C., unpublished.
353. Montgomery, R., and Smith, F., *J. Am. Chem. Soc.*, 79, 695 (1957).
354. Rao, P. S., and White, E. V., *J. Am. Chem. Soc.*, 75, 2617 (1953).
355. Charlson, A. J., Nunn, J. R., and Stephen, A. M., *J. Chem. Soc.*, 1428 (1955).
356. Charlson, A. J., Nunn, J. R., and Stephen, A. M., *J. Chem. Soc.*, 269 (1955).
357. Barker, S. A., Bourne, E. J., Grant, P. N., and Stacey, M., *Nature*, 177, 1125 (1956).
358. Aspinall, G. O., Hirst, E. L., and Wickström, A., *J. Chem. Soc.*, 1160 (1955).
359. Cramer, F. B., *J. Franklin Inst.*, 256, 93 (1953).
360. Rao, P. S., and Beri, R. M., *Proc. Ind. Acad. Sci.*, 34A, 27 (1951); *Chem. Abstracts*, 48, 1039 (1954).
361. Andrews, P., Hough, L., and Jones, J. K. N., *J. Chem. Soc.*, 181 (1956).
362. Büchi, W., and Deuel, H., *Helv. Chim. Acta*, 37, 1392 (1954).
363. Gordon, H. T., Thornburg, W., and Werum, L. N., *Anal. Chem.*, 28, 849 (1956).
364. Moore, S., and Link, K. P., *J. Biol. Chem.*, 133, 293 (1940).
365. Dimler, R. J., and Link, K. P., *J. Biol. Chem.*, 150, 345 (1943).
366. Erickson, J. G., *J. Am. Chem. Soc.*, 77, 2839 (1955).
367. Loring, H. S., Levy, L. W., and Moss, L. K., *Anal. Chem.*, 28, 539 (1956).
368. Forsyth, W. G. C., *Nature*, 161, 239 (1948).
369. Chargoff, E., Levine, Celia, and Green, Charlotte, *J. Biol. Chem.*, 175, 67 (1948).
370. O'Sullivan, C., *J. Chem. Soc.*, 41, 24 (1882).
371. Gilles, K. A., Meredith, W. O. S., and Smith, F., *Cereal Chem.*, 29, 314 (1952).
372. Preece, L. A., and Hobkirk, R., *J. Inst. Brewing*, 59, 385 (1953).
373. Preece, L. A., and Mackenzie, K. G., *J. Inst. Brewing*, 58, 457 (1952).
374. Domenigg, H. S., and Smith, F., unpublished.
375. Morris, D. L., *J. Biol. Chem.*, 142, 881 (1942).
376. Colin, H., and Augem, A., *Bull. soc. chim. biol.* 10, 822 (1928).
377. Augem, A., *Rev. gen. botan.*, 40, 456, 537, 591 (1928); *Chem. Abstracts*, 23, 634 (1929).
378. Wieland, T., and Berg, A., *Angew. Chem.*, 64, 418 (1952).

379. Bauer, L., *Naturwiss.*, **39**, 88 (1952).
380. Kaufmann, H. P., *Fette u. Seifen*, **52**, 331, 713 (1950).
381. Kaufmann, H. P., and Budwid J., *Fette u. Seifen*, **52**, 555 (1950).
382. Kirchner, J. G., and Keller, G. J., *J. Am. Chem. Soc.*, **72**, 1867 (1950).
383. Kowkabany, G. N., and Cassidy, H. G., *Anal. Chem.*, **24**, 643 (1952).
384. Bate-Smith, E. C., and Westall, R. G., *Biochim. Biophys. Acta*, **4**, 427 (1950).
385. Solms, J., *Helv. Chim. Acta*, **38**, 1127 (1955).
386. Fischer, F. G., and Dörfel, H., *Z. physiol. Chem.*, **301**, 224 (1955).
387. Gee, Mildred, and McCready, R. M., *Anal. Chem.*, **29**, 257 (1957).
388. White, L. M., and Secor, Geraldine, E., *Anal. Chem.*, **28**, 1052 (1956).
389. Secor, Geraldine E., and White, L. M., *Anal. Chem.*, **27**, 1998 (1955).
390. White, L. M., and Secor, Geraldine E., *Anal. Chem.*, **27**, 1016 (1955).
391. Schwimmer, S., Bevenue, A., and Weston, W. J., *Arch. Biochem. Biophys.*, **60**, 279 (1956).
392. Ganguli, N. C., *Experientia*, **12**, 38 (1956).
393. Machida, S., and Inano, M., *Bull. Chem. Soc. Japan*, **28**, 629 (1955).
394. Durso, D. F., and Mueller, W. A., *Anal. Chem.*, **28**, 1366 (1956).
395. Cremer, H. D., and Tiselius, A., *Biochem. Z.*, **320**, 273 (1950).
396. Ganguli, N. C., *Anal. Chem.*, **28**, 1499 (1956).
397. Berger, L., and Lee, J., *J. Org. Chem.*, **11**, 84 (1946).
398. Berger, L., Solmssen, U. V., Leonard, F., Wenis, E., and Lee, J., *J. Org. Chem.*, **11**, 91 (1946).
399. Fischer, F. G., and Dörfel, H., *Z. physiol. Chem.*, **302**, 186 (1955).
400. Haworth, W. N., Hirst, E. L., and Smith, F., *J. Chem. Soc.*, 1914 (1939).
401. Frahn, J. L., and Mills, J. A., *Chemistry and Industry*, 578 (1956).
402. Wolfrom, M. L., and Anno, K., *J. Am. Chem. Soc.*, **74**, 5583 (1952).
403. Bell, D. J., in *Methods of Plant Analysis*, ed. by Paech, K., and Tracey, M. V., Springer Verlag Berlin (1955).
404. Williams, K. T., and Bevenue, A., *Anal. Chem.*, **27**, 331 (1955).
405. Porter, W. L., and Hoban, Nancy, *Anal. Chem.*, **26**, 1846 (1954).
406. Kullgren, C., *Svensk Kem. Tidskr.*, **43**, 99 (1931); *Chem. Abstracts*, **25**, 5285 (1931).
407. Hirase, S., Araki, C., and Nakanishi, S., *Bull. Chem. Soc. Japan*, **26**, 183 (1953).
408. Rique, T., and Pardo, L. L., *Rep. Arg., Ministerio Agr. y ganaderia, Publ. tec. No. 19*, (1954); *Chem. Abstracts*, **49**, 7275 (1955).
409. Frahn, J. L., and Mills, J. A., *Chemistry and Industry*, 1137 (1956).
410. Lewis, Bertha A., and Smith, F., unpublished.
411. Jones, J. K. N., and Pridham, J. B., *Biochem. J.*, **58**, 288 (1954).
412. Harris, Pamela, and Lindley, F. W., *Chemistry and Industry*, 922 (1956).
413. Dieckert, J. W., and Morris, Nelle J., *Anal. Chem.*, **29**, 31 (1957).
414. Bourne, E. J., Foster, A. V., and Grant, P. M., *J. Chem. Soc.*, 4311 (1956).
415. Garner, E. F., and Smith, F., unpublished.
416. Gray, G. M., *Chemistry and Industry*, 18 (1957).
417. Mitz, M. A., and Yanari, S. S., *J. Am. Chem. Soc.*, **78**, 2649 (1956).
418. Hoffpauir, C. L., and Guthrie, J. D., *Textile Research J.*, **20**, 617 (1950).
419. Porath, J., *Arkiv för Kemi*, **11**, 97 (1957).
420. Savur, G. R., *J. Chem. Soc.*, 2600 (1956).
421. Stephen, A. M., *J. Chem. Soc.*, 4487 (1956).

422. Amin, El S., *J. Chem. Soc.*, 828 (1956).
423. Dutton, G. G. S., *Can. J. Chem.*, 34, 406 (1956).
424. Bourquelot, E., and Laurent, J., *Compt. rend.*, 130, 1411 (1900).
425. Bourquelot, E., and Laurent, J. *Compt. rend.*, 131, 276 (1900).
426. Araki, C., and Hirase, S., *Bull. Chem. Soc. Japan*, 29, 770 (1956).
427. Keen, J. L., and Opie, J. W., *Tappi*, 40, 100 (1957).
428. Whistler, R. L., and Hickson, J. L., *Anal. Chem.*, 27, 1514 (1955).
429. Hagedorn, H. C., and Jensen, B. N., *Biochem. Z.*, 135, 46 (1923).
430. Stephen, A. M., *J. Chem. Soc.*, 1919 (1957).
431. Myhre, D., and Smith, F., *J. Org. Chem.*, 23, 1229 (1958).
432. Esping, Ulla, *Arkiv för Kemi*, 11, 107 (1957).
433. Hirase, S., Araki, C., and Ito, T., *Bull. Chem. Soc. Japan*, 29, 985 (1956).
434. Fisher, L. S., and Percival, Elizabeth E., *J. Chem. Soc.*, 2666 (1957).
435. Mowery, D. F., *Anal. Chem.*, 29, 1560 (1957).
436. Stepaninko, B. N., Ponomareva, O. N., Afanaseva, E. M., Baksova, R. A., *Doklady Akad. Nauk S.S.S.R.*, 111, 652 (1956); *Chem. Abstracts*, 51, 9190 (1957).
437. Hulyalkar, R. K., Ingle, T. R., and Bhide, B. V., *J. Indian. Chem. Soc.*, 33, 861 (1956); *Chem. Abstracts*, 51, 10103 (1957).
438. McIlroy, R. J., *J. Chem. Soc.*, 4147 (1957).
439. Hulyalkar, R. K., Ingle, T. R., and Bhide, B. V., *J. Indian. Chem. Soc.*, 33, 864 (1956); *Chem. Abstracts*, 51, 10103 (1957).
440. Rao, P. S., and Sharma, R. K., *Proc. Indian. Acad. Sci.*, 45A, 24 (1957); *Chem. Abstracts*, 51, 15160 (1957).
441. Torto, F. G., *Nature*, 180, 864 (1957).
442. Bezanger-Beauquesne, L., and Chosson, J., *Compt. rend.*, 245, 360 (1957); *Chem. Abstracts*, 51, 18665 (1957).
443. Jones, J. K. N., and Smith, F., *Advances in Carbohydrate Chem.*, 4, 243 (1949).
444. Percival, E. G. V., *Quart. Rev. (London)*, 3, 369 (1949).
445. Mori, T., and Tsuchiya, Y., *J. Agr. Chem. Soc. Japan*, 14, 609, 616 (1938); *Chem. Abstracts*, 32, 9175, 9176 (1938).
446. Mori, T., *J. Agr. Chem. Soc. Japan*, 15, 1070 (1939).
446. Mori, T., and Tsuchiya, Y., *J. Agr. Chem. Soc. Japan*, 15, 1065 (1939); *Chem. Abstracts*, 34, 3313 (1940).
447. Yanagigawa, T., *Repts. Imp. Ind. Research Inst., Osaka, Japan*, 17, No. 5 (1936); *Chem. Abstracts*, 31, 6697 (1937).
449. Tadokoro, T., and Yoshimura, K., *J. Chem. Soc. Japan*, 56, 655 (1935); *Chem. Abstracts*, 29, 7390 (1935).
450. Tadokoro, T., Yoshimura, K., and Yanase, M., *J. Chem. Soc. Japan*, 56, 188 (1935); *Chem. Abstracts*, 29, 4406 (1935).
451. Yanagigawa, T., and Yosido, T., *Rept. Imp. Ind. Research Inst., Osaka, Japan*, 20, No. 5 (1939); *Chem. Abstracts*, 34, 4418 (1940).
452. Takahashi, E., *J. Coll. Agr. Hokkaido Imp. Univ.*, 8, 183 (1920); *Chem. Abstracts*, 15, 249 (1921).
453. Tadokoro, T., and Saito, T., *J. Soc. Chem. Ind. Japan*, 38, suppl. binding, 270 (1935); *Chem. Abstracts*, 29, 6388 (1935).
454. Hassid, W. Z., *J. Am. Chem. Soc.*, 55, 4163 (1933).
455. Hassid, W. Z., *J. Am. Chem. Soc.*, 57, 2046 (1935).
456. Haas, P., *Biochem. J.*, 15, 469 (1921).

457. Haas, P., and Russell-Wells, Barbara, *Yearbook British Pharm. Conference*, 644 (1933); *Biochem. J.*, **23**, 425 (1929).
458. Manske, R. H. F., *J. Biol. Chem.*, **86**, 571 (1930).
459. Gruzewska, Z., *Compt. rend.*, **173**, 52 (1921); **170**, 521 (1920).
460. Uyeda, Y., *J. Soc. Chem. Ind. Japan*, **32**, 568 (1929); suppl. binding, **32**, 175B (1929); *Chem. Abstracts*, **23**, 4968 (1929).
461. Kylin, H., *Z. physiol. Chem.*, **83**, 171 (1913); **94**, 337 (1915).
462. Bird, Gladys M., and Haas, P., *Biochem. J.*, **25**, 403 (1931).
463. Hoagland, D. R., and Lieb, L. L., *J. Biol. Chem.*, **23**, 287 (1915).
464. Nelson, W. L., and Cretcher, L. H., *J. Biol. Chem.*, **94**, 147 (1931).
465. Dillon, T., and Mcguinness, Annie, *Sci. Proc. Roy. Dublin Soc.*, **20**, 129 (1932).
466. Haas, P., and Hill, T. G., *Ann. App. Biol.*, **7**, 352 (1921).
467. Dillon, T., and O'Colla, P., *Nature*, **145**, 749 (1940).
468. Lunde, G., Lunde, S., and Jakobsen, A., *Fiskeri dircktor Skriften Ser., Haverundersk (Rept. Norwegian Fishery Marine Investigation)*, **5**, No. 5, 21 (1938).
469. Percival, E. G. V., and Buchanan, J., *Nature*, **145**, 1020 (1940).
470. Barry, V. C., and Dillon, T., *Proc. Roy. Irish Acad.*, **50B**, 349 (1945).
471. Barry, V. C., and Dillon, T., *Nature*, **146**, 620 (1940).
472. Dewar, E. T., and Percival, E. G. V., *Nature*, **156**, 633 (1945).
473. Barry, V. C., *Sci. Proc. Roy. Dublin Soc.*, **21**, 615 (1938).
474. Barry, V. C., *Sci. Proc. Roy. Dublin Soc.*, **22**, 59 (1939).
475. Barry, V. C., *Sci. Proc. Roy. Dublin Soc.*, **22**, 423 (1941).
476. Dillon, T., *Nature*, **155**, 546 (1945).
477. Neuberg, C., and Ohle, H., *Biochem. Z.*, **125**, 311 (1921).
478. Payen, A., *Compt. rend.*, **49**, 521 (1859).
479. Bauer, R. W., *J. prakt. Chem.*, [2], **30**, 367 (1884).
480. Fairbrother, F., and Mastin, H., *J. Chem. Soc.*, **123**, 1412 (1923).
481. Hoffman, W. F., and Gortner, R. A., *J. Biol. Chem.*, **65**, 371 (1925).
482. Lüdtke, M., *Biochem. Z.*, **212**, 419 (1929).
483. Nanji, D. R., Paton, F. J., and Ling, A. R., *J. Soc. Chem. Ind.*, **44**, 253T (1925).
484. Pirie, N. W., *Biochem. J.*, **30**, 369 (1936).
485. Percival, E. G. V., Munro, J., and Somerville, J. C., *Nature*, **139**, 512 (1937).
486. Hands, S., and Peat, S., *Chemistry and Industry*, **57**, 937 (1938).
487. Percival, E. G. V., and Soutar, T. H., *J. Chem. Soc.*, 1475 (1940).
488. Duff, R. B., and Percival, E. G. V., *J. Chem. Soc.*, 830 (1941).
489. Jones, W. G. M., and Peat, S., *J. Chem. Soc.*, 225 (1942).
490. Isaac, W. E., Finlayson, M. H., and Simon, M. G., *Nature*, **151**, 532 (1943).
491. Percival, E. G. V., and Somerville, J. C., *J. Chem. Soc.*, 1615 (1937).
492. Araki, C., *J. Chem. Soc. Japan*, **65**, 725 (1944); *Chem. Abstracts*, **41**, 3496 (1947).
493. Percival, E. G. V., and Forbes, I. A., *Nature*, **142**, 1076 (1938).
494. Colin, H., and Ricard, P., *Compt. rend.*, **188**, 1449 (1929).
495. Nishizawa, K., *J. Chem. Soc. Japan*, **60**, 1020 (1939); [see Mori, T., *Adv. Carb. Chem.*, **8**, 315 (1953)].
496. Lunde, G., Heen, E., and Öy, E., *Z. physiol. Chem.*, **247**, 189 (1937).
497. Johnston, R., and Percival, E. G. V., *J. Chem. Soc.*, 1994 (1950).
498. Araki, C., and Arai, K., *Collected Papers for the Celebration of the forty-fifth Anniversary of the Founding of Kyoto Technical College*, 80 (1948).

499. Dewar, E. T., and Percival, E. G. V., *J. Chem. Soc.*, 1622 (1947).
500. Russell-Wells, Barbara, *Biochem. J.*, **16**, 578 (1922).
501. Buchanan, J., Percival, Elizabeth E., and Percival, E. G. V., *J. Chem. Soc.*, 51 (1943).
502. Mori, T., *Advances in Carbohydrate Chem.*, **8**, 315 (1953).
503. Araki, C., *J. Chem. Soc. Japan*, **59**, 424 (1938); *Chem. Abstracts*, **35**, 7946 (1941).
504. Dillon, T., and McKenna, J., *Nature*, **165**, 318 (1950).
505. Krefting, A., *Tidsskr. Kemi, Farm. Terapi*, 151 (1909); *Pharmacia*, **6**, 151; *Chem. Abstracts*, **4**, 460 (1910).
506. Torup, S., *Tidsskr. Kemi, Farm. Terapi*, 153 (1909); *Pharmacia*, **6**, 153; *Chem. Abstracts*, **4**, 460 (1910).
507. Connell, J. J., Hirst, E. L., and Percival, E. G. V., *J. Chem. Soc.*, 3494 (1950).
508. Percival, E. G. V., and Ross, A. G., *J. Chem. Soc.*, 720 (1951).
509. Naylor, G. L., and Russell-Wells, Barbara, *Ann. Botany (London)*, **48**, 635 (1934).
510. Mirande, R., *Compt. rend.*, **156**, 475 (1913).
511. Dillon, T., and O'Tuama, T., *Nature*, **133**, 837 (1934); *Sci. Proc. Roy. Dublin Soc.*, **21**, 147 (1935).
512. Tadokoro, T., and Takasugi, N., *J. Agr. Chem. Soc. Japan*, **12**, 421 (1936); *Chem. Abstracts*, **30**, 6785 (1936).
513. Araki, C., and Hashi, Y., *Collected Papers for the Celebration of the Forty-fifth Anniversary of the Founding of Kyoto Technical College*, 64 (1948).
514. Percival E. G. V., and Ross, A. G., *J. Chem. Soc.*, 3041 (1949).
515. Percival, E. G. V., and Chanda, S. K., *Nature*, **166**, 787 (1950).
516. Barry, V. C., Dillon, T., Hawkins, Beatrice, and O'Colla, P., *Nature*, **166**, 788 (1950).
517. Barry V. C., Halsall, T. G., Hirst, E. L., and Jones, J. K. N., *J. Chem. Soc.*, 1468 (1949).
518. Kylin, H., *Kgl. Fysiograf. Sällskap. Lund, Förh.*, **13**, 1, 51 (1943); *Chem. Abstracts*, **42**, 4245 (1948).
519. Colin, H., and Augier, J., *Compt. rend.*, **197**, 423 (1933); *Chem. Abstracts*, **28**, 3440 (1934).
520. Kylin, H., *Kgl. Fysiograf. Sällskap. Lund, Förh.*, **13**, 64 (1943).
521. Nunn, J. R., and von Holdt, Mrs. M. M., *Chemistry and Industry*, 467 (1956).
522. Errera, L., *These, Bruxelles* (1882): *Rec. Inst. botan.*, T. 1, Bruxelles (1906).
523. Büschli, O., *Weitere Aufuhrungen über den Bau der Cyanophyceen und Bakterien*, Verlag Wilhelm Engelmann, Leipzig, 1896; *Arch. Protistenk.*, **1**, 41 (1902).
524. Hegler, R., *Jahr. Wiss. Botan.*, **36**, 229 (1901).
525. Fischer, A., *Botan. Ztg.*, **63**, 51 (1905).
526. Nelson, N. L., and Cretcher, L. H., *J. Am. Chem. Soc.*, **51**, 1914 (1929). **52**, 2130 (1930).
527. Frush, Harriet L., and Isbell, H. S., *J. Research Natl. Bur. Standards*, **37**, 321 (1946).
528. Black, W. A. P., and Woodward, F. N., *Advances in Chem. Series*, **11**, 83 (1954).
529. Steiner, A. B., and McNeely, W. A., *Advances in Chem. Series*, **11**, 68 (1954).

530. Dillon, T., and McKenna, J., *Proc. Roy Irish Acad.*, **53B,** 45 (1950).

531. Schoeffel, E., and Link, K. P., *J. Biol. Chem.*, **100,** 397 (1933).

532. Klason, P., *Ber.*, **19,** 2541 (1886).

533. Drake, B., *Biochem. Z.*, **313,** 388 (1943).

534. Pringsheim, H., and Seifert, K., *Z. physiol. Chem.*, **128,** 284 (1923).

535. Karrier, P., and Staub, M., *Helv. Chim. Acta*, **7,** 518 (1924).

536. Lindberg, B., and Mcpherson, J., *Acta Chem. Scand.*, **8,** 985 (1954).

537. Hough, L., Jones, J. K. N., and Wadman, W. H., *J. Chem. Soc.*, 3393 (1952).

538. Hirst, E. L., Percival, Elizabeth, and Williams, R. S., *J. Chem. Soc.*, 1942 (1958).

539. Aspinall, G. O., and Sturgeon, R. J., *J. Chem. Soc.*, 4469 (1957).

540. Tadros, W., and Kamel, M., *J. Chem. Soc.*, 4532 (1952).

541. Whistler, R. L., and Saarnio, J., *J. Am. Chem. Soc.*, **79,** 6055 (1957).

542. French, D., Knapp, Doris, W., and Pazur, J. H., *J. Am. Chem. Soc.*, **72,** 5150 (1950).

543. Vogel, H., and Georg, A., *Tabellen der Zucker und ihrer Derivate*, Springer, Berlin (1931).

544. Boggs, L. A., Cuendet, L. S., Dubois, M., and Smith, F., *Anal. Chem.*, **24,** 1148 (1952).

545. Jones, J. K. N., *Chemistry of Carbon Compounds*, **1B,** Elsevier, Amsterdam (1952) 1197.

CHAPTER 8

DETERMINATION OF THE STRUCTURE OF GUMS AND MUCILAGES

It is of interest to note the following comment of Thomas Graham in reporting (1) upon some preliminary studies on gum arabic: "The equivalent of a colloid appears to be always high, although the ratio between the elements of the substance may be simple. Gummic acid (i.e. the free acid from gum arabic) may be represented by $C_{12}H_{11}O_{11}$ but judging from the small proportions of lime and potash which suffice to neutralize this acid, the true members of its formula must be several times greater. It is difficult to avoid associating the inertness of colloids with their high equivalents, particularly where the high number appears to be attained by the repetition of a smaller number. The inquiry suggests itself whether the colloid molecule may not be constituted by the grouping together of a number of smaller crystalloid molecules, and whether the basis of colloidality may not really be the composite character of the molecule."

The approaches developed for studying the structure of gums and mucilages and the general results thereof, which will form the subject of this chapter, together with the discussion of the structure of the individual gums and mucilages in Chapters 11 and 12, have borne out Graham's insight into the chemistry of these substances.

After purification of the gum or mucilage by one or more fractionation procedures (see Chapter 5), determination of the composition by paper chromatography, and characterization of the component sugars by crystallization or the preparation of derivatives, the investigator is faced with the problem of determining:

(a) the mode of union of the various component sugars, (b) the type of ring structure of each component, (c) the sequential order of the components, (d) the anomeric nature of the glycosidic linkages uniting the components, and (e) the average number of individual sugar residues that make up the molecule of the polymer.

One aspect of such structural studies involves determining the ratio of terminal to nonterminal units which reflects the frequency of branching in

the complex molecule. It will be apparent that these are the problems encountered in the study of any carbohydrate polymer, including the apparently much less complex polysaccharides such as cellulose, starch,
glycogen, and xylan and the reader is referred to other works on this subject (2,3,11).

Graded Hydrolysis of Gums and Mucilages

Information about the structure of gums and mucilages has been derived
from an examination of the products of graded hydrolysis using various
concentrations of mineral acid. In certain instances hydrolysis has been
effected by ultrasonic vibration (4).

The polysaccharide is subjected to the action of dilute (0.01 to 0.1N)
mineral acid whereby the acid-labile sugar residues, L-arabofuranose
(5–8), L-rhamnopyranose (5), and 3,6-anhydro-D- and L-galactose (9,10),
undergo preferential cleavage. If the polysaccharide gum contains uronic
acid units, the free gum acid may undergo autohydrolysis when its aqueous solutions are heated, there being a sufficient concentration of hydrogen ions from the carboxyl groups (5,6).

Following graded hydrolysis it is important to ascertain whether the
sugar residues removed are located on the periphery or in the interior of
the molecule.   This can be accomplished by measuring the molecular
weight of the original polysaccharide and comparing it with that of the
degraded polysaccharide. If we suppose that a polysaccharide of molecular weight 100,000 contains 20 per cent of labile sugar residues located
in the periphery of the molecule, the molecular weight of the residual
degraded gum molecule will be 80,000.   Were the gum molecule constructed with all the acid-labile sugar units in the interior and between
two stable portions of equal size, then the molecular weight of the degraded molecule would be 40,000. It will be apparent that there are many
variations of these possibilities and that only one single labile residue
need be present in a centrally located portion, to cause the molecular
weight to be only half as big as that which results when all labile sugar
residues are cleaved without any effect on the rest of the molecule. To
take a specific example, gum arabic has a molecular weight of approximately 250,000 (12) and contains about 30 per cent of labile sugar residues (L-arabinose, L-rhamnose and a small amount of D-galactose) (see
later, page 242). Now if all these labile residues are mutually joined
so that they can be removed without affecting the rest of the molecule,
composed of D-galactose and D-glucuronic acid, the molecular weight
of the degraded gum arabic should be approximately 175,000.   Experiments have shown that the molecular weight lies somewhere between
10,000 (12) and 20,000 (13). If there are no major defects in the

methods for the measurement of molecular weight, the results show that some of the labile sugar residues must be present in the interior of the gum molecule. It will be seen later (see page 250) that some of the labile residues are located in terminal positions in the molecule.

The use of physical measurements in the constitutional study of gums and mucilages is largely unexplored. It seems reasonable to believe that application of physical methods to purified, degraded molecules will give results of considerable value.

The advantage of applying methods of step-wise degradation is that the degraded molecules are less complicated and more amenable to constitutional studies. After removal of the labile residues, it is generally found that the residual portion, or portions, of the molecule are relatively stable to acidic reagents and much more vigorous treatment is necessary to effect complete hydrolysis. This stability may arise from the fact that the residues, which compose the stable sections of the polysaccharide, are of the pyranose or six membered ring type or from the presence of uronic acid residues which confer stability especially on those linkages which join C_1 of the uronic acids to other sugar residues. If no labile residues are present, mild acid treatment is without effect on a gum molecule. Application of a more vigorous acid treatment results in a general breakdown of the molecule.

Isolation of Aldobiouronic Acids

Many of those gums or mucilages or their corresponding degraded gums containing uronic acid building units give aldobiouronic acids in good yield upon more vigorous hydrolysis. In addition, smaller amounts of aldotriouronic acids may be isolated. It is generally possible to isolate the aldobiouronic acid in good yield because considerable stability is induced in the glycosidic bond between the uronic acid unit and the sugar unit to which it is attached. It is this same phenomenon which enables di-, tri-, and tetra- galacturonic acids to be isolated from the polygalactosiduronic acid, pectic acid, and the corresponding dimers, trimers, etc. from alginic acid.

The aldobiouronic acid, 6-O-(β-D-glucopyranosyluronic acid)-D-galactose, first isolated from gum arabic (14,15), has also been obtained from black wattle gum (16), *Acacia karroo* gum (70), *A. cyanophylla* gum (71), *A. pycnantha* (73), gum ghatti (183) and egg plum gum (17,18). In a similar manner 2-O-(D-glucopyranosyluronic acid)-D-mannose has been obtained from damson gum (6,19), cherry gum (20), and from gum ghatti (183). A 1 → 4-linked aldobiouronic acid, 4-O-(D-glucopyranosyluronic acid)-D-galactose has been isolated from grapefruit (21), *Acacia karroo* (70), and lemon gums (21). It is of interest to note the isolation of the analogous aldobiouronic acid, 4-O-(D-glucopyranosyluronic acid)-D-glucose, from Type III pneumococcus polysaccharide (22). D-Glucuronic acid has been isolated in combination with D-xylose through C_2 from chagual gum (24) and corn cobs (23), through C_3 from wheat straw (25,26), and through C_4 from *Kadsura japonica* Dun (27) and corn cobs (23).

The 4-O-methyl derivative of D-glucuronic acid linked to D-galactose through C_6 (28,33) and C_4 (30) is present in mesquite gum, and in lemon gum the 1 → 4 linked disaccharide is present (32). The 4-O-methyl-D-glucuronic acid residue appears to be quite widely distributed in nature; in the hemicellulose from corn cobs (34) and in that from flax straw (74) it is joined to C_2 of a D-xylose unit, in wheat straw to C_3 (35) and in New Zealand flax (*Phormium tenax*) straw to C_4 of a D-xylose residue. It does not appear to have been present in certain hemicelluloses in prehistoric times (36). The source of a number of aldobiouronic acids is given in Table 34.

TABLE 34. ALDOBIOURONIC ACIDS FROM GUMS AND MUCILAGES CONTAINING D-GLUCURONIC ACID

Aldobiouronic Acid	Sources	References
α-D-GpA-(1 → 2)-D-Xyl$p$	Corn (*Zea mays*) cob (hemicellulose B.)	23
	Chagual (*Puya sp.*) gum	24
α-D-GpA-(1 → 3)-D-Xyl$p$	Wheat (*Triticum vulgare*) straw	25,26
α-D-GpA-(1 → 4)-D-Xyl$p$	*Kadsura japonica* Dun	27
	Corn (*Zea mays*) cob (hemicellulose B.)	23
D-GpA1 → D-Xyl$p$	Cotton (*Gossypium herbaceum*) seed hulls	306
	Prunus serrulata gum	305
β-D-GpA-(1 → 4)-D-Gp	Type III Pneumococcus polysaccharide	22
D-GpA-(1 → 2)-D-Man$p$	Damson (*Prunus insitia*) gum	6,19
	Cherry (*Prunus cerasus*) gum	20
	Gum ghatti (*Anogeissus latifolia*)	183
	Hakea acicularis gum	263
D-GpA1 → D-Man$p$	*Asparagus filicinus* mucilage	304
D-GpA-(1→ 4)-D-Gal$p$	Grapefruit (*Citrus maxima*) gum	21
	Lemon (*Citrus limonia*) gum	21
	Acacia karroo gum	70
β-D-GpA-(1 → 6)-D-Gal$p$	Gum arabic (*Acacia verek*)	14,15
	Black wattle (*Acacia mollissima*, Willd.) gum	16
	Egg plum (*Prunus domestica*) gum	17,18
	Peach (*Prunus persica*) gum	72
	Wheat straw (*Triticum vulgare*) hemicellulose	26
	Acacia karroo gum	70
	Acacia cyanophylla gum	71
	Acacia pycnantha gum	73
	Gum ghatti (*Anogeissus latifolia*)	183

TABLE 34. (*Continued*)

Aldobiouronic Acid	Sources	References
4-*O*-Me-α-D-G*p*A-(1 → 2)- D-Xyl*p*	Corn (*Zea mays*) cob (hemicellulose B.) Flax (*Linum usitatissimum*) straw hemi- cellulose	34 74
4-*O*-Me-α-D-G*p*A-(1 → 3)- D-Xyl*p*	Wheat (*Triticum vulgare*) straw hemicel- lulose	26
4-*O*-Me-D-G*p*A-(1 → 6)- D-Gal*p*	Mesquite (*Prosopsis juliflora DC*) gum	28, 29, 30
4-*O*-Me-D-G*p*A-(1 → 4)- D-Gal*p*	Mesquite (*Prosopsis juliflora DC*) gum *Khaya grandifolia* gum	30 52
α-D-G*p*A-(1 → 4)-β-D- Xyl*p*-(1 → 4)-D-Xyl	Corn (*Zea mays*) cob (hemicellulose B.)	186
D-G*p*A-(1 → 4)-D-Xyl*p*- (1 → 2)-D-Xyl*p*	New Zealand flax (*Phormium tenax*) hemi- cellulose	35

Aldobiouronic acids containing D-galacturonic acid have been isolated in which the reducing end consists of D-galactose (37), D-glucose (38) and D-xylose (39,40). D-Galacturonic acid occurs widely distributed in combination with L-rhamnose (41–43) and in a number of cases the biose linkage has been shown to be of the 1 → 2 type (44–51,126,185) (see Table 35).

At one time it appeared that natural gum exudates and mucilages could be differentiated by the fact that gums contain D-glucuronic acid or its

TABLE 35. ALDOBIOURONIC ACIDS FROM GUMS AND MUCILAGES CONTAINING D-GALACTURONIC ACID

Aldobiouronic Acid	Sources	References
D-Gal*p*A1 → D-Gal*p*	Gum jeol (*Lannea grandis*)	37
D-Gal*p*A1 → D-G*p*	*Asparagus racemosus*	38
D-Gal*p*A1 → D-Xyl*p*	*Plantago arenaria* seed	39, 40
D-Gal*p*A1 → L-Rha*p*	White mustard (*Brassica alba*) seed	41
	Cress (*Lepidum sativum*) seed	42
	Plantago lanceolata seed	307
	Cholla (*Opuntia fulgida*) gum	43
D-Gal*p*A-(1 → 2)-L-Rha*p*	Flax (*Linum usitatissimum*) seed	44–47
	Slippery elm (*Ulmus fulva*) bark	48
	Plantago ovata Forsk. seed	49, 50
	Plantago arenaria seed	51
	Khaya grandifolia gum	52
	Grapes (*Vitis vinifera* L.) fruit	185
	Okra (*Hibiscus esculentus*) pods	126
Aldotriouronic acid composed of D-Gal*p*A; L-Rha; D-Gal	Flax (*Linum usitatissimum*) seed	46
D-Gal*p*A-(1 → 2)-L-Rha*p*- (1 → 4)-D-Gal	*Khaya grandifolia* gum	52

4-methyl ether whereas mucilages contain D-galacturonic acid (272), but this convenient classification has had to be discarded since the gum exudate from *Khaya grandifolia* and that from *Khaya senegalensis* have been shown to contain both D-glucuronic acid and D-galacturonic acid (52).

The structures of many of the aldobiouronic acids referred to above have been ascertained by the classical method of methylation and in certain instances by periodate oxidation.

The methylation method may be illustrated by reference to the proof of the structure of 6-O-(β-D-glucopyranosyluronic acid)-D-galactose (XII) obtained from gum arabic (14), black wattle gum (16), and egg plum gum (17,18). Methylation of XII with methyl sulfate and alkali provides the corresponding crystalline hepta-O-methyl derivative (XIII) (14) which may be recognized after esterification with diazomethane and treatment with ammonia as the crystalline amide (XIV) (33,56). Acid hydrolysis of XIII

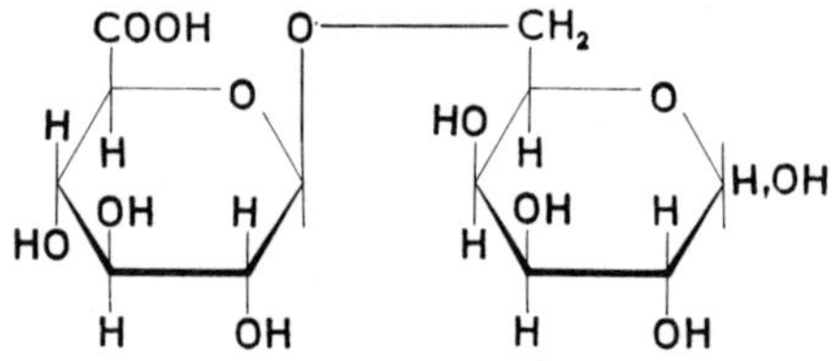

(XII)

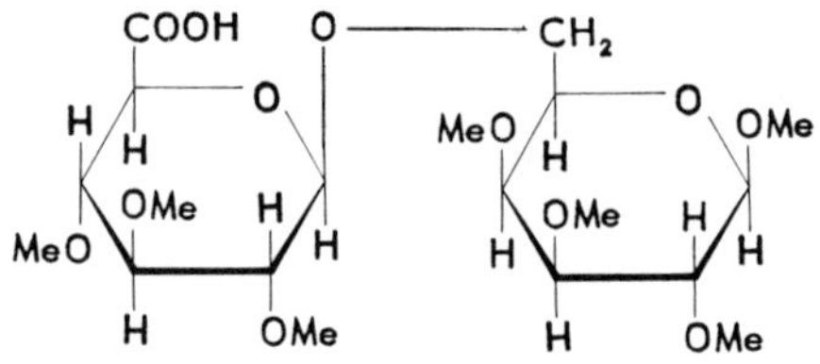

(XIII)

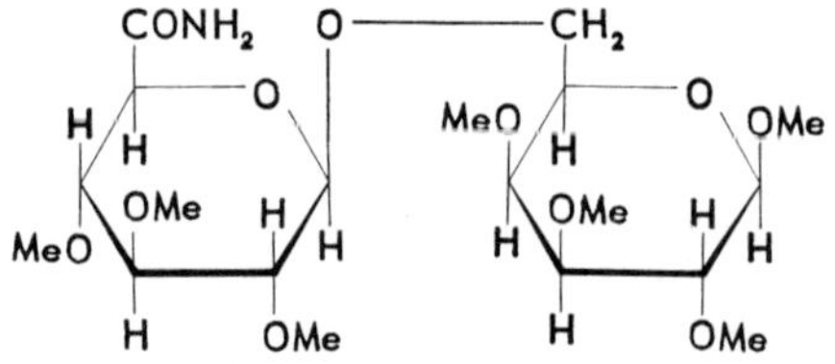

(XIV)

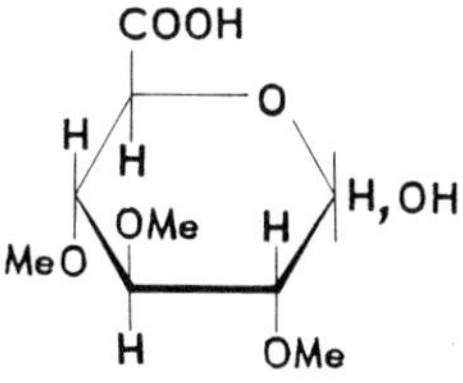

COOH
H
H
OMe   H   H, OH
MeO
H   OMe

(XV)

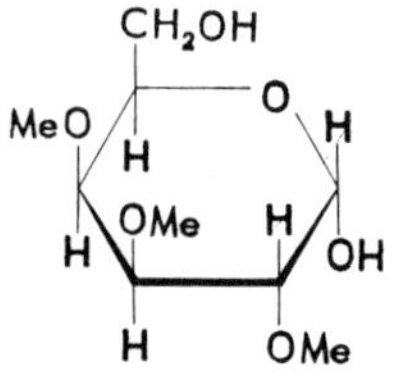

CH$_2$OH
MeO
H
OMe   H   H
H   OH
H   OMe

(XVI)

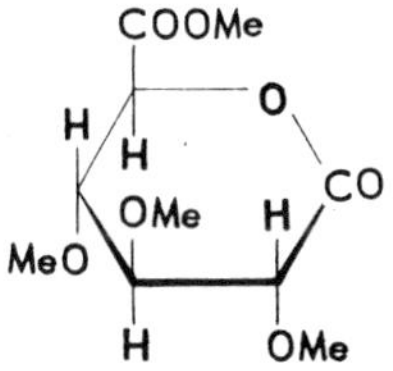

COOMe
H
H
OMe   H   CO
MeO
H   OMe

(XVII)

CONH$_2$
H
H
OMe   H   OMe
MeO
H   OMe

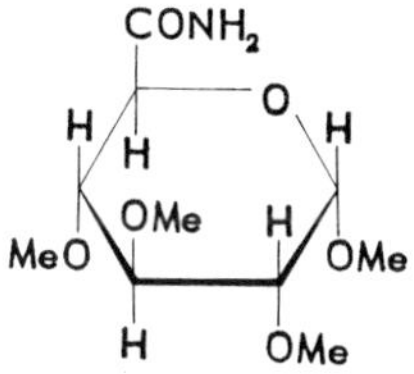

(XVIII)

gives 2,3,4-tri-O-methyl-D-glucuronic acid (XV) and 2,3,4-tri-O-methyl-D-galactose (XVI). The former may be characterized by oxidation with nitric acid followed by esterification and distillation to give 2,3,4-tri-O-methyl-D-glucaric acid lactone methyl ester (XVII) (14), and the latter (XVI) gives rise to a characteristic crystalline aniline derivative (54) and, after oxidation to the lactone with bromine, it readily affords a crystalline phenylhydrazide (55). Perhaps the simplest method for identifying XV is to treat it with methanolic hydrogen chloride to provide the corresponding methyl ester methyl glycoside and then react this with methanolic ammonia to give largely the α-anomer of the amide (XVIII) (55). Further support for the structure (XII) assigned to the aldobiouronic acid follows from its synthesis involving the combination of 2,3,4-tri-O-acetyl-D-glucosyluronic acid bromide with 1,2,3,4-tetra-O-acetyl-D-galactose by the usual Koenigs-Knorr reaction (68,69).

The use of periodate oxidation in the determination of the structure of aldobiouronic acids may be illustrated by reference to 6-O-β (4-O-methyl-D-glucopyranosyluronic acid)-D-galactose (XIX) obtained by acid hydrolysis of mesquite gum (33). When the amide (XX) of the methyl β-glycoside of (XIX) is treated with 0.1N periodic acid at 0–5°, 3 moles of oxidant are consumed per mole of XX to give the tetraaldehyde (XXI) and at the same time 1 mole of formic acid is liberated.

The periodate cleaved uronic acid moiety can be recognized by bromine oxidation, hydrolysis, and isolation of D-2-O-methyl-erythraric acid (XXII) as the characteristic crystalline 1,4-bis-methylamide (XXIII) (28,57,58).

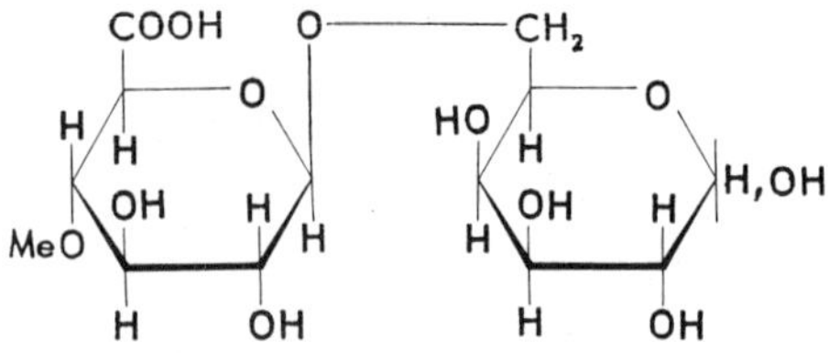

(XIX)

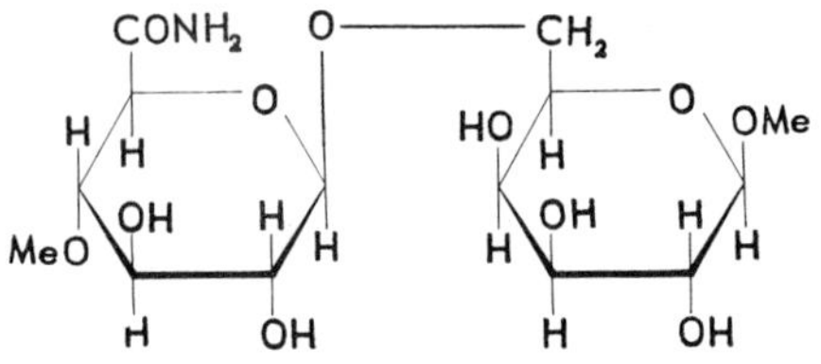

(XX)

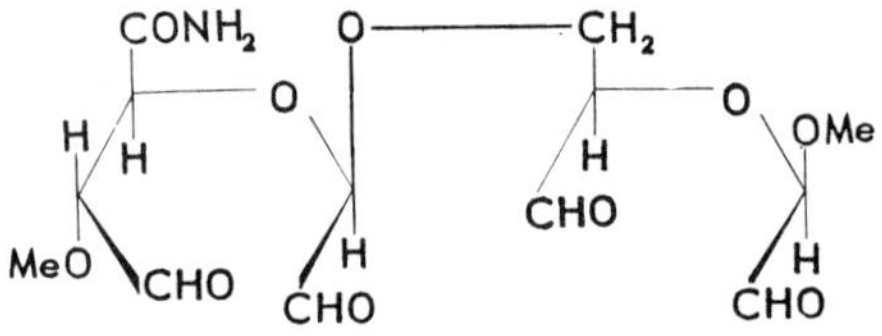

(XXI)

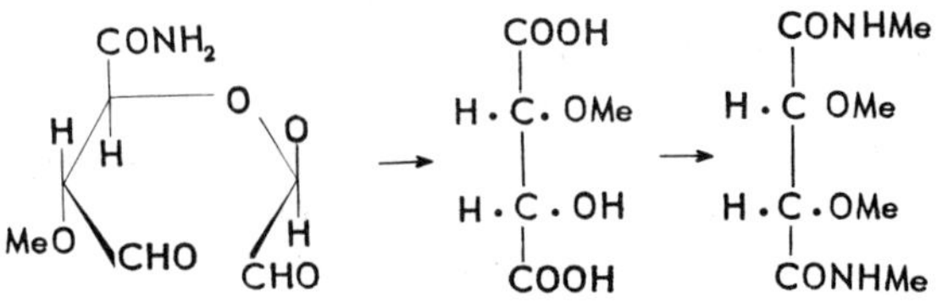

(XXIa)　　　　　(XXII)　　　　(XXIII)

Hydrolysis of the stable aldobiouronic acids usually produces considerable decomposition. The solution of this problem is to reduce the carboxyl to a primary alcoholic group either with hydrogen and a copper chromite catalyst (58,308) or better still with lithium aluminum hydride (58–60). This not only enables the parent sugar of the uronic acid to be identified but the glycosidic linkage of the product behaves normally and may readily be cleaved with dilute mineral acid. In certain cases, where the compounds are not soluble in the dry organic solvents necessary for the use of lithium aluminum hydride, it is possible to use sodium borohydride (61) or better still potassium borohydride (52). Still further improvement is possible by using aluminum chloride in conjunction with sodium borohydride and a suitable solvent such as di-O-methyl diethylene glycol (264,265). This reduction reaction should also be applicable to polyglycosiduronic acids from which neutral polysaccharides should result and these might well be more amenable to structural studies (cf 53).

In the case of the methyl (methyl-4-O-methyl-D-glucosid)uronate (XXIV) from mesquite gum, treatment with lithium aluminum hydride yielded (58) methyl 4-O-methyl-D-glucopyranoside (XXV) which, unlike XXIV, was easily hydrolyzed to give 4-O-methyl-D-glucose (XXVI) and this in turn yielded the characteristic osazone (62).

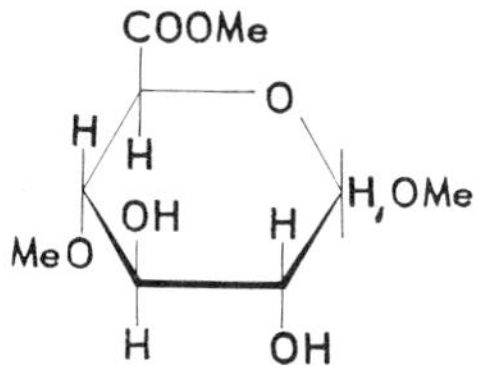

(XXIV) 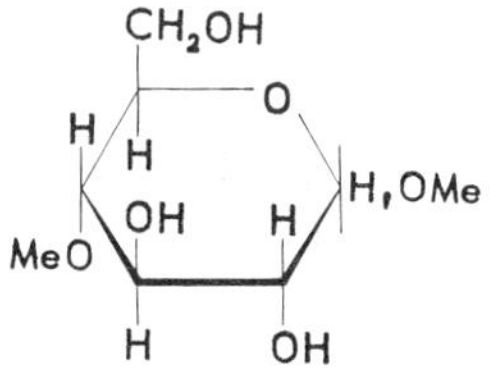   (XXV) 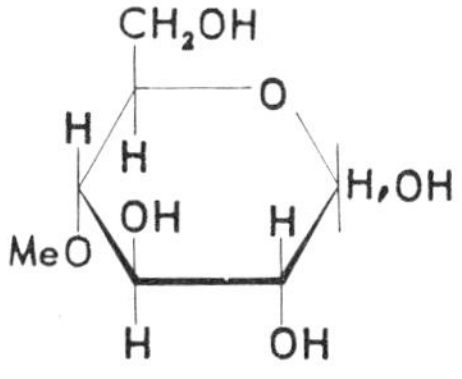   (XXVI)

In a similar fashion the aldobiouronic acid from the hemicellulose of corn cobs (34) was reduced with lithium aluminum hydride to facilitate its identification.

Further illustration of the usefulness of the lithium aluminum hydride reduction method in studies on aldobiouronic acids is shown by the fact that the methyl ester (XXVII) of XIII from gum arabic gave the corresponding crystalline neutral methylated disaccharide (XXVIII) in almost quantitative yield.

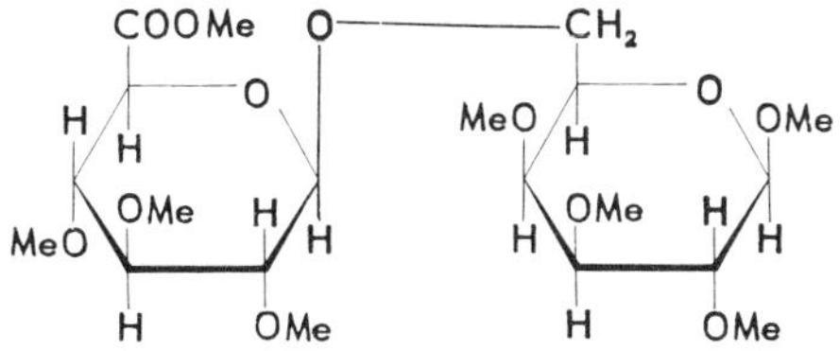

(XXVII)

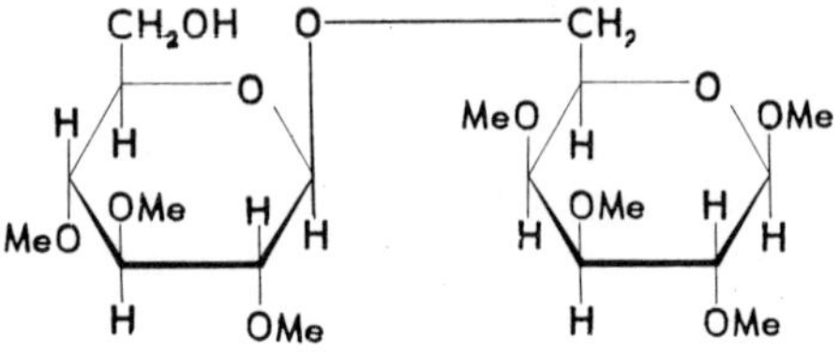

(XXVIII)

It has also been possible (63) to assign the structures XXIX and XXX to two isomeric crystalline acetates of aldobiouronic acids obtained from corn hull gum (64), by making use of this reduction technique. The two corresponding reduced deacetylated products XXXI and XXXII could be identified by the fact that both were cleaved with α-D-glucosidase to give D-glucose which showed that both XXIX and XXX contain an α-biose linkage. Moreover, paper electrophoretic analysis showed that the other product of the reaction of α-D-glucosidase on XXXI was methyl α-D-xylopyranoside and XXXII was found to give methyl β-D-xylopyranoside. Such microenzymic reactions are quite valuable diagnostic tests in structural studies when used in conjunction with paper chromatography (256,257).

Proof of the structure of aldobiouronic acids containing the D-galacturonic unit follows lines similar to those outlined above. One example will suffice to illustrate the general procedure to be followed. The aldobiouronic acid (XXXIII) derived from flax seed (linseed) mucilage gives

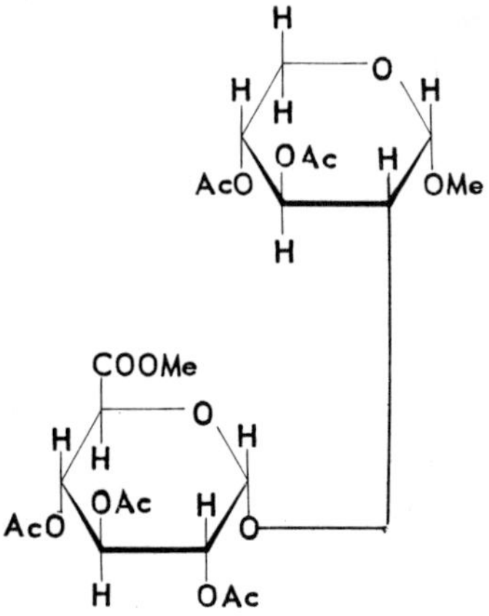

(XXIX)

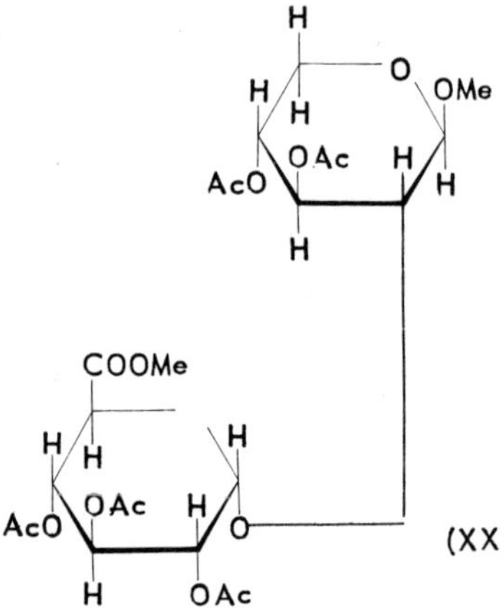

(XXX)

(XXXI)   (XXXII)

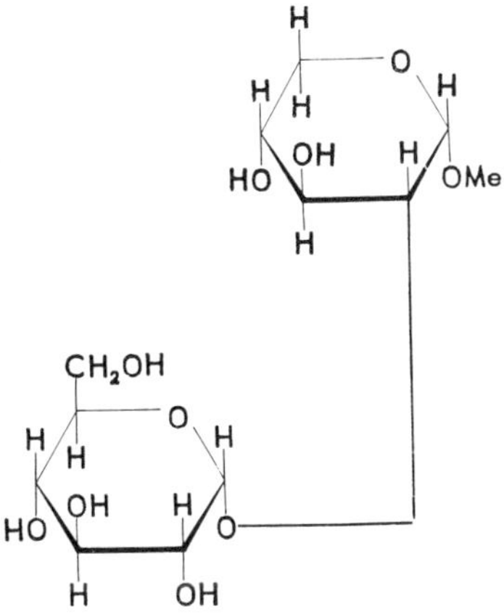

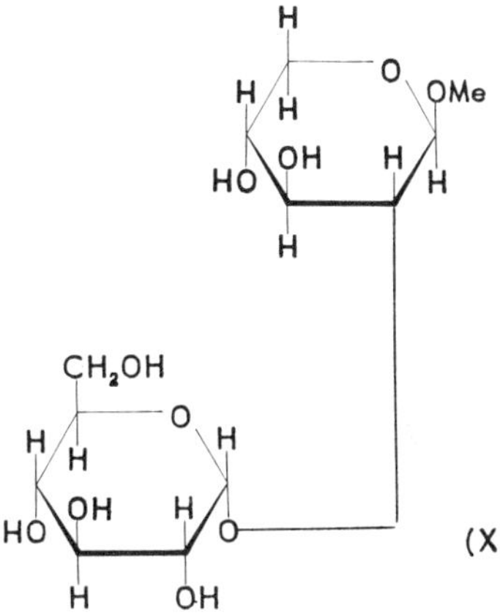

upon hydrolysis L-rhamnose and D-galacturonic acid. Complete methylation of XXXIII provides XXXIV which in turn was shown to give, by hydrolysis, equimolecular amounts of 3,4-di-O-methyl-L-rhamnose (XXXV)
and 2,3,4-tri-O-methyl-D-galacturonic acid (XXXVI). The 3,4-di-O-methyl-
L-rhamnose readily crystallized and its structure was ascertained by oxidation to 2,3-di-O-methyl-L-threaric acid.   The 2,3,4-tri-O-methyl-D-
galacturonic acid was characterized as the amide of the corresponding
methyl glycosiduronic acid (44–47,65).

Less frequently encountered are the acidic fragments of gums and
mucilages containing more than two sugar building units. Although they

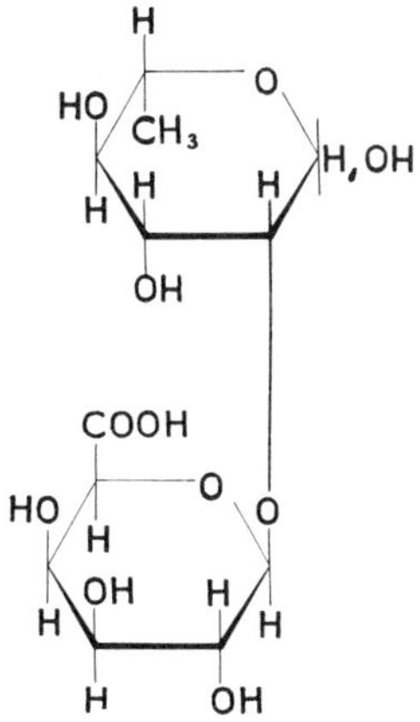

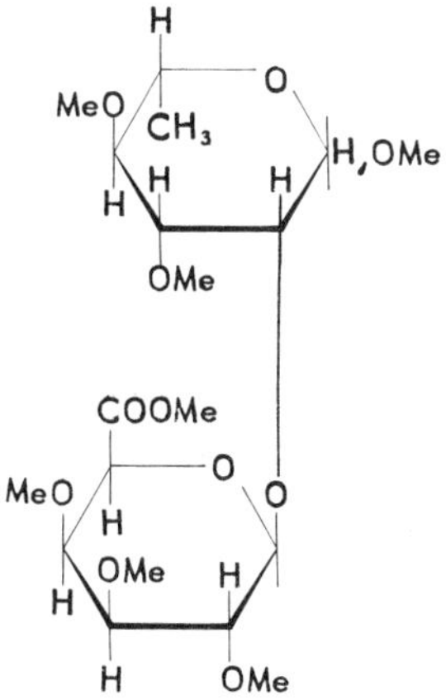

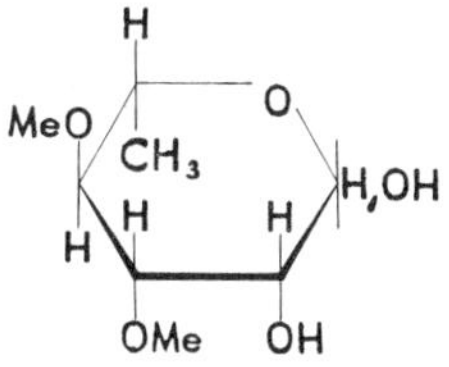

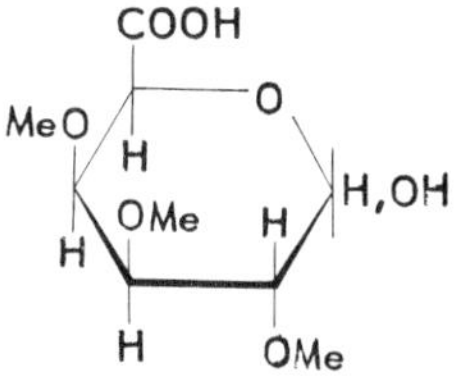

(XXXIII)   (XXXIV)   (XXXVI)

are valuable and highly desirable for structural studies, they are more difficult to isolate in quantity in the pure form than are the aldobiouronic acids discussed above. This is because the stabilizing effect of the uronic acid unit does not extend to the unit preceding the uronic acid residue, nor beyond the first sugar residue following the uronic acid unit.

Nevertheless an aldotriouronic acid has been isolated and characterized from flax seed mucilage (35,46). Another has been obtained from *Khaya grandifolia* gum and shown (52) by classical studies to have the structure O-D-galactosyluronic acid-$(1 \rightarrow 2)$-O-L-rhamnosyl-$(1 \rightarrow 4)$-D-galactose. In a similar fashion the triouronic from New Zealand flax straw hemicellulose has been shown to have the structure O-D-glucopyranosyluronic acid-$(1 \rightarrow 4)$-O-D-xylosyl-$(1 \rightarrow 2)$-D-xylose (35) whereas flax seed mucilage has afforded a triouronic acid composed of D-galacturonic acid, L-rhamnose and D-galactose (46). Mention may also be made of the characterization of the aldotriouronic acid from corn cob hemicellulose, which has the structure D-GpA-$(1 \rightarrow 4)$-D-Xyl$p$-$(1 \rightarrow 2)$-D-Xyl$p$ (186) and that graded hydrolysis of polygalactosiduronic acids gives rise to di-, tri-, and tetra-D-galacturonic acids (66,67) which have been characterized as crystalline brucine salts (67).

Graded Hydrolysis and the Isolation of Neutral Oligosaccharides

Gums may yield neutral disaccharides and higher oligosaccharides as well as monosaccharides when they are subjected to mild acid hydrolysis or autohydrolysis. Thus, arabic acid affords 3-O-α-D-galactopyranosyl-L-arabinose (5,71,75), a result to be traced to the fact that the $1 \rightarrow 3$ biose linkage is more stable than the linkage between the arabinose residue and the rest of the polysaccharide molecule, presumably because the arabinose units are present in the gum molecule in the furanose form (5). The structure of this particular disaccharide (XXXVII) was established by methylation with methyl sulfate and alkali to give XXXVIII from which, by hydrolysis, there were formed 2,3,4,6-tetra-O-methyl-D-galactose (XXXIX) and 2,4-di-O-methyl-L-arabinose (XL), both of which were

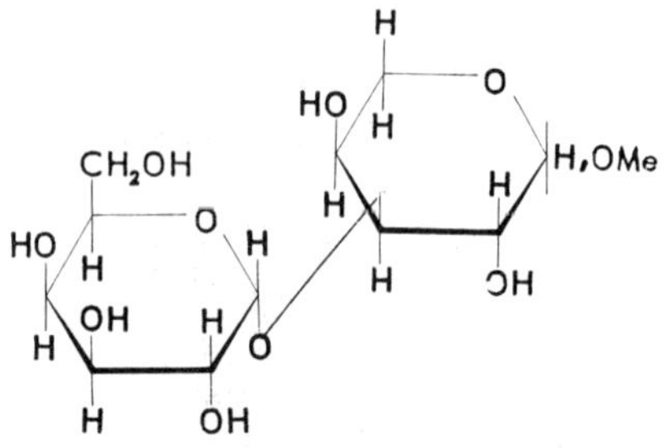

(XXXVII)

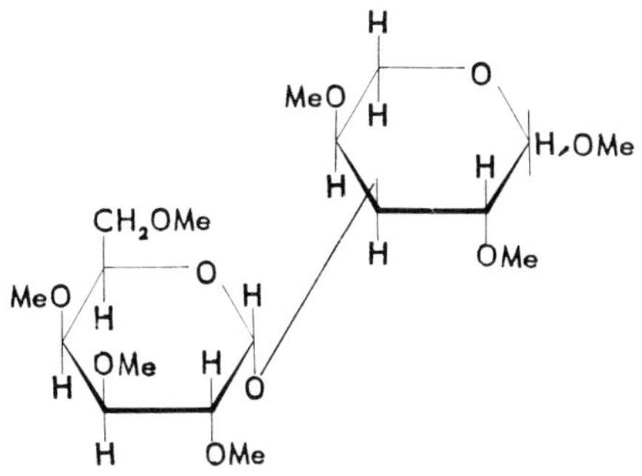

(XXXVIII)

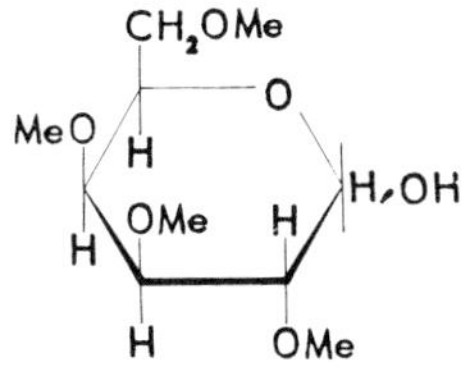

(XXXIX)

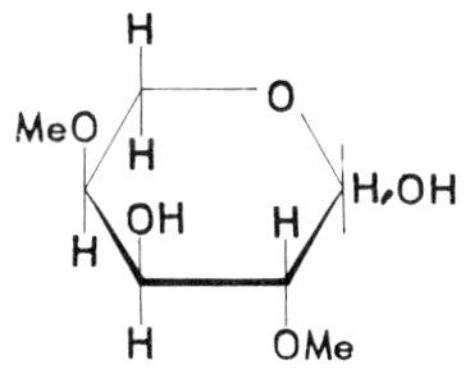

(XL)

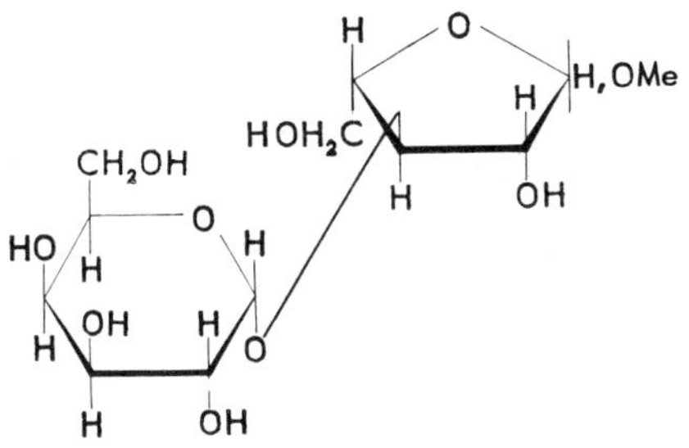

(XLI)

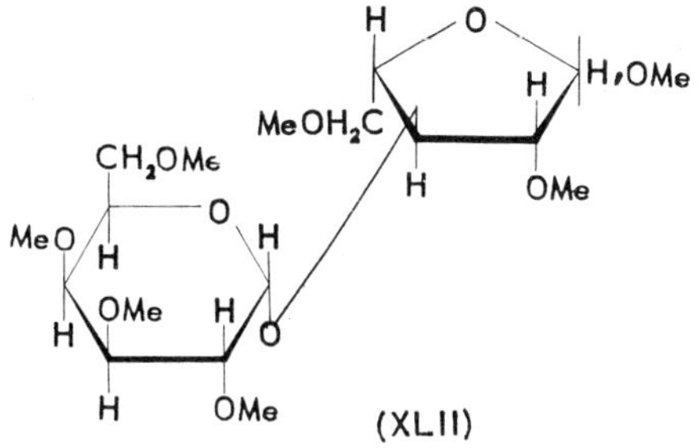

(XLII)

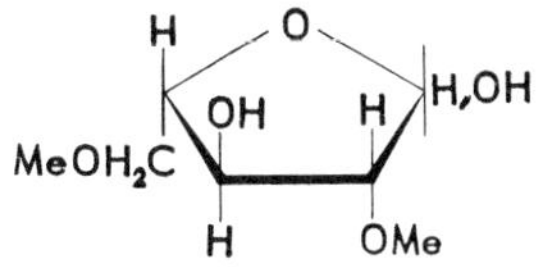

(XLIII)

characterized as their crystalline aniline derivatives (5,71). If the disaccharide is first treated at room temperature with methanolic hydrogen chloride the arabinose moiety adopts a furanose structure and the nonreducing disaccharide glycofuranoside (XLI) is generated. Complete methylation of the latter gave XLII from which by acid hydrolysis there were produced 2,3,4,6-tetra-O-methyl-D-galactose (XXXIX), characterized as the aniline derivative, and 2,5-di-O-methyl-L-arabinose (XLIII), characterized as the crystalline γ-lactone, the corresponding amide, and phenylhydrazide (5). The structure of the above disaccharide (XXXVII) produced from the acacia gums was confirmed by showing that an isomeric disaccharide, 3-O-β-D-galactopyranosyl-D-arabinose, obtained from lactose by a Wohl degradation (76), behaved in an analogous manner (5) and gave rise under the appropriate conditions to the 2,5-, and 2,4-dimethyl ethers of D-arabinose whose crystalline derivatives were identical in every respect, except sign of rotation, with those (XLIII and XL) from the galactose-arabinose disaccharide derived from gum arabic (5).

By suitably interrupting the hydrolysis of the various gums and mucilages, other neutral oligosaccharides have been obtained which aid in the elucidation of the structure of the polysaccharides. Thus, graded hydrolysis of degraded arabic acid was shown to give 3-O-D-galacto-

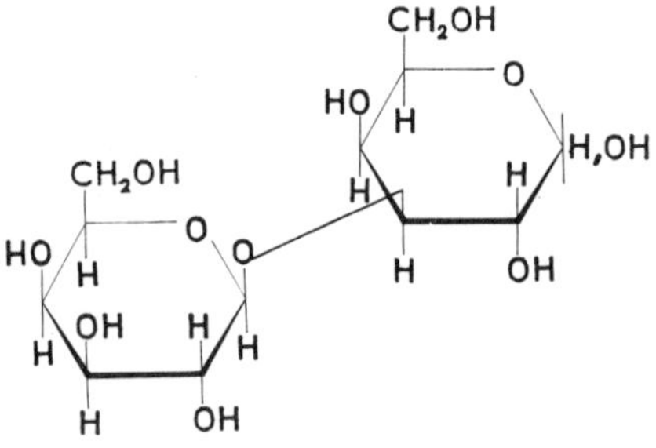

(XLIV)

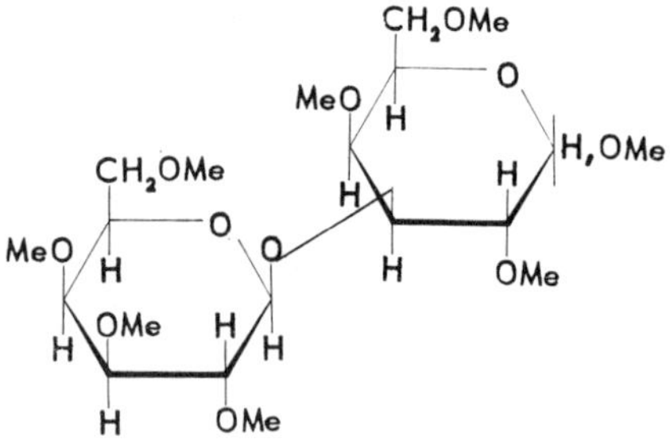

(XLV)

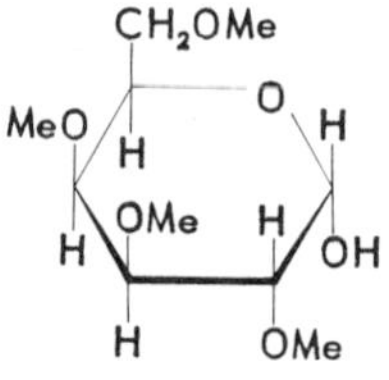

(XXXIX)

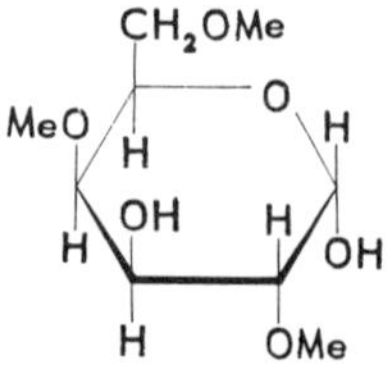

(XLVI)

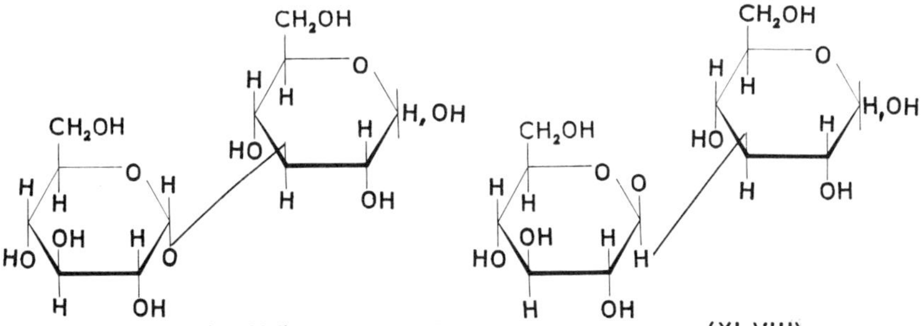

(XLVII)   (XLVIII)

pyranosyl-D-galactose (XLIV), the structure of which was established by methylation studies in which it was shown (77) that the fully methylated disaccharide (XLV) gave, upon hydrolysis, 2,3,4,6-tetra-O-methyl-D-galactose (XXXIX) and 2,4,6-tri-O-methyl-D-galactose (XLVI), both of which were recognized as their crystalline aniline derivatives.

An analogous glucose disaccharide 3-O-α-D-glucopyranosyl-D-glucose, nigerose, (XLVII) has been obtained (128) by hydrolysis of the polysaccharide, nigeran, extracted from *Aspergillus niger* and the isomeric 3-O-β-D-glucopyranosyl-D-glucose, laminaribiose, (XLVIII) has been produced in like manner from laminarin (127) and its structure established by synthesis (187,188).

In a similar manner disaccharides composed of pentose residues have been isolated from gums of the *Prunus* and *Acacia* families. Thus cherry (78), peach (78), golden apple (79), and *Acacia karroo* (70) gums give rise to 3-O-β-L-arabopyranosyl-L-arabinose and another pentose disaccharide, 3-O-α-D-xylopyranosyl-L-arabinose, is obtained from golden-apple gum (79) and corn fiber or corn hull gum (82,83) and yet another 5-O-D-xylopyranosyl-L-arabofuranose is obtained from peach and cholla gum (78).

The procedure adopted for establishing the structure of the pentose disaccharides follows the same general lines as that for the hexose disaccharides. The structure of the 3-O-β-L-arabopyranosyl-L-arabinose (XLIX) was determined with a specimen of the disaccharide obtained from larch E-galactan (75) in the following way.   The disaccharide (XLIX) gave an osazone showing that the biose linkage did not engage C_2. Both the disaccharide and its osazone gave L-arabinose upon hydrolysis.   Methylation of XLIX and hydrolysis gave rise to a mixture of 2,3,4-tri-O-methyl-L-arabinose and 2,4-di-O-methyl-L-arabinose.   The former was identified by bromine oxidation and transformation of the resulting lactone into the characteristic crystalline phenylhydrazide; the latter was recognized as its aniline derivative and by the fact that it gave a δ-lactone upon oxidation with bromine (5). The high positive rotation of XLIX and its hexamethyl ether, $[\alpha]_D + 220°$ and $+ 300°$ respectively,

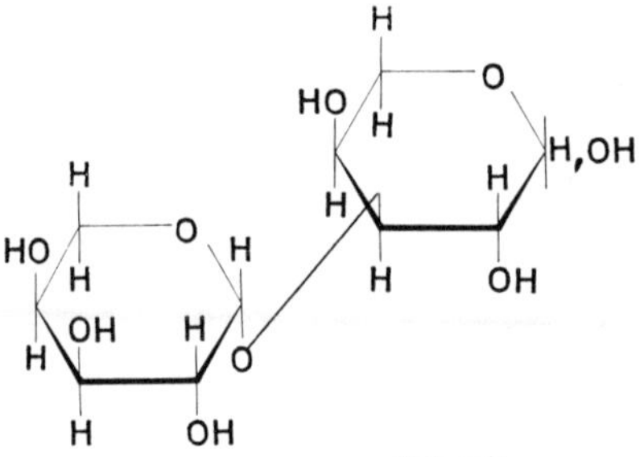

(XLIX) 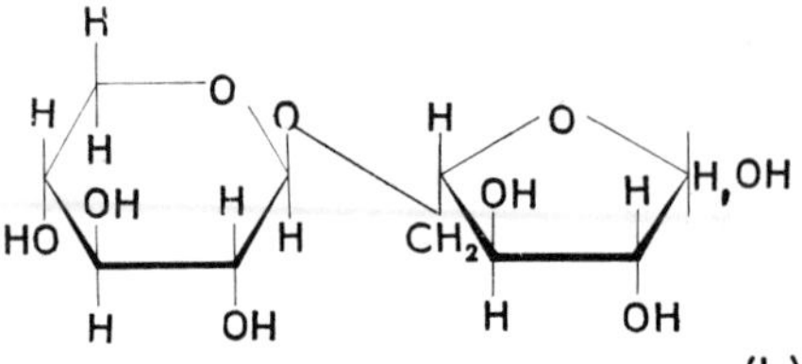   (L)

indicated that the residues were both of the pyranose type and that the biose linkage was the β-D-type.

Of considerable importance in studies on oligosaccharides is the observation that the glycosidic linkage located between the reducing end and the next sugar unit is rendered acid-labile when the oligosaccharide is transformed into an osazone (258).

The structure of the D-xylopyranosyl-L-arabinose disaccharide (L) isolated from peach and cholla gums (78) was based upon the following evidence. Upon hydrolysis L gave D-xylose and L-arabinose whereas hydrolysis of the osazone of L gave D-xylose but no L-arabinose. The arabinose residue was therefore the reducing end of the disaccharide and it is also clear that the biose linkage does not engage C_2 of the arabinose unit because this would prevent osazone formation. Methylation and hydrolysis of L gave rise to 2,3,4-tri-O-methyl-D-xylose and 2,3-di-O-methyl-L-arabinose. The former crystallized and also gave the characteristic aniline derivative whereas the latter was identified by conversion into a lactone and thence to a crystalline amide (80). In order to establish that the biose linkage was at C_5 of the arabinose unit and not at C_4 the disaccharide L was oxidized and methylated according to the classical procedure (81) for this purpose. Hydrolysis of the product so formed yielded 2,3,4-tri-O-methyl-D-xylose and 2,3,4-tri-O-methyl-L-arabonic acid. Although the latter was not identified completely, the fact that the phenylhydrazide of the unknown trimethyl arabonic acid gave no depression of the melting point when mixed with 2,3,4-tri-O-methyl-L-arabonic acid phenylhydrazide indicated that the unknown compound was most likely the 2,3,4-tri-O-methyl derivative. This being the case, the disaccharide is to be designated as 5-O-D-xylopyranosyl-L-arabinose. The negative specific rotation (−34°) of the disaccharide indicated that the biose linkage was of the β-D-type (78).

An interesting case is the isolation from laminarin, by graded hydrolysis, of oligosaccharides containing D-mannitol, namely, 1-O-β-D-gluco-

pyranosyl-D-mannitol (273, cf. 196) and 3-O-β-D-glucopyranosyl-1-O-β-D-glucopyranosyl- D- mannitol (1- O- β- D- laminaribiosyl- D- mannitol) (274). The structure of the latter was established by periodate oxidation and by synthesis wherein the following series of reactions was employed:
laminaribiose ⟶ hepta-O-acetyl-α-D-laminaribiosyl bromide

$$\underset{\text{(D-mannose 1,2,3,4-tetra-acetate)}}{\underline{\hspace{6cm}}} \longrightarrow \text{undeca-}O\text{-acetyl- 6-}O\text{-}\beta\text{- D- laminari -}$$

biosyl- β- D- mannopyranose $\xrightarrow[\text{Na}^3\text{H}_4]{\text{Deacetylation}}$ 1- O- β- D- laminaribiosyl- D -

mannitol.

Further illustration of the employment of controlled hydrolysis in the study of gums and mucilages lies in the demonstration that corn hull or corn fiber gum has been shown to yield the following oligosaccharides, whose structures have been ascertained in general by the methods outlined above: (a) 3-O-α-D-xylopyranosyl-L-arabinose (82,83), (b) 4-O-(D-xylopyranosyl)-D-xylose (84), (c) 4-O-(D-galactopyranosyl)-D-xylose (83), (d) 3-O-(D-galactopyranosyl)-L-arabinose (84), and (e) O-L-galactopyranosyl-(1 ⟶ 4)-O-D-xylosyl-(1 ⟶ 2)-L-arabinose (82).

Similarly, graded hydrolysis of guar gum has been shown to produce 4-O-(β-D-mannopyranosyl)-β-D-mannopyranose, 6-O-(α-D-galactopyranosyl)-β-D-mannopyranose (85), and 4-O-[6-O-(α-D-galactopyranosyl)-β-D-mannopyranosyl]-β- D-mannopyranose (86).

In considering methods for the graded hydrolysis of gums and mucilages, it is pertinent to note the excellent examples of controlled acid hydrolysis in the case of starch (117–121), cellulose (122), dextran (124) and xylan (116,123) whereby a series of oligosaccharides have been obtained.

For the rapid evaluation of the components of a mixture of oligosaccharides, paper electrophoresis (ionophoresis) of the corresponding N-benzylglycosylamines (as salts) (242), the bisulfite, or cyanide addition compounds appears to offer possibilities. Paper chromatography, either directly with a suitable solvent system or after transformation into the N-glycosylamines (242,243) with N-benzylamine or N-(1-napthyl)-ethylenediamine (244), often furnishes valuable data.

Also to be noted in studies on oligosaccharides is a useful method (237) for determining the degree of polymerization of hexosans and pentosans. The oligosaccharide is first treated with the anthrone reagent to determine the total sugar. The oligosaccharide is then reduced to the corresponding alcohol with sodium borohydride and again treated with the anthrone reagent which determines the total sugar less that corresponding to the one reducing end. The total reducing power divided by the decrease in reducing power caused by reduction provides a measure of the degree of polymerization. Although this method in conjunction with the anthrone reagent is not applicable to pentose oligosaccharides, it is very likely that the difficulty could be surmounted by using the phenol-sulfuric acid reagent (238) for sugar determination since this can be used for pentoses as well as for hexoses. The cyanohydrin method (99,259) modified for small amounts (260,261) may also be employed for determining the degree of polymerization.

A general and simple method for determining the molecular weight of reducing oligosaccharides involves reduction with sodium borohydride to transform the terminal reducing sugar to the corresponding sugar alcohol (268). Upon treatment with periodate the sugar alcohol residue furnishes formaldehyde the amount of which may be determined readily by colorimetric methods and used to determine the molecular weight (see Chapter 6) (137,269,270).

Oxidation with lead tetraacetate has been used for determination of the structure of reducing oligosaccharides (239,240). The reaction is carried out on a microscale in the presence of a bicarbonate buffer so that the formic acid generated may be determined by liberation of carbon dioxide. Although some anomalous reactions have been noted, the results to date are promising and worthy of consideration especially when only small amounts of material are available.

The recent observation that a reagent consisting of aniline, diphenylamine and phosphoric acid can be used for the differentiation of $1 \longrightarrow 4$- and $1 \longrightarrow 6$- linked glucosaccharides (241) might prove valuable in structural studies on gums and mucilages.

Acetolysis

Acetolysis is another procedure that can be applied with advantage to the study of gums and mucilages. This method gives a surprisingly high yield of cellobiose octaacetate from cellulose (111) and under the appropriate conditions a series of oligosaccharides is produced (122). Starch has been converted to maltosyl bromide heptaacetate (181,195). There is every reason to expect similar valuable results by applying this method to the more stable gums and especially to those composed of neutral sugar residues (cf 181), such as lichenin from Iceland moss, which affords cellobiose octaacetate (231,232). Decomposition might well take place with such gums as gum arabic or mesquite gum due to labile pentose residues but after their removal by partial hydrolysis the residual degraded molecule would probably react smoothly.

Some indication that the method has merit is provided by its application to konjak mannan from which there appears to be produced a trisaccharide composed of one unit of D-glucose and two of D-mannose (112).

The methods used in this instance lacked the precision necessary to establish the structure of the oligosaccharide, but by using the modern technique of chromatography, which enables structures to be ascertained on minute amounts of compounds, it is believed that the structure of these oligosaccharides could now be ascertained with relative ease.

Recent studies have shown that acetolysis of the Iles glucomannan extracted from *Amorphophallus oncophyllus*, gives a mixture of oligosaccharide acetates which can be separated, after deacetylation, on a cellulose column using the technique of displacement chromatography.

Of the oligosaccharides produced in this way three have been crystallized, namely, 4-O-β-D-glucopyranosyl-D-mannose, 4-O-β-D-mannopyranosyl-D-glucose, and cellobiose (114).

Separation of the acetolysis products directly can be effected on columns of calcium carbonate (177), silica gel (178), other inorganic materials (112) or derivatized cellulose (179).

Mercaptolysis, which is similar in action to acetolysis, has likewise been neglected in the study of gums, but the demonstration that the seaweed gum carrageenin contains 3,6-anhydro-D-galactose by the isolation of the crystalline diethyldithioacetal (275–277) when the gum was treated with ethanethiol and concentrated hydrochloric acid, shows the method merits more attention than it has enjoyed hitherto. A close study of this particular mercaptolysis has not yet been made, but the fact that 3,6-anhydrosugars are sensitive to acid—they are readily transformed into furfural bodies even with dilute mineral acids (115)—would appear to indicate that other identifiable dithioacetals are present in the reaction product besides the one already crystallized, namely, 3,6-anhydro-D-galactose diethylthioacetal. By an analogous series of experiments, the presence of 3,6-anhydro-L-galactose units in agar has been established (278) (see later).

Use of Enzymes

Although much information cencerning the structure of starch and glycogen has resulted from studies of the synthetic and degradative action of enzymes (87,88), very little by comparison has been accomplished in the study of gums by the use of enzymes.

It has been claimed (89) that certain gum exudates contain an enzyme that will effect autolysis under aseptic conditions and that the fungus *Asterula gummipara* Vuill., isolated from the trunks of acacia trees (*Acacia verek*), will completely liquefy cherry gum in three months (90, 91). This seems to be a significant observation and worthy of closer study, inasmuch as well defined steps in the degradation may be realized and thus provide oligosaccharides of constitutional importance.

This approach would be complementary to the work already discussed involving controlled acid degradation.

It seems that a highly-organized, complex system of enzymes must have been involved in the natural synthesis of the gum exudates which contain a diversity of building units and linkages that is rarely encountered in polysaccharides. This complexity is perhaps necessary in order that the plant may seal off its wounds with material immune to the degradative enzymes present in bacteria or fungi (see Chapter 1).

In the field of seaweed gums an enzyme extracted from *Turbo cornutus* has been purified and shown to degrade the mucilage of *Chondrus ocellatus* (92) and the enzyme laminarase, said to be present in malt (279), several seaweeds (189–192), extract of snails (*Helix pomatia, H. aspersa*) (127,193,280), sea-hare (*Tethys puntata*) (281), wheat flour, potato tubers, and hyacinth bulbs (194), has been shown to hydrolyze laminarin to laminaribiose, 3-*O*-(β-D-glucopyranosyl)-D-glucose (127). The unfractionated extracts of *Laminaria digitata, Rhodymenia palmata, Cladophora rupestris*, and *Ulva lactuca* have each been shown to contain a number of carbohydrases including α-D-glucosidase, β-D-glucosidase, amylase, β-D-(1 → 3)-glucanase, β-D-(1 → 4)-glucanase, D-xylanase and D-mannanase (197); when purified these enzymes may prove to be quite useful for structural studies of a wide variety of polysaccharides. The observation was recently made (93–95) that an enzyme preparation ("agarase") from a bacterium, *Pseudomonas kyotoensis* growing on rotting agar is capable of converting agar into a disaccharide, "neoagaribiose," 3-*O*-(3,6-anhydro-L-galactopyranosyl)-D-galactose. With the isolation of agarobiose, 4-*O*-(β-D-galactopyranosyl)-3,6-anhydro-L-galactose, produced by hydrolysis (96,97) and by methanolysis (98), the constitution of agar has been significantly advanced.

Application of an enzymic degradation to tamarind (*Tamarindus indica*) seed gum is said to produce a hexasaccharide composed of D-xylose (2 moles); D-galactose (1 mole), and D-glucose (3 moles) (99). It may well be that this oligosaccharide is an integral portion of the gum itself, but it is now recognized that great care must be exercised in ascertaining that the products of enzymic action are not artifacts produced by synthesis.

Most progress in the study of gums by means of enzymes has been made with the galactomannans. An enzymic breakdown of locust bean or carob gum (*Ceratonia siliqua L.*) was first observed in 1897 when it was shown (100) that an enzyme "carubinase," present in the germ of the locust bean seed, was able to hydrolyze the gum giving "carubinose" (D-mannose) (101). The presence of an enzyme explains why aqueous solutions of locust bean gum and of guar gum become much less viscous when kept at room temperature, and shows that if full use is to be made of the gummy property of these polymers they should be used immediately. Alternatively, the enzyme should be inactivated either by heating the gum before dissolution or heating the aqueous gum solution, preferably the former.

The loss in the viscosity of aqueous solutions of the gums is not accompanied by the development of any marked reducing properties (102). This is perhaps not too surprising for a polymer of high molecular weight, because the cleavage of only one glycosidic bond in the "center" of the molecular chain would reduce the molecular weight by half, yet, at the same time, the generation of only a single reducing group would hardly be detectable by chemical methods.

An enzyme system elaborated by germinating seeds of fenugreek and lucerne has long been known to hydrolyze the corresponding galactomannans in these, giving D-galactose and D-mannose (267). Of particular interest is the observation (101) that the same enzyme system hydrolyzed *Cassia* galactomannan in the same way.

Enzymes capable of hydrolyzing locust bean gum are also present in certain crude preparations from molds, but the nature of the products formed does not appear to have been investigated.

When locust bean gum has been partially degraded by a mold enzyme (Helisol) in aqueous solution, (102) fractionation of the degraded gums affords products in which the D-mannose : D-galactose ratio varies. The less soluble component precipitated with 60 per cent alcohol contained more D-galactose than the more soluble component, precipitated with 95% alcohol. This might be due to the fact that the D-galactose side chains are not attached at regular intervals along the polymannose chain or, more likely, that it is caused by the action of two enzymes, a β-D-mannosidase and an α-D-galactosidase, present in the crude preparation of Helisol. The β-D-mannosidase which cleaves the D-mannose chain may act only after the D-galactose side chains have been removed. That two enzymes were indeed present was shown by the fact that, after treatment of the crude enzyme preparation with alkali, it lost its ability to cleave the chains of D-mannose units but retained its capacity to cleave the D-galactose side chains (see Table 36).

TABLE 36. EFFECT OF ALKALI ON THE ACTIVITY OF AN ENZYME
PREPARATION FOUND IN "HELISOL" (102)

(Enzyme treated with alkali at $20°$ for 2.5 hours. Enzymic hydrolysis carried out for 20 hours on locust bean gum (183 mg.) in 100 ml. aq. solution pH 5.2 at $48°$ with 25 mg. of the enzyme)

Normality of NaOH	0	0.010	0.019	0.036	0.057	0.066	0.100
Liberation of D-galactose	+	+	+	+	+	+	−
Liberation of D-mannose	+	+	+	−	−	−	−

It would appear that a more detailed examination of the reaction products of this enzymic degradation would produce valuable information concerning the constitution of locust bean gum.

Enzyme studies have proved to be highly effective in investigating the structure of the galactomannan, guar gum ("guaran"). Germinated guar seeds contain an enzyme which hydrolyzes the guar gum to give three oligosaccharides: β-D-Manp-$(1 \rightarrow 4)$-D-Manp (103), α-D-Galp-$(1 \rightarrow 6)$-D-Manp (85), and β-D-Manp-$(1 \rightarrow 4)$-β-D-Manp-$(1 \rightarrow 4)$-D-Manp (104), which are of pronounced structural significance. It would be interesting to ascertain whether the enzyme system present in germinated guar beans has any action on the gums derived from the seeds of the related leguminous plants. By this means, perhaps, structural similarities of the galactomannan gums would be detectable (cf 101).

Considerable success has been achieved in the study of xylan-like polymers through the controlled use of a cellulase preparation from *Myrothecium verrucaria* (105) which brings about the formation of a homologous series of xylose oligosaccharides (109). Enzyme preparations from *Aspergillus foetidus* have been shown to transform xylan primarily into xylobiose (106, cf 107,108) and pectic acid into di- and tri-D-galacturonic acids (262). That the judicious use of these enzymes, after purification, will probably throw considerable light on the structure of polymers composed of $1 \rightarrow 4$ linked β-D-xylose units, is illustrated by the observation that treatment of wheat straw xylan with the *M. verrucaria* cellulase, furnishes a trisaccharide, O-L-arabofuranosyl-$(1 \rightarrow 3)$-O-D-xylopyranosyl-$(1 \rightarrow 4)$-D-xylose (110). From this it may be deduced that this xylan contains certain molecules that are terminated by a nonreducing arabofuranose residue.

The effect of an enzyme dextranase on dextran has been shown (129) to give rise to a high yield of 6-O-α-D-glucopyranosyl-D-glucose thus supporting the view (124,130) that this gum, synthesized by microorganisms, contains a large proportion of α-D-$(1 \rightarrow 6)$ linkages.

Promising results have been obtained in some preliminary studies of the enzyme systems in marine algae (197,198) and molluscs (199) which may prove to be valuable in structural studies on seaweed polysaccharides and other carbohydrate polymers.

It is interesting to speculate on the fact that little success appears to have been obtained in cleaving plant gum polyglycosiduronic acids in spite of the fact that β-D-glucuronidase is available from a number of plant and animal sources and is obtainable commercially.

The isolation by chemical and enzymatic means and proof of structure of neutral as well as the acidic oligosaccharides discussed previously provides a valuable approach to the study of polysaccharide gums and mucilages; it is also apparent that the methods now available are capable of wider application (cf 312).

A number of neutral oligosaccharides obtained from gums and mucilages is listed in Table 37.

TABLE 37. NEUTRAL OLIGOSACCHARIDES FROM GUMS AND MUCILAGES

Oligosaccharide	Source	Reference
β-L-Arap-(1 $\rightarrow$ 3)-L-Ara	Acacia karroo gum	70
	Cherry (Prunus cerasus) gum	78
	Golden-apple (Spondias cytheria) gum	79
	Peach (Prunus persica) gum	78
	Western Larch (Larix occidentalis)	75
α-L-Arap-(1 $\rightarrow$ 5)-L-Ara	Virgilia oroboides gum	315
α-D-Xylp-(1 $\rightarrow$ 3)-L-Ara	Corn (Zea mays) "fiber" or hulls	82,83
β-D-Xylp-(1 $\rightarrow$ 5)-L-Ara	Peach (Prunus persica) gum	78
	Cholla (Opuntia fulgida) gum	78
β-D-Xylp-(1 $\rightarrow$ 4)-D-Xyl	Corn (Zea mays) "fiber" or hulls	84
β-D-Xylp-(1 $\rightarrow$ 4)-(D-Xylp)$_{0 \text{ to } 4}$-(1 $\rightarrow$ 4)-D-Xylp	Corn (Zea mays) "fiber" or hulls	84
D-Galp-(1 $\rightarrow$ 5)-L-Ara	Corn (Zea mays) "fiber" or hulls	84
D-Galp-(1 $\rightarrow$ 3)-L-Ara	Gum arabic (Acacia verek)	5
D-Galp-(1 $\rightarrow$ 4)-D-Xylp	Corn (Zea mays) "fiber" or hulls	83
L-Galp-(1 $\rightarrow$ 4)-D-Xylp-(1 $\rightarrow$ 2)-L-Ara	Corn (Zea mays) "fiber" or hulls	82
β-D-Galp-(1 $\rightarrow$ 4)-(3,6-Anhydro-D-Galp)	K-Carrageenin (Chondrus crispus)	276
D-Galp-(1 $\rightarrow$ 3)-D-Galp	Gum arabic (Acacia verek)	75
β-D-Galp-(1 $\rightarrow$ 3)-D-Galp	Golden-apple (Spondias cytheria) gum	302
α-D-Galp-(1 $\rightarrow$ 4)-D-Galp	Okra (Hibiscus esculentus)	125
β-D-Galp-(1 $\rightarrow$ 6)-D-Galp	Golden-apple (Spondias cytheria) gum	302
α-D-Galp-(1 $\rightarrow$ 6)-β-D-Manp	Guar (Cyamopsis tetragonolobus) gum	85
α-D-Galp-(1 $\rightarrow$ 6)-β-D-Manp-(1 $\rightarrow$ 4)-β-D-Manp	Guar (Cyamopsis tetragonolobus) gum	86
α-D-Gp-(1 $\rightarrow$ 3)-D-Gp	Nigeran (Aspergillus niger)	128
β-D-Gp-(1 $\rightarrow$ 3)-D-Gp	Laminarin (Laminaria sp.)	127,188
β-D-Gp-(1 $\rightarrow$ 4)-D-Gp	Iles Mannan (Amorphophallus oncophyllus)	114
α-D-Gp-(1 $\rightarrow$ 6)-D-Gp	Dextran (synthesized by Leuconostoc mesenteroides)	129
β-D-Gp-(1 $\rightarrow$ 6)-D-Gp	Pustulan (Umbilicaria pustulata)	282
β-D-Gp-(1 $\rightarrow$ 4)-D-Gp	Islandican (lichenin) (Cetraria islandica)	231,232

TABLE 37. (CONTINUED)

Oligosaccharide	Source	Reference
β-D-Gp-(1 ⟶ 6)-β-D-Gp-(1 ⟶ 6)-D-Gp	Pustulan (*U. pustulata*)	282
β-D-Gp-(1 ⟶ 6)-(β-D-Gp)$_2$-(1 ⟶ 6)-D-Gp	Pustulan (*U. pustulata*)	282
D-Gp 1 ⟶ D-Manp	Konjak mannan (*Amorphophallus konjak*)	112
D-Gp-(1 ⟶ 4)-D-Manp	Iles mannan (*Amorphophallus oncophyllus*)	114
D-Gp 1 ⟶ D-Man 1 ⟶ D-Man	Konjak mannan (*Amorphophallus konjak*)	112
D-Man p-(1 ⟶ 4) D-Gp	Iles mannan (*Amorphophallus oncophyllus*)	114
β-D-Manp-(1 ⟶ 4)-β-D-Manp	Guar (*Cyamopsis tetragonolobus*) gum	85
D-Man 1 ⟶ D-Man	Konjak mannan (*Amorphophallus Konjak*)	112
β-D-Manp-(1 ⟶ 4)-β-D-Manp-(1 ⟶ 4)-β-D-Manp	Guar (*Cyamopsis tetragonolobus*) gum	104
β-D-Gp-(1 ⟶ 1)-D-Mannitol	Laminarin (*Laminaria Sp.*)	196,228–230, 273
β-D-Gp-(1 ⟶ 3)-β-D-Gp-(1 ⟶ 1)-D-Mannitol	Laminarin (*Laminaria* Sp.)	274

Investigations of Degraded Gums and Mucilages

The deductions made from the above studies on the isolation of the component sugars and simple neutral and acidic oligosaccharides are that the gums and mucilages are highly complex polymers usually composed of different monosaccharide residues which are joined together by a variety of glycosidic bonds. Consequently, attempts have been made to treat the gums and mucilages, usually under mild acid conditions, in order to bring about partial hydrolysis with the formation of a degraded molecule which is still complex but much less so than the original gum and hence more amenable to study in detail.

The observation mentioned above, that gums containing labile residues undergo facile hydrolysis when their acidified aqueous solutions are heated, has been employed in certain instances to provide a degraded molecule having a relatively simple structure. This approach cannot be utilized in the case of gums composed of pyranose sugar residues. The so-called degraded gums or mucilages may then be subjected to methylation studies which furnish enough information for the main structural features to be deduced. However, unless partially methylated oligosaccharides are obtainable, and this is seldom the case except with acid gums which provide aldobiouronic acid fragments, it is not possible, unless special precautions are taken to control the hydrolysis of the methylated degraded gum, to deduce the sequential arrangement of the building units.

The approach to the study of gums making use of the partially hydrolyzed polysaccharide may be illustrated by taking the example of gum arabic. When the latter is heated at 95 to 100° with 0.01N sulfuric acid, a well defined degradation occurs. Essentially the same reaction, referred to as autohydrolysis (5), takes place when the free gum acid, arabic acid, is heated in aqueous solution. The acid-labile sugar residues L-arabinose, L-rhamnose and 3-O-D-galactopyranosyl-L-arabinose are removed, leaving a stable residual polymer that has been designated as degraded arabic acid (5). The general nature of this reaction may be seen from the fact that damson gum (6), egg plum gum (17,18), mesquite gum (133), and gums from other species of *Acacia* (16,70,71) have also been shown to undergo hydrolysis with relative ease when their aqueous solutions are heated with dilute acid, thus indicating a structural similarity that has been traced to the presence in all of these gums of acid labile L-arabofuranose residues (134,272).

Other gums and mucilages behave in an analogous manner as may be recognized by the fact that their aqueous solutions readily lose their viscous character when heated, but the reaction is not as well defined as it is with gum arabic and the other gums referred to above. In the case of gum tragacanth, the reaction is still further complicated because this gum is a mixture of at least two if not more polysaccharides.

Knowledge of the structure of gums from methylation studies on their degraded derivatives may be illustrated by reference to gum arabic, damson gum and mesquite gum. The products formed when the methyl ethers of these substances are hydrolyzed are recorded in Table 38.

Inspection of the results in Table 38 reveals what sugars are present in the degraded gums, and supports results previously derived from a study of the hydrolysis products of the unmethylated degraded gums. The results from Table 38 also show the position of each building unit involved in the construction of the degraded gum molecules and indicate those residues located in terminal positions, at the branch points, and those which constitute nonterminal, nonbranching units.

The production of 2,3,4,6-tetra-O-methyl-D-galactose from the methyl derivative of degraded gum arabic and degraded damson gum shows that D-galactose units of the pyranose type form the terminal nonreducing residues of the degraded gums. The absence of 2,3,4,6-tetra-O-methyl-D-galactose from the components of the hydrolyzate of methylated degraded

TABLE 38. HYDROLYSIS PRODUCTS OF METHYLATED DEGRADED GUMS

Components	Position involved in linkage
Degraded Arabic Acid (55)	
2,3,4,6-tetra-O-methyl-D-galactose	1
2,3,4-tri-O-methyl-D-galactose	1,6
2,4-di-O-methyl-D-galactose	1,3,6
2,3,4-tri-O-methyl-D-glucuronic acid	1
Degraded Damson Gum (19)	
2,3,4,6-tetra-O-methyl-D-galactose	1
2,4,6-tri-O-methyl-D-galactose	1,3
2,3,4-tri-O-methyl-D-galactose	1,6
2,4-di-O-methyl-D-galactose	1,3,6
2,3,4-tri-O-methyl-D-glucuronic acid	1
2,3-di-O-methyl-D-glucuronic acid	1,4
2,3,4-tri-O-methyl-D-xylose	1
Degraded Mesquite Gum (133)	
2,3,4-tri-O-methyl-D-galactose	1,6
2,4,6-tri-O-methyl-D-galactose	1,3
2,4-di-O-methyl-D-galactose	1,3,6
2,3,4-tri-O-methyl-D-glucuronic acid	1

mesquite gum proves that D-galactose units do not occupy terminal non-reducing positions in this degraded gum.   The formation of 2,3,4-tri-O-methyl-D-glucuronic acid from the three methylated degraded gums means that all of them contain terminal nonreducing pyranose units of D-glucuronic acid.   It is also apparent from the identification of 2,3,4-tri-O-methyl-D-xylose as one of the products from the methylated degraded damson gum that the latter also contains terminal nonreducing residues of D-xylopyranose.

The tri-O-methyl hexose sugars, such as 2,3,4-tri-O-methyl-D-galactose, which is obtained from all three methylated degraded gums, arise from doubly linked residues and this is also true for the 2,3-di-O-methyl-D-glucuronic acid obtained from the methylated degraded damson gum. All these derivatives are derived from the nonterminal, nonbranching units.

Such di-O-methyl derivatives as 2,4-di-O-methyl-D-galactose, arise from D-galactose units which occupy branching positions in the molecular complex and it is seen that this structural feature is common to all three degraded gums.

The identification of 2,3,4-tri- and 2,4,6-tri-O-methyl-D-galactose in the case of the methyl derivatives of degraded damson gum and degraded mesquite gum, proves that $1 \rightarrow 6$- and $1 \rightarrow 3$- linked D-galactose units are present in the chains, whereas in the case of degraded arabic acid only $1 \rightarrow 6$ linked D-galactose units are present in the linear portions of the molecule.

To indicate the value of determining the molecular ratio of the various components it may be seen that in the case of the methylated degraded arabic acid, the amount of 2,4-di-O-methyl-D-galactose is the same as the amount of 2,3,4-tri-O-methyl-D-glucuronic acid. This shows that for every branch point in the molecule there is a corresponding terminal residue, a result to be expected from highly branched molecules. Where there is little branched chain character in a molecule it is to be noted that there will be one more terminal nonreducing group than branch points.

Comparison of the results in Table 38 also reveals that the degraded gums from arabic and mesquite gum are simple in comparison with the degraded damson gum; this is deducible from the relatively large number, seven, of different methylated sugars obtained from the methylated degraded damson gum as compared with the four obtained from methylated degraded gum arabic and from methylated degraded mesquite gum.

It is also clear that little decomposition takes place during the methylation of the degraded gums, since their equivalent weights, correspond to those of the unmethylated degraded gums when corrected for methoxyl content.

Further evidence of structural value can sometimes be obtained by studying the products formed by stepwise degradation of the methylated degraded gums. For instance, methylated degraded arabic acid has been shown to give rise to 6-O-(2,3,4-tri-O-methyl-β-D-glucosyluronic acid)-2,3,4-tri-O-methyl-D-galactose (56). When this observation is considered in conjunction with the molecular ratios of the cleavage fragments from the methylated degraded arabic acid (see Table 38), it may be deduced that three aldobiouronic acid residues, 6-O-(β-D-glucopyranosyluronic acid)-D-galactopyranose, probably constitute the branches in the degraded gum molecule (56). Such an observation, therefore, limits the number of possible formulas that may be assigned to degraded arabic acid and in turn this limits the number of formulas for the gum itself (134).

Observations of a similar kind have been made during investigations into corn hull gum. Thus hydrolysis of the methylated gum provided the D-glucuronic acid component of the gum as 2-O-(2,3,4-tri-O-methyl-D-glucosyluronic acid)-3-O-methyl-D-xylose (135). Since the 2,3,4-tri-O-methyl-D-glucuronic acid can only arise from a terminal nonreducing unit and the 3-O-methyl-D-xylose from a xylose unit linked through C_1, C_2

and C_4, which must be a branch point in the molecule, it can be concluded that in this particular gum the uronic acid units constitute the
side chains (135). The same observation was made during the hydrolysis of the methylated hemicellulose of flax straw when 2-O-(2,3,4-tri-O-
methyl-D-glucosyluronic acid)-3-O-methyl-D-xylose was also obtained
(136).

What are now required are a number of oligosaccharides containing
more sugar residues than those hitherto obtained. Constitutional studies
on tri-, tetra- and higher oligosaccharides, with and without uronic acid
units, derived from the degraded and undegraded gums and other methyl
derivatives, would prove of great value in ascertaining more exactly the
structure of these highly branched types of plant gums containing uronic
acid residues (cf 272).

Methylation Studies on Gums and Mucilages Containing Acid-labile Residues

Another approach adopted in the study of the constitution of gums and
mucilages is to apply methylation studies to the undegraded polysaccharides themselves. Generally the methylation proceeds normally with
methyl sulfate and alkali although in certain instances it may be necessary to apply alternative methods of methylation (for details and references
see 137). One method that has proved effective is the use of thallium
hydroxide and methyl iodide (138). Methylation of the acetate of a polysaccharide in tetrahydrofuran with methyl sulfate and solid sodium hydroxide has also been shown to be effective (139, cf 309). Sometimes it
may be necessary to dialyze the reaction mixture after the first methylation
in order to recover the partially methylated gum but, as a general rule,
methylated gums containing uronic acid units are most readily separated
by acidification of the methylation reaction mixture since this causes
precipitation of the methylated polysaccharide acid.

Methylation studies have been applied to some thirty or forty gums
and mucilages with considerable success (see Table 42). As in the
case of methylation studies applied to the degraded gums, the results
obtained will show the composition of the gum, the nature of the building
units, how they are joined together, and the number of residues in the
average repeating unit. The findings also enable the terminal units and
the units at which branching occurs to be designated. However, by
themselves, methylation studies on the polysaccharides provide little
knowledge concerning the exact sequence of the building units unless
the number of structural possibilities is limited by the fact that the
structure of the polysaccharides is relatively simple, being built up of

only one or two types of sugar units. Methylation results are more valuable from a constitutional standpoint if considered in the light of the structure of oligosaccharides that have been prepared from the gum by controlled degradation as described previously (for an example of this see ref. 114). Methylation results sometimes become more diagnostic when considered in conjunction with periodate oxidation studies as well as controlled degradation. For example, the polysaccharide nigeran, extracted from *Aspergillus niger*, has been shown (128) by methylation studies to be composed of D-glucose units joined by 1 → 3- and 1 →4- glycosidic bonds since 2,3,6-tri- and 2,4,6-tri-O-methyl-D-glucose are produced when the methylated polysaccharide is hydrolyzed.   The presence of the 1 → 3 linkage in the polysaccharide was also established by graded hydrolysis which gave 3-O-α-D-glucopyranosyl-D-glucose (nigerose). It was still not possible to deduce the sequential order of the 1 → 3- and 1 → 4-linked units, but oxidation with periodate, treatment of the resulting polyaldehyde with phenylhydrazine, and the isolation therefrom of glucose phenylosazone and not an oligosaccharide osazone, showed that the D-glucose units in the polysaccharide were alternatively linked by 1 → 3 and 1 → 4 glycosidic bonds (128) (see page 214).

Even in the absence of the more recent applications of periodate oxidation, such as that mentioned above, certain significant structural features become apparent if results are available from methylation studies on the degraded and undegraded gums despite the complexity of the polysaccharide. This may be illustrated by reference to mesquite gum. Methylation of degraded mesquitic acid, followed by acid hydrolysis yielded 2,3,4-tri-O-methyl-D-glucuronic acid, 2,3,4-tri-O-methyl-D-galactose, 2,4,6-tri-O-methyl-D-galactose and 2,4-di-O-methyl-D-galactose (see Table 39).

TABLE 39. HYDROLYSIS PRODUCTS OF METHYLATED MESQUITIC ACID
AND METHYLATED DEGRADED MESQUITIC ACID

Mesquitic Acid (140,141)	Degraded Mesquitic Acid (283)
2,3,5-tri-O-methyl-L-arabinose	2,3,4-tri-O-methyl-D-glucuronic acid
3,5-di-O-methyl-L-arabinose	2,3,4-tri-O-methyl-D-galactose
2,3,4-tri-O-methyl-D-glucuronic acid	2,4,6-tri-O-methyl-D-galactose
2,4-di-O-methyl-D-galactose	2,4-di-O-methyl-D-galactose

Inspection of the results in Table 39 will show that in the case of the methylated undegraded gum, in which the arabofuranose units are present, the D-galactose component appears only as the 2,4-di-O-methyl derivative. No tri-O-methyl-D-galactose was produced. It is clear, therefore, that the L-arabinose units are attached to those D-galactose units of the degraded gum which give rise upon methylation and cleavage to the 2,3,4-tri-*O*- and the 2,4,6-tri-*O*-methyl derivatives.

Similar deductions can be made from a comparison of the results of methylation studies on degraded arabic acid (see Table 38) and the undegraded gum (see Table 40).

TABLE 40. HYDROLYSIS PRODUCTS OF METHYLATED ARABIC ACID (134)

Sugar	*O*-Methyl Derivative
L-Arabinose	2,3,5-tri-, 2,5-di-
D-Galactose	2,3,4,6-tetra-, 2,4-di-
L-Rhamnose	2,3,4-tri-
D-Glucuronic acid	2,3,4-tri-, 2,3-di-

It is to be seen that the methylated undegraded arabic acid, with its acid labile residues of L-arabofuranose, L-rhamnopyranose, and 3-*O*-(α-D-galactopyranosyl)-L-arabofuranose still intact, gives no 2,3,4-tri-*O*-methyl-D-galactose, whereas the methylated degraded gum does (see Table 38). The positions of the labile sugar residues have therefore been located on those D-galactose units of the degraded gum which give rise to the 2,3,4-tri-*O*-methyl derivative.   Since the undegraded gum also furnishes 2,3-di-*O*-methyl-D-glucuronic acid, whereas the degraded gum does not, it has been deduced (134) that a certain number of the labile sugar units are attached to C_4 of these particular D-glucuronic acid residues of the undegraded gum.

Damson gum and its degraded derivative have also been subjected to the classical methylation study.   Examination of the nature of the products formed from the methyl derivative of the undegraded and the degraded gum (see Table 41) shows that similar structural deductions to those above can be made.

TABLE 41. HYDROLYSIS PRODUCTS OF METHYLATED DERIVATIVES
OF DEGRADED AND UNDEGRADED DAMSON GUM

Sugar	Degraded Damson Gum (19) *O*-methyl derivative	Damson Gum (140) *O*-methyl derivative
L-Arabinose	...	2,3,5-tri-, 2,3-di-,
D-Xylose	...	2,3,4-tri
D-Galactose	2,3,4,6-tetra-, 2,4,6-tri-, 2,3,4-tri-, 2,4-di-	2,4,6-tri-, 2,4-di-, 2,4-
D-Glucuronic acid	2,3-di-, 2,3,4-tri-	2,3,4-tri-, 2,3-di-

The 2,3,4,6-tetra- and the 2,3,4-tri-*O*-methyl derivatives of D-galactose obtained from the degraded gum are not isolated from the undegraded gum. Hence the acid labile L-arabinose units, removed from the gum when it is converted by mild hydrolysis into the degraded form, are attached to the galactose units of the degraded gum which yield upon methylation and hydrolysis the 2,3,4,6-tetra- and 2,3,4-tri-O-methyl derivatives. The fact that two mono-O-methyl derivatives of D-galactose are formed from the methylated undegraded gum and not from the methylated degraded gum clearly shows that in the original gum these particular galactose units are involved in union with L-arabofuranose units. Further insight into the disposition of the L-arabofuranose units follows from the fact that twice as much 2,3,5-tri- as 2,3-di-O-methyl-L-arabinose is derived from the methylated undegraded damson gum. This means that in the average repeating unit of the gum there are two types of labile side chain groups present in equal amounts, one consisting of single L-arabofuranose units and the other of an arabinose disaccharide joined by a 1 → 5 biose linkage (140).

Such studies as those discussed above involving methylation of the gums and their degraded derivatives require a considerable amount of time and a fair knowledge of the manipulative art of carbohydrate chemistry, but these studies provide a greater insight into the constitution of the gums than is possible from a methylation study of the gum alone. Despite their complex structures a considerable number of gums have been investigated by the methylation technique and as a result, the general structural features at least have been established (see Table 42). Inspection of these results shows that the gums are highly complex polymers composed of different sugars that are joined together by a variety of glycosidic bonds. Undoubtedly these two features, which lead to a highly branched structure whose individual parts cannot become aligned to produce extensive hydrogen bonding, are mainly responsible for the adhesive, gum-like character of the so-called natural plant gum exudates.

Methylation Studies on Gums and Mucilages That Do Not Contain Acid-Labile Residues

Gums and Mucilages Containing D-Galacturonic Acid.* Many gums and mucilages do not contain such acid-labile sugar residues as L-arabofuranose and hence the stepwise degradation that is applicable to gum

---

(*)The division of the subject matter in this section has been adopted for the sake of simplicity. The fact that the acid-labile gums also contain D-glucuronic acid is interesting, but coincidental, and attention is directed to the fact that sapote gum, which contains D-glucuronic acid, contains L-arabinose units of the pyranose type (283); moreover it appears that *Khaya grandifolia* gum contains both D-galacturonic and D-galacturonic and D-glucuronic acid (52).

TABLE 42. THE MONOSACCHARIDE BUILDING UNITS OF GUMS AND MUCILAGES FROM METHYLATION STUDIES

Source	Building Units[a]	Reference
Agar	D-Galp 1→4 3,6-Anhydro-L-Galp 1→4 3,6-Anhydro-L-Galactonic acid 1→3 L-Galp (SO₃H—6, 3)	97,211–215, 224,245, 246
Algal glucan (lichenin) (*Cetraria islandica*) Iceland moss	D-Gp 1→4 D-Gp 1→3 D-Gp 1 / D-Gp 1 (1 mole) (2 moles) (0.6%)	226,227
Algal Gulo-mannuran (Alginic Acid)	D-ManpA 4→1 L-GulpA 1	201, cf 314
Algal Xylan	D-Xylp 1→4 D-Xylp 1→3 D-Xylp 1 D-Xylp 1→4 D-Xylp 1→3 D-Xylp 1	253,254, cf 313

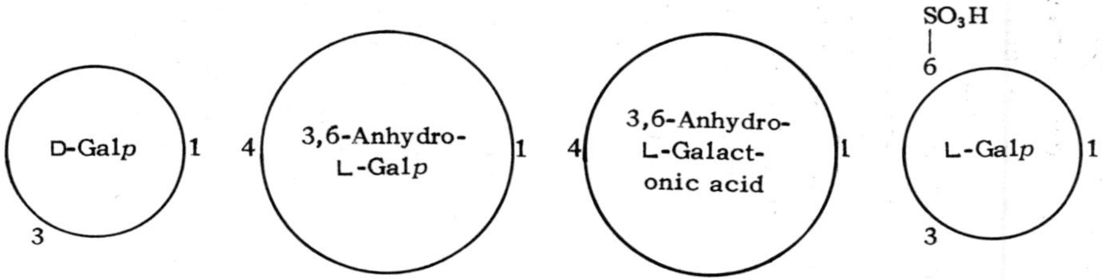

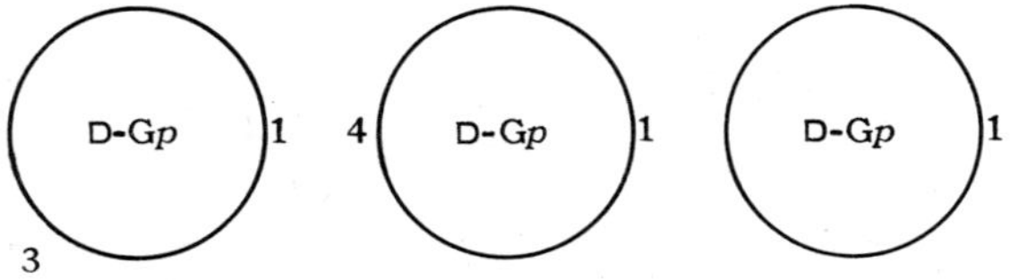

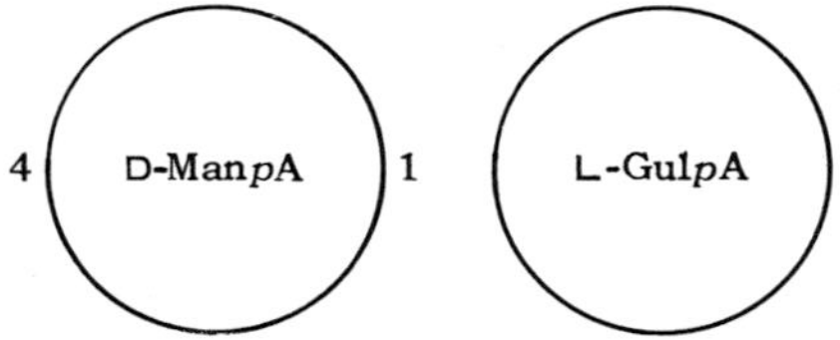

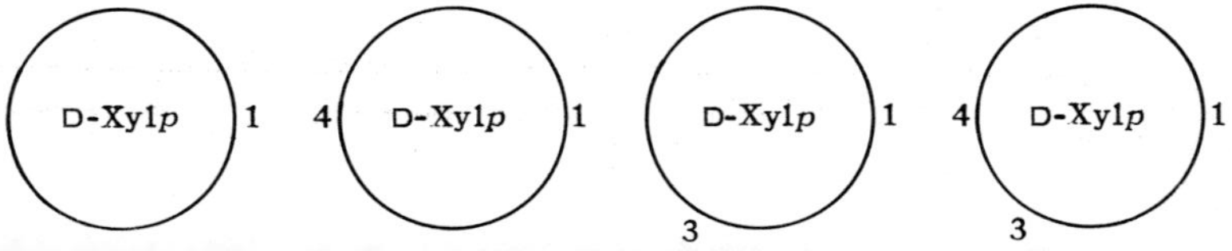

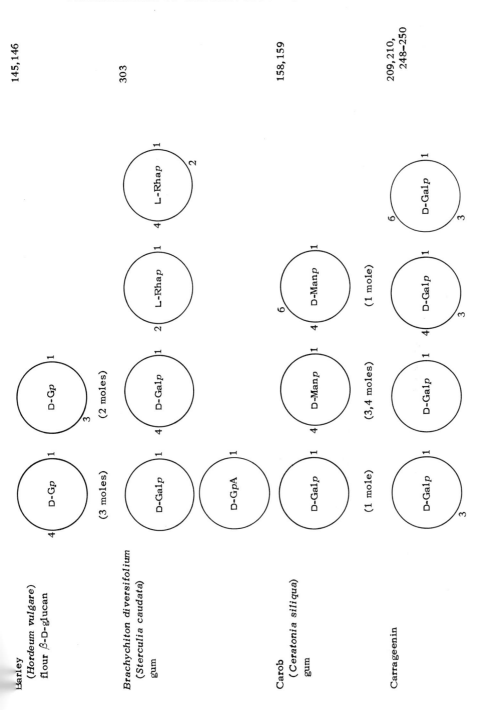

TABLE 42. (CONTINUED)

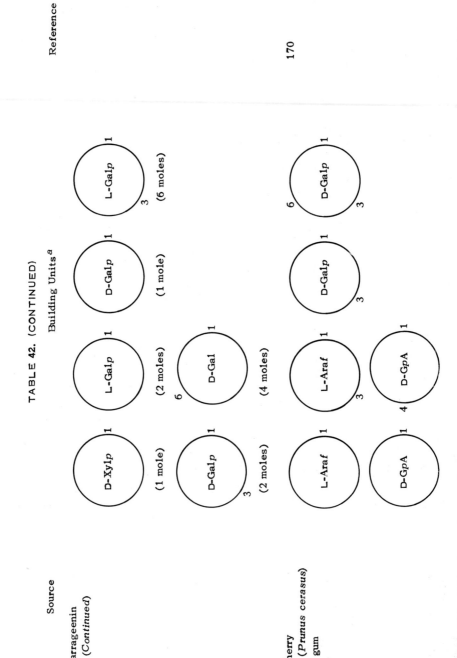

Source	Building Units[a]			Reference

Carrageenin (Continued)

D-Xylp 1 — (1 mole)
L-Galp 1 — (2 moles)
D-Galp 1 — (1 mole)
L-Galp 1 3 — (6 moles)

D-Galp 1 3 — (2 moles)
6 D-Gal 1 — (4 moles)

Cherry (Prunus cerasus) gum

L-Araf 1
L-Araf 1 3
D-Galp 1 3
6 D-Galp 1 3

D-GpA 1
D-GpA 1 4

170

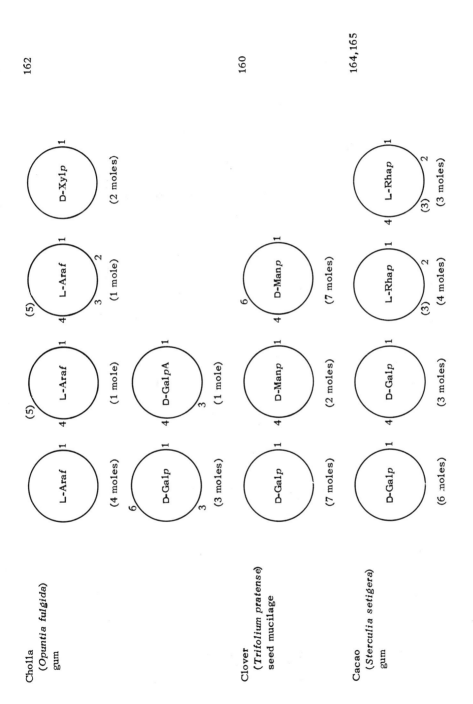

TABLE 42. (CONTINUED)

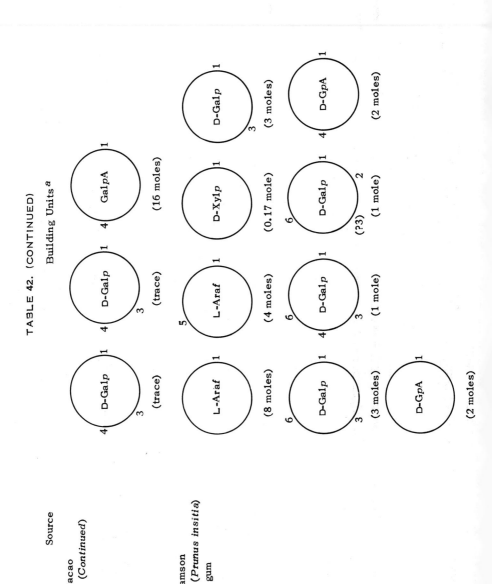

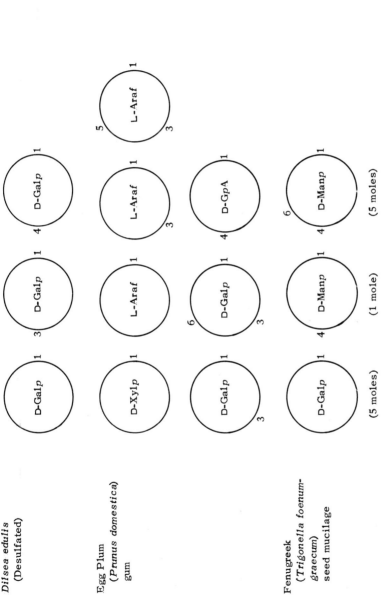

247

Dilsea edulis
(Desulfated)

D-Gal*p* 1 — 3 D-Gal*p* 1 — 4 D-Gal*p* 1

171

Egg Plum
(*Prunus domestica*)
gum

D-Xyl*p* 1 — L-Araf 1 — 3 L-Araf 1 — 3 L-Araf 1
                                         5 — L-Araf 1
                                                3

D-Gal*p* 1 — 3 D-Gal*p* 1 — 4 D-GpA 1
          6

161

Fenugreek
(*Trigonella foenum-
graecum*)
seed mucilage

D-Gal*p* 1 — 4 D-Man*p* 1 — 4 D-Man*p* 1

(5 moles) (1 mole) (5 moles)

TABLE 42. (CONTINUED)

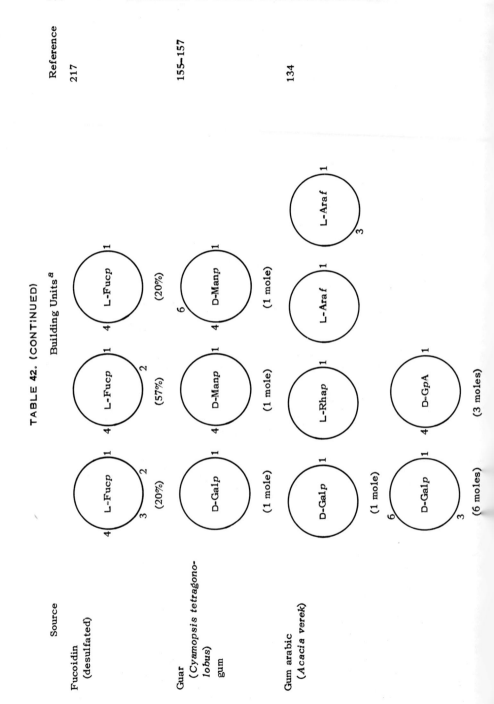

Source	Building Units[a]			Reference
Fucoidin (desulfated)				217
Guar (Cyamopsis tetragono-lobus) gum				155–157
Gum arabic (Acacia verek)				134

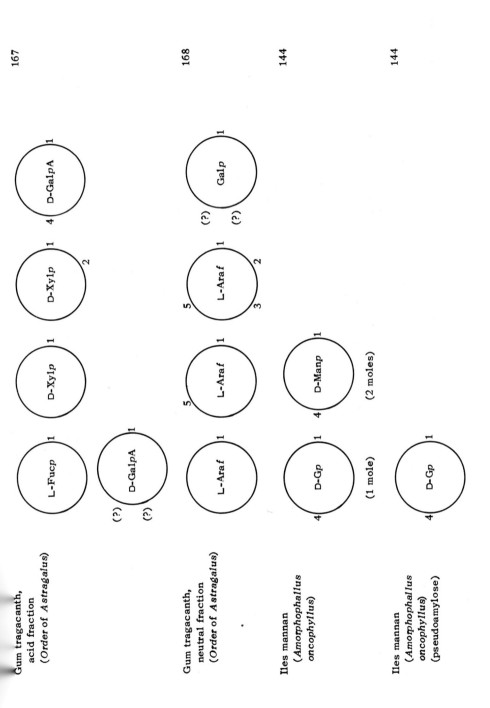

TABLE 42. (CONTINUED)

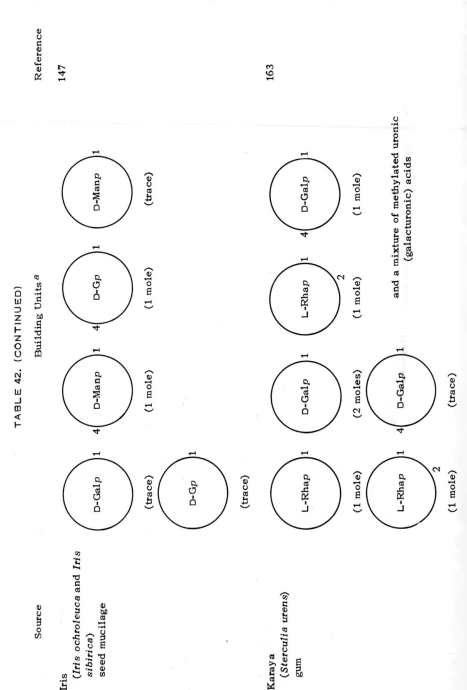

| Source | Building Units[a] | Reference |

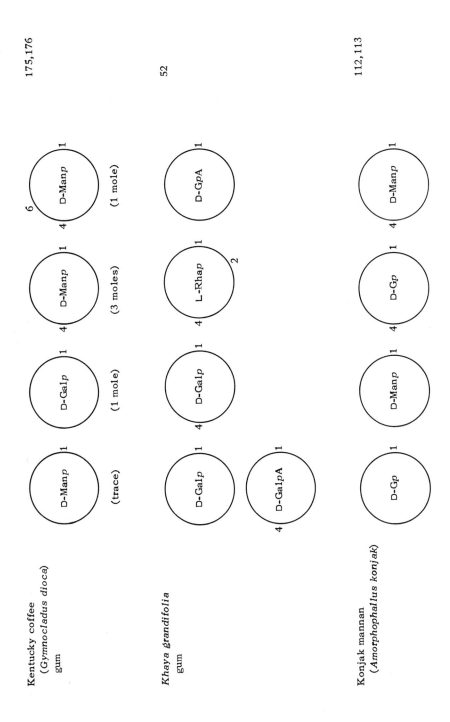

TABLE 42. (CONTINUED)

Source	Building Units[a]			Reference

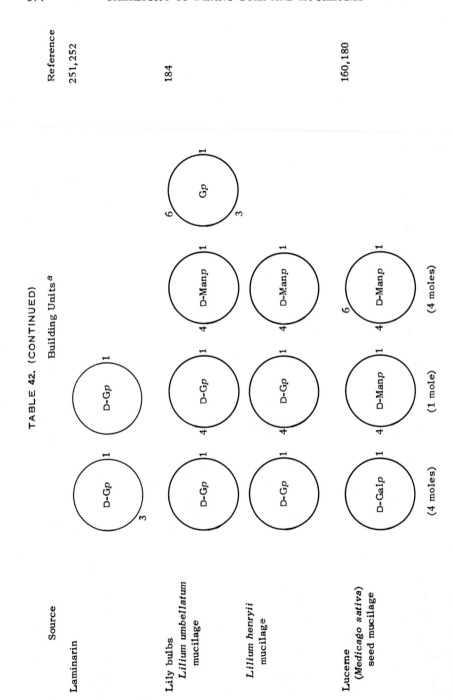

Laminarin — 251,252

Lily bulbs
Lilium umbellatum
mucilage — 184

Lilium henryii
mucilage

Lucerne
(*Medicago sativa*)
seed mucilage — 160,180

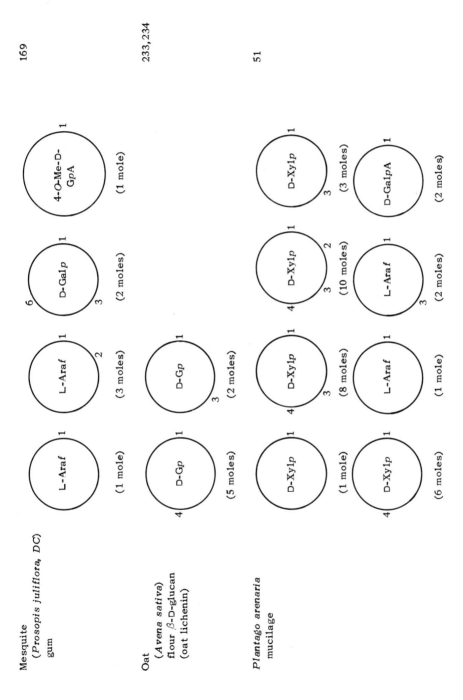

TABLE 42. (CONTINUED)

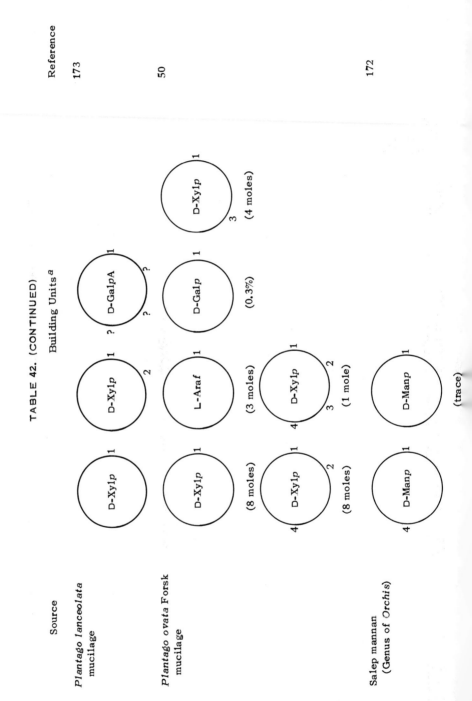

142,143

148,166

Sapote
(*Sapota achras*)
gum

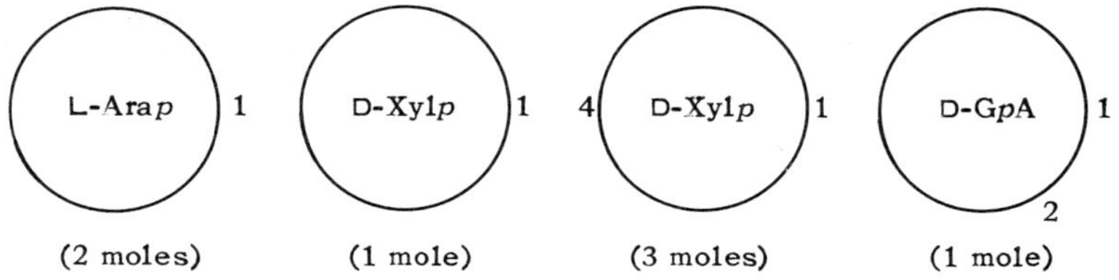

Slippery elm
(*Ulmus fulva*)
mucilage

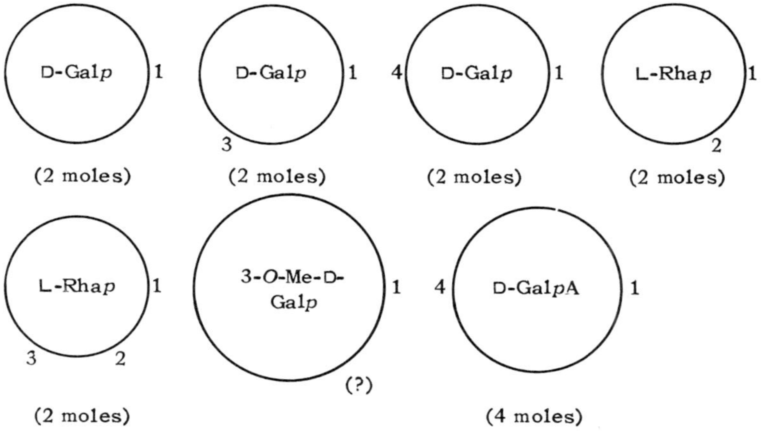

L-Ara*p* 1

(2 moles)

D-Xyl*p* 1 / 4

(1 mole)

D-Xyl*p* 1 / 4

(3 moles)

D-GpA 1 / 2

(1 mole)

D-Gal*p* 1

(2 moles)

D-Gal*p* 1 / 3

(2 moles)

D-Gal*p* 1 / 4

(2 moles)

L-Rha*p* 1 / 2

(2 moles)

L-Rha*p* 1 / 2,3

(2 moles)

3-O-Me-D-Gal*p* 1 / 4

(?)

D-Gal*p*A 1

(4 moles)

TABLE 42. (CONTINUED)

Source	Building Units[a]	Reference
Tamarind (*Tamarindus indica* Linn.) gum	(1 mole) (1 mole) (1 mole) (1 mole) (2 moles)	174

(a) Building units are designated by circles surrounding an appropriate symbol for each sugar. Thus:

L-Ara*f* = L-arabofuranose
L-Ara*p* = L-arabopyranose
L-Fuc*p* = L-fucopyranose
D-G*p* = D-glucopyranose
D-Gal*p* = D-galactopyranose
L-Rha*p* = L-rhamnopyranose
D-Xyl*p* = D-xylopyranose
D-G*p*A = D-glucopyranuronic acid
D-Gal*p*A = D-galactopyranuronic acid
D-Man*p*A = D-mannopyranuronic acid

The numbers on the circumference of the circles indicate the positions of the residues that are involved in linkage. The numbers are located on the circles to approximate the numbering of the carbon atoms in the sugar units. A question mark indicates a linkage whose position is unknown.

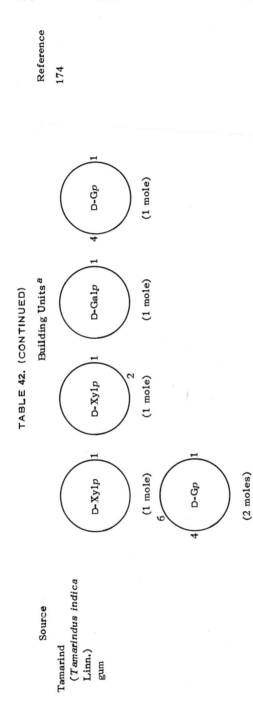

arabic, mesquite gum and damson gum cannot be applied. Such relatively stable gums and mucilages undergo degradation much more slowly than those containing the L-arabofuranose units sensitive to acid hydrolysis and interruption of the acid treatment usually results in no major yield of well-defined degradation products. Instead a mixture of all the possible component sugars together with small amounts of numerous oligosaccharides intermediate in size between the simple sugars and the original gum is obtained. As a consequence of this, methylation studies on these gums and mucilages, whether they are neutral or acidic, has involved procedures very similar to those already laid down in the classical studies of cellulose, starch, glycogen and inulin (2,3).

In the case of the acidic gums and mucilages containing D-galacturonic acid units, advantage is taken of their degradation to an aldobiouronic acid. For example, linseed (or flaxseed) mucilage gives upon hydrolysis L-galactose, D-xylose, and an aldobiouronic acid, 2-O-(D-galactopyranosyluronic acid)-L-rhamnose (44–47). The structure of this aldobiouronic acid, also obtained by acid hydrolysis of slippery elm mucilage (48), has been ascertained in the manner already described for the aldobiouronic acids discussed above. The other components of these and other so-called mucilages containing D-galacturonic acid and the linkages involved in their mutual union have been ascertained by methylation studies in the usual way. The results of such studies on flaxseed mucilage (Linum usitatissimum), cocoa (Sterculia setigera), Plantago arenaria, Plantago lanceolata, slippery elm (Ulmus fulva), karaya (Sterculia urens) and gum tragacanth (Astragalus sp.) are given in Table 42. In addition to D-galacturonic acid these mucilages contain a 6-deoxyhexose, L-rhamnose, found in flaxseed (linseed) mucilage, slippery elm and Plantago arenaria, and L-fucose present in gum tragacanth.

The mucilage from flaxseed (linseed) is also characterized by the uncommon fact that it contains L-galactose, which makes flaxseed the best natural source of this sugar.

Another point of interest is that these mucilages also contain a considerable amount of D-xylose which occurs in the pyranose form.

The chemistry of these so-called mucilages from the seeds, bark, and stems, etc. of plants has not been developed as well as that of the so-called plant gums and it is apparent that there is room for a considerable expansion of knowledge in this field.

The methylation procedure using methyl sulfate and strong alkali is not always applicable to polymers containing esterified uronic acid residues. Attempts to methylate pectin and methyl pectate directly with methyl sulfate and alkali give little or no methylated product. This is probably due to the fact that alkaline saponification of pectin or methyl pectate which occurs during methylation is accompanied by profound decomposition as indicated by osmotic pressure measurements (148). The degradation proceeds even in an atmosphere of nitrogen. The glycosidic or acetal linkage between the uronic acid units is cleaved under the influence of the ester carbonyl group; that this is probably the correct interpretation is shown by the fact that upon completion of the saponification depolymerization stops (148). In support of this may be cited the evidence that neighboring nitro-, halogen, or nitrile groups influence the stability of glycosides towards alkali (149–154).

Neutral Gums and Mucilages. Methylation studies have been extensively applied in determining the constitution of the less complex gums or mucilages, composed of one or two different sugars, that are extracted from the seeds, bulbs, and roots of various plants, for example, the glucans, mannans, glucomannans, and galactomannans (see Table 42). Since these polysaccharides behave normally and present the same problems as those previously encountered in the case of cellulose, starch, glycogen, inulin, the reader is referred to the available text books (2,3) and to Chapters 11 to 14 of this book, for more detailed information. Only the main points of interest will be referred to here.

The glucomannan gums or mucilages, being largely linear in character, give rise to a mixture of the tri-O-methyl derivatives of D-glucose and D-mannose. For example, the methylated derivatives of konjak (113) and of Iles glucomannan (144), like that of iris glucomannan (147), give a mixture of 2,3,6-tri-O-methyl-D-glucose and 2,3,6-tri-O-methyl-D-mannose (144). The characterization of these two components does not present a difficult problem since both give crystalline p-nitrobenzoates and, after oxidation with bromine, crystalline phenylhydrazides. But their quantitative separation is not easily accomplished since they show the same mobility on paper chromatograms and their methyl glycosides have about the same boiling point. However, the 2,3,6-tri-O-methyl-D-glucose undergoes preferential furanoside formation when the mixture is treated with methanolic hydrogen chloride at room temperature, after which separation is readily effected by chromatography (113,144,145).

A similar phenomenon was encountered in methylation studies on barley β-D-glucan (145,146) and the α-D-glucan, nigeran (128), extracted from *Aspergillus niger*, both of which possess 1 → 4- and 1 → 3-linkages and hence give rise to a mixture of 2,3,6-tri-O-methyl-D-glucose and 2,4,6-tri-O-methyl-D-glucose. This mixture could not be separated directly but was readily resolved in the case of the barley β-D-glucan, by taking advantage of the fact that the 2,3,6-tri-O-methyl derivative underwent furanoside formation (145) as described above.

The mannans and galactomannans which fall into the classification of gums and mucilages, and which have been investigated up to the present, undergo smooth methylation. The separation of the mixture of cleavage products of the derived methyl derivatives presents no difficulty, since the mixture usually contains tetra-, tri- and di-O-methyl hexoses, products which are readily separated (see Table 43).

The results of methylation studies of the glucomannans and the galactomannans have been supported and extended by controlled degradation of the polymers to give oligosaccharides using chemical and enzymatic methods (see pages 134–156).

Seaweed Gums and Mucilages. Plants growing in water and especially in sea water constitute an immense source of polysaccharide gums and mucilages which, to all intents and purposes, still remains to be utilized. Once the harvesting difficulties have been overcome, more and more of these polysaccharides will find their way into industry and it is not unlikely that in the absence of cheap labor the collection of gums like gum arabic and gum tragacanth will be abandoned.

The seaweed polysaccharides, which perhaps have proved to be the most difficult to investigate (284,285,311), appear to serve as ion-exchange systems for the plants (255) whereby they show a greater affinity for calcium, potassium, and cesium than for sodium; the plants also exhibit a preferential attraction for certain anions, such as iodide over chloride.

The difficulties encountered in investigating many of the seaweed gums and mucilages have been traced to the presence of sulfate groups and 3,6-anhydrogalactose residues. The sulfate groups hinder methylation probably because of their steric effects; they enhance the solubility of the polysaccharide and make it especially difficult to isolate the methyl derivatives. The 3,6-anhydrogalactose residues, like the other anhydrofuranol ring compounds 3,6-anhydroglucose, and 2,5-anhydroarabinose, are sensitive to acid and readily yield 5- (hydroxymethyl) 2-furaldehyde. This explains the various reports that carrageenin (10) contains a 2-ketohexonic acid (286–292) or 2-keto-D-gluconic acid (182).

The most commonly encountered seaweed polysaccharides are agar, algin, carrageenin, Floridean starch, fucoidin, funorin, and laminarin. With the exception of the alginates, which are composed largely of D-mannuronic acid, many of the seaweed polysaccharides have been found to contain D-galactose. Some, like agar, contain L-galactose as well as the D-form whereas others contain L-fucose, L-arabinose, D-xylose, D-glucose, and D-mannose (see Table 32).

Quite recently D-mannitol and D-mannose (310) have been found in addition to D-glucose as constituents of laminarin and L-guluronic acid as well as D-mannuronic appears to be an integral part of the structure of alginic acid extracted from the brown seaweeds (*Phaeophyceae*) (see Table 33).

One of the major problems emerging from studies on polysaccharides, and this is particularly true of the seaweed polysaccharides, is that of ascertaining the purity or homogeneity of the substances under investigation. Fractionation methods are, at best, crude and capable of bringing about only rough separations since the polysaccharides show a great tendency to associate. Evidence will be presented later to show that many polysaccharides including gums and mucilages can be shown, under certain conditions, to consist of two or more components.

Such neutral seaweed polysaccharides as laminarin, algal cellulose, algal xylan and Floridean starch (see Table 32) can be investigated by the usual procedures developed for polysaccharides in general (see 2,3) and aside from the fact that alginic acid, like pectic acid, is difficult to methylate, it has been investigated with considerable success. However, the procedures for ascertaining the structure of the seaweed polysaccharide sulfates have to take into consideration the fact that these carbohydrate polymers are stable only as salts. The free acids, prepared by dialysis in the presence of acid or by electrodialysis, are substituted sulfuric acids and hence may be considered to be strong acids. Moreover, none of the salts is insoluble so double decomposition reactions cannot be employed in purification; this is in contrast to alginic acid which is readily precipitated as an insoluble calcium salt. Structural studies are also hampered by the difficulty of acetylating and methylating polysaccharide sulfates (284). The acetylation is prevented by the inorganic ion in the polysaccharide sulfate salts and methylation studies are handicapped because the methylated products are soluble in the methylation reaction mixture and cannot be extracted in the usual manner; isolation is accomplished by dialysis after each methylation. Moreover, the sulfate groups appear to hinder methylation in the same manner that the carboxyl groups hinder the methylation of alginic acid (200,201), pectic acid (202,203), Khaya gum (52) and tragacanthic acid (167).

Difficulties attending the study of polyglycosiduronic acids can be largely eliminated by transformation of the carboxyl groups into primary alcoholic groups (59,204) and this would undoubtedly be true of the polysaccharide sulfates if they could be freed from sulfate. However, the sulfate groups cannot be removed from the methylated polysaccharide by alkaline hydrolysis and the use of acid cleaves the glycosidic bonds. For this reason, it is not always possible to ascertain the positions occupied by the sulfate groups and those involved in glycosidic bonds (284,285).

There is some evidence that an enzyme, glucosulfatase, isolated from *Charonia lampas*, will split off the sulfate groups (205-207) and that certain mollusc preparations are capable of effecting desulfation (284). Simultaneous desulfation and acetylation, probably attended by degradation, has been effected in certain cases (208-210,293).

In spite of these difficulties a number of polysaccharide sulfates have been successfully methylated and the identification of the products of hydrolysis of the methylated derivatives has provided considerable insight into the structures of the original polysaccharide sulfates. Agar has been methylated with methyl sulfate and alkali (211-215,224,294-296) and in a similar manner carrageenin has been converted into a methyl derivative (297,298). Likewise, methyl fucoidin has been prepared and the products of hydrolysis identified (217) in the usual way.

To illustrate the results and the structural deductions made from them, reference may be made to the work of Percival and his associates (297, 298). Methylated carrageenin sulfate, prepared from the polysaccharide extracted from *Chondrus crispus* and *Gigantina stellata*, gave upon hydrolysis 2,6-di-O-methyl-D-galactose as the major product. On the assumption that a sulfate group is attached directly to galactose, the following structures are possible:

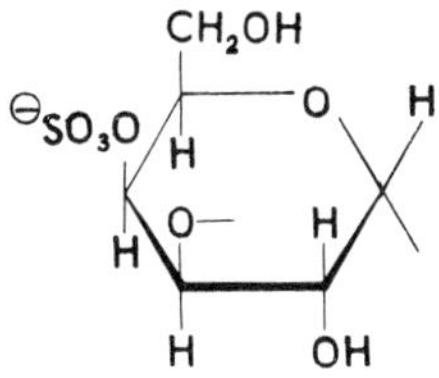

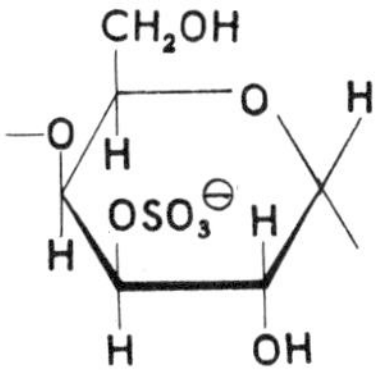

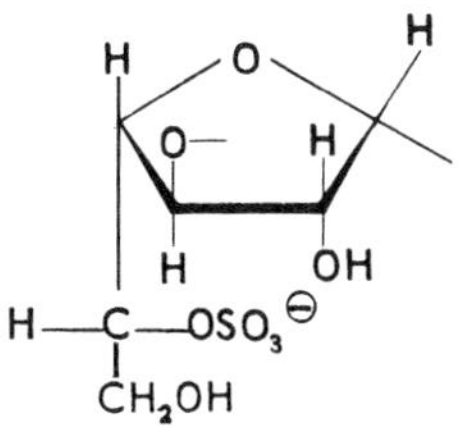

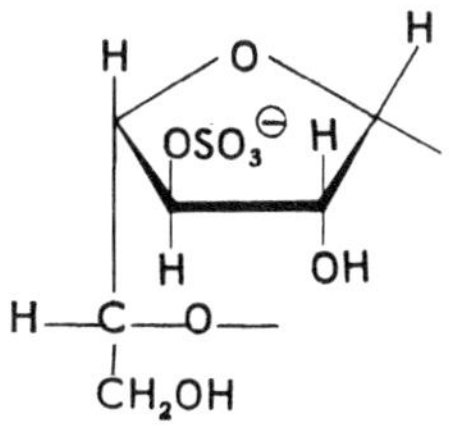

Of these four possible structures for the galactose sulfate unit in carrageenin, LII would readily lose sulfate giving a 2,3- and a 3,6-anhydride; LIII and LIV would likewise form the 5,6- and the 2,3-anhydride, respectively. A residue with the structure (LI) would be stable to alkali since it cannot form an anhydride by *trans* elimination of the elements of sulfuric acid. Inasmuch as the sulfate groups in carrageenin are stable to alkali, the galactose residues must be joined through C_1 and C_3 and they must have a sulfate group at C_4. It is also apparent that furanose residues of the types LIII and LIV would be sensitive to acid hydrolysis whereas, in fact, the carrageenin polysaccharide is relatively stable.

From studies of this type it has become evident that one of the characteristic structural features of the seaweed polysaccharides such as agar (213,214), carrageenin (297,298) and the galactan sulfate of *Dilsea edulis* (293), is that the galactose building units are joined by $1 \rightarrow 3$-glycosidic bonds. In the case of fucose sulfate polysaccharides the linkages are principally of the $1 \rightarrow 2$ type (217). Structural studies of these polysaccharides, made difficult by the presence of sulfate groups, have been simplified by first carrying out a desulfation reaction after which the structural problem of determining the position of the glycosidic linkages is greatly simplified. Simultaneous desulfation and acetylation has also been applied to carrageenin (208,210,284) and to the galactan sulfate of *Dilsea edulis* (293). The procedure generally followed may be illustrated by referring to the latter. Acetylation with acetic anhydride in the presence of chlorine and sulfur dioxide (208,293), a procedure used for acetylating cellulose (218), gave a sulfate-free triacetate which upon methylation and hydrolysis furnished 2,3,4,6-tetra-, 2,4,6-tri- and a small amount of 2,3,6-tri-O-methyl-D-galactose. The major product was 2,4,6-tri-O-methyl-D-galactose thus showing that the polysaccharide was a linear polymer composed of D-galactopyranose residues joined by $1 \rightarrow 3$-glycosidic bonds. Inasmuch as the sulfate groups are stable to alkali they are most likely attached to position 4 of the D-galactose units.

It might be observed in passing that acetylative desulfation has proved to be useful in the study of carbohydrate sulfates of animal origin (219, 220). A mild desulfation procedure (266) developed recently in studies on chondroitin sulfate is worthy of consideration for the desulfation of seaweed polysaccharides.

The isolation of 3,6-anhydro-D-galactose from carrageenin (275–277) and its enantiomorph from agar (97,211,212,221–224,278) has caused considerable speculation as to their origin, but there is now little doubt that they are integral components of the polysaccharides. ·Proof of this has come from the application of mercaptolysis which gives rise to 3,6-anhydrogalactose diethyldithioacetal (275–278).

Investigations into the structure of alginic acid have involved hydrolysis to establish that D-mannuronic and L-guluronic acid are the building units. Methylation was applied to give the di-O-methyl derivative which upon hydrolysis, gave 2,3-di-O-methyl-D-mannuronic acid (201). Reduction with lithium aluminum hydride, in a manner used for the study of pectic acid (59), yielded the corresponding neutral methylated polysaccharide (L-gulo-D-mannan) and subsequent hydrolysis gave 2,3-di-O-methyl-D-mannose (204). Derivatives of the L-guluronic acid component have not yet been obtained.

As will be seen later, periodate oxidation, which usually cleaves adjacent glycol groupings (225), may readily indicate the nature of the glycosidic bonds uniting the uronic acid residues. In the case of alginic acid, the mannuronic acid units are cleaved between C_2 and C_3, since oxidation with bromine followed by hydrolysis yielded erythraric acid (201).

The procedures employed for determining the structure of the neutral seaweed polysaccharide gums have followed very closely those already worked out for neutral polysaccharides in general (213). The polymers may be subjected to graded hydrolysis to give oligosaccharides of constitutional significance. The polysaccharides undergo smooth methylation with methyl sulfate and alkali in the usual manner after which the product can be hydrolyzed and the methylated sugars identified. Thus, for example, the β-D-glucosan, laminarin, gives upon controlled hydrolysis, laminaribiose (299), 1-O-β-D-glucopyranosyl-D-mannitol (273) and 1-O-β-D-laminaribiosyl-D-mannitol (274). Hydrolysis of the methylated laminarin has been shown to give rise to 2,3,4,6-tetra-O-methyl-D-glucose and 2,4,6-tri-O-methyl-D-glucose in a ratio of 1:20. Since this neutral polysaccharide has a low optical rotation, it may be deduced that certain molecules of laminarin consist of a linear chain of β-D-glucopyranose units joined by 1 → 3-glycosidic bonds terminated with a D-mannitol residue (274,299,300,301). The further evidence that only the two ends of the molecule are attacked by periodate oxidation also aids in establishing its structure (225,300).

Many of the methylation studies carried out to determine the structure of various plant gums and mucilages have involved fractional distillation of the methyl glycosides of methylated sugars and their derivatives. The more recent studies, however, have been greatly facilitated by the methods of paper and column partition chromatography discussed in Chapter 8. These methods have usually enabled the components of a mixture of methylated sugars, obtained from methylated polysaccharides, to be separated cleanly and quantitatively, either on a micro- or a macro-scale with relative ease and in a comparatively short time.

Some of the results of the methylation studies on gums and mucilages outlined above are recorded in Table 42.

REFERENCES

1. Graham, T., *J. Chem. Soc.*, **15**, 266 (1862).
2. Percival, E. G. V., *Structural Carbohydrate Chemistry*, Prentice-Hall, Inc., New York (1950).
3. Whistler, R. L., and Smart, C. L., *Polysaccharide Chemistry*, Academic Press, New York (1953).
4. Schlemmer, J., *Chemie (Prague)*, **3**, 73 (1948); *Chem. Abstracts*, **46**, 2888 (1952).
5. Smith, F., *J. Chem. Soc.*, 744 (1939).
6. Hirst, E. L., and Jones, J. K. N., *J. Chem. Soc.*, 1174 (1939).
7. White, E. V., *J. Am. Chem. Soc.*, **69**, 715 (1947).
8. Anderson, E., and Sands, Lila, *J. Am. Chem. Soc.*, **48**, 3172 (1926).
9. Percival, Elizabeth E., *Chemistry and Industry*, 1487 (1954).
10. O'Neill, A. N., *J. Am. Chem. Soc.*, **77**, 2837 (1955).
11. Hirst, E. L., and Jones, J. K. N., *"Modern Methods of Plant Analysis"* Ed. by Paech, K., and Tracey, M. V., Vol. *II*, Springer-Verlag, Berlin (1955) p. 275.
12. Säverborn, S., *The Svedberg (Mem. Vol.)*, 508 (1944).
13. Briggs, D. R., Smith, F., and Spriestersbach, D. R., unpublished.
14. Challinor, S. W., Haworth, W. N., and Hirst, E. L., *J. Chem. Soc.*, 258 (1931).
15. Butler, C. L., and Cretcher, L. H., *J. Am. Chem. Soc.*, **51**, 1519 (1929).
16. Stephen, A. M., *J. Chem. Soc.*, 646 (1951).
17. Hirst, E. L., and Jones, J. K. N., *J. Chem. Soc.*, 1064 (1947).
18. Hirst, E. L., and Jones, J. K. N., *J. Chem. Soc.*, 120 (1948).
19. Hirst, E. L., and Jones, J. K. N., *J. Chem. Soc.*, 1482 (1939).
20. Jones, J. K. N., *J. Chem. Soc.*, 558 (1939).
21. Connell, J. J., Hainsworth, Ruth, Hirst, E. L., and Jones, J. K. N., *J. Chem. Soc.*, 1696 (1950).
22. Hotchkiss, R. D., and Goebel, W. F., *J. Biol. Chem.*, **121**, 195 (1937).
23. Whistler, R. L., and Hough, L., *J. Am. Chem. Soc.*, **75**, 4918 (1953).
24. Hamilton, J. K., Smith, F., and Spriestersbach, D. R., *J. Am. Chem. Soc.*, **79**, 443 (1957).
25. Bishop, C. T., *Can. J. Chem.*, **31**, 134 (1953).
26. Roudier, A., *Compt. rend.*, **237**, 662 (1953).
27. Nishida, K., and Hashima, H., *J. Agr. Chem. Soc., Japan*, **13**, 660 (1937); *Chem. Abstracts*, **32**, 4142 (1938).
28. White, E. V., *J. Am. Chem. Soc.*, **70**, 367 (1948).
29. White, E. V., *J. Am. Chem. Soc.*, **69**, 2264 (1947).
30. Cunneen, J. I., and Smith, F., *J. Chem. Soc.*, 1141 (1948).
31. Hudson, C. S., *J. Am. Chem. Soc.*, **73**, 4038 (1951).
32. Dutton, G. G. S., *Can. J. Chem.*, **34**, 406 (1956).
33. Abdel-Akher, M., Smith, F., and Spriestersbach, D. R., *J. Chem. Soc.*, 3637 (1952).
34. Whistler, R. L., Conrad, H. E., and Hough, L., *J. Am. Chem. Soc.*, **76**, 1668 (1954).
35. McIlroy, R. J., *J. Chem. Soc.*, 121 (1949).
36. Jones, J. K. N., and Merler, E., *Can. J. Chem.*, **34**, 840 (1956).
37. Mukherjee, S. N., and Chakravarti, S. C., *J. Indian Chem. Soc.*, **25**, 113 (1948).

38. Rao, P. S., and Budhiraja, R. P., *J. Sci. Ind. Research (India)*, 11B, 209 (1952); *Chem. Abstracts*, 47, 10882 (1953).
39. Nelson, W. A. G., and Percival, E. G. V., *J. Chem. Soc.*, 58 (1942).
40. Hostettler, F., and Deuel, H., *Helv. Chim. Acta*, 34, 2440 (1951).
41. Bailey, K., and Norris, F. W., *Biochem. J.*, 26, 1609 (1932).
42. Bailey, K., *Biochem. J.*, 29, 2477 (1935).
43. Sands, Lila, and Klass, Rosalind, *J. Am. Chem. Soc.*, 51, 3441 (1929).
44. Anderson, E., and Crowder, J. A., *J. Am. Chem. Soc.*, 52, 3711 (1930).
45. Anderson, E., *J. Biol. Chem.*, 100, 249 (1933).
46. Anderson, E., and Lowe, H. J., *J. Biol. Chem.*, 168, 289 (1939).
47. Tipson. R. S., Christman, C. C., and Levene, P. A., *J. Biol. Chem.*, 128, 609 (1939).
48. Gill, R. E., Hirst, E. L., and Jones, J. K. N., *J. Chem. Soc.*, 1025 (1946).
49. Laidlaw, R. A., and Percival, E. G. V., *J. Chem. Soc.*, 1600 (1949).
50. Laidlaw, R. A., and Percival, E. G. V., *J. Chem. Soc.*, 528 (1950).
51. Hirst, E. L., Percival, E. G. V., and Wylam, Clare B., *J. Chem. Soc.*, 189 (1954).
52. Aspinall, G. O., Hirst, E. L., and Matheson, N. K., *J. Chem. Soc.*, 989 (1956).
53. Jones, J. K. N., and Perry, M. B., *Abstracts 130th A.C.S. Meeting, Atlantic City*, 1956, p. 6D.
54. McCreath, D., and Smith, F., *J. Chem. Soc.*, 387 (1939).
55. Smith, F., *J. Chem. Soc.*, 1724 (1939).
56. Jackson, J., and Smith, F., *J. Chem. Soc.*, 74 (1940).
57. Heslop, Doreen, Salt, Elizabeth, and Smith, F., *J. Chem. Soc.*, 225 (1944).
58. Smith, F., *J. Chem. Soc.*, 2646 (1951).
59. Abdel-Akher, M., and Smith, F., *Nature*, 166, 1037 (1950).
60. Lythgoe, B., and Trippett, S., *J. Chem. Soc.*, 1983 (1950).
61. Adams, G. A., *Can. J. Chem.*, 32, 187 (1954).
62. Shinle, R., *Ber.*, 65, 315 (1932).
63. Montgomery, R., Smith, F., and Srivastava, H. C., *J. Am. Chem. Soc.*, 78, 2837 (1956); 78, 6169 (1956).
64. Wolf, M. J., MacMasters, Majel. M., Cannon, J. A., Rosewall, E. C., and Rist, C. E., *Cereal Chem.*, 30, 451 (1953).
65. Levene, P. A., and Kreider, L. C., *J. Biol. Chem.*, 120, 597 (1937).
66. Derungs, R., and Deuel, H., *Helv. Chim. Acta*, 37, 657 (1954).
67. McCready, R. M., McComb, Elizabeth, A., and Black, D. R., *J. Am. Chem. Soc.*, 76, 3035 (1954).
68. Hotchkiss, R. D., and Goebel, W. F., *J. Am. Chem. Soc.*, 58, 858 (1936).
69. Hotchkiss, R. D., and Goebel, W. F., *J. Biol. Chem.*, 115, 285 (1936).
70. Charlson, A. J., Nunn, J. R., and Stephen, A. M., *J. Chem. Soc.*, 1428 (1955).
71. Charlson, A. J., Nunn, J. R., and Stephen, A. M., *J. Chem. Soc.*, 269 (1955).
72. Jones, J. K. N., *J. Chem. Soc.*, 534 (1950).
73. Hirst, E. L., and Perlin, A. S., *J. Chem. Soc.*, 2622 (1954).
74. Geerdes, J. D., and Smith, F., *J. Am. Chem. Soc.*, 77, 3569 (1955).
75. Jones, J. K. N., *J. Chem. Soc.*, 1672 (1953).
76. Zempl'en, G., *Ber.*, 59, 2402 (1926).
77. Jackson, J., and Smith, F., *J. Chem. Soc.*, 79 (1940).
78. Andrews, P., Ball, D. H., and Jones, J. K. N., *J. Chem. Soc.*, 4090 (1953).

79. Andrews, P., and Jones, J. K. N., *J. Chem. Soc.*, 4134 (1954).
80. Smith, F., *J. Chem. Soc.*, 753 (1939).
81. Haworth, W. N., and Peat, S., *J. Chem. Soc.*, 3094 (1926).
82. Whistler, R. L., and Corbett, W. M., *J. Am. Chem. Soc.*, **77**, 6328 (1955).
83. Montgomery, R., Smith, F., and Srivastava, H. C., *J. Am. Chem. Soc.*, **79**, 698 (1957).
84. Srivastava, H. C., and Smith, F., *J. Am. Chem. Soc.*, **79**, 982 (1957).
85. Whistler, R. L., and Durso, D. F., *J. Am. Chem. Soc.*, **73**, 4189 (1951).
86. Whistler, R. L., and Durso, D. F., *J. Am. Chem. Soc.*, **74**, 5140 (1952).
87. Barker, S. A., and Bourne, E. J., *Quart. Rev. (London)*, **7**, No. 1, 56 (1953).
88. Manners, D. J., *Quart. Rev. (London)*, **9**, No. 1, 73 (1955).
89. Lutz, L., *Bull. sci. pharmacol.*, **47**, 12 (1940).
90. Lutz, L., *Ann. pharm. franc.*, **3**, 9, 58 (1945).
91. Lutz, L., *Compt. rend.*, **218**, 766 (1944).
92. Mori, T., *J. Agr. Chem. Soc., Japan*, **19**, 740 (1943); *Chem. Abstracts*, **45**, 9089 (1951).
93. Fukumoto, J., and Ishimatsu, K., *Bull. of the Osaka Municipal Technical Research Institute*, **13**, 1 (1951).
94. Ishimatsu, K., *Bull. of the Osaka Municipal Technical Research Institute*, **14**, 1 (1953).
95. Araki, C., and Arai, K., *Bull. Chem. Soc. Japan*, **29**, 339 (1956); *Chem. Abstracts*, **51**, 3465 (1957).
96. Araki, C., *J. Chem. Soc. (Japan)*, **65**, 533, 627 (1944).
97. Araki, T., *J. Chem. Soc. Japan*, **65**, 627 (1944); *Chem. Abstracts*, **42**, 1210 (1948).
98. Araki, C., and Hirase, S., *Bull. Chem. Soc. (Japan)*, **27**, 109 (1954); *Chem. Abstracts*, **49**, 9518 (1955).
99. Rao, P. S., and Beri, R. M., *Proc. Indian Acad. Sci.*, **35A**, 1 (1952).
100. Effront, J., *Compt. rend.*, **125**, 38, 309 (1897).
101. Bourquelot, E., and Hérissey, H., *Compt. rend.*, **129**, 614 (1899).
102. Deuel, H., Leuenberger, R., and Huber, G., *Helv. Chim. Acta*, **33**, 942 (1950).
103. Whistler, R. L., and Stein, Joan, T. Z., *J. Am. Chem. Soc.*, **73**, 4187 (1951).
104. Whistler, R. L., and Smith, C. G., *J. Am. Chem. Soc.*, **74**, 3795 (1952).
105. Whitaker, D. R., *Arch. Biochem. Biophys.*, **43**, 253 (1953).
106. Whistler, R. L., and Masak, E., *J. Am. Chem. Soc.*, **77**, 1241 (1955).
107. O'Dwyer, Margaret H., *Biochem. J.*, **33**, 713 (1939); **34**, 149 (1940).
108. Grassmann, W., Stadler, R., and Bender, R., *Ann.*, **502**, 20 (1933).
109. Bishop, C. T., and Whitaker, D. R., *Chemistry and Industry*, 119 (1955).
110. Bishop, C. T., *J. Am. Chem. Soc.*, **78**, 2840 (1956).
111. Friese, H., and Hess, K., *Ann.*, **450**, 40 (1926).
112. Nishida, K., and Hashima, H., *J. Dept. Agr. Kyushu Imp. Univ.*, **2**, 277 (1930).
113. Smith, F., and Srivastava, I. C., *J. Am. Chem. Soc.*, **81**, 1715 (1959).
114. Smith, F., and Srivastava, H. C., *J. Am. Chem. Soc.*, **78**, 1404 (1956).
115. Cifonelli, Margaret, Cifonelli, J. A., Montgomery, R., and Smith, F., *J. Am. Chem. Soc.*, **77**, 121 (1955).
116. Whistler, R. L., and Tu, C. C., *J. Am. Chem. Soc.*, **73**, 1389 (1951).
117. Thompson, A., and Wolfrom, M. L., *J. Am. Chem. Soc.*, **74**, 3612 (1952).

118. Whelan. W. J., Bailey, J. M., and Roberts, P. J. P., *J. Chem. Soc.*, 1293 (1953).
119. Whistler, R. L., and Hickson, J. L., *J. Am. Chem. Soc.*, **76**, 1671 (1954).
120. Whistler, R. L., and Duffy, J. H., *J. Am. Chem. Soc.*, **77**, 1017 (1955).
121. Whistler, R. L., and Moy, B. F., *J. Am. Chem. Soc.*, **77**, 5761 (1955).
122. Dickey, E. E., and Wolfrom, M. L., *J. Am. Chem. Soc.*, **71**, 825 (1949).
123. Whistler, R. L., and Tu, C. C., *J. Am. Chem. Soc.*, **74**, 4334 (1952).
124. Scott, T. A., Jr., and Senti, F. R., *J. Am. Chem. Soc.*, **77**, 3816 (1955).
125. Whistler, R. L., and Conrad, H. E., *J. Am. Chem. Soc.*, **76**, 1673 (1954).
126. Whistler, R. L., and Conrad, H. E., *J. Am. Chem. Soc.*, **76**, 3544 (1954).
127. Barry, V. C., *Sci. Proc. Roy. Dublin, Soc.*, **22**, 423 (1941).
128. Barker, S. A., Bourne, E. J., and Stacey, M.. *J. Chem. Soc.*, 3084 (1953).
129. Jeanes, Allene, Wilham, C. A., Jones, R. W., Tsuchiya, H. M., and Rist, C. E., *J. Am. Chem. Soc.*, **75**, 5911 (1953).
130. Van Cleve, J. W., Schaefer, W. C., and Rist, C. E., *J. Am. Chem. Soc.*, **78**, 4435 (1956).
131. Lohmar, R., *J. Am. Chem. Soc.*, **74**, 4974 (1952).
132. Abdel-Akher, M., Hamilton, J. K., Montgomery, R., and Smith, F., *J. Am. Chem. Soc.*, **74**, 4970 (1952).
133. White, E. V., *J. Am. Chem. Soc.*, **69**, 622 (1947).
134. Smith, F., *J. Chem. Soc.*, 1035 (1940).
135. Montgomery, R., and Smith, F., *J. Am. Chem. Soc.*, **79**, 695 (1957).
136. Geerdes, J. D., and Smith, F., *J. Am. Chem. Soc.*, **77**, 3572 (1955).
137. Smith, F., and Montgomery, R., *Methods of Biochemical Analysis*, **3**, Ed. by D. Glick, Interscience Pub. Inc., New York, (1956), 153.
138. Hirst, E. L., and Jones, J. K. N., *J. Chem. Soc.*, 496 (1938).
139. Falconer, E. L., and Adams, G. A., *Can. J. Chem.*, **34**, 338 (1956).
140. Hirst, E. L., and Jones, J. K. N., *J. Chem. Soc.*, 506 (1946).
141. Nieman, C., and Link, K. P., *J. Biol. Chem.*, **104**, 195, 743 (1934).
142. White, E. V., *J. Am. Chem. Soc.*, **75**, 257 (1953).
143. White, E. V., *J. Am. Chem. Soc.*, **75**, 4692 (1953).
144. Rebers, P. A., and Smith, F., *J. Am. Chem. Soc.*, **76**, 6097 (1954).
145. Gilles, K. A., Huffman, G. W., Meredith, W. O. S., and Smith, F., unpublished.
146. Aspinall, G. O., and Telfer, R. G. J., *J. Chem. Soc.*, 3519 (1954).
147. Andrews, P., Hough, L., and Jones, J. K. N., *J. Chem. Soc.*, 1186 (1953).
148. Vollmert, B., Makromoleculare Chemie, **5**, 110 (1950).
149. Fischer, E., and Strauss, H., *Ber.*, **45**, 2467 (1912).
150. Karrer, P., Nägeli, C., and Weidmann, H., *Helv. Chim. Acta*, **2**, 425 (1919).
151. Helferich, B., and Hase, Marie, *Ann.*, **554**, 261 (1943).
152. Helferich, B., and Lutzmann, H., *Ann.*, **541**, 1 (1939).
153. Helferich, B., and Weber, G., *Z. Naturf.*, **4b**, 193 (1949).
154. Treibs, A., *Angew. Chem.*, (A)**60**, 289 (1948).
155. Ahmed, Z. F., and Whistler, R. L., *J. Am. Chem. Soc.*, **72**, 2524 (1950).
156. Rafique, C. M., and Smith, F., *J. Am. Chem. Soc.*, **72**, 4634 (1950).
157. Swanson, J. W., *J. Am. Chem. Soc.*, **71**, 1510 (1949).
158. Smith, F., *J. Am. Chem. Soc.*, **70**, 3249 (1948).
159. Hirst, E. L., and Jones, J. K. N., *J. Chem. Soc.*, 1278 (1948).
160. Andrews, P., Hough, L., and Jones, J. K. N., *J. Am. Chem. Soc.*, **74**, 4029 (1952).

161. Andrews, P., Hough, L., and Jones, J. K. N., *J. Chem. Soc.*, 2744 (1952).

162. Brown, F., Hirst, E. L., and Jones, J. K. N., *J. Chem. Soc.*, 1761 (1949).

163. Hirst, E. L., and Dunstan, Sonia, *J. Chem. Soc.*, 2332 (1953).

164. Hirst, E. L., Hough, L., and Jones, J. K. N., *J. Chem. Soc.*, 3145 (1949).

165. Hough, L., and Jones, J. K. N., *J. Chem. Soc.*, 1199 (1950).

166. Hirst, E. L., Hough, L., and Jones, J. K. N., *J. Chem. Soc.*, 323 (1951).

167. James, Sybil P., and Smith, F., *J. Chem. Soc.*, 739 (1945).

168. James, Sybil P., and Smith, F., *J. Chem. Soc.*, 749 (1945).

169. White, E. V., *J. Am. Chem. Soc.*, **68**, 272 (1946).

170. Jones, J. K. N., *J. Chem. Soc.*, 1055 (1947).

171. Brown, F., Hirst, E. L., and Jones, J. K. N., *J. Chem. Soc.*, 1757 (1949).

172. Klages, F., and Niemann, R., *Ann.*, **523**, 224 (1936).

173. Mullan, J., Percival, E. G. V., *J. Chem. Soc.*, 1501 (1940).

174. White, E. V., and Rao, P. S., *J. Am. Chem. Soc.*, **75**, 2617 (1953).

175. Boggs, L. A., Cuendet, L. S., Dubois, M., and Smith, F., *Anal. Chem.*, **24**, 1148 (1952).

176. Larson, E. B., and Smith, F., *J. Am. Chem. Soc.*, **77**, 429 (1955).

177. Bredereck, H., Dürr, H., and Ruck, K., *Ber.*, **87**, 526 (1954).

178. Gilbert, Violet E., Smith, F., and Stacey, M., *J. Chem. Soc.*, 622 (1946).

179. Michell, F., and Albers, P., *Ber.*, **89**, 140 (1956).

180. May, F., and Schulz, A. S., *Z. Biol.*, **97**, 201 (1936).

181. Jeanes, Allene, Wilham, C. A., and Hilbert, G. E., *J. Am. Chem. Soc.*, **75**, 3667 (1953).

182. Young, E. G., and Rice, F. A. H., *J. Biol. Chem.*, **156**, 781 (1944); **164**, 35 (1946).

183. Aspinall, G. O., Hirst, E. L., and Wickstrom, A., *J. Chem. Soc.*, 1160 (1955).

184. Andrews, P., Hough, L., and Jones, J. K. N., *J. Chem. Soc.*, 181 (1956).

185. Büchi, W., and Deuel, H., *Helv. Chim. Acta*, **37**, 1392 (1954).

186. Whistler, R. L., and McGilvray, D. I., *J. Am. Chem. Soc.*, **77**, 2212 (1955).

187. Freudenberg, K., and Oertzen, K. v., *Ann.*, **574**, 37 (1951).

188. Bächli, P., and Percival, E. G. V., *J. Chem. Soc.*, 1243 (1952).

189. Davis, A. R., *Ann. Missouri Botan. Garden*, **2**, 771 (1915).

190. Fischer, A., *Bot. Zeit.*, **63**, 51 (1905).

191. Torup, S., *Biochem. Centralbl.*, **8**, 770 (1909).

192. Bartholemew, E. T., *Bot. Gaz.*, **57**, 136 (1914).

193. Gruzewska, Z., *Compt. rend.*, **170**, 521 (1920); **173**, 52 (1921).

194. Dillon, T., and O'Colla, P., *Nature*, **166**, 67 (1950); *Chemistry and Industry*, 111 (1951).

195. Karrer, P., and Nägeli, C., *Helv. Chim. Acta*, **4**, 263 (1921).

196. Lindberg, B., *Acta Chem. Scand.*, **7**, 1119, 1218 (1953).

197. Duncan, W. A. M., Manners, D. J., and Ross, A. G., *Biochem. J.*, **63**, 44 (1956).

198. Bean, R. C., and Hassid, W. Z., *J. Biol. Chem.*, **218**, 425 (1956).

199. Conchie, J., Levvy, G. A., and Marsh, C. A., *Biochem. J.*, **62**, 24P (1956).

200. Hirst, E. L., Jones, J. K. N., and Jones, Winifred O., *Nature*, **143**, 857 (1939).

201. Hirst, E. L., Jones, J. K. N., and Jones, Winifred O., *J. Chem. Soc.*, 1880 (1939).

202. Luckett, S., and Smith, F., *J. Chem. Soc.*, 1106 (1940).

203. Beaven, G. H., and Jones, J. K. N., Chemistry and Industry, 58, 363 (1939).
204. Chanda, S. K., Hirst, E. L., Percival, E. G. V., and Ross, A. G., J. Chem. Soc., 1833 (1952).
205. Soda, T., and Hattori, C., Bull. Chem. Soc. Japan, 6, 258 (1931).
206. Soda, T., and Egami, F., Bull. Chem. Soc. Japan, 8, 148 (1933).
207. Soda, T., Bull. Chem. Soc. Japan, 9, 83 (1934).
208. Dillon, T., and O'Colla, P., Nature, 145, 749 (1940).
209. Dillon, T., and O'Colla, P., Proc. Roy. Irish Acad., 54B, 51 (1951).
210. Mori, T., and Tsuchiya, T., J. Agr. Chem. Soc. Japan, 14, 585 (1941).
211. Hands, S., and Peat, L., Nature, 142, 797 (1938).
212. Hands, S., and Peat, L., Chemistry and Industry, 57, 837 (1938).
213. Percival, E. G. V., and Somerville, J. C., J. Chem. Soc., 1615 (1937).
214. Jones, W. G. M., and Peat, S., J. Chem. Soc., 225 (1942).
215. Araki, C., J. Chem. Soc. Japan, 58, 1362 (1937); Chem. Abstracts, 32, 4172 (1938).
216. Strache, W., Forms and Patterns in Nature, Pantheon Books Inc., New York (1956).
217. Conchie, J., and Percival, E. G. V., J. Chem. Soc., 127 (1950).
218. Barnett, W. L., J. Soc. Chem. Ind., 40, 8T (1921).
219. Wolfrom, M. L., and Montgomery, R., J. Am. Chem. Soc., 72, 2859 (1950).
220. Wolfrom, M. L., Montgomery, R., Karabinos, J. V., and Rathgeb, P., J. Am. Chem. Soc., 72, 796 (1950).
221. Percival, E. G. V., Somerville, J. C., and Forbes, I. A., Nature, 142, 797 (1938).
222. Percival, E. G. V., and Forbes, I. A., Nature, 142, 1076 (1938).
223. Forbes, I. A., and Percival, E. G. V., J. Chem. Soc., 1844 (1939).
224. Araki, T., J. Chem. Soc. Japan, 61, 775 (1940); Chem. Abstracts, 57, 90 (1943).
225. Barry, V. C., J. Chem. Soc., 578 (1942).
226. Boissonnas, R. A., Helv. Chim. Acta, 30, 1703 (1947).
227. Meyer, K. H., and Gurtler, P., Arch. Sci. phys. nat., 27, [v], Suppl. 97 (1945).
228. Lindberg, B., and Paju, J., Acta Chem. Scand., 8, 817 (1954).
229. Lindberg, B., Acta Chem. Scand., 9, 917 (1955).
230. Solberg, Y. J., Acta Chem. Scand., 9, 1234 (1955).
231. Hess, K., and Lauridsen, L. W., Ber., 73, 115 (1940).
232. Karrer, P., and Joos, B., Biochem. Z., 136, 537 (1923).
233. Domenigg, H. S., and Smith, F., unpublished.
234. Acker, L., Diemair, W., and Samhammer, E., Z. Lebensm. Unters. u. Forsch., 102, [4], 225 (1955).
235. Frush, Harriet L., and Isbell, H. S., J. Research Natl. Bur. Standards, 37, 321 (1946).
236. Spoehr, H. A., Arch. Biochem., 14, 153 (1947).
237. Peat, S., Whelan, W. J., and Roberts, J. G., J. Chem. Soc., 2258 (1956).
238. Dubois, M., Gilles, K. A., Hamilton, J. K., Rebers, P. A., and Smith, F., Anal. Chem., 28, 350 (1956).
239. Perlin, A. S., Anal. Chem., 27, 396 (1955).
240. Perlin, A. S., and Lansdown, A. R., Can. J. Chem., 34, 451 (1956).
241. Schwimmer, S., and Bevenue, A., Science, 123, 543 (1956).

242. Barker, S. A., Bourne, E. J., Grant, P. M., and Stacey, M., *Nature*, **177,** 1125 (1956).
243. Bayly, R. J., and Bourne, E. J., *Nature*, **171,** 285 (1953).
244. Wadman, W. H., Thomas, Gwen J., and Pardee, A. B., *Anal. Chem.*, **26,** 1192 (1954).
245. Percival, E. G. V., and Thomson, T. G. H., *J. Chem. Soc.*, 750 (1942).
246. Barry, V. C., and Dillon, T., *Chemistry* and *Industry*, 167 (1944).
247. Dillon, T., and McKenna, J., *Proc. Roy. Irish Acad.*, **53B,** 45 (1950).
248. Mori, T., *J. Agr. Chem. Soc. Japan,* **19,** 297 (1943); *Chem. Abstracts*, **44,** 7783 (1950).
249. Hassid, W. Z., *J. Am. Chem. Soc.*, **57,** 2046 (1935).
250. Johnston, R., and Percival, E. G. V., *J. Chem. Soc.*, 1994 (1950).
251. Barry, V. C., *Sci. Proc. Roy. Dublin Soc.*, **22,** 59 (1939).
252. Connell, J. J., Hirst, E. L., and Percival, E. G. V., *J. Chem. Soc.*, 3494 (1950).
253. Percival, E. G. V., and Chanda, S. K., *Nature*, **166,** 787 (1950).
254. Barry, V. C., Dillon, T., Hawkins, Beatrice, and O'Colla, P., *Nature*, **166,** 788 (1950).
255. Currie, T., *Chemistry* and *Industry*, 116 (1955).
256. Williams, K. T., and Bevenue, A., *Anal. Chem.*, **27,** 331 (1955).
257. Porter, W. L., and Hoban, Nancy, *Anal. Chem.*, **26,** 1846 (1954).
258. Finan, P. A., and O'Colla, P. S., *Chemistry* and *Industry*, 1387 (1955).
259. Militzer, W. E., *Arch. Biochem.*, **9,** 91 (1946); **21,** 143 (1949).
260. Scheurer, P. G., and Smith, F., *Anal. Chem.*, **27,** 1616 (1955).
261. Frampton, V. L., Foley, Lucia P., Smith, L. L., and Malone, Jane G., *Anal. Chem.*, **23,** 1244 (1951).
262. Jones, J. K. N., and Reid, W. W., *J. Chem. Soc.*, 1361 (1956).
263. Stephen, A. M., *J. Chem. Soc.*, 4487 (1956).
264. Brown, H. C., and Subba Rao, B. C., *J. Am. Chem. Soc.*, **77,** 3164 (1955).
265. Brown, H. C., Mead, E. J., and Subba Rao, B. C., *J. Am. Chem. Soc.*, **77,** 6209 (1955).
266. Kantor, T. G., and Schubert, M., *J. Am. Chem. Soc.*, **79,** 152 (1957).
267. Bourquelot, E., and Hérissey, H., *Compt. rend.*, **130,** 42 (1900).
268. Abdel-Akher, M., Hamilton, J. K., and Smith, F., *J. Am. Chem. Soc.*, **73,** 4691 (1951).
269. Hough, L., and Perry, M. B., *Chemistry* and *Industry*, 768 (1956).
270. Unrau, A., and Smith, F., *Chemistry* and *Industry*, 330 (1957).
271. Lindberg, B., *Acta Chem. Scand.*, **7,** 1218 (1953).
272. Jones, J. K. N., and Smith, F., *Advances in Carbohydrate Chem.*, **4,** 243 (1949).
273. Peat, S., Whelan, W. J., and Lawley, H. G., *Chemistry* and *Industry*, 35 (1955).
274. Peat, S., Whelan, W. J., Lawley, H. G., and Evans, J. M., *Biochem. J.*, **61,** [1], x (1955).
275. O'Neill, A. N., *J. Am. Chem. Soc.*, **77,** 2837 (1955).
276. O'Neill, A. N., *J. Am. Chem. Soc.*, **77,** 6324 (1955).
277. Percival, Elizabeth E., *Chemistry* and *Industry*, 1487 (1954).
278. Araki, C., and Hirase, S., *Bull. Chem. Soc. Japan*, **26,** 463 (1953).
279. Kylin, H., *Z. physiol. Chem.*, **83,** 171 (1913); **94,** 337 (1915).
280. Colin, H., and Ricard, P., *Compt. rend.*, **188,** 1449 (1929).

281. Nishizawa, K., J. Chem. Soc. Japan, 60, 1020 (1939).
282. Lindberg, B., and McPherson, J., Acta Chem. Scand., 8, 985 (1954).
283. White, E. V., J. Am. Chem. Soc., 64, 1510 (1942).
284. Percival, E. G. V., Quart. Rev. (London), 3, 369 (1949).
285. Mori, T., Advances in Carbohydrate Chem., 8, 315 (1953).
286. Mori, T., and Tsuchiya, Y., J. Agr. Chem. Soc. Japan, 14, 609, 616 (1938).
287. Mori, T., J. Agr. Chem. Soc. Japan, 15, 1070 (1939).
288. Mori, T., and Tsuchiya, Y., J. Agr. Chem. Soc. Japan, 15, 1065 (1939).
289. Yanagigawa, T., Repts. Imp. Ind. Research Inst., Osaka, Japan, 17, No. 5 (1936).
290. Tadakoro, T., and Yoshimura, K., J. Chem. Soc. Japan, 56, 655 (1935).
291. Tadakoro, T., Yoshimura, K., and Yanase, M., J. Chem. Soc. Japan, 56, 188 (1935).
292. Yanagigawa, T., and Yoshida, T., Repts. Imp. Ind. Research Inst., Osaka, Japan, 20, No. 5 (1939).
293. Dillon, T., and McKenna, J., Proc. Roy. Irish Acad., 53B, 45 (1950).
294. Percival, E. G. V., Somerville, J. C., and Forbes, I. A., Nature, 142, 797 (1938).
295. Percival, E. G. V., and Forbes, I. A., Nature, 142, 1076 (1938).
296. Forbes, I. A., and Percival, E. G. V., J. Chem. Soc., 1844 (1939).
297. Dewar, E. T., and Percival, E. G. V., J. Chem. Soc., 1622 (1947).
298. Buchanan, J., Percival, Elizabeth E., and Percival, E. G. V., J. Chem. Soc., 51 (1943).
299. Barry, V. C., Sci. Proc. Roy. Dublin Soc., 22, 59 (1939).
300. Connell, J. J., Hirst, E. L., and Percival, E. G. V., J. Chem. Soc., 3493 (1950).
301. Percival, E. G. V., and Ross, A. G., J. Chem. Soc., 720 (1951).
302. Lindgren, B. O., Acta Chem. Scand., 11, 1365 (1957).
303. Hirst, E. L., Percival, Elizabeth, and Williams, R. S., J. Chem. Soc., 1942 (1958).
304. Rao, P. S., and Roydon, O. N., Proc. Indian Acad. Sci., 31, 441 (1950); 32, 264 (1950).
305. Tachi, I., and Yamamori, N., Mokuzai Kenkyu, 4, 11 (1950).
306. Anderson, E., and Kinsman, S., J. Biol. Chem., 94, 39 (1931).
307. Percival, E. G. V., and Willox, I, C., J. Chem. Soc., 1608 (1949).
308. Levene, P. A., Tipson, R. S., and Kreider, L. C., J. Biol. Chem., 122, 199 (1937).
309. Lindberg, B., and Wickberg, B., Acta Chem. Scand., 7, 969 (1953).
310. Unrau, A. M., and Smith, F., Chem. and Ind., in press (1959).
311. Hirst, E. L., Proc. Chem. Soc., 177 (1958).
312. Reese, E. T., and Mandels, M., Can. J. Microbiol., 5, 173 (1959).
313. Mackie, J. M., and Percival, E., J. Chem. Soc., 1151 (1959).
314. Fischer, F. G., and Dörfel, H., Z. physiol. chem., 302, 186 (1955); Drummond, D. W., Hirst, E. L., and Percival, E., Chemistry and Industry, 1088 (1958); Whistler, R. L., and Kirby, K. W., Z. physiol. chem., 314, 46 (1959).
315. Stephen, A. M., J. Chem. Soc., 1919 (1957).

CHAPTER 9

PERIODATE OXIDATION
IN STRUCTURAL STUDIES
OF GUMS AND MUCILAGES

In 1928 the important observation was made (1) that periodic acid is capable of cleaving $\alpha\beta$-glycols quantitatively, the *cis*-glycols being attacked more rapidly than the *trans*-glycols, to give two aldehydes thus:

$$R_1CHOHCHOHR_2 + IO_4^\ominus \longrightarrow R_1CHO + R_2CHO + H_2O + IO_3^\ominus$$

When more than two —CHOH— groups are present in adjacent positions, those in excess of two are transformed into formic acid thus:

$$R_1CHOHCHOHCHOHR_2 + 2\ IO_4^\ominus \longrightarrow R_1CHO + R_2CHO + HCOOH +$$
$$H_2O + 2\ IO_3^\ominus$$

The value of periodate oxidation (11,12,17) in the study of gums and mucilages in particular, and of polysaccharides in general, may be illustrated by reference to the behavior of typical sugar residues having the various linkages that may be present in these polymers. D-Xylopyranose residues occupying terminal positions in a polysaccharide and hence linked only through C_1 as in formula LV are oxidized by periodate to give the cleaved residue (LVI) and formic acid. Residues, such as LVII, that are doubly linked through C_1 and C_2 also undergo cleavage to give a dialdehyde grouping (LVIII) without loss of carbon. Similarly, D-xylose residues joined through C_1 and C_4 as in LIX are cleaved without loss of carbon to give the dialdehydic residue (LX). On the other hand, it will be apparent that those xylopyranose residues doubly linked through C_1 and C_3 as in LXI, or triply linked, as for LXII, LXIII, or LXIV, and those quadruply linked, as in LXV will be immune to periodate oxidation. A consideration of these facts will show that the results of periodate oxidation of polymers composed of D-xylopyranose residues will reveal the proportion of residues occupying terminal positions because only these residues afford formic acid. The difference between the total number of residues attacked by periodate including the terminal residues (LV) and also those doubly linked units (LVII and LIX), and the terminal residues attacked will indicate the number of units linked as in LVII and LIX. Those xylose residues that are unaffected by periodate must be of the types shown in formulas LXI, LXII, LXIII, the triply linked residue, LXIV, and the quadruply linked residue, LXV.

These considerations apply to the gums and mucilages containing only D-xylopyranose units and they would also apply to those gums or portions of gums, composed of D-arabopyranose units as in the case of sapote gum.

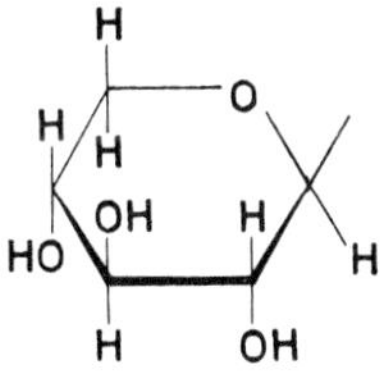

(LV) 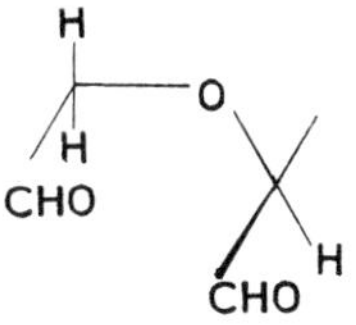   (LVI) 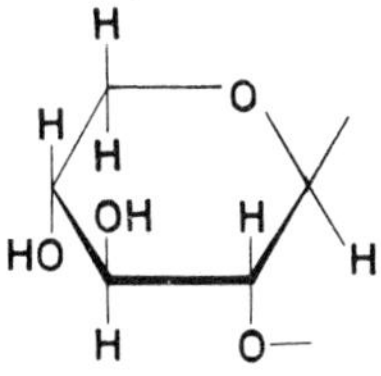   (LVII) 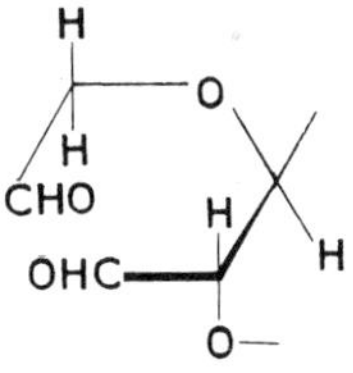   (LVIII) 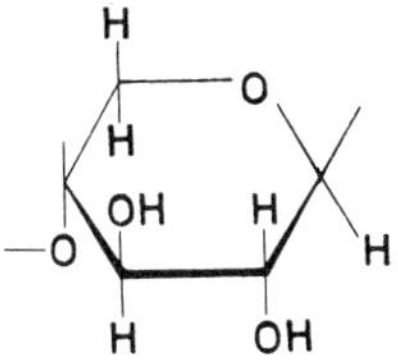   (LIX) 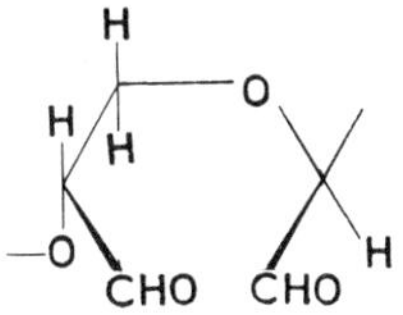   (LX) 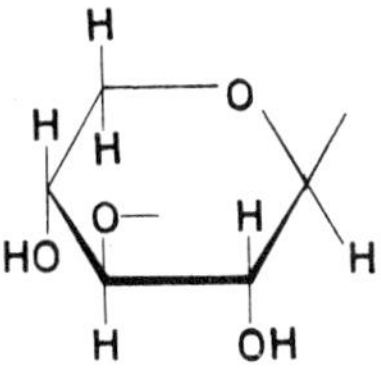   (LXI) 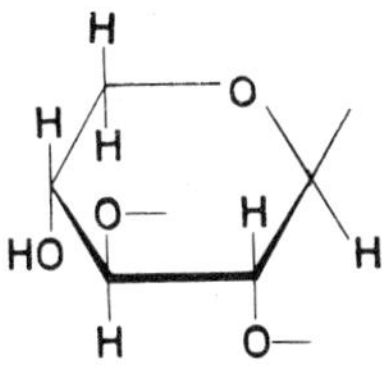   (LXII) 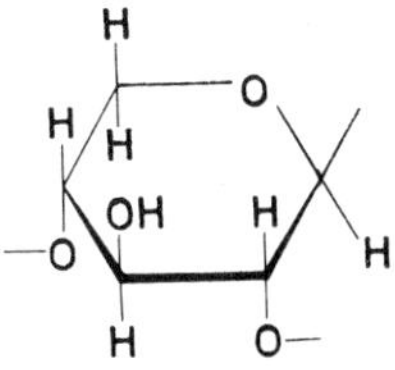   (LXIII)

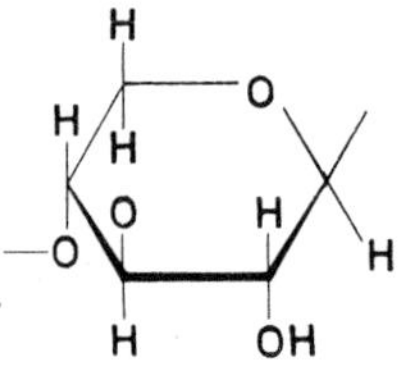

(LXIV) 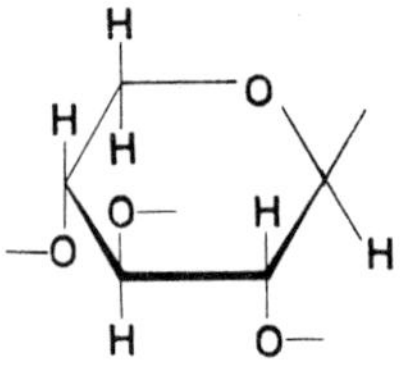   (LXV)

In the case of polysaccharides, composed wholly, or in part, of arabo-furanose units, terminal units such as LXVI are oxidized to give the dialdehydic residue (LXVII) but no formic acid is formed. Residues (LXVIII) linked through C_1 and C_5 undergo oxidation to give LXIX. Those residues linked through C_2 and C_2 (LXX), or C_1 and C_3 (LXXI) and those residues linked through C_1, C_2 and C_3 (LXXII), C_1, C_2 and C_5 (LXXIII), C_1, C_3, C_5 (LXXIV) as well as those joined to other units through all available positions as in LXXV, will not undergo oxidation by periodate. The proportion of the araban polymer oxidized by perio-date will therefore indicate the number of terminal and $1 \longrightarrow 5$ linked arabofuranose units in the complex. All the other types of residues will be indicated by the amount of arabinose remaining in the polysaccharide after oxidation of all α,β-glycol groups is complete.

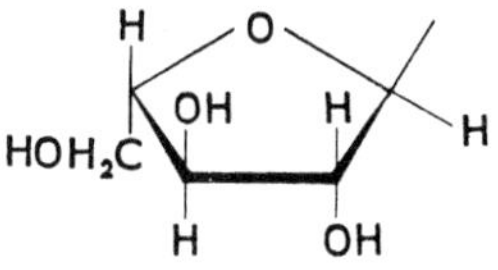

(LXVI) 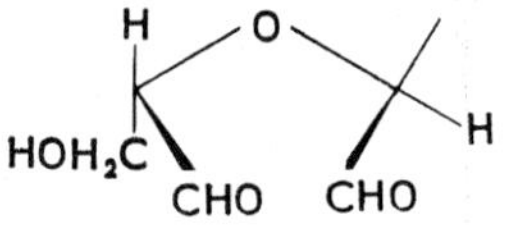   (LXVII)

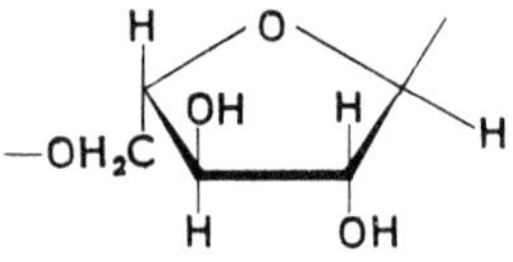

(LXVIII) 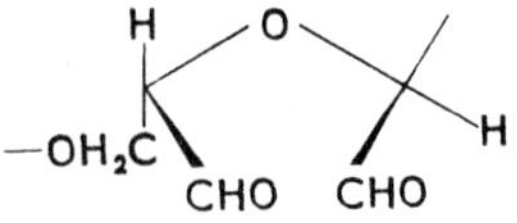   (LXIX)

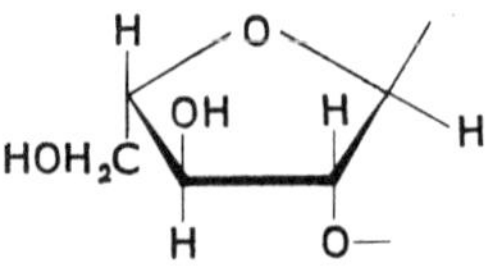

(LXX) 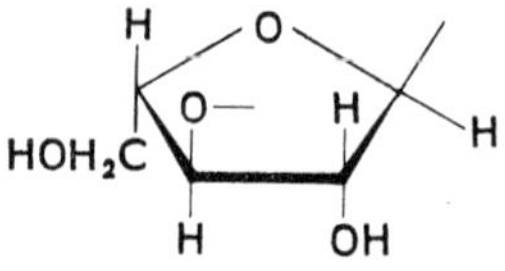   (LXXI) 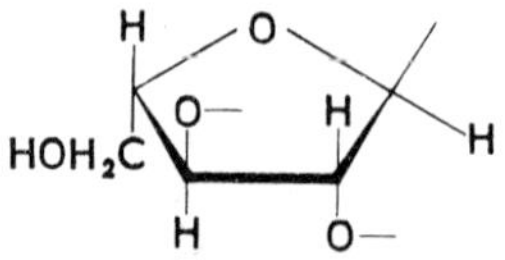   (LXXII)

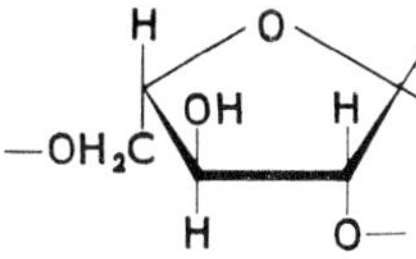

(LXXIII)

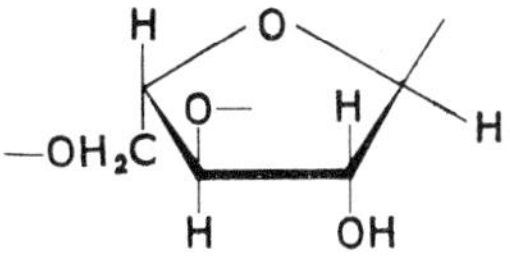

(LXXIV)

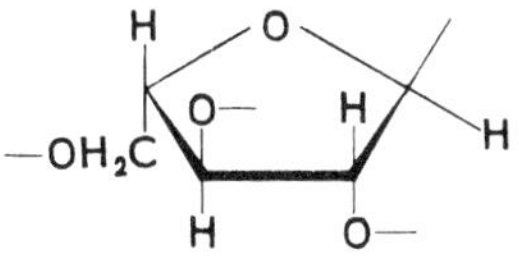

(LXXV)

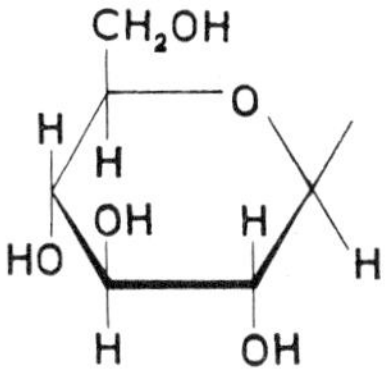

(LXXVI)

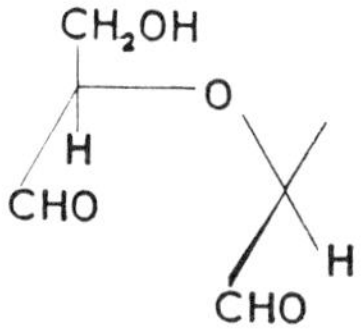

(LXXVII)

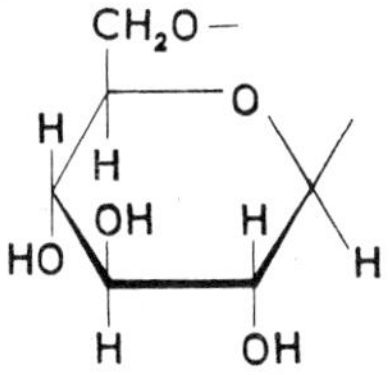

(LXXVIII)

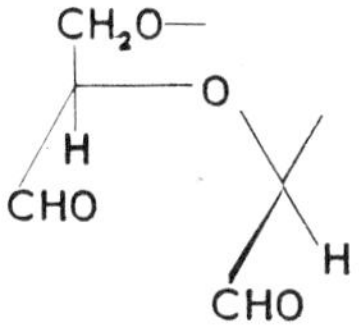

(LXXIX)

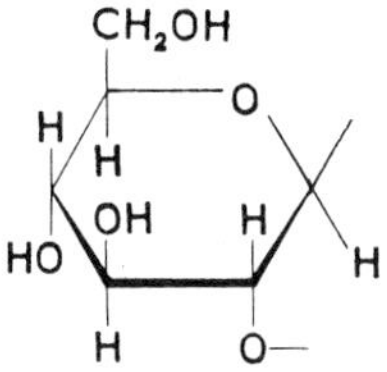

(LXXX)

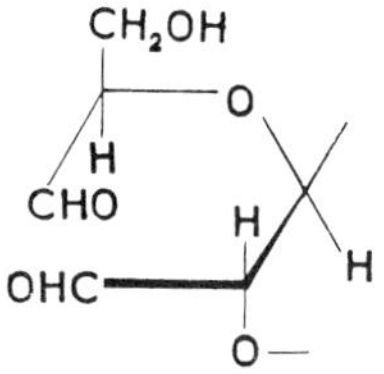

(LXXXII)

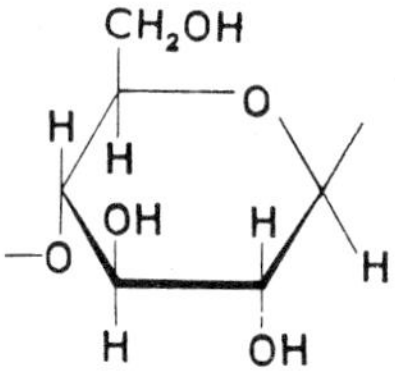

(LXXXI)

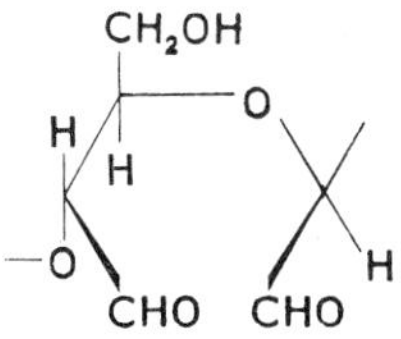

(LXXXIII)

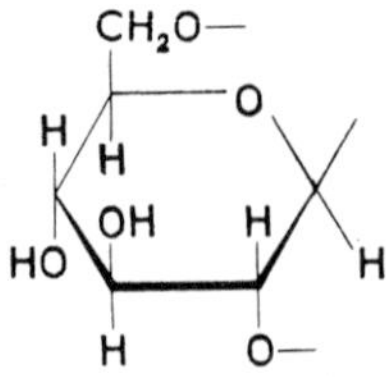

CH₂O—

(LXXXIV)

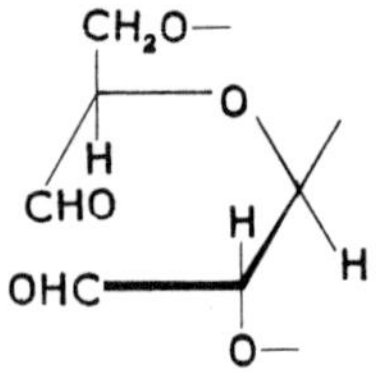

CH₂O—

(LXXXVI)

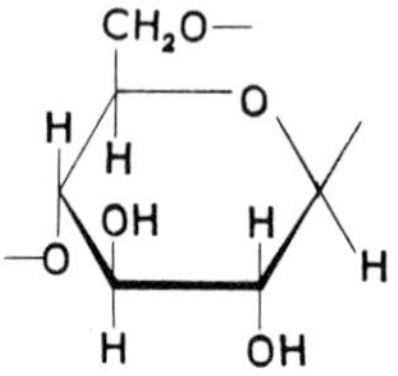

CH₂O—

(LXXXV)

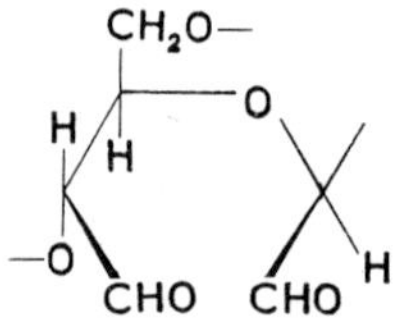

CH₂O—

(LXXXVII)

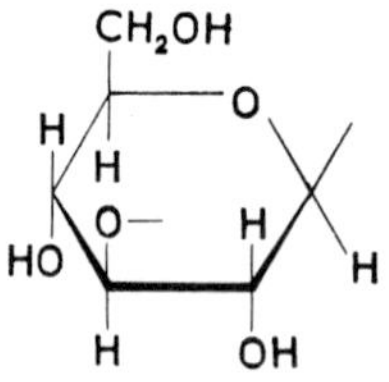

CH₂OH

(LXXXVIII)

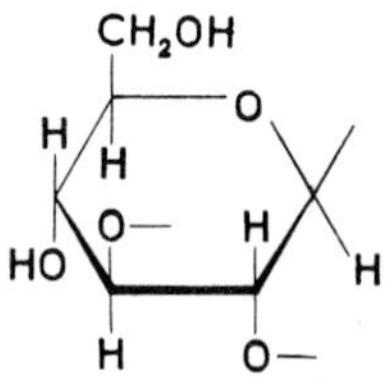

CH₂OH

(LXXXIX)

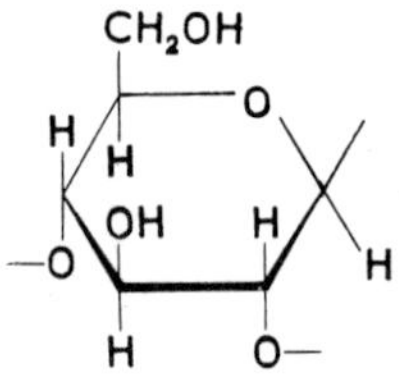

CH₂OH

(XC)

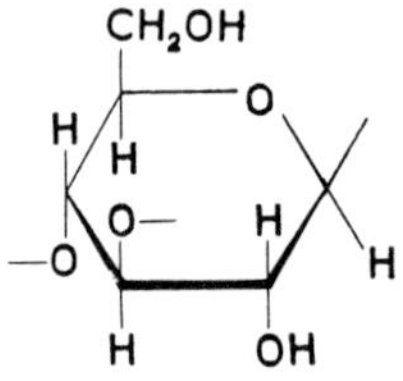

CH₂OH

(XCI)

CH₂O—

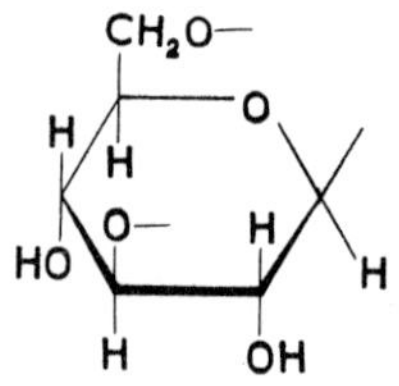

(XCII)

Application of the same considerations to the aldohexopyranose residues (such as D-glucose) that occur in gums will show that terminal units (LXXVI) of glucose for example undergo oxidation to give the dialdehyde (LXXVII) together with formic acid. A 1 ⟶ 6 linked aldopyranose residue (LXXVIII) behaves like a terminal residue inasmuch as it gives the dialdehyde (LXXIX) and formic acid. Doubly linked aldopyranose residues linked through C_1 and C_2 (LXXX), or C_1 and C_4 (LXXXI), undergo cleavage without yielding formic acid to give the dialdehydes (LXXXII) and (LXXXIII), respectively.

Those residues joined through C_1, C_2 and C_6 (LXXXIV) or C_1, C_4 and C_6 (LXXXV) undergo cleavage to give the dialdehyde residues LXXXVI and LXXXVII, respectively, no formic acid being formed in either case. Those residues doubly linked through C_1 and C_3 (LXXXVIII), triply linked through positions C_1, C_2 and C_3 (LXXXIX), or C_1, C_2 and C_4 (XC), C_1, C_3 and C_4 (XCI), C_1, C_3 and C_6 (XCII), and any residues linked through four or all five possible hydroxyls, will not be affected by periodate; all or any of these residues can be recognized and quantitatively determined by suitable analysis, after periodate oxidation, by hydrolysis of the polysaccharide polyaldehyde or better still, the corresponding reduced polymer, the polyalcohol.

Inspection of the structure of the 6-deoxyhexoses, such as L-rhamnose and L-fucose, which thus far have only been found to occur naturally in the pyranose form, would react as in the case of the pentopyranose residue given above. A terminal residue (XCIII) of L-rhamnose, for example, would give formic acid from C3 and yield a dialdehyde (XCIV) thus:

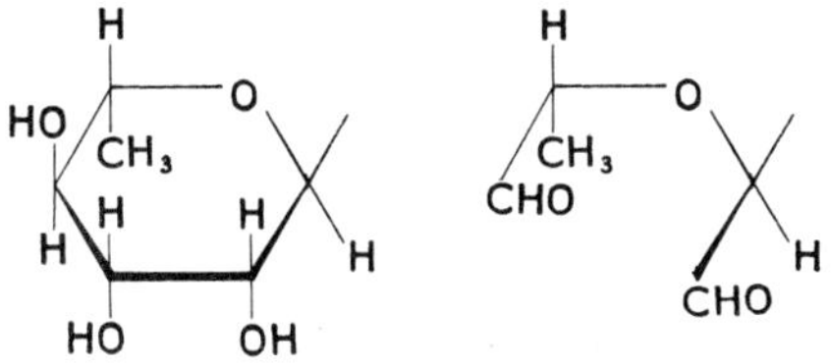

(XCIII)   (XCIV)

A $1 \rightarrow 2$ (XCV) and a $1 \rightarrow 4$ (XCVI) linked residue would consume 1 mole of periodate to give dialdehydes XCVII and XCVIII, respectively, whereas the $1 \rightarrow 3$ linked residue (XCIX) would not be affected by periodate.

Methyl pentose residues triply linked through C_1,C_2 and C_3, C_1,C_2 and C_4, C_1,C_3 and C_4 or those quadruply linked would not react with periodate since none contains the α,β-glycol grouping.

As far as the uronic acids are concerned, the evidence shows that terminal nonreducing residues, such as (C), behave abnormally and un-

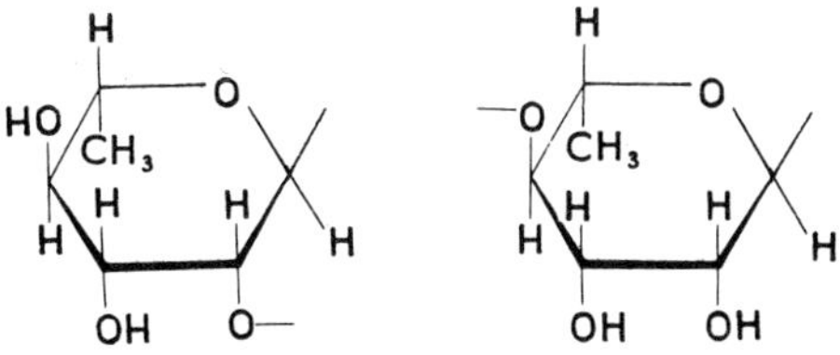

(XCV)   (XCVI)

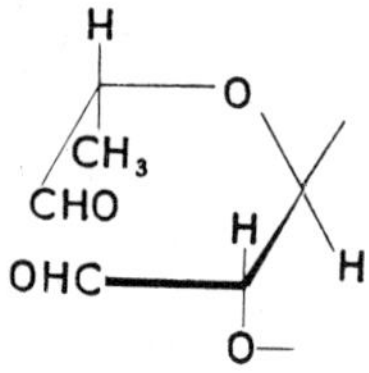

(XCVII) 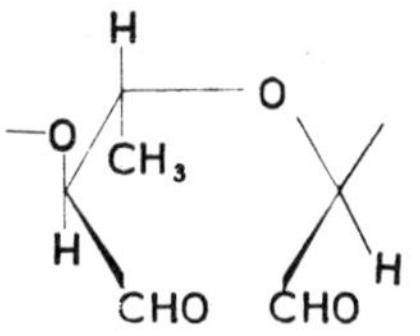   (XCVIII) 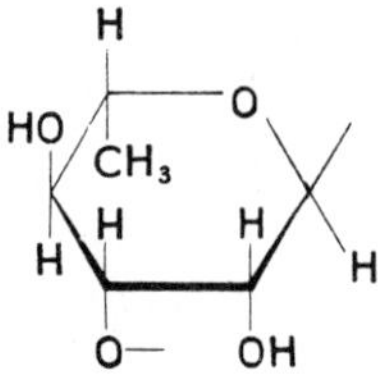   (XCIX)

dergo complete oxidation to formic and oxalic acid as indicated below, unless temperature and pH are controlled (2–7). However, by using periodic acid instead of the sodium periodate or buffered periodate solutions, the intermediate dialdehyde stage (CI) has been realized (8) in studies on gum arabic, mesquite gum (4), pectic acid (10), and alginic acid (9).

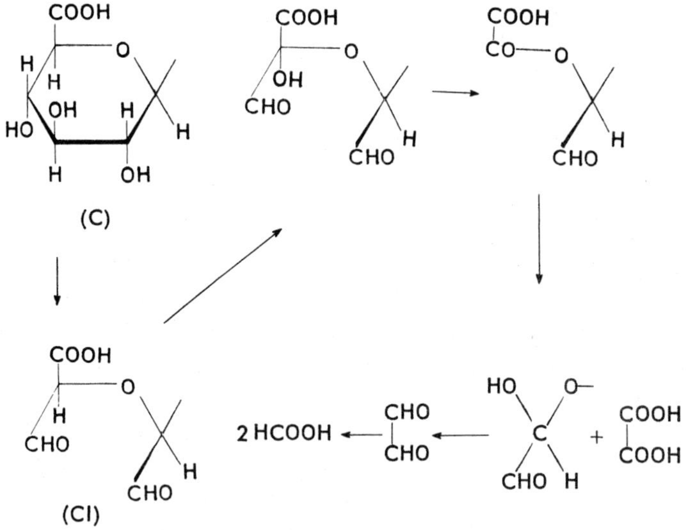

(C)

(CI)   2 HCOOH ←   + COOH COOH

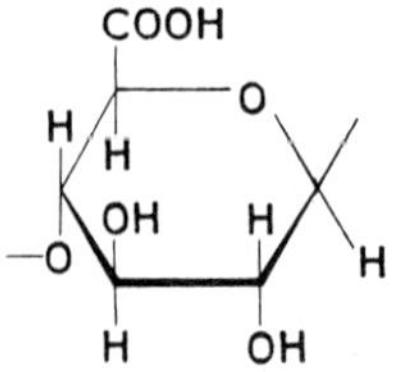

(CII) 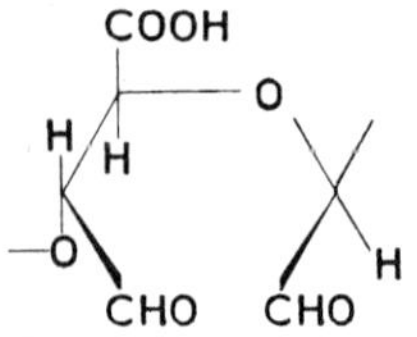   (CIII)

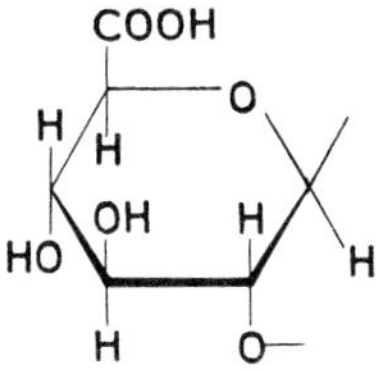

COOH   COOH

H / H — O   H — O

H   H

OH   H   CHO   H

HO   H   OHC———   H

H   O—   O—

(CIV) 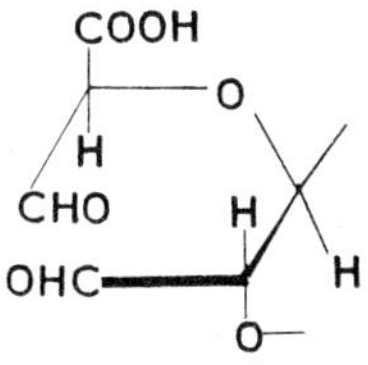   (CV)

Those uronic acid residues joined by $1 \longrightarrow 4$ bonds as in CII undergo cleavage to give a dialdehyde (CIII) (4) and $1 \longrightarrow 2$ linked residues (CIV), which should give rise to CV, would also be subject to complete oxidation as in the case of C, unless the pH is maintained on the acid side (8). The $1 \longrightarrow 3$ linked uronic acid units and those triply linked through C_1, C_2 and C_3, C_1, C_2 and C_4, or C_1, C_3 and C_4 would not be susceptible to attack by periodate. A uronic acid unit linked through all its available hydroxyl groups would likewise be stable to periodate oxidation.

Although these periodate oxidation reactions have not been extensively applied to gums and mucilages in structural studies, there are enough examples with model compounds to show that the above considerations are essentially correct. Thus periodate oxidation has been extensively used in establishing and correlating the structure of simple glycosides (11–13), the general procedure being to oxidize the glycosides, such as methyl α-D-glucopyranoside (CVI), with periodate to the dialdehyde (CVII), which is then further oxidized with bromine in the presence of barium or strontium carbonate to give the corresponding acid (CVIII).

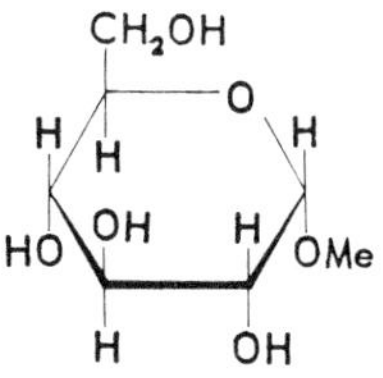

CH$_2$OH   CH$_2$OH   CH$_2$OH

O   O   O

H   H   H   H

H   H   H

HO   OH   H   OMe   CHO   OMe   COOH   OMe

H   OH   OHC   HOOC

(CVI) 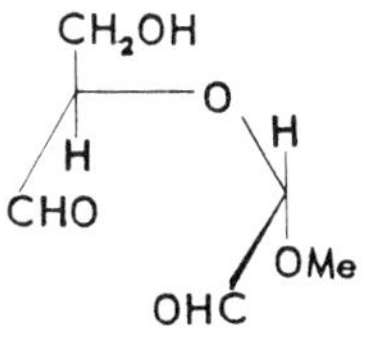   (CVII) 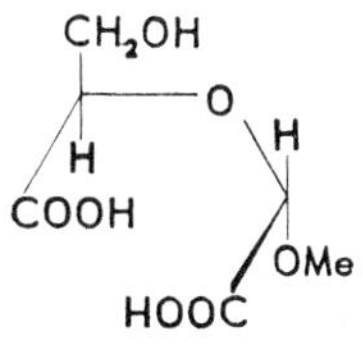   (CVIII)

In the case of methyl pentopyranosides, the reaction proceeds in an analogous manner. Thus, for example, methyl α-D-xylopyranoside (CIX) gives the dialdehyde (CX) which in turn can be recognized by oxidizing it to the dibasic acid (CXI) (11).

The method is equally applicable to glycosides of the L-series of pentoses, 6-deoxyhexoses, and hexoses.

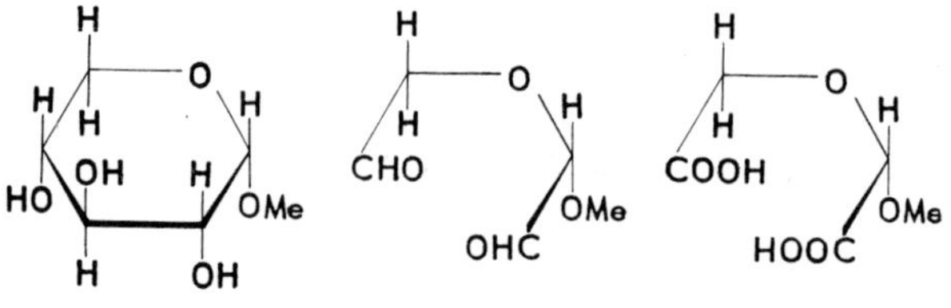

(CIX) (CX) (CXI)

In an alternative procedure for the utilization of periodate oxidation products in structural studies, the dialdehydes, such as CVII and CX, may be reduced either catalytically or with sodium borohydride to the corresponding alcohols (18,19,21) which are obtainable in high yield and are readily purified by distillation. These alcohols are identified as benzoates or p-nitrobenzoates. The method may be illustrated by reference to methyl α-D-xylopyranoside (CIX), methyl α-D-galactopyranoside (CXII), and methyl β-L-arabofuranoside (CXIII). The first of these (CIX), like all other methyl α-D-pentopyranosides, behaves as follows to give the alcohol (CXIV).

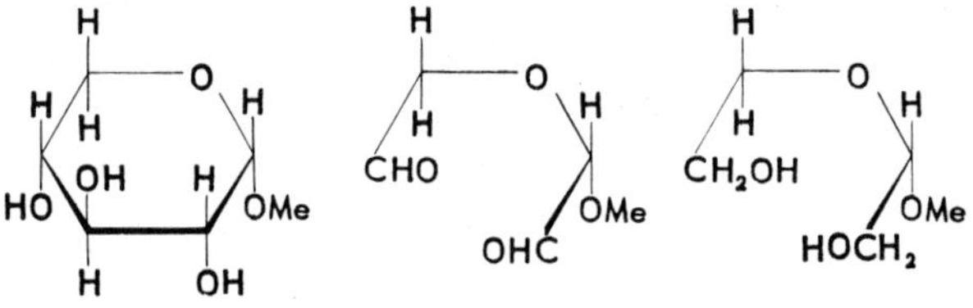

(CIX) (CX) (CXIV)

The second glycoside, methyl α-D-galactopyranoside (CXII) and all other methyl α-D-hexopyranosides behave as follows to give the alcohol (CXV).

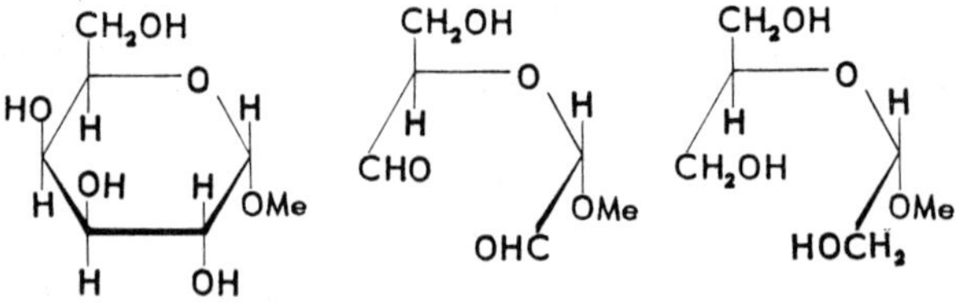

(CXII) (CVII) (CXV)

The third glycoside, methyl β-L-arabofuranoside (CXIII), gives first the dialdehyde (CXVI) and then by reduction the alcohol (CXVII); all other methyl β-L-pentofuranosides behave in the same manner.

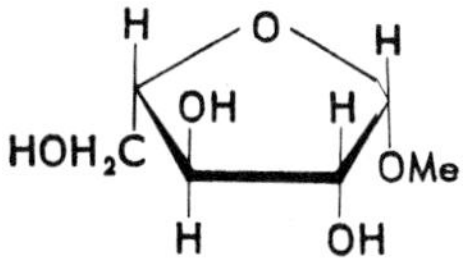

(CXIII) 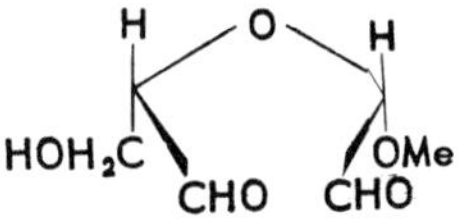   (CXVI) 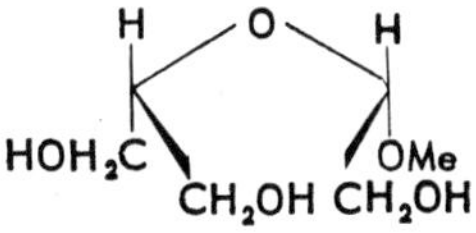   (CXVII)

It is to be noted that although the dialdehyde from CXIII is isomeric with that from CXII it is formed without loss of carbon, whereas oxidation of CXII causes the loss of one carbon atom as formic acid. It is also apparent that the alcohols CXV and CXVII are identical; this facilitates the structural correlations (18,19). Methyl glycopyranosides and furanosides of the 6-deoxyhexoses, such as L-rhamnose and L-fucose, behave in an analogous fashion. Thus methyl α-L-rhamnopyranoside (CXVIII) gives the dialdehyde (CXIX) and then by reduction the alcohol (CXX), whereas the corresponding methyl furanoside (CXXI) affords the dialdehyde (CXXII) and finally the alcohol (CXXIII).

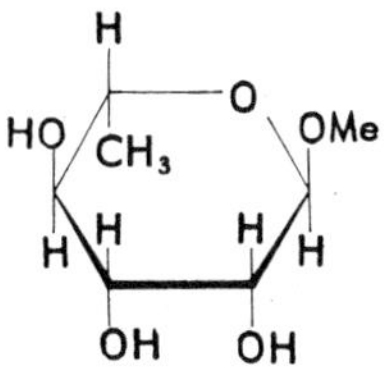

(CXVIII) 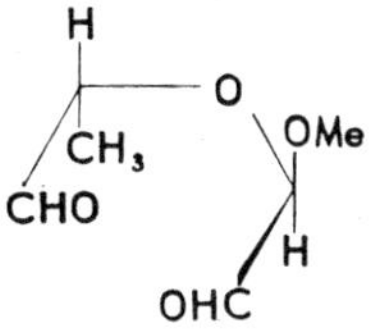   (CXIX) 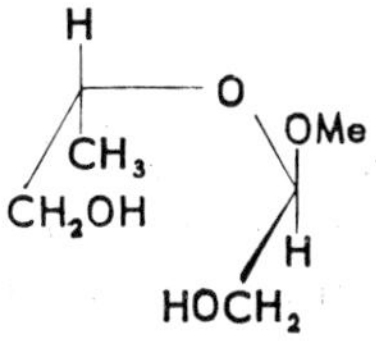   (CXX)

For the structural correlations that may be made of the above alcohols and the corresponding acids derived from the dialdehydes by reduction (18,21) and oxidation (13,14), respectively, the reader is referred to the original publications.

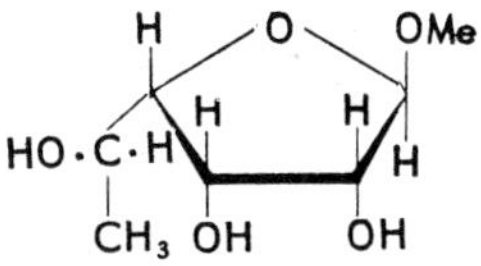

(CXXI) 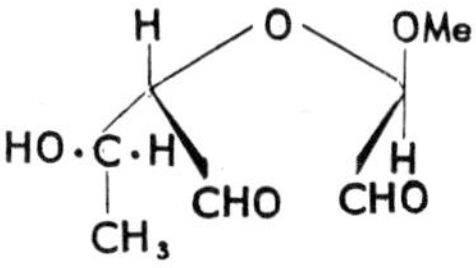   (CXXII) 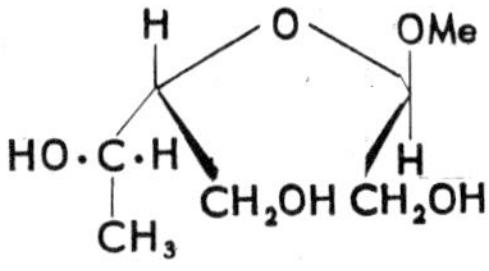   (CXXIII)

In other model experiments, it has been shown that the glycosides of oligosaccharides behave in a similar manner. Thus methyl β-D-lactoside (CXXIV) affords the tetraaldehyde (CXXV) which in turn yields the alcohol (CXXVI) (22).

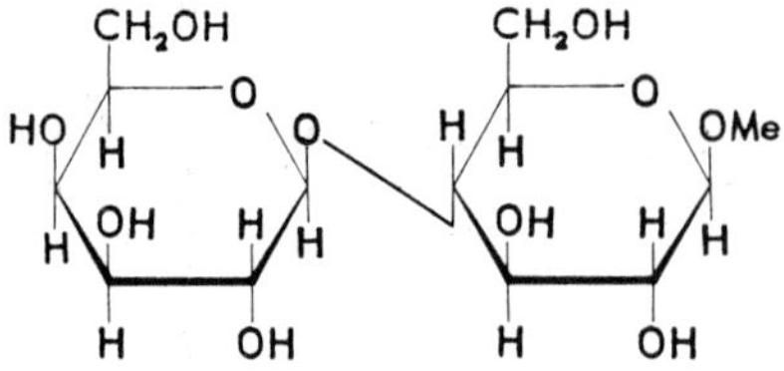

(CXXIV)

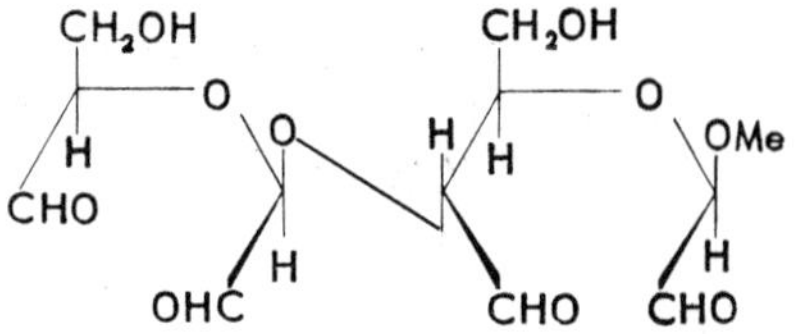

(CXXV)

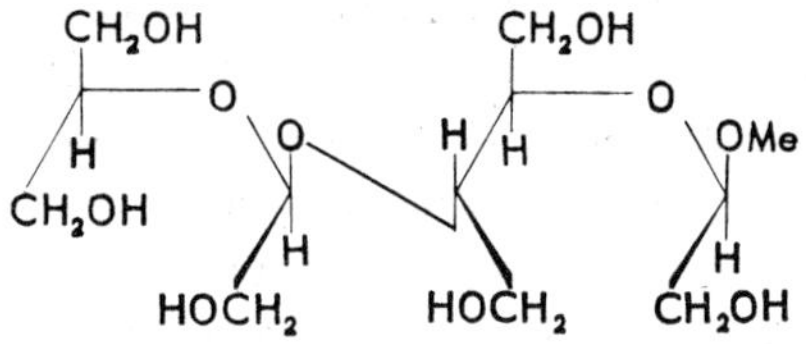

(CXXVI)

Reactions based on the above fundamental investigations are useful in the study of gums and mucilages. Thus, for example, the structure of the methyl 4-*O*-methyl-D-glucosiduronic acid (CXXVII), obtained originally from mesquite gum (4,23,24), has been proved by the fact that periodate oxidation of CXXVII, followed by oxidation and hydrolysis afforded D-2-*O*-methyl-erythraric acid (CXXX) *via* CXXVIII and CXXIX, respectively. This finding proved that the methoxyl group is located at C_4.

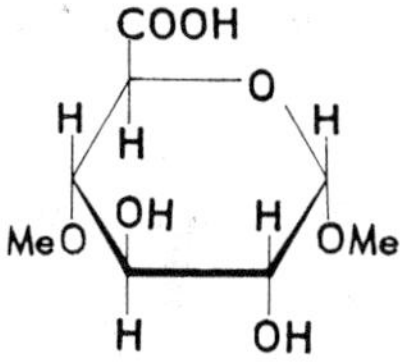

(CXXVII) 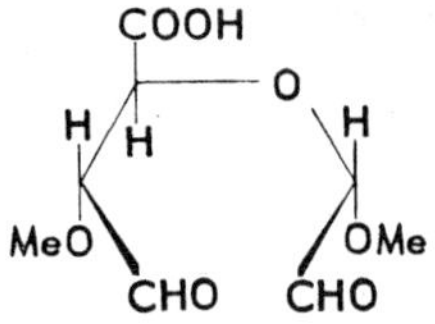   (CXXVIII) 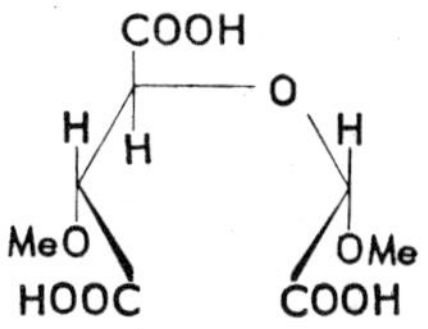   (CXXIX) 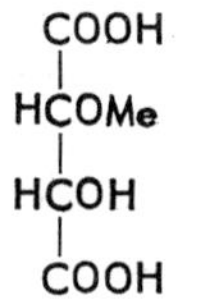   (CXXX)

Similarly, methyl 6-*O*-(4-*O*-methyl-β-D-glucopyranosyluronic acid)-D-galactopyranoside (CXXXI), also obtained from mesquite gum (7), undergoes oxidation with periodate in the expected manner to give CXXXII thus:

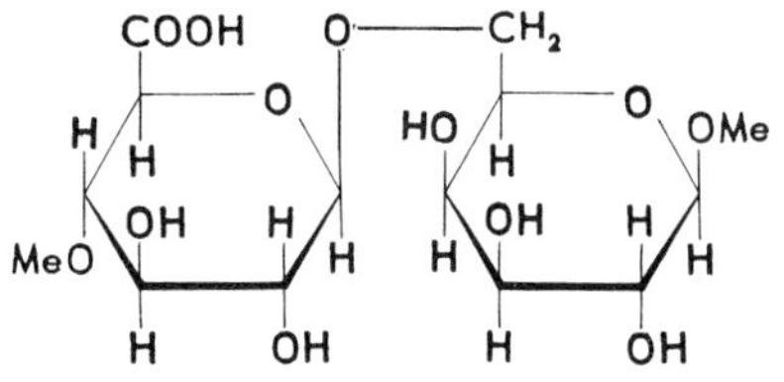

COOH O——CH₂ HO O OMe
H O
H H
MeO OH H OH H
H H H
H OH H OH

(CXXXI)

COOH O——CH₂ O OMe
H O
H H
MeO CHO
CHO CHO OHC H

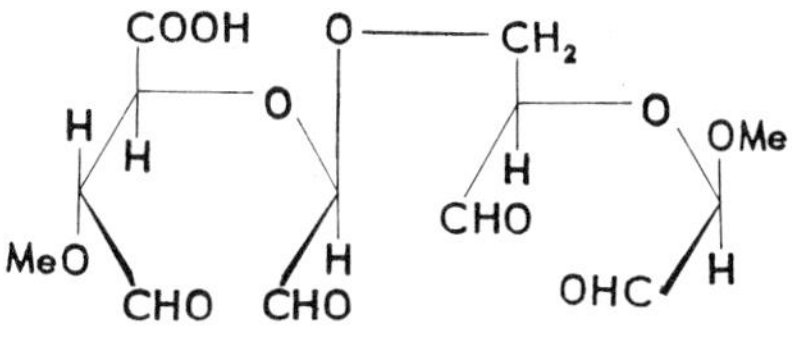

(CXXXII)

Clear-cut periodate oxidation reactions as they have been depicted above do not always apply and care must be exercised in interpreting the results, particularly the negative ones. Compounds with fixed *trans* hydroxyl groups on adjacent carbon atoms, are stable to periodate. For example, the compound 1,6-anhydro-β-D-glucofuranose and 1,6 anhydro-α-D-galactofuranose, which have rigid structures, possess adjacent hydroxyl groups at C_2 and C_3, yet both are stable to periodate (25–27, cf 99). A similar phenomenon has been noted with methyl α-D-glucoside-4,6 (phenyl phosphate) (28).

It is also to be noted that terminal reducing groups may lead to over-consumption ("over-oxidation") of periodate and consequent extensive breakdown of the molecules as in the case of laminarin (29,30) and amylose (31,40). The same drawback, due to over-consumption of periodate, may apply to those compounds containing terminal nonreducing uronic acid residues (see above). This type of deviation from the normal can be controlled by adjustment of the pH and by carrying out the reaction in the dark at low temperature (0–5°). In some cases deliberate attempts to effect over-oxidation may prove useful in locating 1 ⟶ 6-linkages since they alone are stable to periodate under alkaline conditions (94).

In spite of these difficulties, periodate oxidation when judiciously applied can be used to reveal certain structural features (32,33) of gums and mucilages. This may be illustrated by reference to some selected examples. Laminarin (CXXXIII) which is a linear polymer composed of D-glucopyranose units joined by β-D-(1 ⟶ 3) glycosidic bonds (29,34, 35), has been reported to be attacked by periodate at the terminal ends of the molecule (29,36), one molecular proportion of formic acid being liberated from the nonreducing end of the molecule giving CXXXIV.

Unless the reaction conditions are controlled (37,38) (acid pH), the formyl grouping generated from C_1 of the terminal reducing residue will be hydrolyzed and leave the residue open to still further oxidation (29, 30). This is evidently only a partial explanation because recent studies have shown that some of the laminarin molecules are terminated by a mannitol residue (42,43,100).

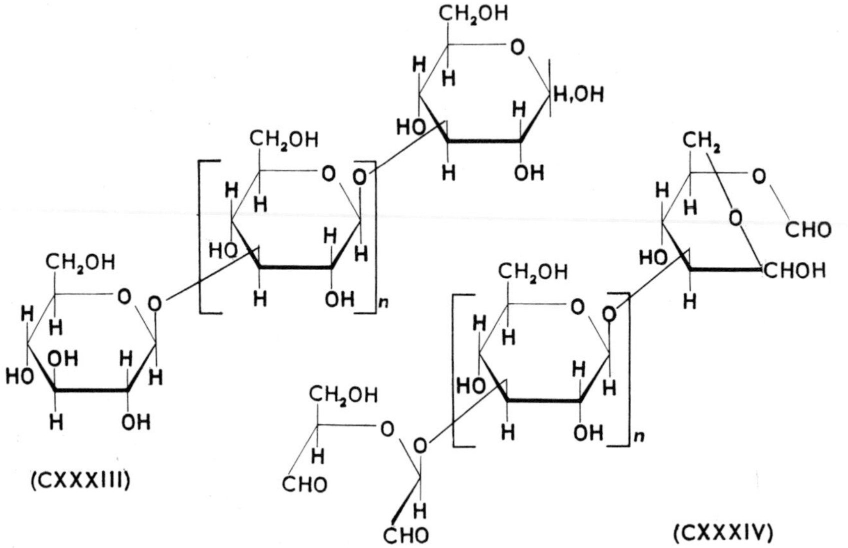

(CXXXIII)

(CXXXIV)

The amount of formic acid produced (6,33,39–41,44–46) from polysaccharides can be used to determine the number of terminal residues per average repeating unit, provided that no $1 \rightarrow 2$ or $1 \rightarrow 6$ linkages are present in the molecule, since residues linked in this manner would also give rise to formic acid. The method may be illustrated by reference to the repeating units of guar gum (CXXXV).

Although all the residues are cleaved by periodate, only the terminal units of D-galactose give rise to formic acid (see CXXXVI). The analytical results of this reaction show that 4 moles of periodate are con-

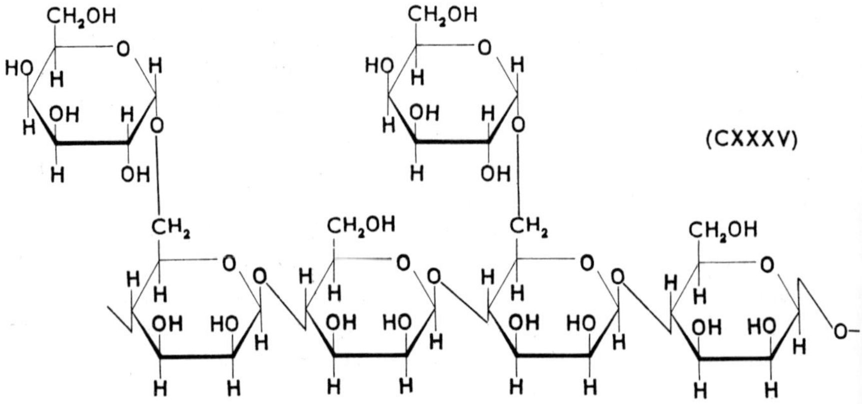

(CXXXV)

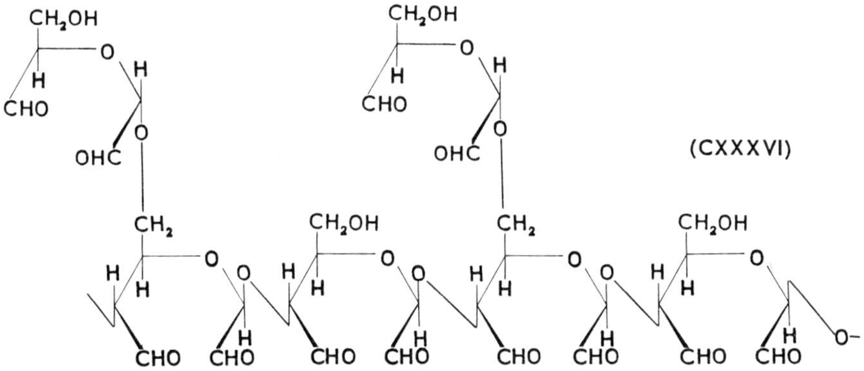

(CXXXVI)

sumed for every three hexose residues and that one mole of formic acid is produced (47,48).

This method has been extensively applied to gums, such as locust bean gum (49), Kentucky coffee bean gum (50), dextran (32) and yeast gum (51), to cite only a few examples. The method is so well established that it has become almost a routine experiment in polysaccharide studies (for other examples, see Chapters 11–14) and it invariably gives valuable results unless uronic acid units are present. Some of the earlier pioneering experiments were carried out with amylopectin (39) and glycogen (33) which lend themselves particularly well to this type of analysis, since the reducing terminal unit (if there is such an entity!) comprises only a very small part of the large molecules, whereas the terminal nonreducing residues giving rise to formic acid constitute about 5% and 10% respectively of the total number of D-glucose residues in the molecules.

The value of the periodate oxidation technique may be further illustrated by reference to the β-D-glucosan (lichenin) component of barley gum (52,53). This linear polymer consumes 1 mole of periodate for about every two D-glucose units without the formation of formic acid. Hydrolysis of the periodate oxidized polysaccharide, before or after reduction, shows that about half the glucose survives the oxidation and this is traced to the presence of 1 ⟶ 3-linkages in the polymer (52,53). Similar results have been obtained for the so-called lichenin of oat flour (54–56) and that of Iceland moss (*Cetraria islandica*) (57). The presence of 1 ⟶ 3-linkages in yeast mannan established by methylation studies (51,58,59) is also in agreement with periodate oxidation results which show that certain mannose units (those linked by 1 ⟶ 3-bonds) survive the oxidation (51). On the other hand periodate oxidation of Kentucky coffee bean gum, guar gum or locust bean gum results in complete cleavage of all the sugar residues, a result in agreement with structures assigned to these compounds from methylation studies (see Chapter 12).

Periodate oxidation has also shown that alginic acid contains $1 \longrightarrow 4$ linked D-mannuronic acid units (CXXXVII) since bromine oxidation of the alginic acid polyaldehyde (CXXXVIIa) followed by hydrolysis has been shown to give erythraric acid (CXXXVIII) (9) thus:

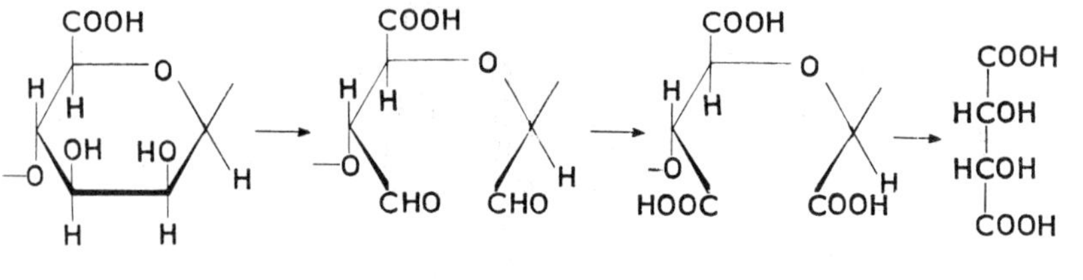

(CXXXVII)   (CXXXVIIa)   (CXXXVIII)

In view of the recent discovery that L-guluronic acid is also present in alginic acid (60) a closer inspection of the mother liquors after separating the erythraric acid, should reveal the presence of L-threaric acid if these units of L-guluronic are also joined by $1 \longrightarrow 4$-glycosidic bonds.

Investigations into the reduced products of the periodate oxidation of the simple glycosides discussed above (18) have furnished a new approach to the study of gums and mucilages and indeed of all polysaccharides (20,61–64). One or two examples will serve to illustrate the procedure. The building unit (LXXXI) of a D-glucose polymer joined by $1 \longrightarrow 4$-glycosidic bonds is transformed by periodate oxidation into LXXXIII and this in turn upon reduction, either with sodium borohydride or catalytically using Raney nickel, gives the residue (CXXXIX).

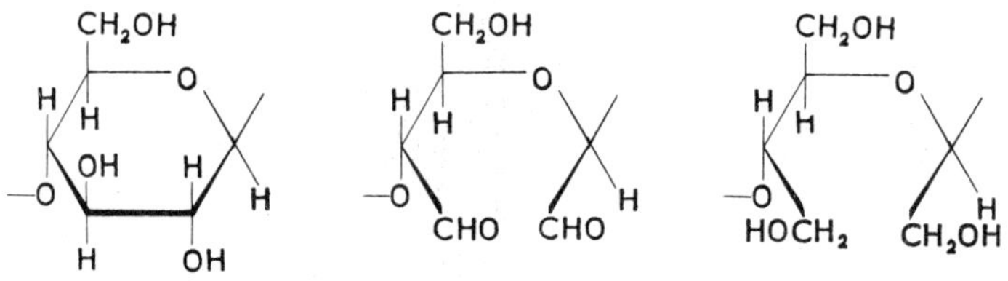

(LXXXI)   (LXXXIII)   (CXXXIX)

That the reaction proceeds in this fashion has been established by demonstrating that hydrolysis of the polyalcohol (CXXXIX) furnishes erythritol and glycolic aldehyde.

A similar reaction ensues in the case of 1 ⟶ 6 linked polymers. For example the polysaccharide (LXXVIII) gives first the polyaldehyde (LXXIX) and then the polyalcohol (CXL), which is recognized by the fact that upon hydrolysis it gives glycerol and glycolic aldehyde.

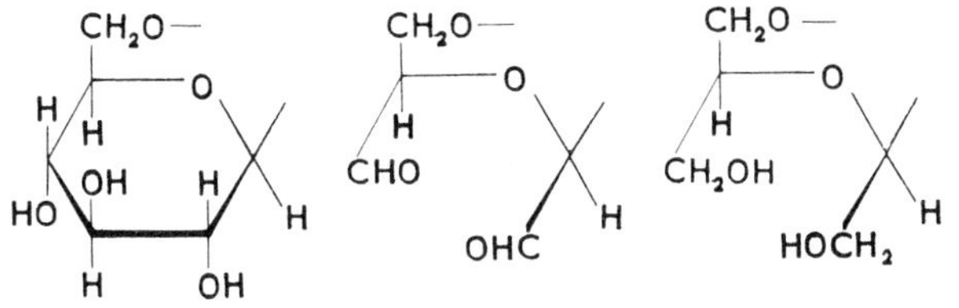

CH$_2$O—
H
H
OH   H
HO
H   OH

CH$_2$O—
H
CHO
OHC

CH$_2$O—
H
CH$_2$OH
HOCH$_2$

(LXXVIII)   (LXXIX)   (CXL)

Likewise, with the 1 ⟶ 2 linked polymers (LXXX), the polyaldehyde formed has the structure (LXXXII) and, as in the case of LXXXI but unlike that of LXXVIII, it is produced without loss of a carbon atom. Reduction of LXXXII affords the polyalcohol (CXLI) which upon cleavage yields glycerol and D-glyceraldehyde.

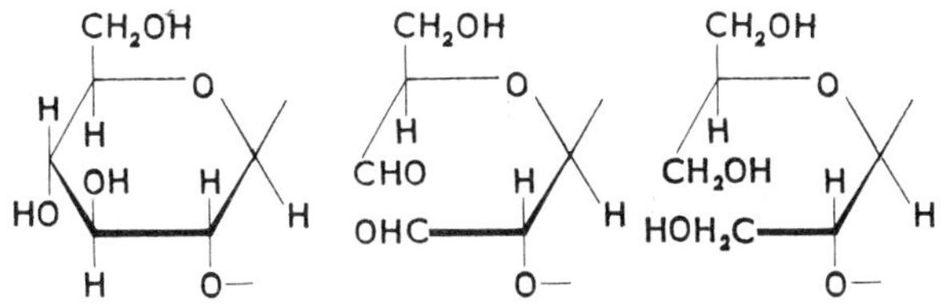

CH$_2$OH
H
H
OH   H
HO
H   O—

CH$_2$OH
H
CHO   H
OHC
O—

CH$_2$OH
H
CH$_2$OH   H
HOH$_2$C
O—

(LXXX)   (LXXXII)   (CXLI)

It will be apparent that the presence of any 1 ⟶ 3-linked hexose residues in a polymer will be shown by the fact that these residues will survive the periodate oxidation and will appear after the final hydrolysis step as free sugar. The structural significance of this type of information has already been pointed out (61).

The above considerations by themselves are subject to limitation as far as structural deductions are concerned. Thus both the 1 ⟶ 2 and the 1 ⟶ 6 linked polymers give rise to polyalcohols which yield glycerol upon hydrolysis; they may, of course, be distinguished by the identification of the other products of the hydrolysis of the polyalcohol, namely, glyceraldehyde from the 1 ⟶ 2 linked glucan and glycolic aldehyde from the 1 ⟶ 6 linked polymer. To confirm these results and to obtain more information about other structural features in the carbohydrate polymers, it is sometimes an advantage to investigate the hydrolysis products of the methylated polyalcohols.

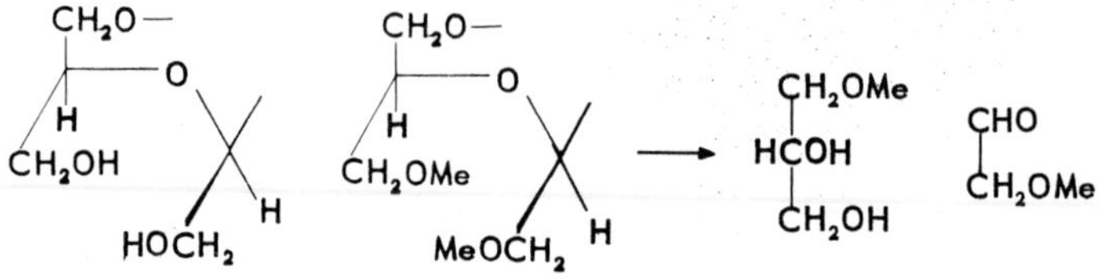

CH_2O- ... O ... H ... CH_2OH ... $HOCH_2$

(CXL)

CH_2O- ... O ... H ... CH_2OMe ... $MeOCH_2$ ... H →

(CXLII)

CH_2OMe
$HCOH$
CH_2OH

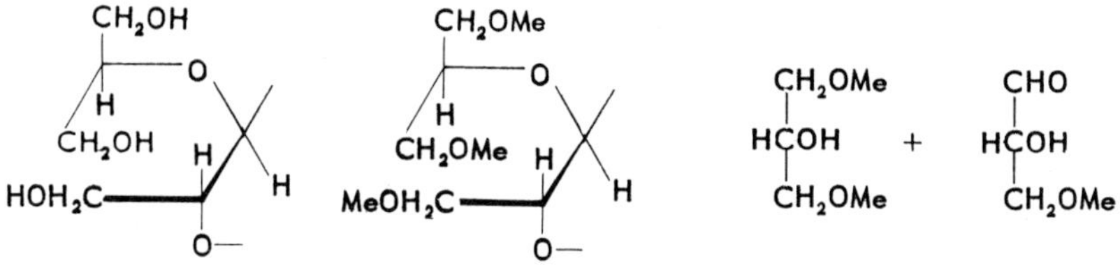

(CXLIII)

CHO
CH_2OMe

(CXLVI)

CH_2OH ... O ... H ... CH_2OH ... HOH_2C- ... H ... $O-$

(CXLI)

CH_2OMe ... O ... H ... CH_2OMe ... $MeOH_2C-$ ... H ... $O-$

(CXLIV)

CH_2OMe
$HCOH$
CH_2OMe

(CXLV)

$+$

CHO
$HCOH$
CH_2OMe

(CXLVII)

The methylated polyalcohol (CXLII) obtained from the 1 → 6 linked polymer is readily distinguished from the 1 → 2 linked polymer since the former yields optically active D-1-O-methyl-glycerol (CXLIII), while the methylated polyalcohol (CXLIV) from the latter gives 1,3-di-O-methyl-glycerol (CXLV). The two polymers LXXVIII and LXXX are also distinguishable by the fact that the corresponding methylated polyalcohols CXLII and CXLIV furnish methoxyacetaldehyde (CXLVI) and 3-O-methyl-D-glyceraldehyde (CXLVII), respectively.

The above method, based on the identification of the products of the hydrolysis of polysaccharide polyalcohols, is applicable also to pentose residues in carbohydrate polymers. Thus pentopyranose residues joined by 1 → 2 or 1 → 4 glycosidic linkages behave as follows:

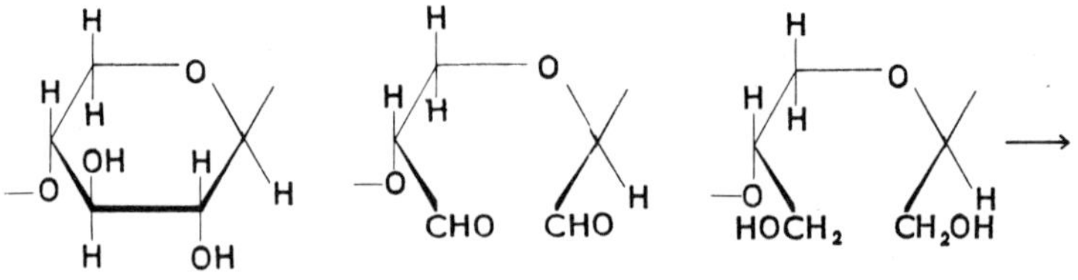

H ... O ... H ... H ... $-O$ ... OH ... H ... H ... H ... OH

(LIX)

H ... O ... H ... H ... $-O$ ... CHO ... CHO ... H

(LX)

H ... O ... H ... H ... $-O$ ... $HOCH_2$ ... CH_2OH ... H →

(CXLVIII)

CH_2OH
$CHOH$
CH_2OH

$+$

CHO
CH_2OH

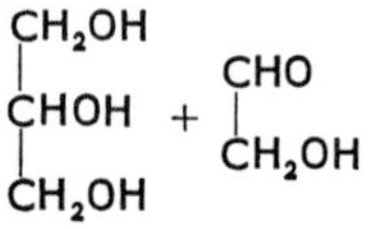

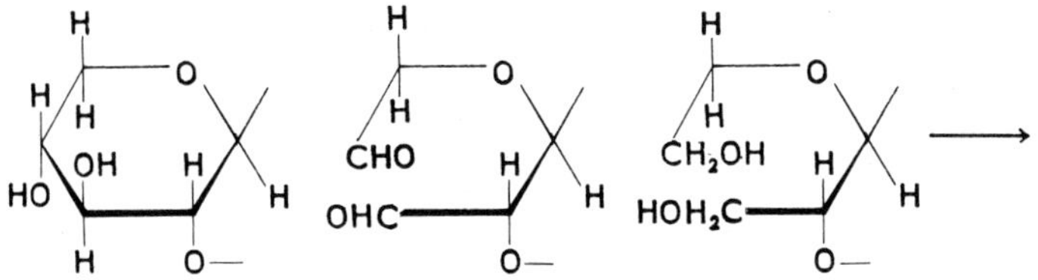

(LVII)   (LVIII)   (CXLIX)

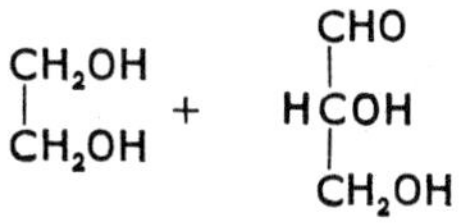

$$CH_2OH \atop CH_2OH \quad + \quad {CHO \atop H\overset{|}{C}OH \atop CH_2OH}$$

Furanose units of L-arabinose, for example, in polysaccharide gums, joined by 1 ⟶ 5 linkages may be recognized according to the following reaction:

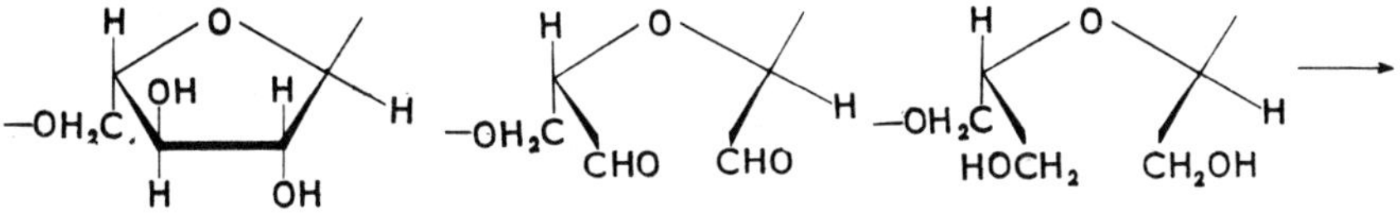

(LXVIII)   (LXIX)   (CL)

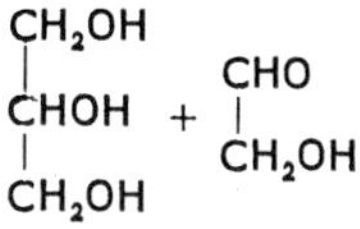

$$CH_2OH \atop CHOH \atop CH_2OH \quad + \quad {CHO \atop CH_2OH}$$

It will be apparent that methylation studies on the above polyalcohols, CXLVIII, CXLIX and CL, will also provide results of structural significance (see below).

The behavior and recognition of residues of 6-deoxyhexoses and uronic acids in polysaccharides proceeds along analogous lines.

Those units of the polysaccharide gums not cleaved by periodate oxidation for the reason that they do not possess adjacent hydroxyl groups, will be recognized in the hydrolysis products of the polyalcohol by the formation of intact sugar residues.

Similar information has been obtained from an examination of the products of hydrolysis of the polyaldehyde derived from polysaccharide gums. For example, periodate oxidation of egg plum (*Prunus domestica*) gum indicates that both the D-galactose and the L-arabinose units are joined in such a way as to render them stable to periodate, thus showing that these particular units do not possess adjacent hydroxyl groups (65,66).

Some difficulty, however, is encountered with this procedure since the aldehydic cleavage fragments undergo decomposition and condensation. In contrast, the polyalcohols can be hydrolyzed with dilute mineral acid without decomposition (61).

The utilization of this information derived from a study of simple carbohydrates has not been extensively applied, as yet, but some idea of its potential value may be illustrated by reference to the polysaccharide glycogen. The polyalcohol derived from this polysaccharide gives, upon hydrolysis, erythritol and glycerol in the ratio of 10:1; this is the same as the ratio of non-terminal to terminal residues of D-glucose, a result which agrees with those from other chemical methods (61,67).

Applied to the synthetic gum, dextran, produced by the action of *Leuconostoc mesenteroides* NRRL 512B on sucrose, the new method shows that hydrolysis of the dextran polyalcohol provides glycerol and glucose in a ratio of 20:1 which corresponds to the ratio of 1 ⟶ 6 to 1 ⟶ 3 linkages in the parent dextran gum (61,64). This also agrees reasonably well with the results of methylation studies on the dextran in question.

Another illustration is furnished by studies on the pentosan from wheat straw. The 1 ⟶ 4-linked D-xylose residues (LIX) in this polymer

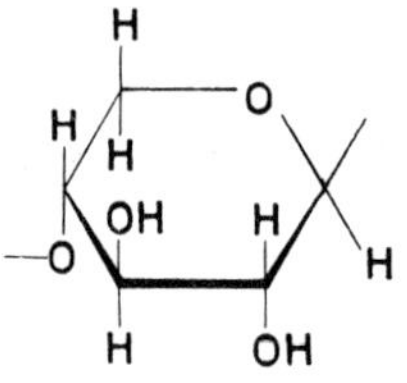

(LIX) 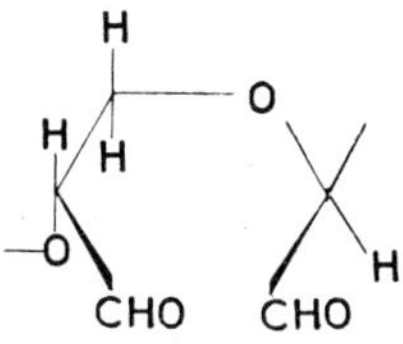   (LX)

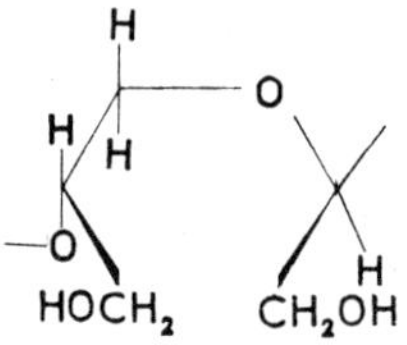

(CXLVIII) 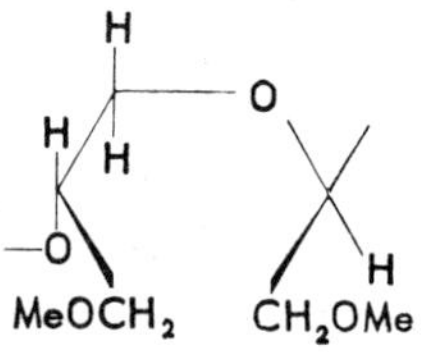   (CLI)

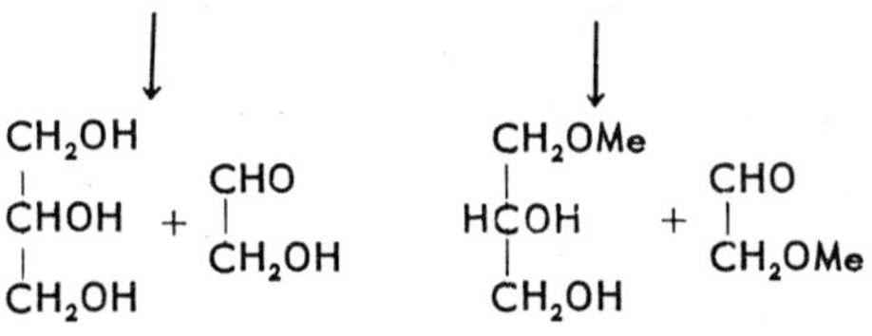

$$\begin{array}{ccc} CH_2OH & & CHO \\ | & & | \\ CHOH & + & CH_2OH \\ | & & \\ CH_2OH & & \end{array}$$

$$\begin{array}{ccc} CH_2OMe & & CHO \\ | & & | \\ HCOH & + & CH_2OMe \\ | & & \\ CH_2OH & & \end{array}$$

(CXLIII)   (CXLVI)

have been shown to undergo cleavage between C_2 and C_3 to give a polyaldehyde with LX as the monomeric unit. Reduction of LX gives the alcoholic residue (CXLVIII) which has been recognized, not only by the fact that upon hydrolysis it gives glycerol and glycolic aldehyde, but also by the observation that the methyl derivative (CLI) of CXLVIII yields upon hydrolysis D-1-*O*-methyl-glycerol (CXLIII) and methoxyacetaldehyde (CXLVI).

Branch points in carbohydrate polymers are also readily recognizable. The presence in starch of D-glucose residues linked through C_1, C_4 and C_6 is proved by the fact that this particular residue (LXXXV) undergoes the transformations below, giving finally D-1-*O*-methyl-erythritol (CLIV) *via* the polyalcohol (CLII) and its methyl ether (CLIII). This observation clearly distinguishes this triply linked residue from the more commonly occurring glucopyranose units linked through C_1 and C_4 which also furnishes erythritol upon periodate oxidation followed by reduction and hydrolysis, inasmuch as the latter gives rise to 1,4-di-*O*-methyl-erythritol (CLVII) when the methylated polyalcohol CLVI from CLV is hydrolyzed.

(LXXXV)

(LXXXVII)

(CLII)

(CLIV) (CXLVI) (CLIII)

(LXXXI)

(LXXXIII)

(CLV)

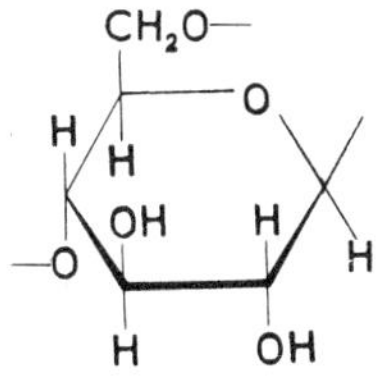

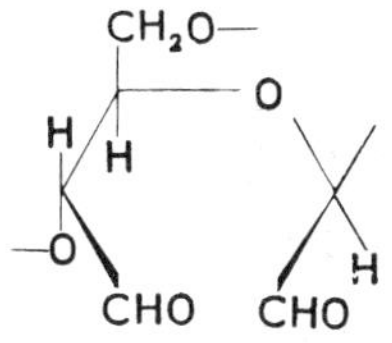

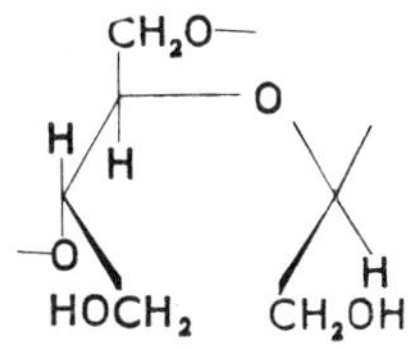

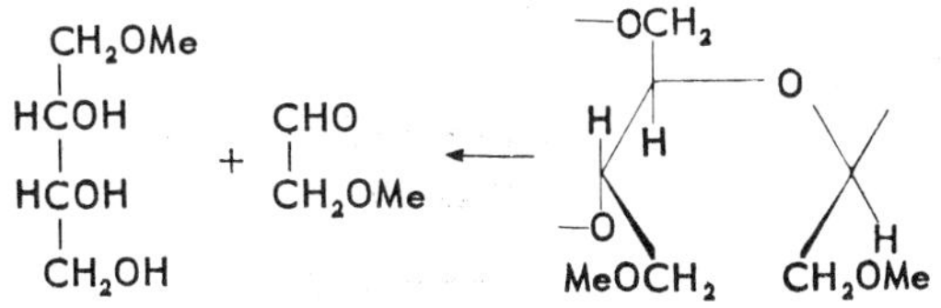

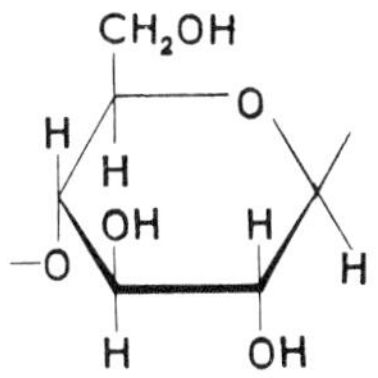

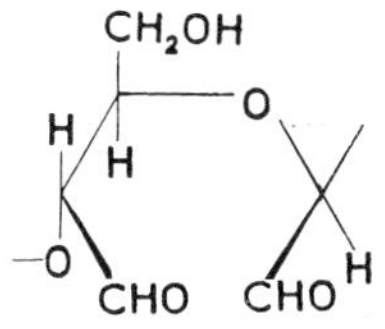

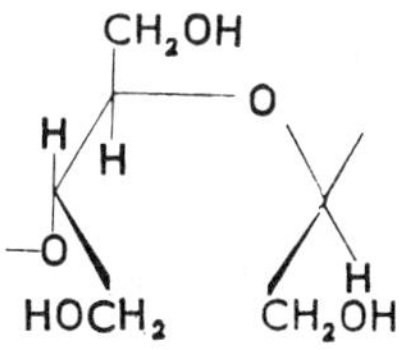

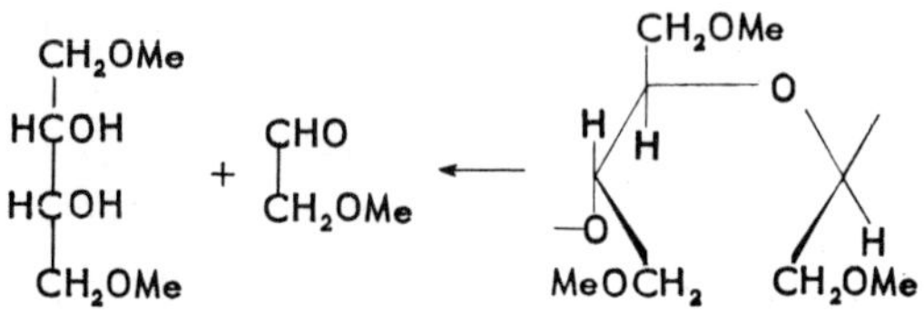

(CLVII)   (CLVI)

The concepts discussed above may be used not only to ascertain the nature of linkages by which one sugar residue is joined to another, but it may also be employed in certain cases to determine the relative positions of periodate stable and periodate oxidizable residues. A case in point is nigeran (CLVIII), the glucose polysaccharide extracted from *Aspergillus niger*. When CLVIII is treated with periodate, about half of the glucose remains unaffected by the oxidant, because of the presence of $1 \rightarrow 3$ linkages (68). That at least some of the D-glucose

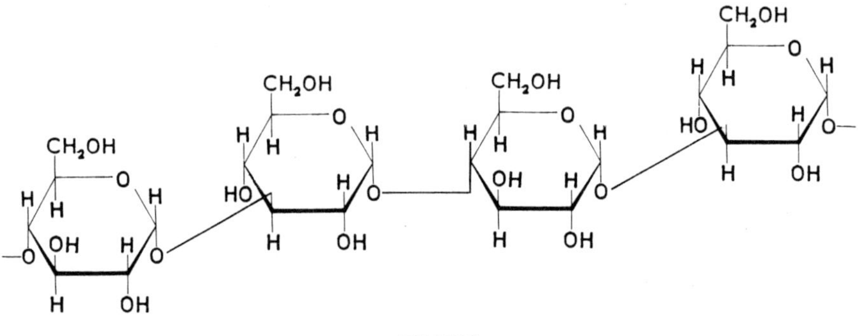

(CLVIII)

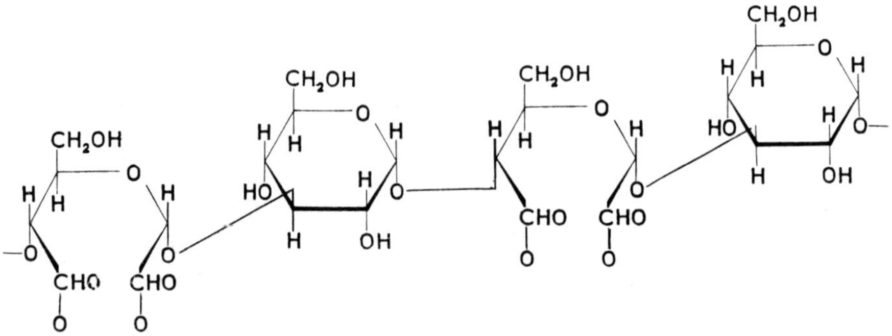

(CLIX)

units, stable to periodate, are separated from each other by periodate susceptible units, is demonstrated by the observation that treatment of the periodate oxidized polysaccharide (CLIX) with phenylhydrazine affords D-glucose phenylosazone; no oligosaccharide osazone was isolated (68).

Excellent use has been made of the capacity of phenylhydrazine (69–71), cyclohexylamine, and other hydrazines (75), to sever polysaccharide molecules at those sugar residues that have been oxidized by periodate. For instance, the conversion of gum arabic into a periodate-resistant galactan, by repetition of the alternate action of periodate and phenylhydrazine, provides evidence that at least a certain portion of the gum arabic molecule consists of D-galactopyranose units joined by 1 → 3-glycosidic linkages (69) (see Chapter 11 page 252).

The same general procedure has been employed to show that the neutral portion of the mucilages derived from *Dilsea edulis* is composed of D-galactopyranose residues joined by 1 → 3 linkages (76).

Diazotized aniline will react with the phenylhydrazine derivative, CLX, of periodate oxidized polysaccharides such as cellulose, starch and xylan to give formazans (CLXI) (73).

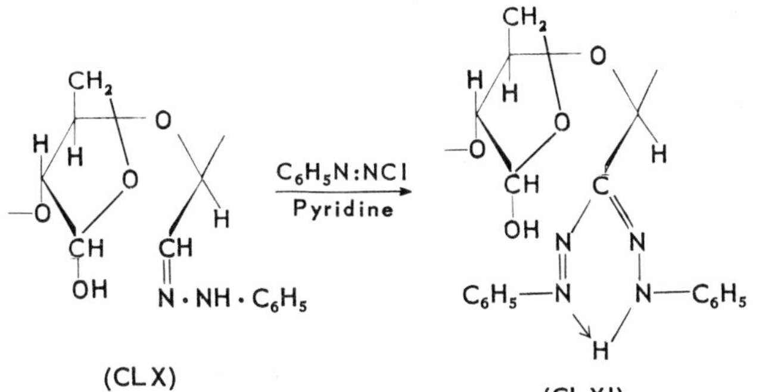

This reaction (72) has been taken to indicate that the phenylhydrazine derivative (CLX) possesses a cyclic structure (cf 71). This reaction might well prove to be valuable in the study of the more complicated polysaccharide gums and mucilages. It would be of some interest to ascertain whether the cyclic erythrose residue is indeed present in CLXI; this could be ascertained by reduction of CLXI followed by hydrolysis and the identification of erythritol.

The reduced products of periodate-oxidized glycosides, such as CXIV and CXV (see above), are much more sensitive to acid hydrolysis than are the parent periodate-oxidized compounds. Thus the alcohol (CXV) is

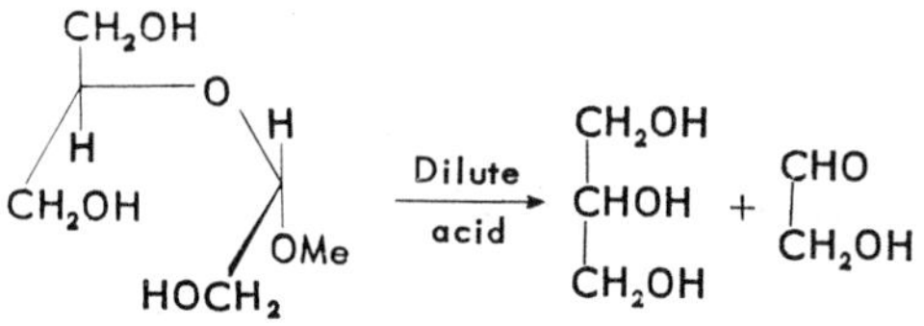

(CXV)

readily hydrolyzed with dilute acid to give glycerol and glycolic aldehyde and little or no decomposition occurs. The acetal linkage in CXV
is far more sensitive to acid than is the sugar ring system and hence the
former can be cleaved without affecting the latter. By oxidizing the
molecule of degraded gum arabic with periodate to cleave the outer-
most units of 6-$O(\beta$-D-glucopyranosyluronic acid)-D-galactopyranose and
then reducing the resulting product with sodium borohydride or with
hydrogen and Raney nickel, there is formed a galactan nucleus to which
are attached the now acid sensitive alcoholic residues (CLXII) which
can readily be removed by mild treatment with dilute acid to give a poly-

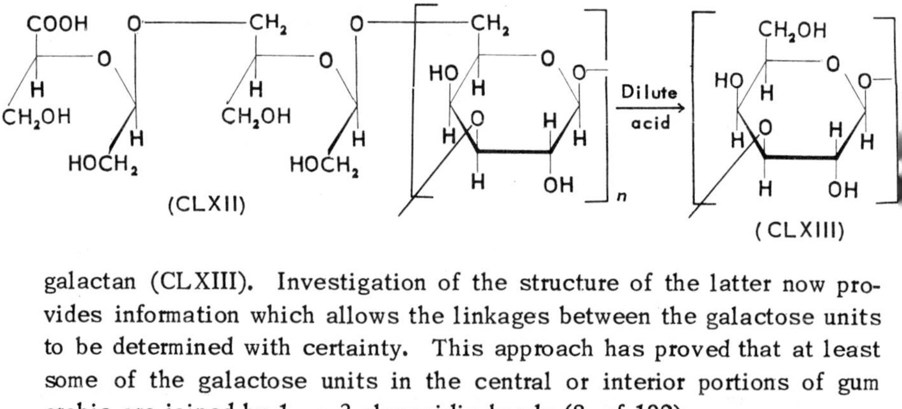

galactan (CLXIII). Investigation of the structure of the latter now provides information which allows the linkages between the galactose units
to be determined with certainty. This approach has proved that at least
some of the galactose units in the central or interior portions of gum
arabic are joined by 1 → 3 glycosidic bonds (8, cf 102).

In the previous sections of this chapter, attention has been focused
on the use of periodic acid and its salts in determining the structure of
carbohydrate polymers. It must be noted, however, that this excellent
oxidizing agent is capable of wide application in the determination of
the structure of the building units of polysaccharides and the cleavage
products of their methylated derivatives.

For example the amount of L-rhamnose or L-fucose present in the
hydrolyzate of a gum may be determined (77) from the amount of acetaldehyde formed upon oxidation with periodate thus:

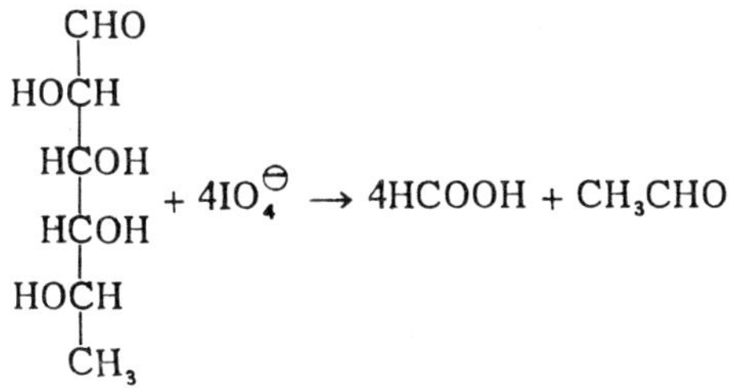

$$
\begin{array}{c}
\text{CHO} \\
| \\
\text{HOCH} \\
| \\
\text{HCOH} \\
| \\
\text{HCOH} \\
| \\
\text{HOCH} \\
| \\
\text{CH}_3
\end{array}
\; + \; 4\text{IO}_4^{\ominus} \;\rightarrow\; 4\text{HCOOH} + \text{CH}_3\text{CHO}
$$

Periodate oxidation has also been employed in the determination of those compounds, such as glycerol, D-glucitol, amylitol, and laminaritol (80), possessing the grouping CH_2OH—$CHOH$— since all of them give rise to formaldehyde which may then be determined by some colorimetric (81–83) or gravimetric (44,84–87) procedure. This provides a new route to the determination of the average molecular weight of reducing polysaccharides.

The degree of polymerization, DP, of polysaccharides, (see Chapter 6), possessing a terminal reducing residue can be ascertained by first treating the polysaccharide with sodium or potassium borohydride to give the corresponding "polysaccharitol," which is oxidized with periodate. The amount of formaldehyde produced is determined by some suitable colorimetric reagent, such as chromotropic acid (93). Since the hydrolysis products of the periodate-oxidized polysaccharides interfere with the formaldehyde determination by the chromotropic acid method, it is advisable to separate the formaldehyde by dialysis before carrying out the analysis (93). This is particularly important for reducing polysaccharides but for polymers having a DP of about 10–20 the formaldehyde can be determined directly (94). If the terminal reducing unit is an aldohexose residue it will give rise upon reduction and periodate oxidation to 2 moles of formaldehyde if it is joined to the rest of the molecule through C_3 or C_4, whereas it furnishes only one mole of formaldehyde if the linkage is through C_2, C_5 or C_6 (see below).

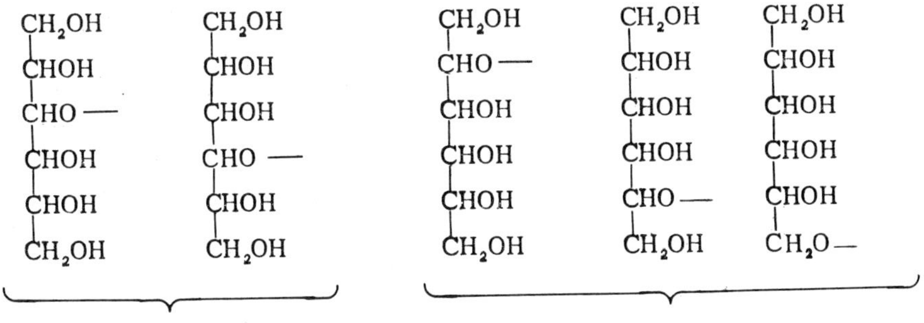

CH_2OH	CH_2OH	CH_2OH	CH_2OH	CH_2OH
$CHOH$	$CHOH$	CHO—	$CHOH$	$CHOH$
CHO—	$CHOH$	$CHOH$	$CHOH$	$CHOH$
$CHOH$	CHO—	$CHOH$	$CHOH$	$CHOH$
$CHOH$	$CHOH$	$CHOH$	CHO—	$CHOH$
CH_2OH	CH_2OH	CH_2OH	CH_2OH	CH_2O—

2 moles CH_2O 1 mole CH_2O

A terminal aldopentose residue will give rise to 2 moles of formaldehyde only if it is linked through C_3, whereas linkage through positions C_2, C_4 or C_5 will result in the production of 1 mole of formaldehyde thus:

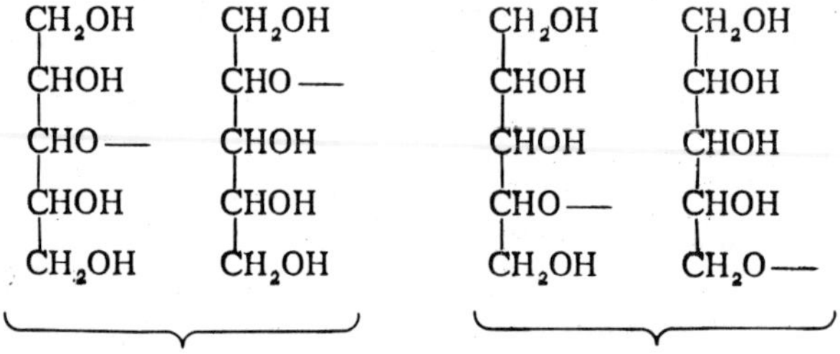

$$
\begin{array}{llll}
CH_2OH & CH_2OH & CH_2OH & CH_2OH \\
CHOH & CHO- & CHOH & CHOH \\
CHO- & CHOH & CHOH & CHOH \\
CHOH & CHOH & CHO- & CHOH \\
CH_2OH & CH_2OH & CH_2OH & CH_2O-
\end{array}
$$

$$\underbrace{\hphantom{CH_2OH \quad CH_2OH}}_{\text{2 moles } CH_2O} \qquad \underbrace{\hphantom{CH_2OH \quad CH_2OH}}_{\text{1 mole } CH_2O}$$

The determination of formaldehyde after periodate or lead tetraacetate oxidation is reported to distinguish between $1 \rightarrow 4$ and $1 \rightarrow 6$ linked disaccharides (78,79).

It is to be noted that oxidation of 2,3-di-O-methyl-L-fucose (CLXIV) provides the dialdehyde (CLXV) which in turn may be further oxidized to di-O-methyl-D-threaric acid, thus establishing the position of the two methoxyl groups.

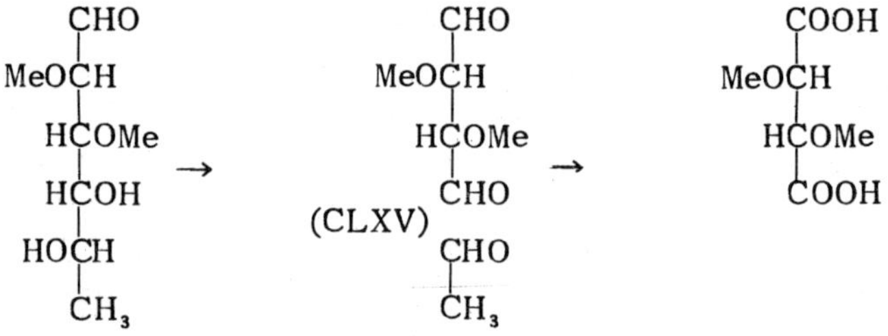

$$
\begin{array}{ccc}
CHO & CHO & COOH \\
MeOCH & MeOCH & MeOCH \\
HCOMe & HCOMe & HCOMe \\
HCOH \; \rightarrow & CHO & COOH \\
HOCH & CHO & \\
CH_3 & CH_3 & \\
(CLXIV) & (CLXV) \; \rightarrow &
\end{array}
$$

In a similar manner, it has been shown that periodate oxidation of 3,6-di-O-methyl-D-glucose affords 2,5-di-O-methyl-D-arabinose, the enantiomorph of the di-O-methyl-L-arabinose derivative obtained from methylated gum arabic. Similarly, periodate oxidation of 3,5-di-O-methyl-D-glucose gives 2,4-di-O-methyl-D-arabinose, the enantiomorph of the 2,4-di-O-methyl-L-arabinose obtained from the methylation studies of 3-O-(D-galactopyranosyl)-L-arabopyranose (37,88) produced from gum arabic. The products formed when the 2-, 3-, 4-, and 6-mono-O-methyl derivatives of D-glucose and various di-O-methyl glucoses are oxidized with periodate have been recognized by paper chromatography (98), and an attempt has been made to utilize the reaction for the quantitative determination of various methylated derivatives of glucose (86,96) and fructose (97).

In order to avoid complications from the formation of intermediate cyclic acetals during periodate oxidation (89), it is advisable to reduce the sugars to the corresponding alditols before applying the periodate oxidation. This can be done quantitatively with sodium borohydride (80,90) and it is unnecessary to isolate the glycitol before proceeding with the oxidation.

Periodate oxidation of phenylosazones has been used for the determination of the type of biose linkage in disaccharides (91,92). The method is based upon the observation that a hexose phenylosazone (CLXVII) consumes the theoretical amount of periodate and liberates 2 moles of formic acid and 1 mole of formaldehyde according to the equation:

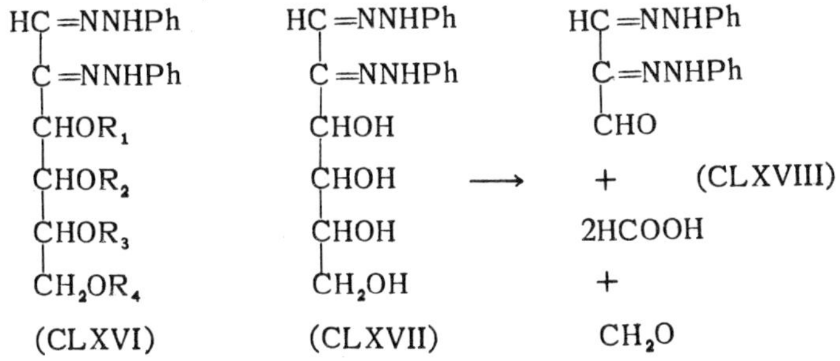

$$
\begin{array}{lll}
\text{HC}=\text{NNHPh} & \text{HC}=\text{NNHPh} & \text{HC}=\text{NNHPh} \\
\text{C}=\text{NNHPh} & \text{C}=\text{NNHPh} & \text{C}=\text{NNHPh} \\
\text{CHOR}_1 & \text{CHOH} & \text{CHO} \\
\text{CHOR}_2 & \text{CHOH} \longrightarrow & +\quad\text{(CLXVIII)} \\
\text{CHOR}_3 & \text{CHOH} & \text{2HCOOH} \\
\text{CH}_2\text{OR}_4 & \text{CH}_2\text{OH} & + \\
\text{(CLXVI)} & \text{(CLXVII)} & \text{CH}_2\text{O}
\end{array}
$$

At the same time mesoxaldehyde 1:2-bisphenylhydrazone (CLXVIII) crystallizes directly from the solution (92). Now in the case of a disaccharide osazone such as maltosazone (CLXVI, $R_2 = Gp$, $R_1 = R_3 = R_4 = H$) periodate oxidation of the osazone moiety of the disaccharide will yield 1 mole of formaldehyde while consuming 1 mole of periodate; no formic acid is formed in the reaction. The glucopyranosyl residue of the disaccharide will consume 2 moles of periodate and 1 mole of formic acid will be produced. If the disaccharide osazone possesses a 1 → 6 linkage as in the case of gentiobiosazone (CLXVI, $R_4 = Gp$ and $R_1 = R_2 = R_3 = H$), periodate oxidation affords 1 mole of formic acid from the osazone residue and 1 mole of formic acid from the glucopyranosyl unit of the disaccharide. In all, 4 moles of periodate are consumed without the formation of any formaldehyde. Inspection will show that the 1 → 3 linked disaccharide osazones will also give rise to formaldehyde.

The method has proved to be valuable in confirming the structures assigned to 5-O-L-arabofuranosyl-L-arabinose and 3-O-L-arabofuranosyl-L-arabinose. Precise titrimetric methods for periodate consumption and formic acid production and a colorimetric method for formaldehyde using a modified phenylhydrazine-ferricyanide method have enabled the procedure to be applied to semimicro amounts of material (91). It is also apparent that the method is applicable to the determination of the structure of certain partially methylated sugars provided that they can be transformed into crystalline osazones, as in the case of 3-O-methyl-D-glucose.

REFERENCES

1. Malaprade, L., *Bull. soc. chim.*, **43**, 683 (1928); *Compt. rend.*, **186**, 382 (1928).
2. Huebner, C. F., Lohmar, R., Dimler, R. J., Moore, S., and Link, K. P., *J. Biol. Chem.*, **159**, 503 (1945).
3. Sprinson, D. B., and Chargaff, E., *J. Biol. Chem.*, **164**, 433 (1946).
4. Smith, F., *J. Chem. Soc.*, 2646 (1951).
5. Grangaard, D. H., Gladding, E. K., and Purves, C. B., *Paper Trade J.*, **115**, (No. 7), 41 (1942).
6. Halsall, T. G., Hirst, E. L., and Jones, J. K. N., *J. Chem. Soc.*, 1427 (1947).
7. Abdel-Akher, M., Smith, F., and Spriestersbach, D. R., *J. Chem. Soc.*, 3637 (1952).
8. Smith, F., and Spriestersbach, D. R., *Abstracts 128th A.C.S. Meeting, Minneapolis, Minn.*, (1955).
9. Hirst, E. L., Jones, J. K. N., and Jones, Winifred O., *J. Chem. Soc.*, 1880 (1939).
10. Levene, P. A., and Kreider, L. C., *J. Biol. Chem.*, **120**, 591 (1937).
11. Jackson, E. L., in *"Organic Reactions,"* **II**, John Wiley and Sons, New York, (1944) 341.
12. Bobbitt, J. M., *Advances in Carbohydrate Chem.*, **11**, 1 (1956).
13. Jackson, E. L., and Hudson, C. S., *J. Am. Chem. Soc.*, **58**, 378 (1936).
14. Jackson, E. L., and Hudson, C. S., *J. Am. Chem. Soc.*, **59**, 994 (1937).
15. Jackson, E. L., and Hudson, C. S., *J. Am. Chem. Soc.*, **60**, 989 (1938).
16. Jackson, E. L., and Hudson, C. S., *J. Am. Chem. Soc.*, **61**, 959 (1939).
17. Dyer, J. R., *"Methods of Biochemical Analysis,"* Vol. 3, Interscience Pub., New York, (1956) 111.
18. Smith, F., and Van Cleve, J. W., *J. Am. Chem. Soc.*, **77**, 3091 (1955).
19. Smith, F., Presented at the 115th A. C. S. Meeting, San Francisco (1949).
20. Meyer, K. H., and Baldwin, G., *Helv. Chim. Acta*, **36**, 597 (1953).
21. Abdel-Akher, M., Cadotte, J. E., Lewis, B. A., Montgomery, R., Smith, F., and Van Cleve, J. W., *Nature*, **171**, 474 (1953).
22. Hamilton, J. K., Huffman, G. W., and Smith, F., unpublished.
23. Anderson, E., and Otis, Louise, *J. Am. Chem. Soc.*, **52**, 4461 (1930).
24. White, E. V., *J. Am. Chem. Soc.*, **70**, 367 (1948).
25. Dimler, R. J., Davis, H. A., and Hilbert, G. E., *J. Am. Chem. Soc.*, **68**, 1377 (1946).
26. Alexander, B. H., Dimler, R. J., and Mehltretter, C. L., *J. Am. Chem. Soc.*, **73**, 4658 (1951).
27. Klosterman, H., and Smith, F., *J. Am. Chem. Soc.*, **74**, 5336 (1952).

28. Baddiley, J., Buchanan, J. G., and Szalbó, L., *J. Chem. Soc.*, 3826 (1954).
29. Connell, J. J., Hirst, E. L., and Percival, E. G. V., *J. Chem. Soc.*, 3494 (1950).
30. Neumüller, G., and Vasseur, E., *Arkiv för Kemi*, **5,** 235 (1953).
31. Potter, A. L., and Hassid, W. Z., *J. Am. Chem. Soc.*, **70,** 3488 (1948).
32. Jeanes, Allene, Haynes, W. C., Wilham, C. A., Rankin, J. C., Melvin, E. H., Austin, Marjorie J., Cluskey, J. E., Fisher, B. E., Tsuchiya, H. M., and Rist, C. E., *J. Am. Chem. Soc.*, **76,** 5041 (1954).
33. Halsall, T. G., Hirst, E. L., and Jones, J. K. N., *J. Chem. Soc.*, 1399 (1947).
34. Barry, V. C., *Sci. Proc. Roy. Dublin Soc.*, **22,** 59 (1939).
35. Percival, E. G. V., and Ross, A. G., *J. Chem. Soc.*, 720 (1951).
36. Barry, V. C., *J. Chem. Soc.*, 578 (1942).
37. Huffman, G. W., Lewis, B. A., Smith, F., and Spriestersbach, D. R., *J. Am. Chem. Soc.*, **77,** 4346 (1955).
38. Barker, G. R., and Smith, D. C. C., *Chemistry and Industry*, 1035 (1952).
39. Hirst, E. L., Jones, J. K. N., and Roudier, A. J., *J. Chem. Soc.*, 1779 (1948).
40. Morrison, M., Kuyper, A. C., and Orten, J. M., *J. Am. Chem. Soc.*, **75,** 1502 (1953).
41. Perlin, A. S., *J. Am. Chem. Soc.*, **76,** 4101 (1954).
42. Peat, S., Whelan, W. J., and Lawley, H. C., *Chemistry and Industry*, 35 (1955).
43. Peat, S., Whelan, W. J., Lawley, H. G., and Evans, J. M., *Biochem. J.*, **61,** [1], *Proc.* x (1955).
44. Reeves, R. E., *J. Am. Chem. Soc.*, **63,** 1476 (1941).
45. Hirst, E. L., and Jones, J. K. N., *J. Chem. Soc.*, 1659 (1949).
46. Abdel-Akher, M., and Smith, F., *J. Am. Chem. Soc.*, **73,** 1994 (1951).
47. Ahmed, Z. F., and Whistler, R. L., *J. Am. Chem. Soc.*, **72,** 2524 (1950).
48. Rafique, C. M., and Smith, F., *J. Am. Chem. Soc.*, **72,** 4634 (1950).
49. Hirst, E. L., and Jones, J. K. N., *J. Chem. Soc.*, 1278 (1948).
50. Larson, E. B., and Smith, F., *J. Am. Chem. Soc.*, **77,** 429 (1955).
51. Cifonelli, J. A., and Smith, F., *J. Am. Chem. Soc.*, **77,** 5682 (1955).
52. Aspinall, G. O., and Telfer, R. G. J., *J. Chem. Soc.*, 3519 (1954).
53. Gilles, K. A., Huffman, G. W., Meredith, W. O. S., and Smith, F., unpublished.
54. Acker, L., Diemair, W., Samhammer, E., *Z. Lebensm. Unters. u. Forsch.*, **100,** 180 (1955).
55. Acker, L., Diemair, W., and Samhammer, E., *Z. Lebensm. Unters. u. Forsch.*, **102,** 225 (1955).
56. Domenigg, H. S., and Smith, F., unpublished.
57. Meyer, K. H., and Gürtler, P., *Helv. Chim. Acta*, **30,** 751 (1947).
58. Haworth, W. N., Heath, R. L., and Peat, S., *J. Chem. Soc.*, 833 (1941).
59. Haworth, W. N., Hirst, E. L., and Isherwood, F. A., *J. Chem. Soc.*, 784 (1937).
60. Fischer, F. G., and Dörfel, H., *Z. physiol. Chem.*, **302,** 186 (1955).
61. Abdel-Akher, M., Hamilton, J. K., Montgomery, R., and Smith, F., *J. Am. Chem. Soc.*, **74,** 4970 (1952).
62. Jayme, G., and Maris, S., *Ber.*, **77,** 383 (1944).
63. Lohmar, R., *J. Am. Chem. Soc.*, **74,** 4974 (1952).

64. Sloan, J. W., Alexander, B. H., Lohmar, R. L., Wolff, I. A., and Rist, C. E., *J. Am. Chem. Soc.*, **76**, 4429 (1954).
65. Hirst, E. L., and Jones, J. K. N., *J. Chem. Soc.*, 1064 (1947).
66. Hirst, E. L., and Jones, J. K. N., *J. Chem. Soc.*, 120 (1948).
67. Abdel-Akher, M. and Smith, F., *Arch. Biochem. Biophys.*, **78**, 451 (1958).
68. Barker, S. A., Bourne, E. J., and Stacey, M., *J. Chem. Soc.*, 3084 (1953).
69. Dillon, T., O'Ceallachan, Donnachadha, F., and O'Colla, P., *Proc. Roy. Irish Acad.*, **55B**, 331 (1953).
70. Barry, V. C., *Nature*, **152**, 537 (1943).
71. Barry, V. C., and Mitchell, P. W. D., *J. Chem. Soc.*, 4020 (1954).
72. Mester, L., *J. Am. Chem. Soc.*, **77**, 5452 (1955).
73. Mester, L., and Major, A., *J. Am. Chem. Soc.*, **77**, 4297 (1955).
74. Mester, L., *J. Am. Chem. Soc.*, **77**, 4301 (1955).
75. Barry, V. C., and Mitchell, P. W. D., *J. Chem. Soc.*, 3610 (1953).
76. Barry, V. C., and Dillon, T., *Proc. Roy. Irish Acad.*, **50B**, 349 (1945).
77. Nicolet, B. H., and Shinn, L. A., *J. Am. Chem. Soc.*, **63**, 1456 (1941).
78. Ahlborg, K., *Svensk Kem. Tidskr.*, **54**, 205 (1942).
79. Jeanloz, R., *Helv. Chim. Acta*, **27**, 1501 (1944).
80. Abdel-Akher, M., Hamilton, J. K., and Smith, F., *J. Am. Chem. Soc.*, **73**, 4691 (1951).
81. MacFadyen, D. A., *J. Biol. Chem.*, **158**, 107 (1945).
82. Lambert, Marguerite, and Neish, A. C., *Can. J. Res.*, **B28**, 83 (1950).
83. Frisell, W. R., Meech, L. A., and Mackenzie, C. G., *J. Biol. Chem.*, **207**, 709 (1954).
84. Vorländer, D., *Z. anal. Chem.*, **77**, 241 (1929).
85. Yoe, J. H., and Reid, L. C., *Ind. Eng. Chem., Anal. Ed.*, **13**, 238 (1941).
86. Bell, D. J., *J. Chem. Soc.*, 992 (1948).
87. Fleury, P., and Courtois, J., *Bull. soc. chim.*, **8**, 75 (1941).
88. Fried, J. and Walz, Doris E., *J. Am. Chem. Soc.*, **74**, 5468 (1952).
89. Cadotte, J., Dutton, G. G. S., Goldstein, I. J., Lewis, B. A., Smith, F., and Van Cleve, J. W., *J. Am. Chem. Soc.*, **79**, 691 (1957).
90. Frush, Harriet L., and Isbell, H. S., *J. Am. Chem. Soc.*, **78**, 2844 (1956).
91. Hough, L., Powell, D. B., and Woods, B. M., *J. Chem. Soc.*, 4799 (1956).
92. Stodola, F. H., Sharpe, E. S., and Koepsell, H. J., *J. Am. Chem. Soc.*, **75**, 2514 (1956).
93. Unrau, A. M., and Smith, F., *Chemistry and Industry*, 330 (1957).
94. Hough, L., and Perry, M. B., *Chemistry and Industry*, 768 (1956). Hough, L., Woods, B. M., and Perry, M. B., *Chemistry and Industry*, 1100 (1957).
95. Smith, F., and Montgomery, R., in "*Methods of Biochemical Analysis*," Vol. 3, Interscience, New York (1956), 153.
96. Bell, D. J., Palmer, Anne, and Johns, A. T., *J. Chem. Soc.*, 1536 (1949).
97. Mitchell, W. E. A., and Percival, Elizabeth, *J. Chem. Soc.*, 1423 (1954).
98. Lemieux, R. V., and Bauer, H. F., *Can. J. Chem.*, **31**, 814 (1953).
99. Taylor, J. E., *J. Am. Chem. Soc.*, **75**, 3912 (1953).
100. Goldstein, I. J., Smith, F., and Unrau, A. M., *Chemistry and Industry*, 124 (1959).
101. Whistler, R. L., and Kirby, K. W., *Z. Physiol. Chem.*, **314**, 46 (1959).
102. Goldstein, I. J., Hay, G. W., Lewis, B. A., and Smith, F., Abstracts 135th A.C.S. Meeting, Boston, Mass., (1959), 3D.

CHAPTER 10

SEPARATION AND IDENTIFICATION
OF THE CLEAVAGE PRODUCTS
OF METHYLATED GUMS AND MUCILAGES

Mixtures of methylated sugars were formerly separated by fractional distillation of their methyl glycosides (1). Losses occur in this procedure and for quantitative work more material is necessary than is available in most investigations of polysaccharides. Improvements in the separation of methylated sugars resulted from the application of solvent extraction (110) and from the resolution of the colored azoyl derivatives on columns of inorganic material, such as aluminum oxide or silica using the classical adsorption chromatographic techniques (2–6). Difficulties were encountered, however, since the α- and β-anomers tended to separate, but by reducing the methyl sugars to the corresponding alcohols this problem is eliminated (7). The separation of the methyl glycosides of methylated sugars has been brought about on columns of alumina (8,9). Thus, methyl 2,3,4,6-tetra-O- and methyl 2,3,6-tri-O-methyl-D-glucoside were resolved. A partial separation of a mixture of methyl 2,3,4-tri-O-methyl-D-xyloside and methyl 2,3,5-tri-O-methyl-L-arabofuranoside obtained from methylated damson gum was also effected although the experiment was complicated by the fact that the α- and β-glycosides of the two methylated sugars were also resolved (10). A somewhat similar separation of mixtures of 2,3,4,6-tetra-, 2,3,6-tri- and 2,3-di-O-methyl-D-glucose, can be carried out with silica gel (10,100) and with alumina (11), the sugars on the latter column being recognized by their fluorescence in ultraviolet light.

These methods are seldom used at the present time since the technique is rather more complicated and exacting than those employed using partition chromatography. The same disadvantage applies to the use of columns of Silene EF (12) although this has proved to be an excellent material for separating sugar acetates. Celite has recently been recommended for separating sugars and their methyl derivatives (117).

Vapor phase chromatography has not yet been applied to the separation of the methyl glycosides of methylated sugars but it is to be noted that some success has attended the separation, using thermal diffusion, of a mixture of methyl 2,3,4,6-tetra-O-methyl-D-galactoside and methyl 2,3,6-tri-O-methyl-D-glucoside (101).

The methods preferred at the present time for the separation of mixtures of methylated sugars, sugar acids, and alcohols, obtained by hydrolysis of methylated gums and mucilages are those making use of partition chromatography. The general techniques developed for the unmethylated compounds (see Chapter 7) are usually applicable, the only difference being in the nature of the irrigating solvents and, in certain instances, in somewhat different spray reagents for detecting the methylated sugars. The development of these methods has made it possible to determine on a microscale the composition and hence the general structure of a methylated polysaccharide. Whereas anything from 1 to 100 g. of methylated polysaccharide was formerly necessary for a methylation study (1), the same results can now be achieved with only a few hundred milligrams.

Solvents that have been found particularly useful in partition chromatography for separating methylated sugars and their derivatives are: 1-butanol: ethanol: water (4: 1: 5) (13,14), benzene: ethanol: water (169: 47: 15 and 200: 47: 15) (15,16) and butanone: water azeotrope (17,18). In the case of the last irrigant, ammonia should be added to suppress trailing of the sugars. Addition of boric acid to the irrigating solvent is reported (20) to improve the separation of methylated sugars. For methylated uronic acids 1-butanol: water: acetic acid has been recommended (21,27).

The methods of detecting the methylated sugars on chromatograms are similar to those used for the unmethylated sugars (see Chapter 7), emphasis, however, being on those reagents which transform the sugars into furfural derivatives since these give colors with aromatic amines. Silver nitrate can be used for the methylated sugars containing one or two methoxyl groups, but it is less sensitive for the more highly methylated derivatives than are the amine reagents. These last named reagents also have the advantage over most silver nitrate reagents in that no interfering background color is produced.

The amine reagents, when suitably chosen, are capable of distinguishing certain of the methylated sugars by the different colors formed (17,21). Thus N,N-di-methyl-p-aminoaniline readily distinguishes 2, 3, 4-tri-O-methyl-D-xylose from 2, 3, 5-tri-O-methyl-L-arabinose (17) even though their R_F values are quite similar; likewise urea oxalate will differentiate 2,3,4,6-tetra-O-methyl-D-glucose from 1,3,4,5-tetra-O-methyl-D-fructose (19). And almost all aromatic amine reagents give different colors with the di-, tri- and tetra-O-methyl sugars.

The R_F values of some methyl sugars using 1-butanol : ethanol : water (13) and butanone : water azeotrope (17), two of the more commonly used irrigating solvents are recorded in Table 43. For other useful solvents and R_F values the reader is referred to references 23–26. The values quoted in Table 43 are not absolute values and in practice it is advisable to put a known compound on the chromatogram as the standard of reference; all unknown methylated sugars should be compared directly on the same chromatogram with known standard methylated sugars.

TABLE 43. PAPER CHROMATOGRAPHIC SEPARATION OF METHYLATED SUGARS

Substance	Solvent	
	$R_G{}^a$(1-Butanol:ethanol:water (4 : 1 : 5)) (13,14)	R_F(Butanone:water azeotrope) (17)
L-*Arabinose*	0.12	0.04
2-O-methyl	0.38	0.14
2,3-di-O-methyl	0.64	. . .
2,4-di-O-methyl	. . .	0.26
2,5-di-O-methyl	. . .	0.58
2,3,4-tri-O-methyl	. . .	0.58
2,3,5-tri-O-methyl	0.95	0.82
D-*Lyxose*		
2,3,5-tri-O-methyl	. . .	0.72
D-*Xylose*	0.15	0.058
2-O-methyl	0.38	0.21
3-O-methyl	. . .	0.23
2,3-di-O-methyl	0.74	0.58
2,4-di-O-methyl	0.66	. . .
3,4-di-O-methyl	. . .	0.57
3,5-di-O-methyl	. . .	0.63
2,3,4-tri-O-methyl	0.94	0.80
L-*Fucose*	0.21	0.05
2-O-methyl	0.51	. . .
3-O-methyl (digitalose)	0.45	. . .
3,4-di-O-methyl	0.67	. . .
2,3,4-tri-O-methyl	. . .	0.72
L-*Rhamnose*	0.30	0.086
4-O-methyl	0.57	. . .
2,4-di-O-methyl	. . .	0.64
3,4-di-O-methyl	0.84	. . .
2,3,4-tri-O-methyl	1.01	0.87

(a)The R_G value is the distance moved by the methylated sugar divided by the distance moved by 2,3,4,6-tetra-O-methyl-D-glucose.

TABLE 43. (CONTINUED)

Substance	Solvent	
	R_G(1-Butanol:ethanol:water (4:1:5)) (13,14)	R_F(Butanone:water azeotrope) (17)
D-*Galactose*	0.07	0.011
2-*O*-methyl	0.23	0.06
4-*O*-methyl	0.16	...
6-*O*-methyl	...	0.043
2,4-di-*O*-methyl	0.41	0.14
2,6-di-*O*-methyl	0.44	...
3,4-di-*O*-methyl	0.32	...
4,6-di-*O*-methyl	0.42	...
2,3,4-tri-*O*-methyl	0.64	0.36
2,3,6-tri-*O*-methyl	0.71	0.48
2,4,6-tri-*O*-methyl	0.67	0.37
3,4,6-tri-*O*-methyl	...	0.33
2,3,4,6-tetra-*O*-methyl	0.88	0.68
2,3,5,6-tetra-*O*-methyl	...	0.88
D-*Glucose*	0.090	0.013
2-*O*-methyl	0.22	0.061
3-*O*-methyl	0.26	0.08
4-*O*-methyl	...	0.07
6-*O*-methyl	0.27	0.053
2,3-di-*O*-methyl	0.57	0.28
2,4-di-*O*-methyl	...	0.20
2,6-di-*O*-methyl	0.51	0.18
3,4-di-*O*-methyl	0.52	...
3,5-di-*O*-methyl	...	0.33
3,6-di-*O*-methyl	0.51	0.20
4,6-di-*O*-methyl	0.46	...
2,3,4-tri-*O*-methyl	0.85	0.58
2,3,6-tri-*O*-methyl	0.83	0.56
2,4,6-tri-*O*-methyl	0.76	0.48
3,4,6-tri-*O*-methyl	...	0.49
2,3,4,6-tetra-*O*-methyl	1.00	0.78
2,3,5,6-tetra-*O*-methyl	1.01	...
D-*Mannose*	0.11	0.023
4-*O*-methyl	0.32	0.13
2,3-di-*O*-methyl	0.54	0.22
3,4-di-*O*-methyl	0.58	0.32
4,6-di-*O*-methyl	0.57	...
2,3,6-tri-*O*-methyl	0.81	0.50
2,3,4-tri-*O*-methyl	...	0.60
2,4,6-tri-*O*-methyl	...	0.55
3,4,6-tri-*O*-methyl	0.79	...
2,3,4,6-tetra-*O*-methyl	0.96	0.78

Sometimes separation of isomeric methylated sugars is not possible by paper partition chromatography. In such cases, however, it is usually possible to devise a chemical reaction that will affect only one component so as to facilitate the separation. Thus, for example, chromatographic separation of 2,4,6-tri-O- and 3,4,6-tri-O-methyl-D-mannose can be effected by treatment of the mixture with acetone in the presence of an acid catalyst which reacts only with the 3,4,6-tri-O-methyl isomer yielding the corresponding 1,2-O-isopropylidene derivative. The latter moves much more rapidly on the chromatogram and can readily be separated from the unchanged 2,4,6-tri-O-methyl-D-mannose in the usual way. Alternatively, this problem may be solved by treating the mixture of tri-O-methyl-mannoses with periodate to transform the 3,4,6-tri-O-methyl derivative into 2,3,5-tri-O-methyl-D-arabinose which is readily separated from 2,4,6-tri-O-methyl-D-mannose (28). In a similar manner 3,4,6-tri-O-methyl-D-fructose can be separated from 1,3,4-tri-O-methyl-D-fructopyranose by reacting the mixture with acetone; this converts the former into 1,2-O-isopropylidene-3,4,6-tri-O-methyl-D-fructose (31) after which the mixture is readily resolved either chromatographically (29) or by solvent extraction.

For the separation of a methylated aldose from an isomeric methylated ketose the former may be oxidized with bromine to the corresponding aldonic acid and then removed from the unchanged methylated ketose by absorption on an anion exchange column. In this way 2,3,4-tri-O-methyl-D-glucose has been separated from 1,3,4-tri-O- and 3,4,6-tri-O-methyl-D-fructose (19,29). Similarly, 2,3,4,6-tetra-O-methyl-D-glucose can be separated from 1,3,4,6-tetra-O-methyl-D-fructose (32) or, alternatively, the amount present can be determined by hypoiodite oxidation since only aldoses are affected in this reaction (19).

Selective furanoside formation may also be used to separate mixtures of methyl sugars that cannot be resolved directly. Thus 2,3,6-tri-O-methyl-D-glucose can be separated in this manner from 2,4,6-tri-O-methyl-D-glucose (95) and it may be separated in the same way from 2,3,6-tri-O-methyl-D-mannose. The latter does not readily form a furanoside, although the C_4 hydroxyl group is available for ring formation, since the stereochemistry of the mannose molecule in this case prevents it (64).

It has long been known that polyhydroxy compounds including the sugars form complexes with the borate ion (96,97). By making use of this fact it has been found possible to separate sugars and sugar derivatives that are otherwise difficult to separate, by means of paper electrophoresis in the presence of a borate buffer (33–40). Thus, at pH 8.6 D-glucose is readily separated from D-mannose whereas by the usual paper chromatography, separation, except with ethyl acetate:pyridine:water or butanone:water, is difficult at best.

The method is equally, or even more, effective in resolving mixtures of methylated sugars; those that form complexes are easily separated from those that do so only weakly or not at all. Thus 2,3,6-tri-O-methyl-D-mannose and 3,4,6-tri-O-methyl-D-mannose cannot be separated by paper chromatography either with 1-butanol:ethanol:water or with butanone:water azeotrope, but by paper electrophoresis in the presence of a borate buffer they are easily distinguished since the 3,4,6-tri-O-methyl derivative forms a complex which consequently moves more rapidly towards the anode. Inspection of Table 44 shows that the 2,4-, 3,4-, 3,6- and 4,6-di-O-methyl derivatives of D-glucose are readily separated from each other by paper electrophoresis, whereas their separation by paper partition chromatography presents some difficulty. This technique has not been used extensively in the study of partially methylated sugars, but its possibilities can be judged by reference to the electrophoretic (ionophoretic) mobilities of certain methylated sugars recorded in Table 44 (41-43). It is clear that used in conjunction with a colorimetric method of sugar determination this electrophoretic technique can form the basis of a quantitative procedure for determining certain methylated sugars.

TABLE 44. SEPARATION OF METHYLATED SUGARS BY
PAPER ELECTROPHORESIS

(Borate buffer; 600 volts)

Substance	M_G Values[a]	
	pH 10 (41)	pH 9.2 (43)
D-Xylose	...	0.44
2-O-methyl	...	0.00
3-O-methyl	...	0.00
2,3-di-O-methyl	...	0.71
2,3,6-tri-O-methyl	...	0.56
L-Rhamnose	0.52	0.73
2,3-di-O-methyl	0.02	...
2,4-di-O-methyl	0.05	...
3,4-di-O-methyl	0.36	...
D-Fructose	0.90	0.90
3,4-di-O-methyl	...	0.46
1,3,4-tri-O-methyl	...	0.00
1,3,4,6-tetra-O-methyl	...	0.00

TABLE 44. (CONTINUED)

Substance	M_G Values [a]	
	pH 10 (41)	pH 9.2 (43)
D-Glucose	1.00	1.00
2-O-methyl	0.23	0.24
3-O-methyl	0.82	0.59
4-O-methyl	0.00	0.20
6-O-methyl	0.71	0.63
2,3-di-O-methyl	0.12	...
2,4-di-O-methyl	0.05	0.07
3,4-di-O-methyl	0.31	0.29
3,6-di-O-methyl	...	0.52
4,6-di-O-methyl	...	0.18
5,6-di-O-methyl	...	0.67
2,3,4-tri-O-methyl	0.00	...
2,3,6-tri-O-methyl	...	0.00
3,5,6-tri-O-methyl	0.23	...
2,3,4,6-tetra-O-methyl	0.00	0.00
D-Galactose	0.93	0.92
2-O-methyl	0.37	...
D-Mannose	0.72	0.85
2,3,6-tri-O-methyl	...	0.02
3,4,6-tri-O-methyl	...	0.24

[a] $M_G = \dfrac{\text{True migration of substance}}{\text{True migration of D-glucose}}$

The true migration is the observed value corrected for movement due to electroendosmotic flow by reference to 2,3,6-tri- or 2,3,4,6-tetra-O-methyl-D-glucose which do not form borate complexes (41).

From the results in Tables 43 and 44 it can be seen that whereas the di-O-methyl derivatives of L-rhamnose cannot be separated by chromatography the 3,4-di-O-methyl derivative is readily separated from the other two by the electrophoretic method, since it has hydroxyl groups on adjacent carbon atoms which enable it to form a complex with the borate ion.   The same effect may be seen with respect to the 2,3-, 2,4-, and 3,4-di-O-methyl derivatives of D-glucose.   Similarly 3,5,6-tri-O-methyl-D-glucose, which can form a borate complex, shows a greater mobility than 2,3,4-tri-O-methyl-D-glucose.

Paper electrophoresis has also been applied effectively for the identification of certain methyl ethers of fructose (44) and of galactose (133).   It was also found that a urea:hydrochloric acid spray reagent (45) served to distinguish certain of the methyl fructose derivatives which could form complexes with borate from those which could not (see Table 45).

TABLE 45. PAPER ELECTROPHORESIS OF METHYLATED DERIVATIVES
OF D-FRUCTOSE (44)

Potential, 220 v; Borate buffer, 0.05M; pH, 9.2; Time 6 hours.

Derivative	Distance travelled from the starting line (cm.)	Ratio of distance travelled by derivative compared with distance travelled by 3-O-methyl D-fructose	Color with Urea spray
1-O-methyl-	14.7	1.02	ochre
3-O-methyl- (standard)	14.0	1.00	ochre
3,4-di-O-methyl-	10.8	0.77	grey-green
4,5-di-O-methyl-	13.0	0.93	ochre
1,4,6-tri-O-methyl-	12.5	0.89	grey-green
1,4,5-tri-O-methyl-	9.7	0.69	ochre
3,4,6-tri-O-methyl-	10.5	0.77	grey-green
methyl β-pyranoside	9.3	0.67	ochre

The migration of sugars and their methyl derivatives as determined by paper electrophoresis is dependent upon the pH of the solution, the temperature, potential difference, width of paper, and capillary movement. It is of the utmost importance, therefore, that a known reference substance be put on the paper every time an unknown compound is examined. It is also important to have the starting line at the same place on the paper strip, usually the center, and, if possible, the paper should be wetted with buffer to the same extent. Unless all these precautions are strictly adhered to, the migration values will be variable and hence of limited value.

For certain substances, especially those that cannot be readily detected by the usual spray reagents for reducing sugar, such as ammoniacal silver nitrate or an amine:acid reagent, it is an advantage to replace the cellulose paper by one made from an inert material such as glass or asbestos (46). These inert papers seem to work equally as well as the cellulose papers and they have the added advantage that highly reactive spray reagents such as a modified Molisch reagent, composed of concentrated sulfuric acid and 1-naphthol (46), or alkaline permanganate can be used. This method employing glass papers has been found to be useful for the separation of higher molecular weight, non-reducing, carbohydrate compounds including polysaccharides (see Chapter 6).

For the quantitative determination of methyl sugars after separation by paper partition chromatography or by paper electrophoresis, a colorimetric method (53) is recommended. All types of methylated sugars and their derivatives possessing a free or a combined reducing group can be determined by the phenol-sulfuric acid procedure (47).

Methods using p-anisidine trichloroacetate (18), aniline phthalate (48), benzidine acetate (51), 4-aminodiphenylamine (54), and aniline trichloroacetate (49) have been proposed for the methylated aldoses. A simplified method, in which the colors are developed directly on the paper with p-anisidine hydrochloride and then extracted and measured, has been developed for the unmethylated sugars (50) and it would appear to offer possibilities for the analysis of the methylated aldose sugars. A colorimetric procedure using 3,5-dinitrosalicylic acid has found limited use (52). Sodium hypoiodite has also been extensively used for the reducing methylated aldoses (13) but this method requires rather more material than those employing colorimetric procedures.

When considerable amounts of methylated polysaccharide are available resolution of the mixture of sugars in the hydrolyzate can be carried out using column chromatography on cellulose (55), a mixture of cellulose and hydro-cellulose (56), celite (117) or carbon (57,58), using the techniques already described (see Chapter 7) and such solvents as 1-butanol: ethanol:water (55), butanone:water azeotrope (132), or 1-butanol:petroleum ether; water (30). Partially methylated sugars are only sparingly soluble in 1-butanol: petroleum ether: water and move down the column rather slowly; to overcome this 1-butanol alone and 1-butanol half saturated with water have been employed (22).

All of these methods can be used for the quantitative analysis of mixtures of methylated sugars as well as for the isolation of enough of each component for identification purposes. If, however, the components of mixtures of methylated sugars are already known it is simpler to carry out the analysis using paper chromatography as described above. (For the experimental details of the principal methods see reference 53).

Identification of Methylated Sugars

A certain number of the methylated sugars crystallize directly but many do not, especially in the presence of small amounts of impurity. In such cases, it is advisable to prepare the N-phenyl- (59,60), N-p-nitrophenyl- (61–63), or N-p-bromophenyl glycosylamine (63).

Derivatives with p-nitrobenzoyl chloride (3,64) offer good promise for identifying methylated sugars; the yields are usually good and as in the case of the N-phenyl-glycosylamines, the products consist largely of one anomeric form. The azoates (2) have also been found useful in a few instances; these derivatives, like the N-p-nitrophenyl glycosides have the advantage of displaying numerically large specific rotations; this is an important factor to consider when only small amounts are available and when sugars of both the D- and the L- series may be present.

Certain methylated sugars will give rise to well-defined crystalline phenylosazones (77); when the methylated sugar possesses a methoxyl group at C_2 osazone formation results in the elimination of this group (69).

If a derivative cannot be made directly in the above manner, the methyl sugar can be oxidized with bromine (65–67) or alkaline iodine (71) to the corresponding lactone from which crystalline derivatives such as the amide (67), phenylhydrazide (68), or p-bromphenylhydrazide (102), can usually be obtained. Methylated aldonic acids having a free hydroxyl group at C_2 might well form well-defined benzimidazoles since the unmethylated aldonic acids readily do (98,99). Methylated uronic acids may also be identified as their amides (69) or phenylhydrazides (72) after first treating them with methanolic hydrogen chloride to give the methyl glycoside methyl ester (69). Alternatively the methylated methylglycosiduronates can be reduced with sodium borohydride (73) or potassium borohydride (74) or lithium aluminum hydride (70,75,76) to the methyl glycosides of the corresponding methylated sugars which may then be hydrolyzed and characterized as above.

The methylated sugars may also be reduced to the corresponding alditols which may be transformed into characteristic crystalline derivatives, such as the azoates (7) or p-nitrobenzoates (78). Suitable derivatives for the identification of methylated sugars are given in Appendix II.

Proof of Structure of Methyl Sugars

The general procedure for ascertaining the structure of an unknown methylated sugar may incorporate the following steps:

(1) When the methylated compound has been purified by recrystallization, distillation, or one of the chromatographic methods discussed above, its mobility on a paper chromatogram should be compared with those of standard methyl sugars using two, or better still three, different irrigating solvents to ascertain approximately the number of methoxyl groups it contains. The color formed on spraying the chromatogram with an aromatic amine reagent should be noted since it is sometimes possible thereby to classify the methyl sugars. The behavior of the methyl sugar when examined by paper electrophoresis, using a borate buffer, should be noted to see whether adjacent cis-hydroxyl groups are present. A micro-furfural test using the phenol-sulfuric acid reagent followed by determination of the absorption band will indicate whether the substance is a derivative of a hexose or of a pentose.

(2) Meanwhile the substance is submitted for elemental analysis including methoxyl to establish the molecular formula and the degree of

methylation. If the methylated sugar is a liquid, a crystalline derivative such as the *N*-phenyl-, *N-p*-nitrophenyl-, or *N-p*-bromophenyl-glycosylamine should be obtained and likewise analyzed.

(3) If the polysaccharide giving rise to the unknown methylated sugar is a heteroglycan it may be necessary to ascertain the parent sugar. This can be achieved either by demethylation with hydrobromic acid and subsequent paper chromatography (21) or alternatively by complete methylation, hydrolysis and identification of the fully methylated reducing sugar, provisionally by chromatography and conclusively by preparation of one or more suitable derivatives discussed above. Sometimes the process can be greatly simplified by directly methylating the aniline derivative of the unknown methylated sugar with silver oxide and methyl iodide to the characteristic fully methylated *N*-phenyl glycosylamine (79).

It is important to determine whether the substance belongs to the D- or the L-series as soon as possible. This is best done by measuring the specific rotation of one of the known derivatives, for example, the *N*-phenyl glycosylamine of the fully methylated reducing sugar now under discussion.

(4) The next problem is to locate the positions of the methoxyl groups. If the methylated sugar gives an osazone without loss of a methoxyl group then it follows that a free hydroxyl group is present at C_2, whereas the loss of a methoxyl group during osazone formation proves that a methoxyl group is at C_2. The Weerman test for α-hydroxyamides is also useful in this connection (see later).

(5) Another useful diagnostic test and one from which the substance can be recovered (a point that may be of great importance when only minute amounts of the unknown are available) is to ascertain whether the methylated sugar will form a furanoside when treated at room temperature with 0.5 to 1 percent methanolic hydrogen chloride. A positive reaction, usually recognized by a rapid change in rotation, proves that a free hydroxyl group must be at C_4, but as noted above a negative test does not necessarily mean that C_4 carries a methoxyl group. Thus certain methylated derivatives of mannose with a free hydroxyl group at C_4 such as 2,3,6-tri-O-methyl-D-mannose, do not form furanosides in this manner, because of the particular stereochemical arrangement of the mannose molecule; on the other hand, the corresponding 2,3,6-tri-O-methyl-D-glucose readily forms a furanoside under these conditions and, as a matter of fact, this difference in behavior provides an easy method for their separation (64). The rate of furanoside formation depends on the number of carbon atoms in the parent sugar. Thus, in general, hexoses react more slowly than pentoses and these in turn react more slowly than the tetroses which form glycosides at room temperature almost instanta-

neously (81). Confirmation of furanoside formation should be sought by ascertaining whether the glycoside undergoes hydrolysis under mild acid conditions.

(6) Oxidation of the methyl sugar to the corresponding lactone with bromine or with alkaline iodine also provides valuable information since the rate of hydrolysis of the lactones in water indicates the size of the lactone ring (80). Rapid hydrolysis indicates a δ-lactone and a free hydroxyl group at C_5 whereas a slow hydrolysis indicates a γ-lactone and hence a free hydroxyl group at C_4. Since a γ- is more stable than a δ-lactone the formation of the latter not only proves that there is a hydroxyl group at C_5 but also that γ-lactone ring formation is prevented and hence there must be a methoxyl group at C_4. By the same reasoning, the formation of a γ-lactone does not prove that there is not a free hydroxyl group at C_5 (86).

(7) A positive Weerman test on the amide, obtained by the action of ammonia on the lactone of a partially methylated sugar acid, usually shows that a free hydroxyl group is present at C_2 (82,83).

(8) A primary hydroxyl group at C_6 can generally be recognized by the formation of a trityl ether (84). This valuable reaction is not absolutely specific since some compounds which do not possess a primary alcoholic group generally react though much more slowly (85).

(9) The reaction with p-toluenesulfonyl chloride is sometimes useful for detecting the presence of a primary alcoholic grouping since in general only a tosyl group attached to such a position is replaced by iodine when the tosyl derivative is treated with sodium iodide in acetone, a positive reaction being revealed by the formation of sodium p-toluenesulfonate which is sparingly soluble in the reaction medium (87,88). Acetone can be replaced by the higher boiling acetylacetone or acetic anhydride with advantage since the sealed tube, necessary for the acetone: sodium iodide reaction, can be dispensed with (89).

(10) If, at this stage, the methyl sugar has not been identified, it may be advisable to ascertain the action of periodic acid on the methyl sugar, the corresponding acid, glycoside, or glycitol, to ascertain whether adjacent hydroxyl groups are present and where they are located. This reaction can be applied to the methylated uronic acids after they have been reduced to the corresponding sugar or sugar alcohol (76). The reaction should be carried out quantitatively if possible (108,118,119) and the cleavage products should be identified. Thus, free hydroxyl groups at C_5 and C_6 will result in the formation of formaldehyde which can readily be recognized as its dimedone derivative (107–109). Similarly free hydroxyl groups at C_4 and C_5 in a 6-deoxy sugar or its acid, can be established by the liberation of acetaldehyde which may be determined colori-

metrically with sodium nitroprusside (114,115) and identified as its 2,4-dinitrophenylhydrazone or bis-methone derivative (112,113). Glyoxylic acid is formed by degradation of a lactone having hydroxyl groups at C_2 and C_3 and is recognized by a specific color reaction with tryptophan in the presence of sulfuric acid and characterized as its 2,4-dinitrophenylhydrazone or bis-methone derivative. Anomalous results (9,106–108,111) are obtained with certain methyl sugars, only part of the expected amounts of cleavage products being found. This is no doubt due to the stability of the sugar ring or to the formation, in the initial stages of the oxidation, of intermediate cyclic acetals or formyl esters which are relatively stable to periodate. This difficulty can be avoided by reducing the methyl sugar to the corresponding glycitol before periodate oxidation (116). Periodate cleavage of a 2-O-methyl- (A) or a 2,6-di-O-methyl-hexopyranoside (B) between C_3 and C_4 or of a 5-O-methylpentoside (C) between C_2 and C_3 may be recognized by reducing the aldehydic derivatives with sodium borohydride. Hydrolysis of the products formed gives 1-O-methylglycerol from B and C and glycerol from A both of which can be identified chromatographically and with a few milligrams they are readily characterized as the p-nitrobenzoates (90).

(11) If reasonably large amounts of the unknown methylated sugar are available, the classical degradation reaction with nitric acid (91) can be applied and the methyl ethers of trihydroxyglutaric acids or dihydroxysuccinic acids identified as their amides or N-methylamides (68,91–94). Nitric acid oxidation can be used to establish the structure of methylated uronic acids (72). Under controlled conditions certain methylated sugars give rise to crystalline derivatives of the corresponding hexaric acids; this is particularly applicable to galactose. Quite frequently hydrolysis of a methylated polysaccharide containing uronic acid units affords a methylated aldobiouronic acid in which the biose linkage is relatively stable to acids. Proof of the structure of such compounds can be established by reduction of the carboxyl group to a primary alcohol group with lithium aluminum hydride (22,70,74–76,103–105). This gives a neutral methylated disaccharide whose structure is determined in the classical manner as described previously, unless, of course, it has been characterized before and can be identified by reference to the literature (see Appendix II).

Saccharinic Acid Formation in Determination of Structure of Partially Methylated Sugars

A study of the mechanism of the action of alkali in an inert atmosphere upon substituted aldoses has revealed that the nature of the saccharinic acid formed depends upon the position occupied by the substituent.

The action of alkali on the 3-O-methyl- derivatives CLXVIIa and CLXVIIIa of D-fructose and D-glucose, respectively, gives rise (122) to a mixture of the α- and β-isomeric D-glucometasaccharinic acids, CLXIX, (120,121) according to the following scheme (122).

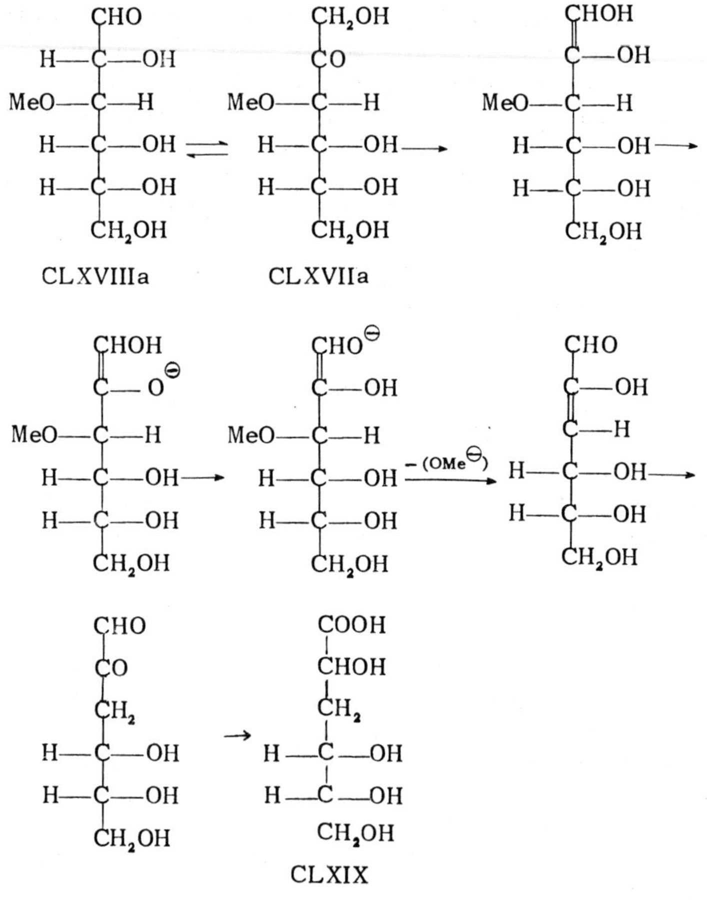

$$
\begin{array}{ccc}
\text{CHO} & \text{CH}_2\text{OH} & \text{CHOH} \\
\text{H—C—OH} & \text{C=O} & \text{C—OH} \\
\text{MeO—C—H} & \text{MeO—C—H} & \text{MeO—C—H} \\
\text{H—C—OH} \rightleftharpoons & \text{H—C—OH} \longrightarrow & \text{H—C—OH} \longrightarrow \\
\text{H—C—OH} & \text{H—C—OH} & \text{H—C—OH} \\
\text{CH}_2\text{OH} & \text{CH}_2\text{OH} & \text{CH}_2\text{OH} \\
\text{CLXVIIIa} & \text{CLXVIIa} &
\end{array}
$$

$$
\begin{array}{ccc}
\text{CHOH} & \text{CHO}^{\ominus} & \text{CHO} \\
\text{C—O}^{\ominus} & \text{C—OH} & \text{C—OH} \\
\text{MeO—C—H} & \text{MeO—C—H} & \text{C—H} \\
\text{H—C—OH} \longrightarrow & \text{H—C—OH} \xrightarrow{-(\text{OMe}^{\ominus})} & \text{H—C—OH} \longrightarrow \\
\text{H—C—OH} & \text{H—C—OH} & \text{H—C—OH} \\
\text{CH}_2\text{OH} & \text{CH}_2\text{OH} & \text{CH}_2\text{OH}
\end{array}
$$

$$
\begin{array}{ccc}
\text{CHO} & & \text{COOH} \\
\text{C=O} & & \text{CHOH} \\
\text{CH}_2 & & \text{CH}_2 \\
\text{H—C—OH} & \rightarrow & \text{H—C—OH} \\
\text{H—C—OH} & & \text{H—C—OH} \\
\text{CH}_2\text{OH} & & \text{CH}_2\text{OH} \\
& \text{CLXIX} &
\end{array}
$$

Similarly the alkaline decomposition of the 4-O-methyl- derivatives CLXX and CLXXI of D-glucose and D-fructose, respectively, affords (123) the same two D-glucoisosaccharinic acids CLXXII. Recent studies have shown that 2,3-di-O-methyl-D-glucose yields 5-(hydroxymethyl)-2-furaldehyde (130) whereas the 3,6-di- and 4,6-di-O-methyl derivatives of D-glucose afford 6-O-methyl-meta- and 6-O-methyl-isosaccharinic acid (131).

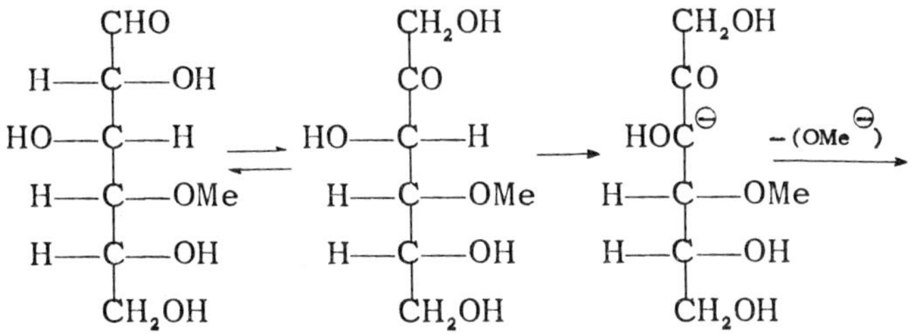

$$\begin{array}{ccc}
\text{CHO} & \text{CH}_2\text{OH} & \text{CH}_2\text{OH} \\
\text{H---C---OH} & \text{C=O} & \text{C=O} \\
\text{HO---C---H} \rightleftharpoons & \text{HO---C---H} \rightarrow & \text{HOC}^{\ominus} \quad -(\text{OMe}^{\ominus}) \rightarrow \\
\text{H---C---OMe} & \text{H---C---OMe} & \text{H---C---OMe} \\
\text{H---C---OH} & \text{H---C---OH} & \text{H---C---OH} \\
\text{CH}_2\text{OH} & \text{CH}_2\text{OH} & \text{CH}_2\text{OH} \\
\text{CLXX} & \text{CLXXI} &
\end{array}$$

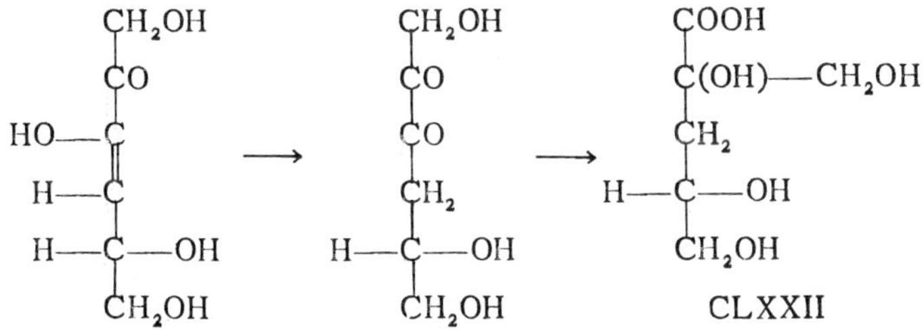

$$\begin{array}{ccc}
\text{CH}_2\text{OH} & \text{CH}_2\text{OH} & \text{COOH} \\
\text{C=O} & \text{C=O} & \text{C(OH)---CH}_2\text{OH} \\
\text{HO---C} \rightarrow & \text{C=O} \rightarrow & \text{CH}_2 \\
\text{H---C} & \text{CH}_2 & \text{H---C---OH} \\
\text{H---C---OH} & \text{H---C---OH} & \text{CH}_2\text{OH} \\
\text{CH}_2\text{OH} & \text{CH}_2\text{OH} & \text{CLXXII}
\end{array}$$

Since these saccharinic acids can be separated by paper chromatography either directly or after transformation to the corresponding anilides, the method may prove to be of value in locating the position of methoxyl groups in methylated sugars which contain the β-hydroxy- or β-alkoxycarbonyl system susceptible to alkaline degradation (123). The method also appears to be useful for ascertaining the types of the linkages in oligosaccharides (124–127) and polysaccharides (128,129).

REFERENCES

1. Haworth, W. N., and Machemer, H., *J. Chem. Soc.*, 2270 (1932).
2. Freudenberg, K., and Boppel, H., *Ber.*, **73,** 609 (1940).
3. Freudenberg, K., and Plankenhorn, E., *Ber.*, **73,** 621 (1940).
4. Myrbäck, K., and Tamm, C. O., *Svensk Kem. Tidskr.*, **53,** 441 (1941); *Chem. Abstracts*, **37,** 3406 (1943).
5. Mertzweiller, J. K., Carney, D. M., and Farley, F. F., *J. Am. Chem. Soc.*, **65,** 2367 (1943).
6. Coleman, G. H., Rees, D. E., Sundberg, R. L., and McCloskey, C. M., *J. Am. Chem. Soc.*, **67,** 381 (1945).
7. Boissonnas, R. A., *Helv. Chim. Acta*, **30,** 1689 (1947).
8. Jones, J. K. N., *J. Chem. Soc.*, 333 (1944).
9. Conchie, J. and Percival, E. G. V., *J. Chem. Soc.*, 827 (1950).
10. Bell, D. J., *J. Chem. Soc.*, 473 (1944).
11. Norberg, Ethelda J., Auerbach, I., and Hixon, R. M., *J. Am. Chem. Soc.*, **67,** 342 (1945).
12. Georges, L. W., Bower, R. S., and Wolfrom, M. L., *J. Am. Chem. Soc.*, **68,** 2169 (1946).

13. Hirst, E. L., Hough, L., and Jones, J. K. N., *J. Chem. Soc.*, 928 (1949).
14. *Chromatographic Analysis, General Discussion*, Faraday Society, 7, 1949.
15. Andrews, P., Hough, L., and Jones, J. K. N., *J. Chem. Soc.*, 1186 (1953).
16. Adams, G. A., *Can. J. Chem.*, **33**, 56 (1955).
17. Boggs, L. A., Cuendet, L. S., Ehrenthal, I., Koch, R., and Smith, F., *Nature*, **166**, 520 (1950).
18. Schaefer, W. C., and Van Cleve, J. W., *Anal. Chem.*, **28**, 1290 (1956).
19. Hirst, E. L., McGilvray, D. I., and Percival, E. G. V., *J. Chem. Soc.*, 1297 (1950).
20. Barker, G. R., and Smith, D. C. C., *Chemistry* and *Industry*, 19 (1956).
21. Hough, L., Jones, J. K. N., and Wadman, W. H., *J. Chem. Soc.*, 1702 (1950).
22. Chanda, S. K., Hirst, E. L., and Percival, E. G. V., *J. Chem. Soc.*, 1240 (1951).
23. Lederer, E., and Lederer, M., *"Chromatography: A Review of Principles and Applications."* 2nd Ed. Elsevier, New York (1957).
24. Cramer, F., *Papier Chromatographie*, 2nd Ed., Verlag. Chemie, Weinheim (1953).
25. Kowkabany, G. N., *Advances in Carbohydrate Chem.*, **9**, 303 (1954).
26. Hough, L., *Methods of Biochemical Analysis*, Vol. I, Ed. D. Glick, Interscience Pub., New York (1954), p. 205.
27. Chanda, S. K., Hirst, E. L., Percival, E. G. V., and Ross, A. G., *J. Chem. Soc.*, 1833 (1952).
28. Cifonelli, J. A., and Smith, F., *J. Am. Chem. Soc.*, **77**, 5682 (1955).
29. Boggs, L. A., and Smith, F., *J. Am. Chem. Soc.*, **78**, 1880 (1956).
30. Arni, P. C., and Percival, E. G. V., *J. Chem. Soc.*, 1822 (1951).
31. Montgomery, T. N., *J. Am. Chem. Soc.*, **56**, 419 (1934).
32. Montgomery, R., and Smith, F., *J. Am. Chem. Soc.*, **79**, 446 (1957).
33. Consden, R., and Stanier, Winifred M., *Nature*, **169**, 783 (1952).
34. Jaenicke, L., *Naturwissenschaften*, **39**, 86 (1952).
35. Michl, H., *Monatsh.*, **83**, 737 (1952).
36. Micheel, F., and Kamp, F. P., Van de, *Angew. Chem.*, **64**, 607 (1952).
37. Woodin, A. M., *Biochem. J.*, **51**, 319 (1952).
38. Foster, A. B., *J. Chem. Soc.*, 982 (1953).
39. Briggs, D. R., Garner, E. F., Montgomery, R., and Smith, F., *Anal. Chem.*, **28**, 1333 (1956).
40. Durrum, E. L., *J. Am. Chem. Soc.*, **72**, 2943 (1950).
41. Foster, A. B., and Stacey, M., *J. Appl. Chem.*, **3**, 19 (1953).
42. Foster, A. B., *Chemistry* and *Industry*, 828, 1050 (1952).
43. Garner, E. F., *Ph.D., Theis.*, University of Minnesota, (1956).
44. Bell, D. J., and Northcote, D. H., *Chemistry* and *Industry*, 1328 (1954).
45. Dedonder, R., *Bull. soc. chim. biol.*, **34**, 144 (1952).
46. Briggs, D. R., Garner, E. F., and Smith, F., *Nature*, **178**, 154 (1956).
47. Dubois, M., Gilles, K. A., Hamilton, J. K., Rebers, P. A., and Smith, F., *Anal. Chem.*, **28**, 350 (1956).
48. Bartlett, J. K. (Miss), Hough, L., and Jones, J. K. N., *Chemistry* and *Industry*, 76 (1951).
49. Blass, Judith, Macheboeuf, M., Nunez, G., *Bull. soc. chim. biol.*, **32**, 130 (1950).
50. Pridham, J. B., *Anal. Chem.*, **28**, 1967 (1956).
51. Jones, J. K. N., and Pridham, J. B., *Biochem. J.*, **58**, 288 (1954).
52. Bell, D. J., Manners, D. J., and Palmer, Anne, *J. Chem. Soc.*, 3760 (1952).

53. Smith, F., and Montgomery, R., *"Methods of Biochemical Analysis,"* Vol. III, ed. D. Glick, Interscience Pub. Inc., New York (1956).
54. Timell, T. E., Glaudemans, C. P. J., and Currie, A. L., *Anal. Chem.*, **28**, 1916 (1956).
55. Hough, L., Jones, J. K. N., Wadman, W. H., *J. Chem. Soc.*, 2511 (1949).
56. Geerdes, J. D., Lewis, Bertha A., Montgomery, R., and Smith, F., *Anal. Chem.*, **26**, 264 (1954).
57. Lindberg, B., and Wickberg, B., *Acta Chem. Scand.*, **8**, 569 (1954).
58. Whelan, W. J., and Morgan, K., *Chemistry and Industry*, 78 (1954).
59. Sorokin, B., *Ber.*, **19**, 513 (1886); *J. prakt. Chem.*, [2], **37**, 291 (1888).
60. Irvine, J. C., and McNicoll, D., *J. Chem. Soc.*, **97**, 1448 (1910).
61. Weygand, F., Perkow, W., and Kuhner, P., *Ber.*, **84**, 594 (1951).
62. Antaki, H., and Petrow, V., *J. Chem. Soc.*, 2873 (1951).
63. Van Cleve, J. W., and Schaefer, W. C., *J. Am. Chem. Soc.*, **77**, 5341 (1955).
64. Rebers, P. A., and Smith, F., *J. Am. Chem. Soc.*, **76**, 6097 (1954).
65. Kiliani, H., *Ann.*, **205**, 145 (1880).
66. Purdie, T., and Irvine, J. C., *J. Chem. Soc.*, **83**, 1021 (1903).
67. Pryde, J., Hirst, E. L., and Humphreys, R. W., *J. Chem. Soc.*, **127**, 348 (1925).
68. Haworth, W. N., Hirst, E. L., and Miller, E. J., *J. Chem. Soc.*, 2436 (1927).
69. Smith, F., *J. Chem. Soc.*, 1724 (1939).
70. Smith, F., *J. Chem. Soc.*, 2646 (1951).
71. Willstätter, R., and Schudel, G., *Ber.*, **51**, 780 (1918).
72. Smith, F., *J. Chem. Soc.*, 1035 (1940).
73. Adams, G. A., *Can. J. Chem.*, **32**, 186 (1954).
74. Aspinall, G. O., Hirst, E. L., and Matheson, N. K., *J. Chem. Soc.*, 989 (1956).
75. Abdel-Akher, M., and Smith, F., *Nature*, **166**, 1037 (1950).
76. Lythgoe, B., and Trippett, S., *J. Chem. Soc.*, 1983 (1950).
77. Anderson, C. G., Charlton, W., and Haworth, W. N., *J. Chem. Soc.*, 1329 (1929).
78. Smith, F., and co-workers, unpublished.
79. Ehrenthal, L, Rafique, M. C., and Smith, F., *J. Am. Chem. Soc.*, **74**, 1341 (1952).
80. Drew, H. D. K., Goodyear, E. H., and Haworth, W. N., *J. Chem. Soc.*, 1237 (1927).
81. Hamilton, J. K., Lewis, Bertha A., Montgomery, R., and Smith, F., unpublished.
82. Weerman, R. A., *Rec. trav. chim.*, **37**, 16 (1918).
83. Ault, R. G., Haworth, W. N., and Hirst, E. L., *J. Chem. Soc.*, 1722 (1934).
84. Helferich, B., *Angew. Chem.*, **41**, 871 (1928).
85. Hockett, R. C., and Hudson, C. S., *J. Am. Chem. Soc.*, **56**, 945 (1934).
86. Haworth, W. N., *"The Constitution of the Sugars,"* Edward Arnold and Co., London, 1929.
87. Oldham, J. W. H., and Rutherford, Jean, K., *J. Am. Chem. Soc.*, **54**, 366 (1932).
88. Hann, R. M., Ness, A. T., and Hudson, C. S., *J. Am. Chem. Soc.*, **66**, 73 (1944).
89. Murray, G. E., and Purves, C. B., *J. Am. Chem. Soc.*, **62**, 3195 (1940).
90. Goldstein, I. J., Hamilton, J. K., and Smith, F., *J. Am. Chem. Soc.*, **79**, 1190 (1957).

91. Hirst, E. L., *J. Chem. Soc.*, 350 (1926).
92. Avery, J., Haworth, W. N., and Hirst, E. L., *J. Chem. Soc.*, 2308 (1927).
93. Purdie, T., and Irvine, J. C., *J. Chem. Soc.*, **79**, 957 (1901).
94. Haworth, W. N., and Jones, D. I., *J. Chem. Soc.*, 2349 (1927).
95. Gilles, K. A., Huffman, G. W., Meredith, W. O. S., and Smith, F., unpublished.
96. Boesekin, J., **Ber.**, 46, 2612 (1919).
97. Macpherson, H. T., and Percival, E. G. V., *J. Chem. Soc.*, 1920 (1937).
98. Moore, S., and Link, K. P., *J. Biol. Chem.*, **133**, 293 (1940).
99. Dimler, R. J., and Link, K. P., *J. Biol. Chem.*, **150**, 345 (1943).
100. Schlubach, H. H., and Heesch, Annemarie, *Ann.*, **572**, 114 (1951).
101. Ball, D. H., Butler, R. M., Cook, W. H., and Jones, J. K. N., *Chemistry and Industry*, 1740 (1955).
102. Hampton, H. A., Haworth, W. N., and Hirst, E. L., *J. Chem. Soc.*, 1739 (1929).
103. Montgomery, R., Smith, F., and Srivastava, H. C., *J. Am. Chem. Soc.*, **78**, 2837 (1956).
104. Dutton, G. G. S., and Smith, F., *J. Am. Chem. Soc.*, **78**, 2505 (1956).
105. Whistler, R. L., Conrad, H. E., and Hough, L., *J. Am. Chem. Soc.*, **76**, 1668 (1954).
106. Percival, E. E., and Percival, E. G. V., *J. Chem. Soc.*, 690 (1950).
107. Jeanloz, R., *Helv. Chim. Acta*, **27**, 1509 (1944).
108. Bell, D. J., *J. Chem. Soc.*, 992 (1948).
109. Reeves, R. E., *J. Am. Chem. Soc.*, **63**, 1476 (1941).
110. Bell, D. J., *Biochem. J.*, **29**, 2031 (1935).
111. Brown, F., Hough, L., and Jones, J. K. N., *J. Chem. Soc.*, 1125 (1950).
112. Horning, E. C., and Horning, M. G., *J. Org. Chem.*, **11**, 95 (1946).
113. Sprinson, D. B., and Chargoff, E., *J. Biol. Chem.*, **164**, 417 (1946).
114. Desnuelle, P., and Naudet, M., *Bull. soc. chim. France*, **12**, 871 (1945).
115. Wickstrom, A., *Ann. pharm. franc.*, **8**, 86 (1950).
116. Lemieux, R. U., and Bauer, H. F., *Can. J. Chem.*, **31**, 814 (1953).
117. Lemieux, R. U., Bishop, C. T., and Pelletier, G. E., *Can. J. Chem.*, **34**, 1365 (1956).
118. Bell, D. J., Palmer, Anne, and Johns, A. T., *J. Chem. Soc.*, 1536 (1949).
119. Mitchell, W. E. A., and Percival, Elizabeth, E., *J. Chem. Soc.*, 1423 (1954).
120. Nef, J. U., *Ann.*, **376**, 1 (1910).
121. Evans, W. L., *Chem. Reviews*, **31**, 537 (1942).
122. Kenner, J., and Richards, G. N., *J. Chem. Soc.*, 278 (1954).
123. Kenner, J., and Richards, G. N., *J. Chem. Soc.*, 1810 (1955).
124. Corbett, W. M., Kenner, J., and Richards, G. N., *Chemistry and Industry*, 154 (1953).
125. Corbett, W. M., and Kenner, J., *J. Chem. Soc.*, 2245 (1953).
126. Aspinall, G. O., Carter, Mary E., and Los, M., *J. Chem. Soc.*, 4807 (1956).
127. Whistler, R. L., and Corbett, W. M., *J. Am. Chem. Soc.*, **78**, 1003 (1956).
128. Kenner, J., and Richards, G. N., *Chemistry and Industry*, 1483 (1954).
129. Corbett, W. M., and Richards, G. N. *Svensk Papperstidning*, **60**, 791 (1957).
130. Kenner, J., and Richards, G. M., *J. Chem. Soc.*, 2921 (1956).
131. Kenner, J., and Richards, G. M., *J. Chem. Soc.*, 2916 (1956).
132. Boggs, L. A., Cuendet, L. S., Dubois, M., and Smith, F., *Anal. Chem.*, **24**, 1148 (1952).
133. Bouveng, H., and Lindberg, B., *Acta Chem. Scand.*, **10**, 1283 (1956).

CHAPTER 11

THE STRUCTURE OF THE GUM EXUDATES

Gum Arabic

Gum arabic exudes from the stems and branches of the *Acacia* tree which is located in many semi-arid tropical and sub-tropical regions of the world. *Acacia senegal* (syn. *Acacia verek*) constitutes the principle varietal source of the gum, the exudation of which is stimulated by mechanical injury. Of the many other varieties of *Acacia* gum only that of *A. mollissima* (Black-wattle gum) (36), *A. pycnantha* (8), *A. cyanophylla* (39) and *A. karroo* (40) have been subjected to detailed structural investigations. These are lower grade gums and have not yet received commercial application.

Acacia Senegal Gum

Gum arabic is the salt of an organic acid, arabic acid, with metals such as calcium, magnesium and potassium (1). The free acid is obtained by the addition of a slight excess of mineral acid to a solution of the gum in cold water and when the aqueous solution is poured into alcohol the arabic acid is obtained as an amorphous powder.

The sugar units of which gum arabic is composed are D-galactose (4–8), L-arabinose (3,4), L-rhamnose and D-glucuronic acid; L-fucose has been reported in the gum from *Acacia sieberiana*. a tree found in the Belgian Congo (2). The presence of L-rhamnose was indicated (9) and later proved by the isolation of the sugar in the crystalline state (8,10) and in the form of crystalline derivatives (11). L-Rhamnose is reportedly a variable constituent of gum arabic. It is pertinent, therefore, to consider the immunological studies whereby it was shown that Type II antipneumococcus horse serum gives a precipitin reaction with gum arabic. Furthermore, analysis of the fraction of the gum precipitated with the serum protein, showed that it contained only one-third to one-fifth of the L-rhamnose in the parent gum, thus suggesting that gum arabic is a mixture of at least two polysaccharide components (13). It is perhaps unfortunate that the history of the gum used in this work is not known, since it may well have been a composite commercial sample. The view that gum arabic is a mixture is supported by electrophoretic studies in free solution (14) and on glass paper (15).

Analysis of gum arabic shows it to be composed of 30.3 per cent of L-arabinose, 11.4 per cent of L-rhamnose, 36.8 per cent of D-galactose and 13.8 per cent of D-glucuronic acid (12).

When a solution of arabic acid in 0.1N sulfuric acid is heated, hydrolysis takes place with the formation of a mixture of sugars (from which L-arabinose is readily isolated) (16) and a more resistant nucleus, degraded arabic acid. The mixture of sugars and the degraded acid are produced in approximately equal proportions. Degraded arabic acids have been described by O'Sullivan (4), but the method of preparation was such that the presence of acids of small molecular size could not be avoided. A 10 per cent aqueous solution of arabic acid has a pH of 2.2 and hydrolysis can be smoothly effected by simply heating the aqueous solution. This process, termed autohydrolysis, produces the same mixture of sugars and the same degraded arabic acid as is obtained by hydrolysis with 0.01N sulfuric acid. Although autohydrolysis proceeds more slowly than the hydrolysis of arabic acid with 0.01N sulfuric acid it is an advantage to use the former procedure since the process is more easily reproducible. It is also apparent that application of heat in the preparation of the free polysaccharide acid, arabic acid, should be avoided because partial hydrolysis may occur.

Autohydrolysis of arabic acid results in the liberation of labile sugar residues which have been identified (11) as L-arabinose, L-rhamnose and 3-O-D-galactopyranosyl-L-arabinose CLXXIII (cf 8). The structure of this disaccharide CLXXIII which probably possesses an α biose linkage (39) was proved (11) by the fact that methylation yielded the heptamethyl ether (CLXXIV), which gave on hydrolysis 2,3,4,6-tetra-O-methyl-D-galactose (XXXIX) and 2,4-di-O-methyl-L-arabinose (XL). Preliminary

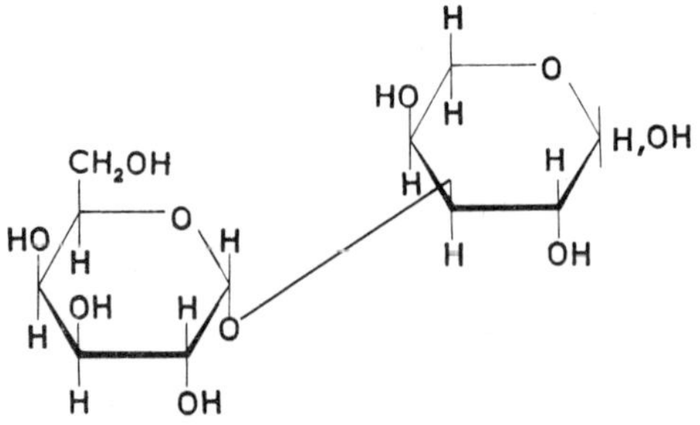

(CLXXIII)

treatment of the disaccharide (CLXXIII) with methanolic hydrogen chloride at room temperature followed by methylation afforded the hepta-O-methyl ether (CLXXV) the hydrolysis of which afforded 2,3,4,6-tetra-O-methyl-D-galactopyranose (XXXIX) and 2,5-di-O-methyl-L-arabinose (XLIII). The identification of the two di-O-methyl derivatives of L-arabinose (XL) and (XLIII) proved that the D-galactopyranose moiety is linked to C_3 of the L-arabinose unit and since the disaccharide is removed so easily from the basic nucleus of arabic acid, the arabinose moiety is considered to be present in the furanose form in the arabic acid. Similarly, the L-arabinose residues which are formed together with the disaccharide (CLXXIII) in the autohydrolyzate of arabic acid are likewise present in the furanose form. It will be seen later, from methylation studies, that the labile L-rhamnose is in the pyranose form.

More drastic hydrolysis of gum arabic or degraded arabic acid leads to the formation of 3-O-D-galactopyranosyl-D-galactose (CLXXVI) (17) and an aldobiouronic acid 6-O-(β-D-glucopyranosyluronic acid)-D-galactose (CLXXVII) (18,19).

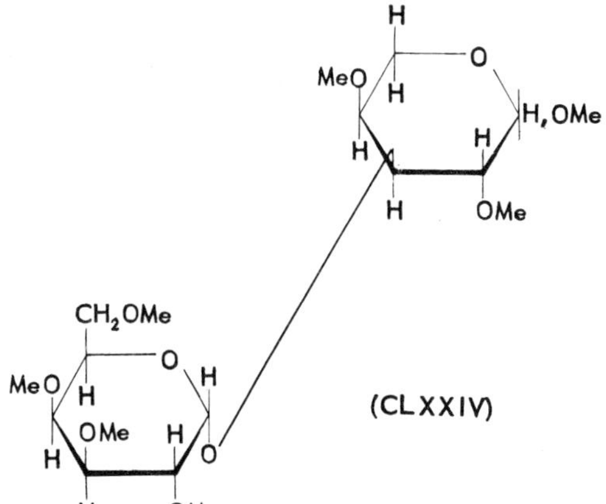

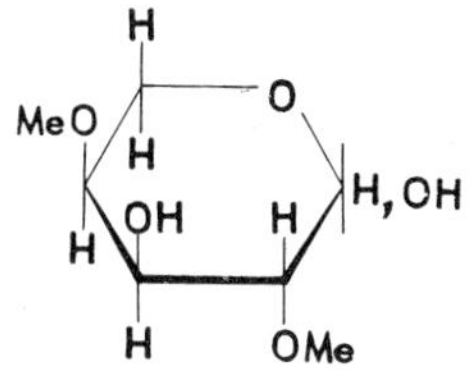

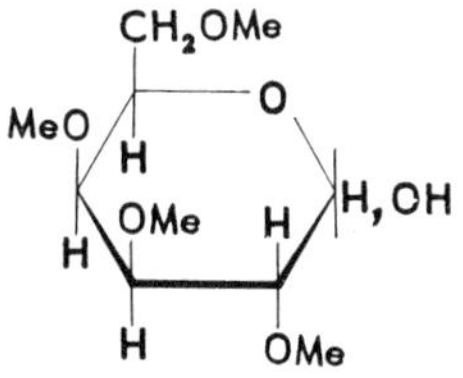

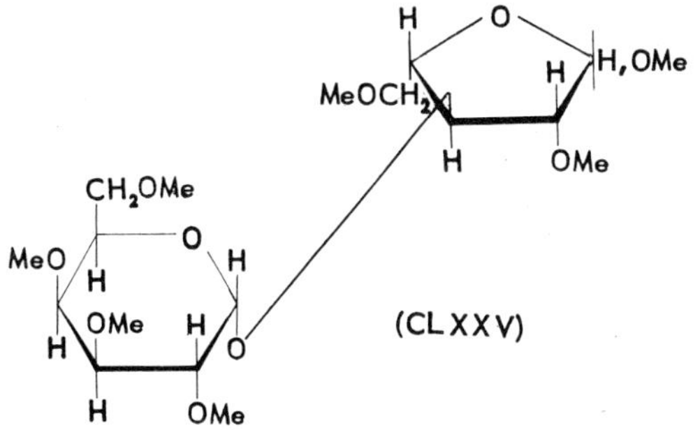

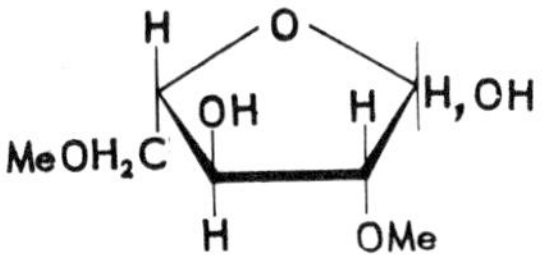

The structures of the disaccharide (CLXXVI) and the aldobiouronic acid (CLXXVII) were proved by methylation studies in the manner described previously for 3-O-D-galactopyranosyl-L-arabinose (CLXXIII). Treatment of the disaccharide (CLXXVI) with methyl sulfate and alkali gave the octa-O-methyl derivative (CLXXVIII) which upon hydrolysis afforded 2,3,4,6-tetra-O-methyl-D-galactose (XXXIX) and 2,4,6-tri-O-methyl-D-galactose (XLVI). The methyl ether (CLXXIX) of the aldobiouronic acid (CLXXVII) gave upon methanolysis methyl (methyl 2,3,4-tri-O-methyl-D-glucosid)uronate (CLXXX) and methyl 2,3,4-tri-O-methyl-D-galactoside (CLXXXI). In addition the structure of the aldobiouronic acid (CLXXVII) was confirmed by synthesis (19).

The nature and mode of linking of the D-galactose and D-glucuronic acid residues contained in degraded arabic acid was ascertained by subjecting the latter to methylation (20). When the methyl derivative, which had a molecular weight approximately 4800 by osmotic pressure measurements (20), was hydrolyzed there were formed three moles[a] of 2,3,4-tri-O-methyl-D-glucuronic acid (XV), one mole of 2,3,4,6-tetra-O-methyl-D-galactose (XXXIX), five moles of 2,3,4-tri-O-methyl-D-galactose (XVI), and three moles of 2,4-di-O-methyl-D-galactose CLXXXII. If the methyl-

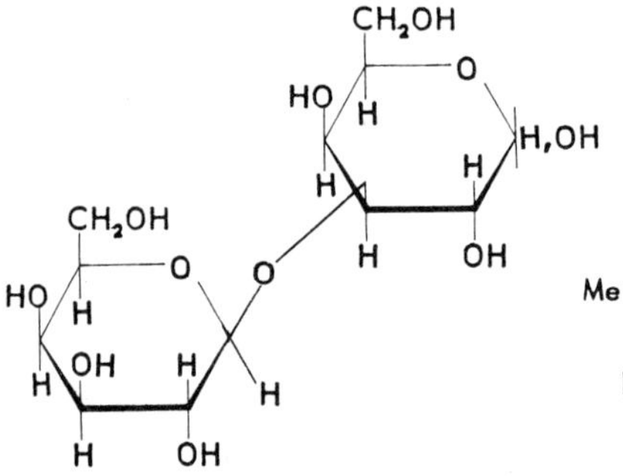

(CLXXVI) 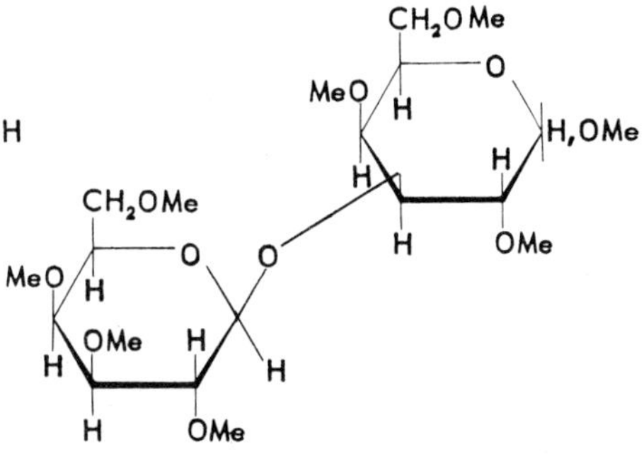   (CLXXVIII)

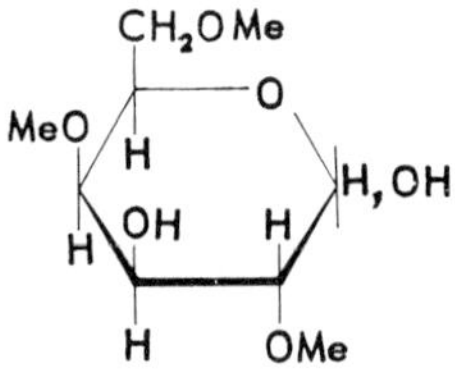

(XLVI)

[a] Here and elsewhere the term "mole" refers to molecular proportion.

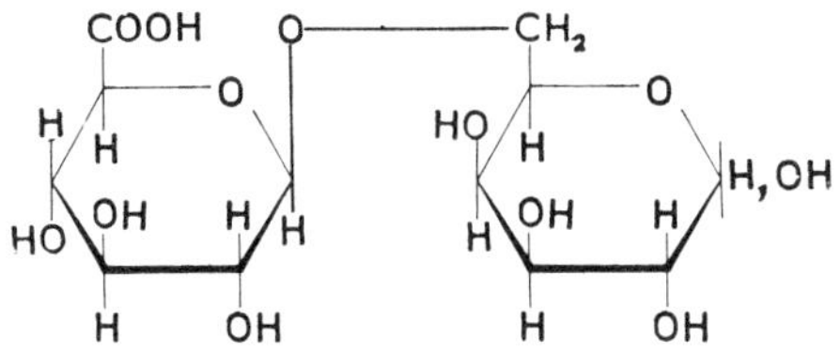

(CLXXVII)

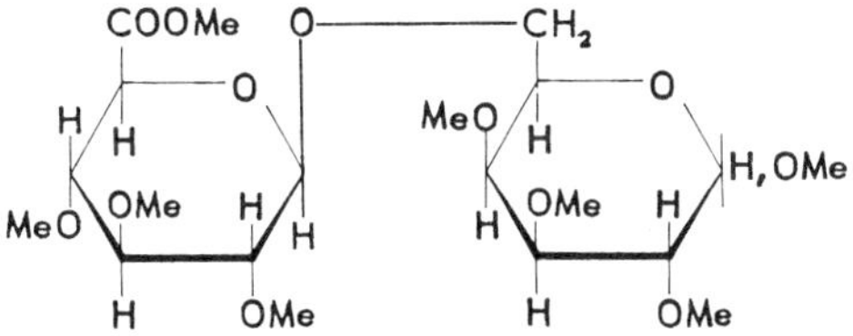

(CLXXIX)

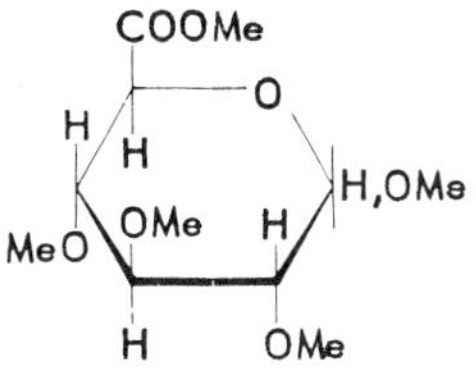

(CLXXX) 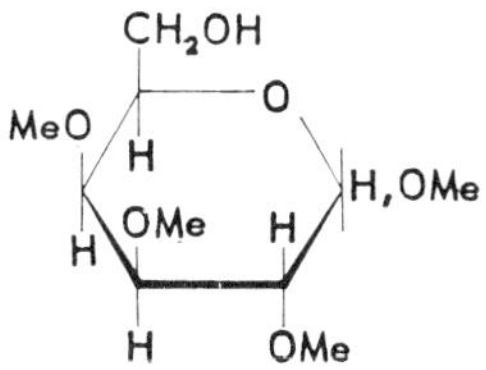   (CLXXXI)

ated degraded arabic acid is reduced with lithium aluminum hydride before hydrolysis, the cleavage products are the same except that 2,3,4-tri-O-methyl-D-glucose is formed instead of 2,3,4-tri-O-methyl-D-glucuronic acid (21).

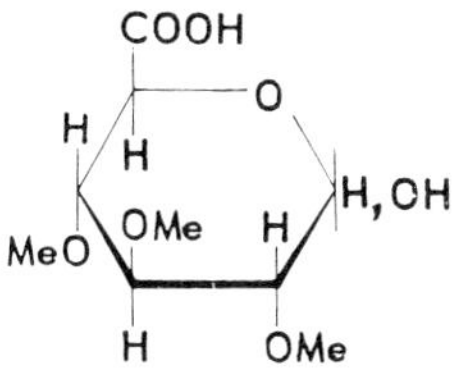

(XV) 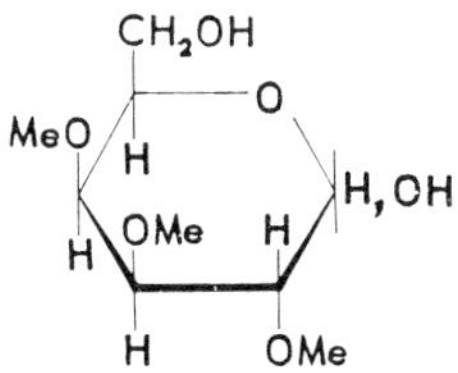   (XVI) 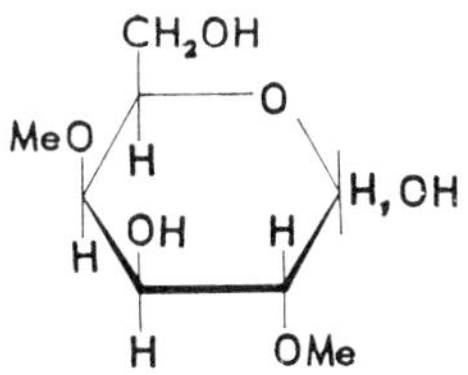   (CLXXXII)

On the assumption that the methylation of the degraded arabic acid was complete, the locations of the hydroxyl groups in the four cleavage fragments indicate the positions through which the monosaccharide units are involved in union with the other residues. Thus the isolation of three moles of 2,3,4-tri-O-methyl-D-glucuronic acid (XV), and one mole of 2,3,4,6-tetra-O-methyl-D-galactose (XXXIX) demonstrates that these residues constitute the four end groups in the average repeating unit of the molecular complex since they are linked only through the reducing group at C_1, as shown in CLXXXIII and CLXXXIV respectively. Similarly the isolation of 2,3,4-tri-O-methyl-D-galactose (XVI) shows that this component arises from a D-galactose residue linked to other units in the complex through hydroxyl groups at C_1 and C_6, as in CLXXXV. Those D-galactose residues which give rise to 2,4-di-O-methyl-D-galactose CLXXXII must be combined with other monosaccharide units through C_1, C_3 and C_6, as shown in CLXXXVI.

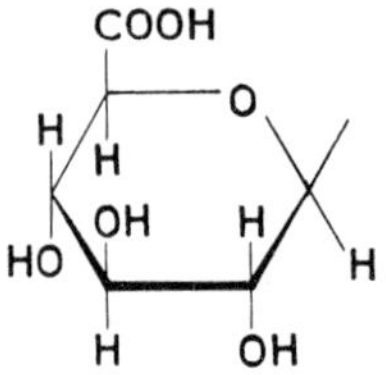

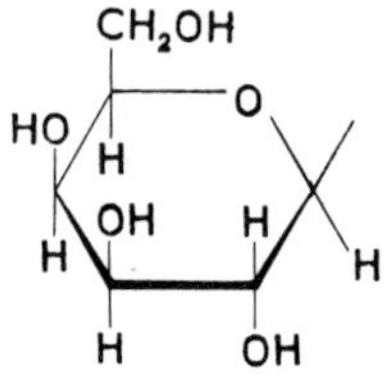

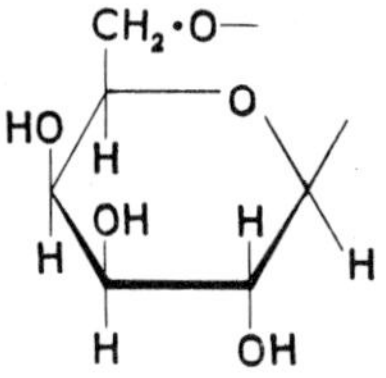

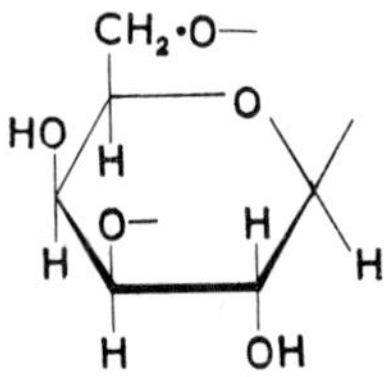

The existence of four end groups in a molecular complex consisting of twelve members demonstrates the branched-chain character of the degraded arabic acid. Furthermore, the branching occurs at those D-galactose units which give rise to 2,4-di-O-methyl-D-galactose (CLXXXII).

The isolation of the four cleavage fragments from methylated degraded arabic acid, listed in Table 46, column 1, shows that all the D-galactose and D-glucuronic acid residues have the pyranose structure and that all the units are joined either by 1 → 3 or 1 → 6 linkages. The several possible structures which could accommodate these experimental facts were limited by the isolation of 6-O-(2,3,4-tri-O-methyl-β-D-glucosyluronic acid)- 2, 3, 4 - tri - O - methyl - D - galactose (CLXXXVII) (22), the structure of which was ascertained by the fact that upon hydrolysis CLXXXVII afforded 2,3,4-tri-O-methyl-D-glucuronic acid (XV) and 2,3,4-

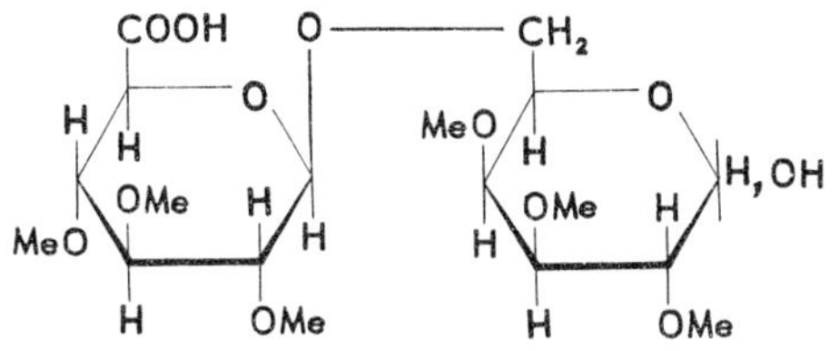

(CLXXXVII)

tri-O-methyl-D-galactose (XVI). The isolation of the aldobiouronic (CLXXXVII) from methylated degraded arabic acid indicated that the side chains containing the D-glucuronic acid must be linked with the main D-galactose chain through at least one D-galactose residue otherwise the galactose moiety of the methylated aldobiouronic acid (CLXXXVII) would have been 2,4-di-O-methyl-D-galactose (CLXXXII). One possible structure advanced for degraded arabic acid is shown in CLXXXVIII. The D-galactopyranose unit, D-Galp, is known to be united to other units through C_3 and C_6, since it affords 2,4-di-O-methyl-D-galactose (CLXXXII). The unit is so represented in the formula, however, because the methylation data cannot define whether it is joined to other D-galactose units in the main galactose chain by a 1 → 3 linkage and to the side chain, aldobiouronic acid residues by a 1 → 6 linkage or whether the reverse is the case.

TABLE 46. HYDROLYTIC CLEAVAGE FRAGMENTS FROM METHYLATED DEGRADED ARABIC ACID AND METHYLATED ARABIC ACID

Methylated Degraded Arabic Acid	Methylated Arabic Acid
2,3,4,6-Tetra-O-methyl-D-galactose (XXXIX) (1 mole)	2,3,4,6-tetra-O-methyl-D-galactose (XXXIX)
2,3,4-Tri-O-methyl-D-galactose (XVI) (5 moles)	2,3,4-tri-O-methyl-L-rhamnose (CLXXXIX)
2,4-Di-O-methyl-D-galactose (CLXXXII) (3 moles)	2,3,5-tri-O-methyl-L-arabinose (CLXL)
2,3,4-Tri-O-methyl-D-glucuronic acid (XV) (3 moles)	2,5-di-O-methyl-L-arabinose (XLIII)
	2,4-di-O-methyl-D-galactose (CLXXXII)
	2,3-di-O-methyl-D-glucuronic acid (CLXLI)
	2,3,4-tri-O-methyl-D-glucuronic acid (XV)

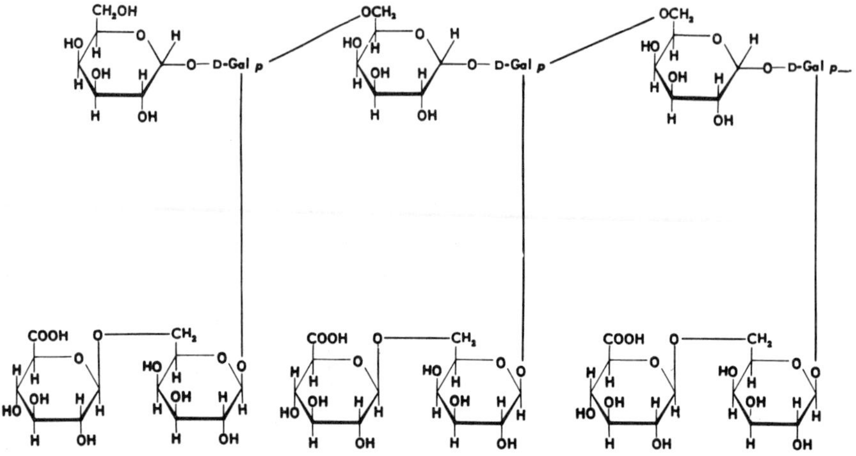

(CLXXXVIII) (D-Gal p = CLXXXVI)

The methylated derivative of gum arabic can be readily formed by the action of methyl sulfate and sodium hydroxide (10). Upon hydrolysis it gives 2,3,4,6-tetra-O-methyl-D-galactose (XXXIX), 2,3,4-tri-O-methyl-L-rhamnose (CLXXXIX), 2,3,5-tri-O-methyl-L-arabinose (CLXL), 2,5-di-O-methyl-L-arabinose (XLIII), 2,4-di-O-methyl-D-galactose (CLXXXII), 2,3-di-O-methyl-D-glucuronic acid (CLXLI), and 2,3,4-tri-O-methyl-D-glucuronic acid (XV).

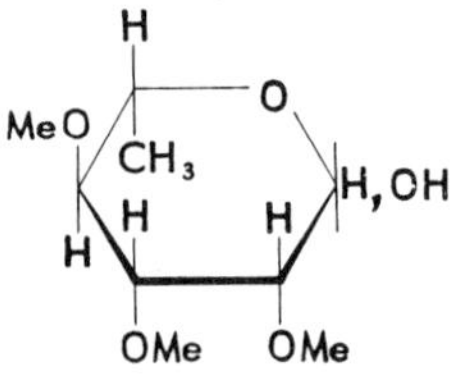

(CLXXXIX)

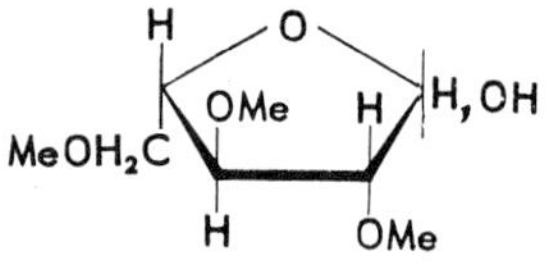

(CLXL)

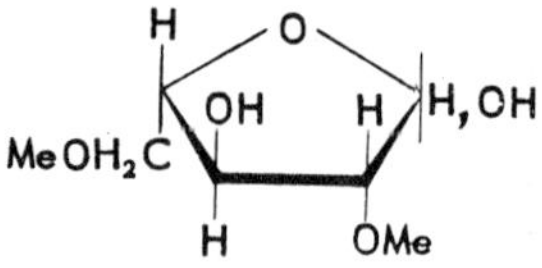

(XLIII)

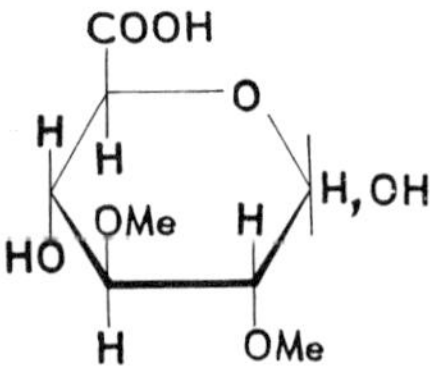

(CLXLI)

The identification of these products demonstrates that those labile sugar residues, L-arabinose, L-rhamnose, and 3-*O*-D-galactopyranosyl-L-arabinose, which are liberated during the autohydrolysis of arabic acid, are joined to the stable nucleus of degraded arabic acid in the form of L-arabofuranose (CLXLII), L-rhamnopyranose (CLXLIII), and 3-*O*-D-galactopyranosyl-L-arabofuranose (CLXLIV). Furthermore, it will be noted that whereas the methylated degraded arabic acid gave 2,3,4-tri-*O*-methyl-D-galactose (XVI) upon hydrolysis, the only partially methylated D-galactose derivative isolated from methylated gum arabic was 2,4-di-*O*-methyl-D-galactose (CLXXXII). It follows, therefore, that the labile sugar residues were attached at C_3 to those galactose units in degraded arabic acid which gave rise to 2,3,4-tri-*O*-methyl-D-galactose (XVI) upon hydrolysis of the methylated degraded arabic acid. Also, the D-glucuronic acid residues of methylated gum arabic afford principally the 2,3-di-*O*-methyl-D-glucuronic acid (CLXLI) and only a small amount of 2,3,4-tri-*O*-methyl-D-glucuronic acid (XV) which was the only methyl derivative of D-glucuronic acid isolated from the methylated degraded arabic acid. Some of the labile, sugar residues are therefore attached through C_4 of the D-glucuronic acid residues. The small amount of the 2,3,4-tri-*O*-methyl-D-glucuronic acid (XV) component of methylated gum arabic may arise from some degradation of the gum during methylation or it may be derived from a small number of terminal glucuronic acid groups in arabic acid.

A portion of the arabinose constituent of arabic acid is isolated from the methylated arabic acid as 2,5-di-*O*-methyl-L-arabinose (XLIII) and this must represent arabinose units which are interposed between the terminal groups of the side chain and the nucleus of degraded arabic acid. The isolation of 3-*O*-D-galactopyranosyl-L-arabinose (CLXXIII) from arabic acid is in agreement with this view and the presence of 2,5-di-*O*-methyl-L-arabinose residues in methylated arabic acid strongly suggests that in the polysaccharide the disaccharide (CLXXIII) is present in the form of 3-*O*-D-galactopyranosyl-L-arabofuranose (CLXLIV).

One of the simplest structures that explains the facts derived from the study of the methylated derivatives of arabic acid and degraded arabic acid is represented by CLXLV. As in the case of the structure of degraded arabic acid (CLXXXVIII) D-Gal*p* represents a D-galactopyranose unit which is here linked to other units through C_3 and C_6. The results of the methylation studies do not unambiguously establish the linkages of the D-galactose units in the main chain, which may all be of the 1 → 3 type with the aldobiouronic acid side chain attached to the main chain by a 1 → 6 linkage or, *vice versa*.

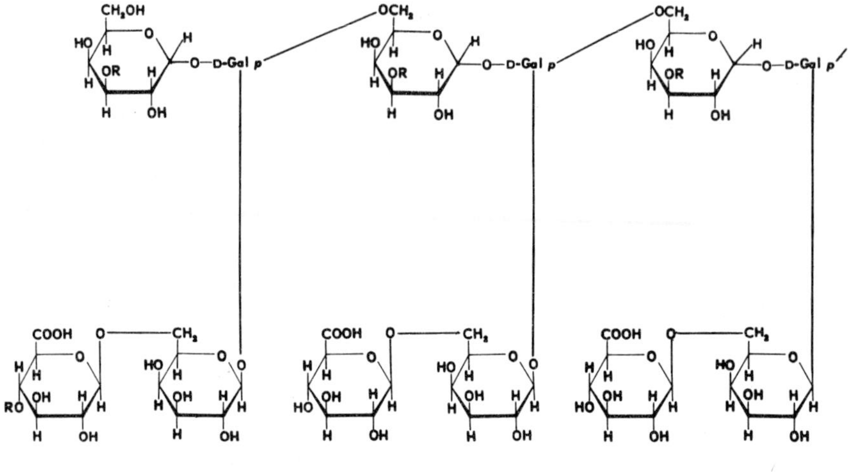

(CLXLV)

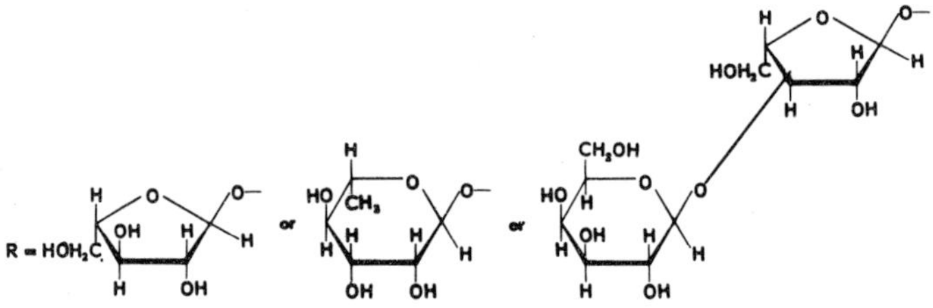

(CLXLII)   (CLXLIII)   (CLXLIV)

However, the possibility that the linkages in the main chain of D-galactose units are exclusively 1 ⟶ 6 is minimized by the isolation of 3-O-D-galactopyranosyl-D-galactose (CLXXVI) from degraded arabic acid. Alternatively, the linkages of the D-galactose units of the main chain and the linkages by which the aldobiouronic acid side chains are joined, may be both 1 ⟶ 3 and 1 ⟶ 6.

As was stated earlier, the structure CLXLV is the simplest representation of the methylation data for arabic acid. Equally compatible, for example, would be one in which the labile sugar residues, designated by R- in CLXLV, are joined to the more stable molecular complex through one or more L-arabofuranose units at C_3.

Throughout the constitutional studies of polysaccharides by methylation techniques, such as have been described above in the study of gum arabic, very little definite information can be obtained concerning the anomeric nature of the linkages between the component monosaccharide units. This is particularly true of the plant gums where several different sugars constitute the building units and where these are frequently of the D- and L-series. However, inferences may be drawn from polarimetric data which indicate the most probably predominant anomeric type. Arabic acid, $[\alpha]_D$ $-28°$ in water, when hydrolyzed with mineral acid shows a concomitant increase in the optical rotation of the solution to a high positive value, this direction of change usually being associated with β-D-linkages. That β-D-linkages are present has been proved by the synthesis of 6-O-β-D-glucopyranosyluronic acid)-D-galactose (CLXXVII) (19), which has been shown to be present in gum arabic (18,22). Further support for the presence of β-D-linkages in the main chain of D-galactose units is derived from the low rotation of the octa-O-methyl derivative of 3-O-D-galactopyranosyl-D-galactopyranose (CLXXVIII), $[\alpha]_D$ $+0.5°$ (approx.) in water (17), which increases to a high positive rotation upon hydrolysis. In view of the above facts the linkages in the formulae for degraded arabic acid (CLXXXVIII) and arabic acid (CLXLV) are shown as the β-D-type with the understanding, however, that they may not be exclusively so.

In an effort to reduce the number of alternative structures which are possible for arabic acid, the reaction originally described by Barry (24) has been applied to the degradation of gum arabic (23). It was shown that a sugar residue which has been oxidized by periodate to the corresponding dialdehyde suffers cleavage upon reaction with phenylhydrazine. The general scheme of the reactions is as follows:

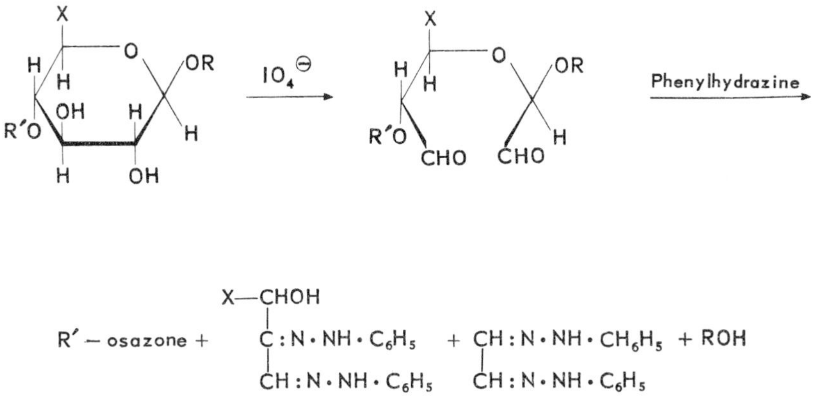

where X = H, CH_3, CH_2OH, COOH and R and R′ = H or any portion of the polysaccharide which is not oxidized by periodate.

The theoretical result of this series of reactions, therefore, is the removal of those sugar residues from the polysaccharide complex which are oxidized by periodate, namely, those which have α,β-glycol groupings. The molecule may be simply degraded from the reducing and non-reducing ends as in the case of laminarin (25) or it may be extensively degraded if several sugar residues in the main chain of the polysaccharide are oxidized, demonstrated by the amylopectin component of starch. The resistant fragments so produced will have new end groups and they may also have other residues in the chain which are now susceptible to further oxidation with periodate. By repeating this series of reactions the polysaccharide can be progressively degraded until a nucleus is obtained which is resistant to periodate or until all the residues of the polysaccharide have been cleaved. It will be seen from the proposed structure for arabic acid (CLXLV) that a repetition of this series of degradations will eventually expose the main chain of D-galactopyranose units. At this point, if only 1 ⟶ 6 linkages are present, oxidation with periodate will completely oxidize all the D-galactose residues. If 1 ⟶ 3 linkages are present exclusively, the only D-galactose unit to be oxidized will be that at the nonreducing end of the chain which would result in a very small degradation. If both types of linkage are present in the main chain, the products resulting will depend on the frequency of the two types of linkages, and they will have a molecular size smaller than if only 1 ⟶ 3 linkages were present.

After the first oxidation-degradation step, a product, A, was obtained from gum arabic which contained D-galactose and L-arabinose, confirming the outer structure of the gum depicted in CLXLV. The degradation of A in a similar manner gave a substance B which again was found to be composed of galactose and arabinose suggesting that one or more L-arabofuranose units are present between the galactosylarabofuranose disaccharide side chain, (CLXLIV), and the nucleus of the molecule in CLXLV. Further degradation of B gave a product composed solely of D-galactose units, which was only slightly degraded on a further treatment with periodate followed by phenylhydrazine. The conclusion was drawn, therefore, that the main chain of D-galactose units in arabic acid is linked by 1 ⟶ 3 glycosidic bonds.

A structural study of the polysaccharide A has thrown further light on the constitution of gum arabic (26). A quantitative analysis of A shows that half of the L-arabinose but less than 1 percent of the D-galactose residues are cleaved by the periodate oxidation of undegraded gum arabic. Several deductions can be drawn from this. The D-galactopyranose residue in the side chains, which is attached glycosidically to an L-arabofuranose unit, must have another sugar attached to it at C_3 in order that it will be resistant to periodate oxidation. Also, since all the D-glucuronic acid is oxidized by periodate and removed in the subsequent treatment with phenylhydrazine it cannot have the D-galactosyl-L-arabofuranose unit attached to it at C_4 otherwise D-galactose would be lost from the degraded polysaccharide A. Considering that D-glucuronic acid and L-rhamnose are present in gum arabic in approximately equimolecular proportions and that both are completely cleaved by periodate, it is probable that the L-rhamnose is attached to the uronic acid.

Acetylation of the degraded polysaccharide A followed by methylation with methyl sulfate and alkali gives a methylated derivative. The latter upon hydrolysis affords a complex mixture of methyl sugars which is reported to be composed of 2,4-di-O-methyl-D-galactose (8 moles), 2,4,6-tri-O-methyl-D-galactose (6 moles), 2,3,4,6-tetra-O-methyl-D-galactose (3 moles), 2,3-di-O-methyl-L-arabinose (2 moles), 2,5-di-O-methyl-L-arabinose (2 moles), 2,3,5-tri-O-methyl-L-arabinose (2 moles), and 2,3,4-tri-O-methyl-L-arabinose (2 moles). The quantitative analysis of the mixture of sugars was carried out by the chromatographic separation on cellulose sheets followed by extraction of the fractions, which were freed from solvent and weighed. Such a procedure is extremely difficult when applied to a mixture of sugars more simple than that encountered in this case so that the mole ratios quoted above must be looked upon as approximations until verified on a larger scale.

The cleavage fragments of methylated polysaccharide A were identified chromatographically except for the methylated galactose residues which were characterized by the formation of crystalline derivatives. However, support for the existence of L-arabopyranose residues in gum arabic, which was indicated by the presence of 2,3,4-tri-O-methyl-L-arabinose in the cleavage fragments, is forthcoming from the identification of 3-O-β-L-arabopyranosyl-L-arabinose in the partial hydrolysis products of gum arabic (27). Since this residue is present in polysaccharide A, it must be in the inner portion of the molecule and with a residue attached to it at C_3 or C_2 and C_4.

An alternative method for determining the types of linkages in the main chain of arabic acid takes advantage of the fact that periodate oxidized sugar residues, when reduced with sodium borohydride or catalytically with hydrogen, give polyalcohols (28) which can be easily hydrolyzed with mineral acid. This method avoids the practical difficulties inherent in the use of phenylhydrazine for degradation, difficulties which were obvious to the original workers (29). The general reaction is as follows:

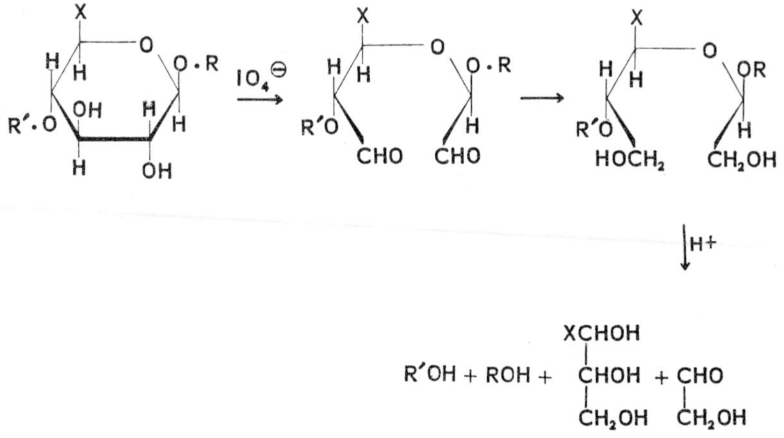

$$R'OH + ROH + \begin{array}{c} X\underset{|}{C}HOH \\ \underset{|}{C}HOH \\ CH_2OH \end{array} + \begin{array}{c} CHO \\ \underset{|}{C}H_2OH \end{array}$$

where X = H, CH₃, CH₂OH or COOH

Degraded arabic acid when treated with periodic acid at 0° consumes 1.2 mols. of periodate per anhydrohexose unit (30). The degraded arabic acid polyaldehyde so produced gives, upon reduction with sodium borohydride, the corresponding polyalcohol. Since the cleaved residues are now joined to the unoxidized portions of the molecule and to each other by acetal linkages they are easily hydrolyzed by mineral acid. Hydrolysis of the degraded arabic acid polyalcohol at pH 2, under which condition the original degraded arabic acid is stable, results in the formation of a galactan polymer which was found to be composed of D-galactose and D-lyxitol (D-arabitol). The D-lyxitol arises from the following series of reactions:

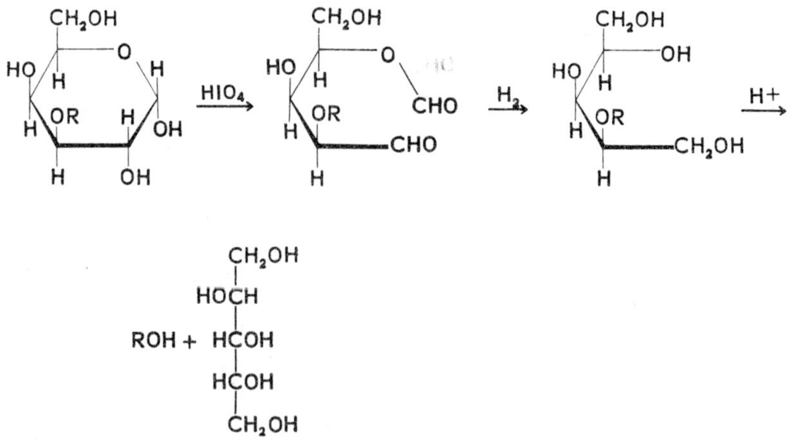

$$ROH + \begin{array}{c} CH_2OH \\ HO\underset{|}{C}H \\ H\underset{|}{C}OH \\ H\underset{|}{C}OH \\ CH_2OH \end{array}$$

The formyl ester group at C_5 of the original molecule is stable under the conditions of periodate oxidation (31,32) and so arrests further oxidation.

The galactan, upon further oxidation with periodic acid as before consumed one mole of periodate per anhydrohexose unit with the formation of one mole of formic acid for every two anhydrohexose units. Methylation of the galactan by the method of Menzies (33), followed by hydrolysis of the resulting methyl ether, afforded 2,3,4,6-tetra-O-methyl-D-galactose (XXXIX) and 2,4,6-tri-O-methyl-D-galactose (XLVI). Since no 2,3,4-tri-O-methyl-D-galactose was present, all the linkages in the galactan are of the 1 $\longrightarrow$ 3 type. This result agrees with the findings from the application of periodate oxidation and reaction with phenylhydrazine (23).

From the work of Dillon (23), which was applied to undegraded gum arabic, it might be inferred that the main chain of D-galactose units in gum arabic is joined entirely by 1 $\longrightarrow$ 3-linkages Since this type of linkage is comparatively resistant to hydrolysis with mineral acid, such a structure is difficult to reconcile with the properties of a degraded arabic acid formed by the mild hydrolysis of gum arabic. Both the barium salt and the free degraded arabic acid reduce Fehling solution (20) and it would seem that this portion of the arabic acid molecule is of finite size and relatively small in comparison with the parent polysaccharide, arabic acid. The comparatively small molecular size of the degraded arabic acid is born out by osmotic pressure determinations of molecular weight, a figure of approximately 4800 being obtained for methylated degraded arabic acid (20), compared with 220,000 for the molecular weight of gum arabic by similar methods of measurement (34). Sedimentation experiments also show that the molecular weight of degraded arabic acid is no greater than 20,000 (35). Furthermore, the linear 1 $\longrightarrow$ 3 linked galactan obtained by Smith and Spriestersbach (30) gave upon periodate oxidation an amount of formic acid which corresponds to only three or four galactose units in the molecule. It would seem, therefore, that gum arabic is best considered to be a molecule composed of blocks of degraded arabic acid units joined to each other possibly by arabofuranose units, which are sensitive to acid hydrolysis. The main chain of D-galactose units in the degraded arabic acid blocks are principally linked through C_1 and C_3 although the presence of 1 $\longrightarrow$ 6 linkages at the end or near the middle of this main chain are not excluded by the experimental facts known to date.

Other Acacia Gums

Most of the constitutional studies of gum arabic have been carried out with commercial specimens of gum and although these are obtained principally from *Acacia senegal*, contamination with gums from other varieties of *Acacia* is quite possible. In connection with chemical studies this is unfortunate, since it is now known that the composition of the gum depends upon the variety of *Acacia* tree from which the gum is collected. In three cases, *Acacia* gums of botanical homogeneity have been studied.

Black wattle gum is an exudate from the bark of *Acacia mollisima* Willd., produced upon mechanical injury or pathologically as a result of "gummosis" (36), has not, as yet, been put to commercial use. The qualitative chemical properties of the gum are similar to those of gum arabic. An elementary analysis of black-wattle gum indicates 71 percent pentosan and 16 percent galactose (37) with the free gum acid having an equivalent weight of about 1900 compared with 1,000–1,400 for gum arabic. It is composed of L-arabinose (38), L-rhamnose, D-galactose, and D-glucuronic acid in the molecular ratio 6: 1: 5: 1, respectively.

Upon autohydrolysis of the free acid, the labile residues of L-arabinose and L-rhamnose are liberated in amounts which together correspond to that of the resulting degraded acid; 3-O-β-L-arabopyranosyl-L-arabinose has also been detected in the hydrolysis products (40). The degraded acid consists of D-galactose and D-glucuronic acid in the molecular ratio 5: 1 and partial hydrolysis results in the formation of D-galactose and an aldobiouronic acid, 6-O-(β-D-glucopyranosyluronic acid)-D-galactose (CLXXVII) the identity of which was established by methylation studies as in the case of gum arabic. It is suggested therefore, that the degraded acid of black wattle gum differs from degraded arabic acid in that one aldobiouronic acid side chain is attached to a main chain of four D-galactopyranose units compared with degraded arabic acid, which has three aldobiouronic side chains and a main chain of six D-galactopyranose units.

The gum exudate of *Acacia pycnantha*, a tree found in South Australia, is composed of D-galactose (65 percent), L-arabinose (27 percent) and D-glucuronic acid (5 percent) with a small amount of L-rhamnose (1 to 2 percent) which may be an impurity (8). The gum acid, equivalent weight 3700, upon mild hydrolysis with 0.1N sulfuric acid readily affords L-arabinose and L-rhamnose; D-galactose and a crystalline disaccharide (m.p. 159–160°, $[\alpha]_D$ + 62° in water), believed to be 3-O-D-galactopyranosyl-D-galactose (CLXXVI), are produced upon prolonged hydrolysis. More vigorous hydrolysis of the gum with N sulfuric acid gives an aldobiouronic acid which was proved by methylation studies to be 6-O-(β-D-glucopyranosyluronic acid)-D-galactose (CLXXVII). Preliminary methylation studies on the gum indicate that it has a highly branched structure.

Acacia cyanophylla Lindl. (Port Jackson willow: golden willow) is closely related botanically to *A. pycnantha* and produces a gum which is composed of D-galactose (11 moles), L-arabinose (2 moles), L-rhamnose (5 moles), and D-glucuronic acid (5 moles) (39). The ash-free polysaccharide having $[\alpha]_D$ − 20° in water and equivalent weight 740, undergoes autohydrolysis at 45° with the liberation after 4 hours of L-rhamnose, L-arabinose, and 3-*O*-α-D-galactopyranosyl-L-arabinose (CLXXIII); after 23 hours, D-galactose and 6-*O*-(β-D-glucopyranosyluronic acid)-D-galactose (CLXXVII) are produced. The degraded gum remaining after autohydrolysis is composed of D-galactose (4 moles) and D-glucuronic acid (1 mole) and is reported to have an equivalent weight of 700.

Acacia karroo Hayne, ("doringboom"; Karroo thorn; mimosa), is indigenous to South Africa and found extensively in the semi-arid inland regions. It produces a gum which, when freed from ash, has an equivalent weight of 1660 and shows $[\alpha]_D$ + 54° (sodium salt in water) (40). The positive specific rotation differentiates this gum from the other examples of this type known to date. Karroo gum acid is composed of L-rhamnose (2 percent), L-arabinose (36 percent), D-galactose (50 percent), and D-glucuronic acid (12 percent) and, like gum arabic, undergoes autohydrolysis giving L-arabinose which is detectable chromatographically after 2 hours; two disaccharides are liberated after 3.5 hours hydrolysis; L-rhamnose after 12 hours and both D-galactose and aldobiouronic acid after 17 hours. The resulting degraded gum has an equivalent weight of 1270 and is composed of D-galactose and uronic acid, the ratio of which, calculated from the equivalent weight, would be approximately 7 : 1.

The neutral disaccharides produced by autohydrolysis are 3-*O*-α-D-galactopyranosyl-L-arabinose (CLXXIII) (identified chromatographically) and 3-*O*-β-L-arabopyranosyl-L-arabinose (CLXLVI), which was identified as its crystalline phenylosazone. This disaccharide had been previously identified in larch *E*-galactan (41), peach gum (42), cherry gum (42), golden apple gum (43), and it is most probably present in lemon gum (27).

Hydrolysis of *A. karroo* gum with 0.5*N* sulfuric acid gave a mixture of two aldobiouronic acids, 6-*O*-(β-D-glucopyranosyluronic acid)-D-galactose (CLXXVII) and 4-*O*-(α-D-glucopyranosyluronic acid)-D-galactose (CLXLVII). The latter aldobiouronic acid had not been encountered before in an *Acacia* gum. It is also the first *Acacia* gum to contain glucuronic acid units linked by 1 ⟶ 4 and 1 ⟶ 6 linkages although it should be borne in mind that the parent gum may have been a mixture of two polysaccharides.

Thus, with the exception of *Acacia karroo* gum, the gums of *Acacia mollissima* Willd., *Acacia pycnantha*, and *Acacia cyanophylla* which are compared in Table 47, resemble gum arabic in that they contain the same constituent sugars and they yield the same aldobiouronic acid upon acid hydrolysis (see Table 47). However, the proportions of these compo-

TABLE 47. COMPARISON OF PROPERTIES AND COMPOSITION OF
ACACIA GUMS

Properties	A. cyano-phylla	A. senegal	A. karroo	A. mollis-sima	A. py-cnantha
Equivalent Weight	740	1000 to 1400	1660	1880	3700
$[\alpha]_D$ (ash-free gum in water)	-20°	-28°	$+54^\circ$(Na salt)	-49°	-8°
Composition (%)					
L-Rhamnose	18	11	2	8	1-2
L-Arabinose	7	30	36	46	27
D-Galactose	50	37	50	38	65
D-Glucuronic acid	25	14	12	8	5
Degraded Gum					
Equivalent Weight	700	660	1270	930	
Composition (mol. ratio)					
D-Galactose		3		5	
D-Glucuronic acid		1		1	
Oligosaccharides identified from partial hydrolysis of gum					
β-L-Ara*p*-(1 ⟶ 3)-L-Ara		+	+	+	
α-D-Gal*p*-(1 ⟶ 3)-L-Ara	+	+	+		
D-Gal*p*-(1 ⟶ 3)-D-Gal		+			+(?)
β-D-GA*p*-(1 ⟶ 6)-D-Gal	+	+	+	+	+
α-D-GA*p*-(1⟶ 4)-D-Gal		+			

nents are markedly different, an observation which must be a reflection of the detailed structures of the individual gums. In particular, the proportion of uronic acid in the three gums is different and consequently if the general structural features of the *Acacia* gums are the same, it would appear that they differ in the ratio of acidic side chains to D-galactose residues in the backbone. For *A. verek* this ratio is 3 : 6, for *A. cyanophylla* 5 : 6, for *A. mollissima* 1 : 4, and for *A. pycnantha* 1 : 12. These ratios may be significant in comparing the physical properties of the respective gums.

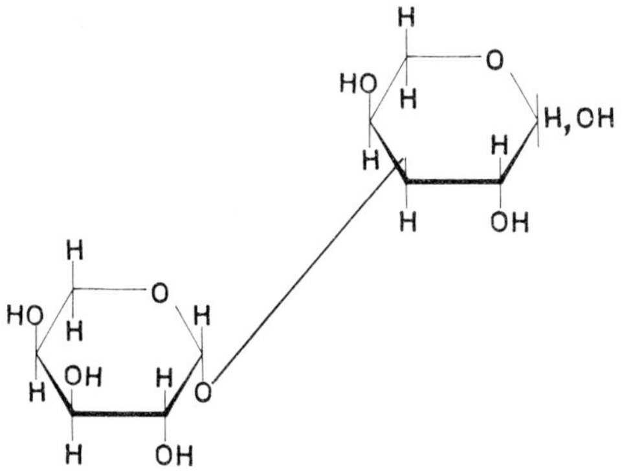

(CLXLVI)

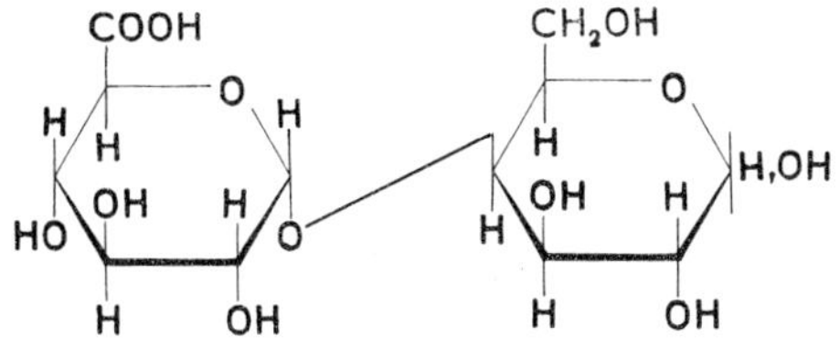

(CLXLVII)

Damson Gum

Damson gum exudes from the bark of the tree, *Prunus insitia,* as brownish semi-solid nodules. The gum is the neutral salt of a complex polysaccharide acid (44). In appearance and properties the substance resembles gum arabic to which it seems to be structurally related. Although samples of the gum, collected from trees in different parts of England, are found to be essentially the same in physical and chemical properties significant chemical differences have been noted.

The ash-free polysaccharide, obtained by precipitation from an acidified aqueous solution of the gum with ethanol shows $[\alpha]_D - 26°$ (sodium salt in water) and analysis indicates 36.2 per cent of pentosan and 16.4 per cent uronic anhydride. Examination of the products formed on hydrolysis with mineral acid shows that the pentose is principally L-arabinose with traces of D-xylose and that the uronic acid is D-glucuronic acid; D-galactose and D-mannose are also present. D-Galactose, L-arabinose and D-glucuronic acid are therefore common to both gum arabic and damson gum; the latter, however, also contains D-mannose and

D-xylose but no L-rhamnose.   As with arabic acid, the damson gum acid undergoes autohydrolysis, during which all of the L-arabinose is liberated leaving a more resistant nucleus of degraded polysaccharide. This would indicate that all the L-arabinose is present in damson gum in the furanose form. The degraded polysaccharide obtained by autohydrolysis gives analytical values for uronic acid and pentosan which are in agreement with those required by a polysaccharide containing one uronic acid residue combined with three hexose residues, together with a pentosan present in much smaller stoichiometric ratio.   Controlled hydrolysis of the degraded damson gum with N sulfuric acid gives two moles of D-galactose, a small amount of D-xylose, and one molecular proportion of an aldobiouronic acid 2-O-(β-D-glucopyranosyluronic acid)-D-mannose (CLXLVIII).   The gum therefore consists of repeating units which contain L-arabinose (3 moles), D-galactose (2 moles), D-mannose (1 mole), D-glucuronic acid (1 mole), and D-Xylose (3 per cent) (44).

The aldobiouronic acid (CLXLVIII), isolated as the barium salt from the hydrolyzate of degraded damson gums gave upon methylation methyl 2-O-[methyl (2,3,4-tri-O-methyl-β-D-glucosyl)uronate]-3,4,6-tri-O-methyl-D-mannoside (CLXLIX) which upon hydrolysis afforded 2,3,4-tri-O-methyl-D-glucuronic acid (XV) and 3,4,6-tri-O-methyl-D-mannose (CC). This clearly indicates that the D-glucuronic acid is in the pyranose form

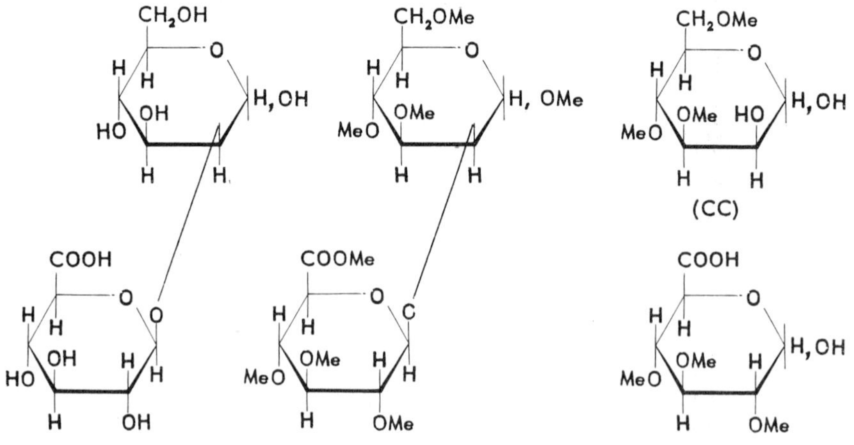

(CLXLVIII)   (CLXLIX)   (XV)   (CC)

and that it is attached by a glycosidic link to C_2 of the D-mannopyranose moiety.   From the rotation of the fully methylated derivative (CLXLIX) ($[\alpha]_D^{20} - 16°$) it is inferred that the linkage is of the β-D-type.

Further evidence concerning the structure of damson gum is obtained from a study of the products of hydrolysis of the methylated degraded polysaccharide. A mixture of methylated sugars is obtained which is more complex than that obtained from methylated degraded arabic acid. The cleavage fragments, isolated and identified by the formation of crystalline derivatives, are listed in the first column of Table 48 (45). Also present are 2 parts of D-mannose which is present as a di-O-methyl derivative.

Methylation of the undegraded gum by treatment of the thallium salt with methyl iodide, the same procedure as was used for the degraded gum, gave the corresponding methylated material which afforded upon hydrolysis those methylated sugars listed in the second column of Table 48, together with methylated derivatives of D-mannose and D-xylose not yet characterized (46).

TABLE 48. METHYLATED SUGARS FROM THE HYDROLYSIS OF METHYLATED DAMSON GUM AND METHYLATED DEGRADED DAMSON GUM

Methylated Degraded Damson Gum	Methylated Damson Gum
2,3,4,6-Tetra-O-methyl-D-galactose (XXXIX) (1 part)	2,3,5-Tri-O-methyl-L-arabinose (CLXL) (8 parts)
2,4,6-Tri-O-methyl-D-galactose (XLVI) (1 part)	2,3-Di-O-methyl-L-arabinose (CCI) (4 parts)
2,3,4-Tri-O-methyl-D-galactose (XVI) (1 part)	2,4,6-Tri-O-methyl-D-galactose (XLVI) (3 parts)
2,4-Di-O-methyl-D-galactose (CLXXXII) (1 part)	2,4-Di-O-methyl-D-galactose (CLXXXII) (3 parts)
2,3,4-Tri-O-methyl-D-glucuronic acid (XV) (1 part)	2-O-Methyl-D-galactose (CCIII) (1 part)
2,3-Di-O-methyl-D-glucuronic acid (CLXLI) (1 part)	4-O-Methyl-D-galactose (CCIV) (1 part)
2,3,4-Tri-O-methyl-D-xylose (CCXII) (1/6 part)	2,3,4-Tri-O-methyl-D-glucuronic acid (XV) (2 parts)
4,6-Di-O-methyl-D-galactose (CCXIII) (trace)	2,3-Di-O-methyl-D-glucuronic acid (CLXLI) (2 parts)

Despite the achievement of the identification of these highly complex mixtures of sugars from the methylated damson gum and the methylated degraded gum and the estimation of the quantities of each present in the mixtures, it is not yet possible to assign a single structural formula to this gum. Nevertheless, a comparison of the products formed from the methyl derivatives of the degraded and undegraded gum shows that 2,3,4,6-tetra-O-methyl-D-galactose (XXXIX) and 2,4,6-tri-O-methyl-D-

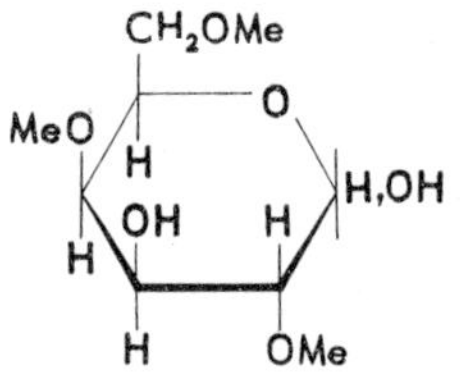

CH₂OMe structure (XLVI)

CH₂OMe
MeO — O
H
OH   H,OH
H
H   OMe

(XLVI)

H
H — O
H
MeO OMe   H,OH
H
H   OMe

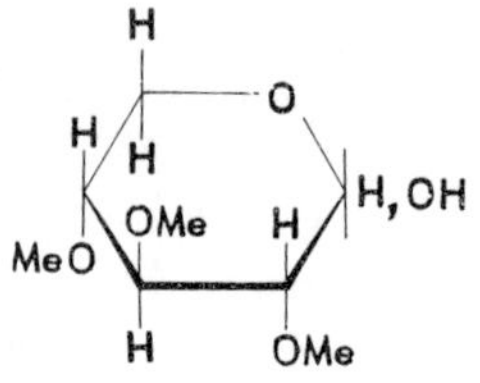

(CCXII)

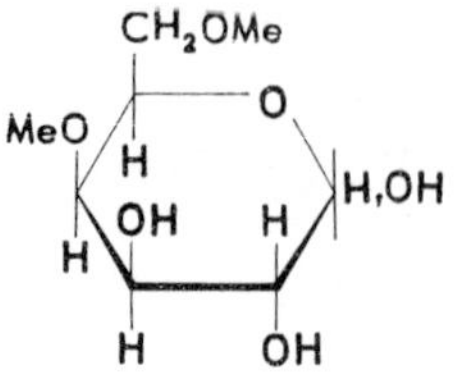

CH₂OMe
MeO — O
H
OH   H,OH
H
H   OH

(CCXIII)

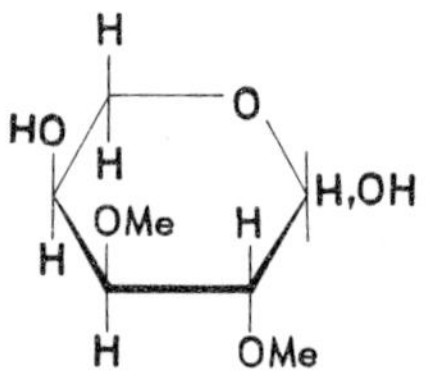

H
HO — O
H
OMe   H,OH
H
H   OMe

(CCI)

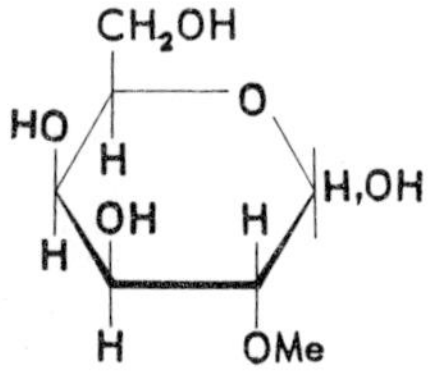

CH₂OH
HO — O
H
OH   H,OH
H
H   OMe

(CCIII)

CH₂OH
MeO — O
H
OH   H,OH
H
H   OH

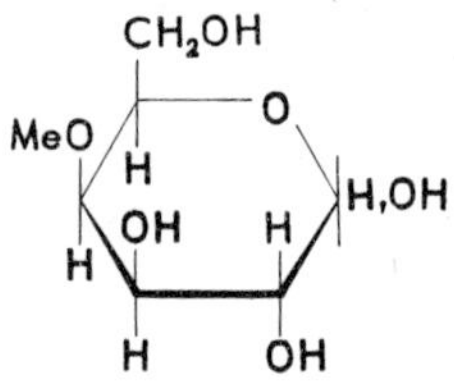

(CCIV)

galactose (XLVI) do not occur among the cleavage fragments of the methylated gum. It may be inferred therefore, that the L-arabofuranose residues are attached to C_3 and C_6 of the D-galactopyranose units which give rise to 2,3,4,6-tetra-(XXXIX) and 2,4,6-tri-O-methyl-D-galactose (XLVI) in the methylated degraded gum. Furthermore, since 2,3-di-O-methyl-L-arabinose (CCI) and 2,3,5-tri-O-methyl-L-arabinose (CLXL) are present in the hydrolysis products of the methylated gum in the ratio 1 : 2 it follows that there must be two side chains one consisting of single L-arabofuranose units (CLXLII) and the other composed of two L-arabofuranose units in one chain mutually joined by a 1 → 5 linkage as in CCII. The arabinose side chains (CLXLII) and (CCII) also appear to be joined to those D-galactose residues of the methylated gum which afford 2-O-methyl-D-galactose (CCIII) and 4-O-methyl-D-galactose (CCIV). Since the molecular ratio of the 2,3,4-tri-O-methyl-D-glucuronic acid (XV) to 2,3-di-O-methyl-D-glucuronic acid (CLXLI) are the same in the methyl derivatives of degraded and undegraded gum, it would seem that neither of these acid units constitutes a point of attachment for the L-arabinose side chains.

From methylation studies it is clear that the gum contains D-galactopyranose units linked through C_1 and C_3 (CCV), C_1, C_3 and C_6 (CCVI), C_1, C_3, C_4 and C_6 (CCVII), and C_1, C_2, C_3 and C_6 (CCVIII), L-arabinose side chains, (CLXLII and CCII), D-glucuronic acid linked through C_1

(CCIX), and C_1 and C_4 (CCX) but there are D-xylopyranose and D-manno-pyranose units linked in an undetermined way. However, it is known that the D-mannose residues are linked through C_2 to D-glucuronic acid residues, and that, in part at least, they must also be linked through one other position since some of the mannose residues from the methylated un-degraded gum appear as a di-O-methyl derivative. Neglecting the small proportion of D-xylose, the role of which is unknown, one of the many possible structures for degraded damson gum is depicted in CCXI for purposes of illustration (47), where D-Man$p$ is a D-mannopyranose resi-due linked through C_1 and C_2 and one other carbon atom. The glycosidic bonds are all assigned a β-D-configuration because of the negative ro-tation of the gum. It is possible, however, that some α-D-glycosidic linkages are also present. At this stage it is obvious that only an outline of the type of possible structure of damson gum can be advanced.

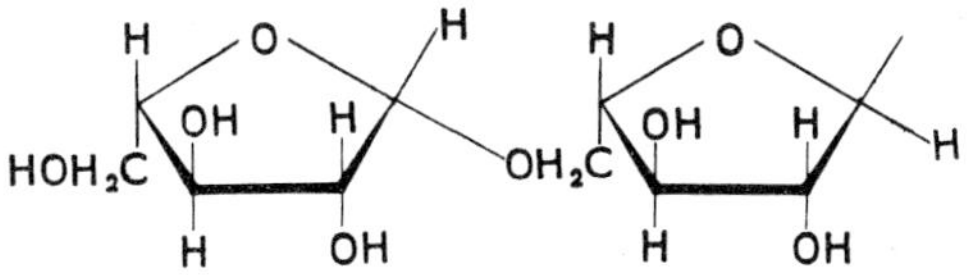

(CCII)

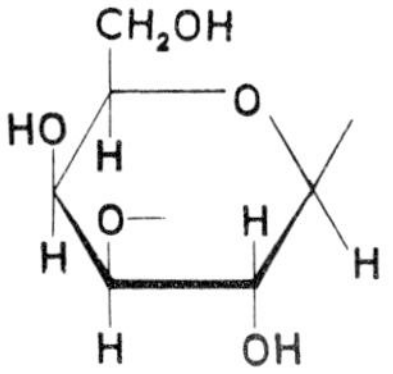

(CCV) 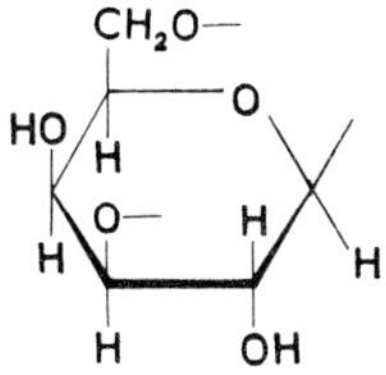   (CCVI) 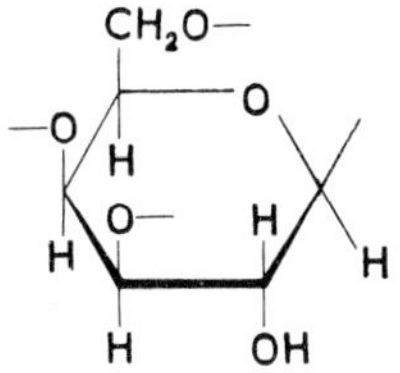   (CCVII)

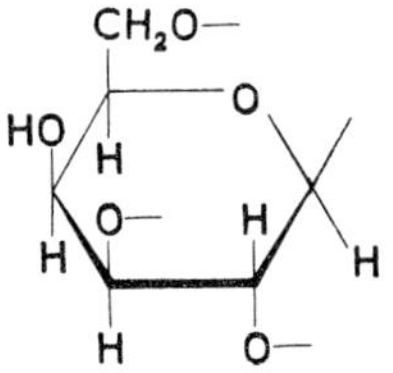

(CCVIII) 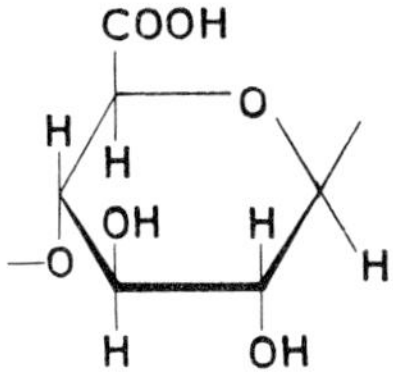   (CCX) 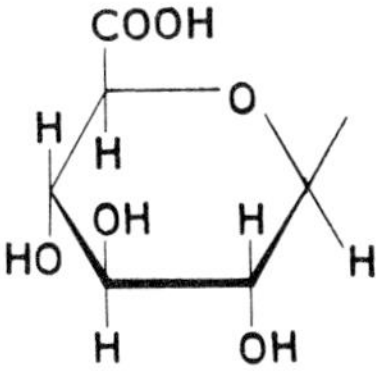   (CCIX)

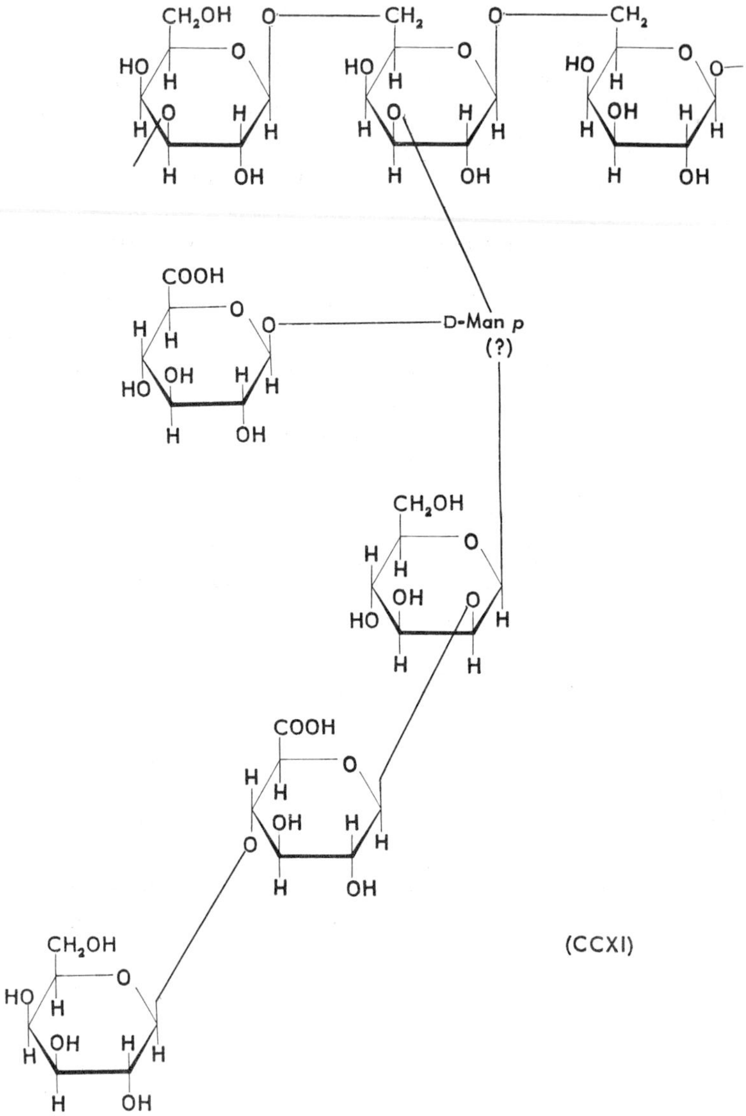

(CCXI)

Cherry Gum

Gums exude from the bark of cherry trees as semi-solid nodules, resembling damson gum very closely. They are sometimes collected during off-season periods and find some use in the pharmaceutical and medicinal fields. The supplies however, are not constant.

Two specimens of cherry (*Prunus cerasus*) gum obtained from cultivated trees growing in England differed in some respects from the gum
obtained from wild cherry trees (*Prunus virginiana* L.) in the State of
Indiana, U.S.A. The gum from wild cherry, which dissolves only partially
in water, has an equivalent weight of 1790. The free gum acid consists
of L-arabinose (8 moles), D-xylose (6 moles), D-galactose (6 moles), D-
mannose (3 moles), and D-glucuronic acid (48). The acid gum from the
English trees consists of L-arabinose (6 moles), D-galactose (2 moles),
D-mannose (1 mole), D-glucuronic acid (1 mole) and small amounts (1.5
per cent) of D-xylose, and has an equivalent weight of 1450 (49,50). Extraction with 70 per cent alcohol, the usual method for the extraction of
araban (51), failed to separate a polysaccharide differing in physical
properties from the original gum. It may be important to note that cherry
trees can be grown as grafts on different stocks, the types of which may
determine the nature of the exuded gum. However, all samples of English
cherry gum appear to have very similar properties and bear many resem-
blances to damson gum. For instance, both gums upon prolonged hydrolysis give the same aldobiouronic acid, 2-*O*-(β-D-glucopyranosyluronic
acid)-D-mannose (CLXLVIII) (49).

Graded hydrolysis of the free acid of cherry (*P. cerasus*) gum with N
mineral acid affords various oligosaccharides, one of which has been
shown to be 3-*O*-β-L-arabopyranosyl-L-arabinose (CLXLVI) (42). This
is one of the first instances of the identification of arabopyranose residues in a gum (cf 41,52). The structure of the disaccharide (CLXLVI)
was proved by methylation with methyl sulfate and sodium hydroxide to
the hexamethyl ether (CCXIV) which on hydrolysis yielded 2,3,4-tri-*O*-
methyl-L-arabinose (CCXV) and 2,4-di-*O*-methyl-L-arabinose (XL).

The fully methylated cherry gum may be prepared by treatment of the
thallium salt of the gum with methyl iodide (53). The methylated gum,
like methylated damson gum, readily undergoes partial methanolysis with
2 per cent of methanolic hydrogen chloride, but there remains a resistant
residue which requires prolonged treatment before hydrolysis is complete. Six different sugars, (see Table 49, Column 2), have been identi-

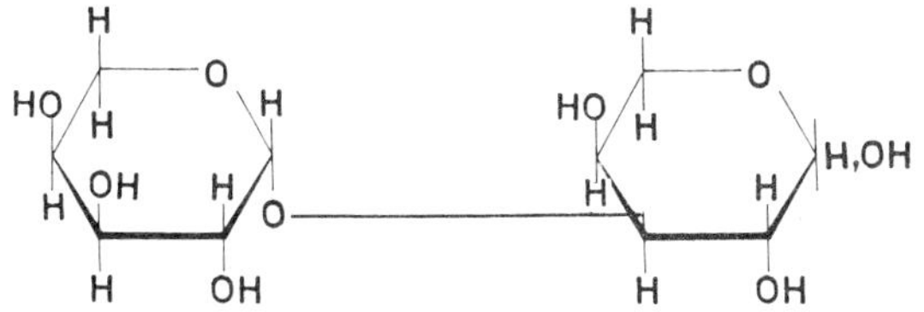

(CLXLVI)

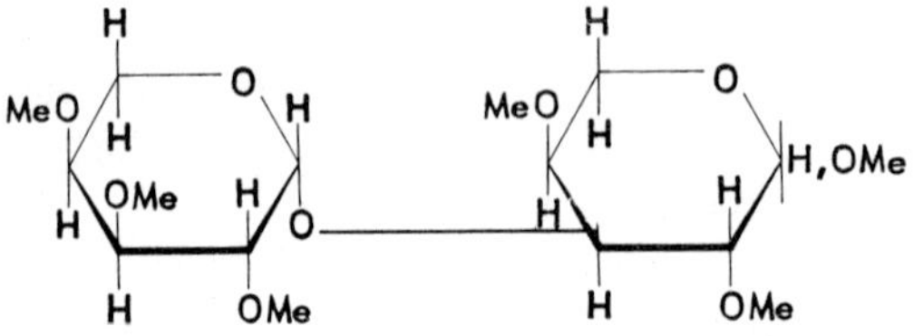

(CCXIV)

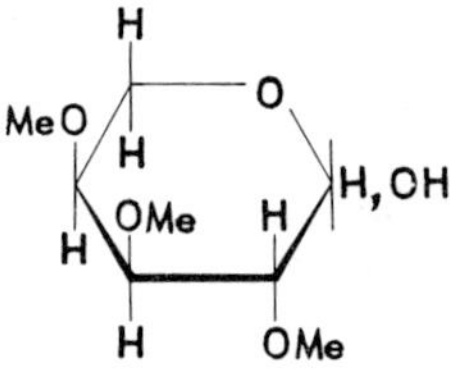

(CCXV) 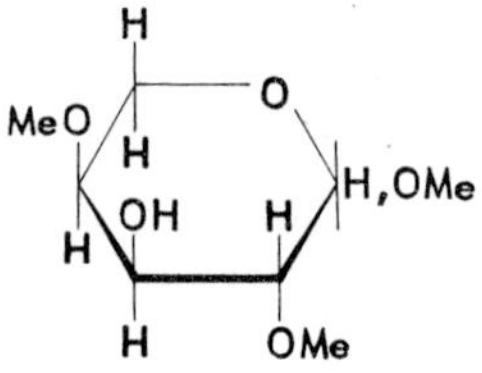　　　　　　　(XL)

fied after fractional distillation of the methanolysis products. However, because of the difficulty encountered in the separation of such complex mixtures of methylated sugars by fractional distillation, the methylated residues of D-mannose and D-xylose were not identified. It is also possible that other methylated derivatives of galactose are present as

TABLE 49. METHYLATED SUGARS FROM THE HYDROLYSIS OF METHYLATED CHERRY GUM AND METHYLATED DEGRADED CHERRY GUM

Methylated Degraded Cherry Gum	Methylated Cherry Gum
2,3,4,6-Tetra-O-methyl-D-galactose (XXXIX)	2,3,5-Tri-O-methyl-L-arabinose (CLXL)
2,3,4-Tri-O-methyl-D-xylose (CCXII)	2,5-Di-O-methyl-L-arabinose (XLIII)
2,4,6-Tri-O-methyl-D-galactose (XLVI)	2,4,6-Tri-O-methyl-D-galactose (XLVI)
2,4-Di-O-methyl-D-xylose (CCXVI)	2,4-Di-O-methyl-D-galactose (CLXXXII)
2,6-Di-O-methyl-D-galactose (CCXVII)	2,3,4-Tri-O-methyl-D-glucuronic acid (XV)
2,4-Di-O-methyl-D-galactose (CLXXXII)	2,3-Di-O-methyl-D-glucuronic acid. (CLXLI)
2,3,4-Tri-O-methyl-D-glucuronic acid (XV)	
2,3-Di-O-methyl-D-glucuronic acid (CLXLI)	

well as a methylated arabopyranose residue; the latter must be present in view of the identification of 3-O-β-L- arabopyranosyl- L - arabinose (XLIX). Such a methylated arabopyranose cleavage fragment was indicated in the methanolysis products of methylated cherry gum, but was ruled out at that time since the opinion was held that all the arabinose units were in the furanose form (53).

The free acid of cherry gum undergoes autohydrolysis; this removes all the L-arabinose together with a little D-xylose, leaving a degraded cherry gum which resembles very closely the degraded polysaccharide from damson gum (50). The arabinose-free degraded gum was methylated by the thallium-methyl iodide method (33). Cleavage of the methylated degraded gum gives a complex mixture of methylated sugars whose separation by partition chromatography on a cellulose column (54) illustrates the elegance of this technique and enables a much clearer picture to be drawn. The sugars which are obtained from methylated degraded cherry gum by this procedure are listed in Table 49, column 1. A tri-O-methyl- and a di-O-methyl-D-mannose are also indicated by paper chromatographic analysis but their identity is not yet known.

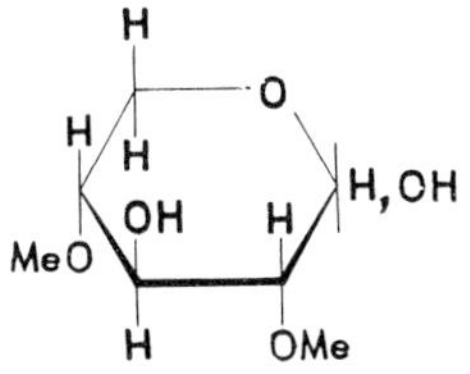

(CCXVI) 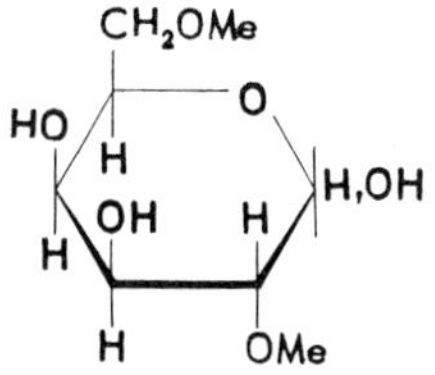   (CCXVII)

Further information of the mode of union of the sugar units is forthcoming from a study of the action of periodate on cherry gum. Oxidation of the gum with periodate is found to produce two moles of formic acid per equivalent of the gum with the concomitant consumption of seven moles of periodate (50). In view of the fact that D-glucuronic acid residues are present as end-groups in the gum, it is doubtful whether the yield of formic acid has any structural significance (62), but since the production of two moles of formic acid requires the reduction of four moles of periodate approximately three sugar residues per equivalent of gum are oxidized, in addition to the uronic acid residue. Analysis of the polyaldehyde of the gum indicates that no D-galactose residues are oxidized but that approximately 50 per cent of the L-arabinose residues are cleaved. No D-xylose was found in the gum polyaldehyde despite the isolation of 2,4-di-O-methyl-D-xylose from the hydrolysis of the methylated degraded cherry gum which indicates that some of the D-xylose residues in the gum have no free adjacent hydroxyl groups. The fate of the D-mannose residues during the periodate oxidation of the gum is not settled.

In the absence of quantitative separation and identification of the cleavage fragments of the methylated gum, it is not possible to select any one formula for cherry gum. The main structural features of the gum, however, are apparent as may be seen from the following considerations. Since the two methylated arabinose derivatives (CLXL and XLIII) formed by methanolysis have the furanose structure some L-arabinose units must be present in the gum as furanose residues and in view of their ease of removal, both from the methylated and unmethylated gum by treatment with acid, it appears that they must be joined as side chains to the acid-resistant nucleus of the degraded cherry gum. Similar considerations would also indicate that the arabinose moiety of the disaccharide (CLXLVI) which is joined to the degraded gum nucleus is in the furanose and not in the pyranose form as is shown in CLXLVI. Since the hydroxyl groups at C_4 and C_5 of the reducing arabinose moiety of the disaccharide are free, then isomerization of the more labile furanose structure to the pyranose form which is more stable would take place upon hydrolysis of this glycosidic bond. The identification of 2,4-di-O-methyl-D-xylose (CCXVI) excludes a part of the D-xylose residue from an end-group position. The periodate oxidation studies show that no D-galactose units in this gum have free α-glycol groups and from the methylation data these residues are linked through C_1 and C_3, C_1, C_3 and C_6, and C_1, C_3 and C_4, since they give rise in the case of the methylated degraded gum to 2,4,6-tri-O-methyl-D-galactose (XLVI), 2,4-di-O-methyl-D-galactose (CLXXXII), and 2,6-di-O-methyl-D-galactose (CCXVII). Cherry and damson gums, like gum arabic, possess terminal units of D-glucuronic acid since the 2,3,4-tri-O-methyl derivative (XV) is produced as one of the cleavage fragments of the methylated gum and methylated degraded gum; in addition, units of D-glucuronic acid which have a $1 \rightarrow 4$ linkage occur in each of these three gums since 2,3-di-O-methyl-D-glucuronic acid (CLXLI) is formed by hydrolysis of the methylated gums. In the case of damson and cherry gum, these D-glucuronic acid residues are linked through their reducing groups to C_2 of the D-mannose residues. The latter are also linked in part through another position, as yet unknown, since chromatographic analysis of the hydrolyzate of methylated degraded cherry gum reveals the presence of a di-O-methyl mannose. One point of difference between cherry and damson gum is that cherry gum has its L-arabofuranose units mutually joined by 1 → 3 linkages as is the case with gum arabic, since 2,5-di-O-methyl-L-arabinose (XLIII) is formed from the methylated gum, whereas in damson gum the L-arabofuranose residues are joined by 1 → 5 glycosidic bonds, 2,3-di-O-methyl-L-arabinose (CCI) being obtained from the methylated gum.

A sample of gum exuded from a cultivated Black Republican cherry tree (*Prunus* sp.) collected during the summer of 1956 is reported (151) to yield a gum acid which was completely water soluble and showed $[\alpha]_D^{23}$ -9° (c 1, water) and an intrinsic viscosity of 4.0 in cupriethylene-diamine.

Complete hydrolysis of the gum followed by paper partition chromatographic analysis showed the presence of large and approximately equal amounts of galactose and arabinose, smaller amounts of xylose, mannose, and glucuronic acid as well as very small amounts of rhamnose.

Graded hydrolysis by heating for 8 hours at 100° with N sulfuric acid gave the above mentioned sugars and two aldobiouronic acids one composed of galactose and glucuronic acid and the other of mannose and glucuronic acid. Autohydrolysis for 24 hours at 100° produced large amounts of arabinose, smaller amounts of rhamnose, and a trace of xylose as well as several oligosaccharides.

Periodate oxidation studies showed that the gum consumed 5 moles of periodate and the production of 1.5 moles of formic acid per kilogram of gum acid. A fraction of the gum (about 30 per cent) was resistant to periodate oxidation and, upon hydrolysis, was found to contain arabinose, mannose, and galactose.

Egg Plum Gum

Recent researches on a gum from the egg or yellow Pershore plum tree, *Prunus domestica*, belonging to the family *Rosaceae* have demonstrated that this gum resembles gum arabic more closely than do the damson and cherry gums (55,56).

The gum acid, which appears to be a homogeneous substance, has an equivalent weight of 1220 and does not reduce Fehling solution. The gum consists of L-arabinose (3 parts), D-xylose (1 part), D-galactose (3 parts), and D-glucuronic acid (1 part). An aqueous solution of the gum acid undergoes autohydrolysis upon heating at 100°. In this way, all the L-arabinose units of the gum are readily detached from the stable nucleus and the D-xylose, although eliminated less readily than the L-arabinose, nevertheless can be removed almost completely without dislocation of the main chain structure of the gum. Upon hydrolysis with *N*-sulfuric acid, the degraded polysaccharide affords D-galactose and an aldobiouronic acid, 6-*O*-(β-D-glucopyranosyluronic acid)-D-galactose (CLXXVII), the structure of which is identical with that of the aldobiouronic acid from gum arabic and other gums (see page 136). Analysis shows that the degraded egg-plum gum contains a repeating unit consisting of two molecules of D-galactopyranose and one molecule of the aldobiouronic acid (CLXXVII).

The methylated degraded gum, formed by the treatment of the thallium salt of the polysaccharide gum acid with methyl iodide, when subjected to methanolysis gave a mixture of sugar glycosides which upon fractional distillation followed by hydrolysis yielded the methyl sugars listed in Table 50.

TABLE 50. METHYLATED SUGARS FROM THE HYDROLYSIS
OF METHYLATED EGG-PLUM GUM AND METHYLATED
DEGRADED EGG-PLUM GUM

Methylated Degraded Egg-Plum Gum	Methylated Egg-Plum Gum
2,3,4,6-Tetra-*O*-methyl-D-galactose (XXXIX)	2,3,4-Tri-*O*-methyl-D-xylose (CCXII)
2,4,6-Tri-*O*-methyl-D-galactose (XLVI)	2,3,5-Tri-*O*-methyl-L-arabinose (CLXL)
2,3,4-Tri-*O*-methyl-D-galactose (XVI)	2,5-Di-*O*-methyl-L-arabinose (XLIII)
2,4-Di-*O*-methyl-D-galactose (CLXXXII)	2-*O*-Methyl-L-arabinose (CCXIX)
2,3-Di-*O*-methyl-D-glucuronic acid (CLXLI)	2,4,6-Tri-*O*-methyl-D-galactose (XLVI)
	2,4-Di-*O*-methyl-D-galactose (CLXXXII)
	2,3-Di-*O*-methyl-D-glucuronic acid (CLXLI)

Some of the partly methylated glucuronic acid (CLXLI) listed in Table 50, column 1, was found to be present as a methylated aldobiouronic acid (CCXVIII) which upon hydrolysis afforded 2,3-di-*O*-methyl-D-glucuronic acid (CLXLI) and 2,4-di-*O*-methyl-D-galactose (CLXXXII). It is likely that this partially methylated aldobiouronic acid arises from that portion of the molecule which gives rise to 6-*O*-(β-D-glucopyranosyluronic acid)-D-galactose (CLXXVII) upon hydrolysis of the degraded egg-plum gum. This being the case, the isolation of CCXVIII indicates that in the degraded polysaccharide there are D-galactopyranose units attached to C$_4$ of the D-glucuronic acid residues and also to C$_3$ of those D-galactose residues which occur in the aldobiouronic acid (CLXXVII). Indications

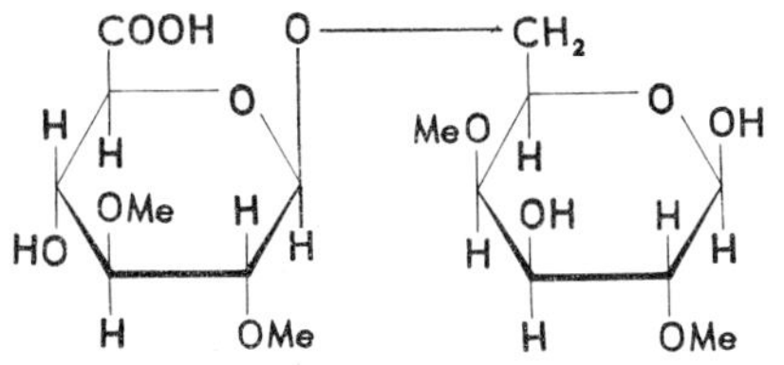

COOH O————CH₂

H   O   MeO   O   OH
H   H
OMe   H   OH   H
HO   H   H
H   OMe   H   OMe

(CCXVIII)

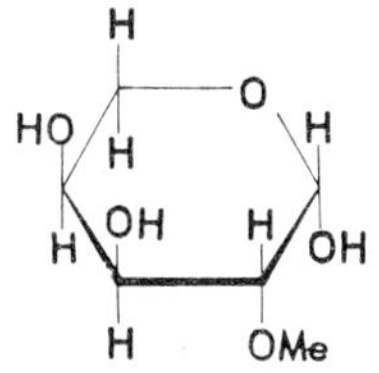

H
HO   O   H
H
OH   H   OH
H   OMe

(CCXIX)

are found for the presence of small amounts of 2,3,4-tri-O-methyl-D-xylose in the hydrolysis products of the methylated degraded gum, so that some of the D-glucuronic acid residues may be linked at C_4 with D-xylose units.

The absence of 2,3,4-tri-O-methyl-D-glucuronic acid (XV) among the cleavage fragments of methylated degraded egg-plum gum shows that none of the D-glucuronic acid residues is in a terminal position. Support for this conclusion is also found in periodate oxidation studies on the egg-plum gum. Thus, when the gum is oxidized with potassium periodate approximately one mole of formic acid is produced and five moles of periodate are consumed per equivalent (1220) of gum. Since under the conditions of oxidation there is no continual rise in formic acid titer followed by a subsequent liberation of iodine, the glucuronic acid is not an end-group (57–62) and does not have free hydroxyl groups at C_3 and C_4.

The periodate-oxidized polysaccharide contains D-galactose and L-arabinose in amounts which would indicate that approximately half of each of these residues in the gum are involved in union with other sugar units in such a way that the D-galactose and L-arabinose residues do not possess adjacent free hydroxyl groups.

An examination of the product isolated from the reaction between the gum and triphenylmethylchloride in pyridine indicates that there may be approximately four primary alcohol groups (63) per equivalent of 1220.

Hydrolysis of the methylated egg-plum gum (64) affords the methyl sugars listed in Table 50, column 2. The identification of the components, together with the data given above, reveals the main structural features of the gum. Since two of the methylated arabinose derivatives, CLXL and XLIII, formed by methanolysis have a furanose structure they must be present in the original gum in the furanose form. Like those in cherry gum and gum arabic these units in egg-plum gum are mutually joined by 1 → 3 linkages but it is apparent that in egg-plum gum the L-arabinose side chains consist of more than two units since 2-O-methyl-L-arabinose (CCXIX) has also been identified. The L-arabinose residue which gives rise to 2-O-methyl-L-arabinose upon methylation may be in either the pyranose or furanose form; if the former possibility is correct it is unlikely that this unit is linked directly to the more acid-stable nucleus since all the arabinose residues in the gum are known to be easily liberated upon autohydrolysis. For the same reason, it is unlikely that the sugar residues attached to this branch point in the arabinose side chain are other than L-arabinose. Also, the possibility that the three methylated arabinose derivatives (CLXL, XLIII and CCXIX) arise from an araban which is associated with the gum is minimized by the failure to extract by solvents any fractions differing in elementary and physical properties from the original gum. Other side chains in egg-plum gum contain 6-O-(β-D-glucopyranosyluronic acid)-D-galactose with D-galactose or D-xylose linked through C_4 of the D-glucuronic acid moiety. In the former case either D-xylose or L-arabinose is linked to C_3 or positions C_3 and C_6 of this D-galactose unit, since D-galactose units do not form end-groups in the gum as evidenced by the absence of 2,3,4,6-tetra-O-methyl-D-galactose (XXXIX) in the hydrolysis products of the methylated gum.

In some of the side chains containing the aldobiouronic acid, the D-galactose moiety is linked to other sugars through C_3. The main chain of the egg-plum gum consists of D-galactose units linked through C_1 and C_3 and C_1, C_3 and C_6.

Peach Gum

The exuded gum of the peach tree, *Prunus persica* L., is composed of D-galactose (5 parts), L-arabinose (6 parts), D-xylose (2 parts), D-glucuronic acid (1 part) and L-rhamnose (2 per cent approx.) (65). Graded hydrolysis of the peach gum acid, equivalent weight 2040, leads to the isolation of 6-O-(β-D-glucopyranosyluronic acid)-D-galactose (CLXXVII) identical with that isolated from gum arabic and egg-plum gum, 3-O-β-L-arabopyranosyl-L-arabinose (CLXLVI) (42) also obtained from cherry gum, and a third disaccharide, 5-O-β-D-xylopyranosyl-L-arabinose (CCXX) (42).

Methylation of CCXX followed by hydrolysis of the methyl derivative (CCXXI) afforded 2,3,4-tri-O-methyl-D-xylose (CCXII) and 2,3-di-O-methyl-L-arabinose (CCI). The isolation of these two methyl sugars indicates a linkage between the reducing group of the D-xylose and either C_4 or C_5 of the L-arabinose moiety. Oxidation of the disaccharide (CCXX) with bromine to the corresponding aldobionic acid (CCXXII), followed by methylation and hydrolysis of the methylated derivative (CCXXIII), yields 2,3,4-tri-O-methyl-D-xylose (CCXII) and a derivative of L-arabonic acid which had physical constants closely resembling those of 2,3,4-tri-O-methyl-L-arabonic acid (CCXXIV). The structure of the disaccharide, therefore, is most probably that shown in CCXX, a deduction supported by the fact that it is readily liberated by autohydrolysis of the peach gum acid indicating that in the gum the L-arabinose residue of CCXX is of the furanose type.

The negative rotation of the disaccharide (CCXX), $[\alpha]_D$ -34° in water, indicates that the biose linkage is probably of the β-D-type.

A disaccharide containing only D-galactose, and oligosaccharides composed of L-arabinose are also produced by graded hydrolysis of peach gum, but the structures have not yet been determined. It is pointed out, however, that the presence of L-arabinose oligosaccharides may indicate the presence of arabinose side chains of more than two units as in the case of egg-plum gum.

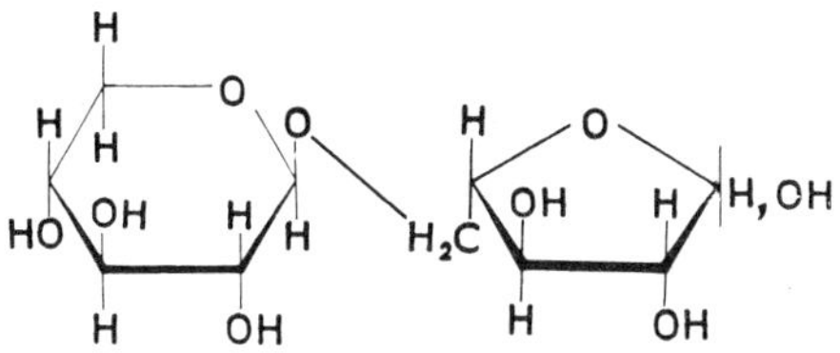

(CCXX)

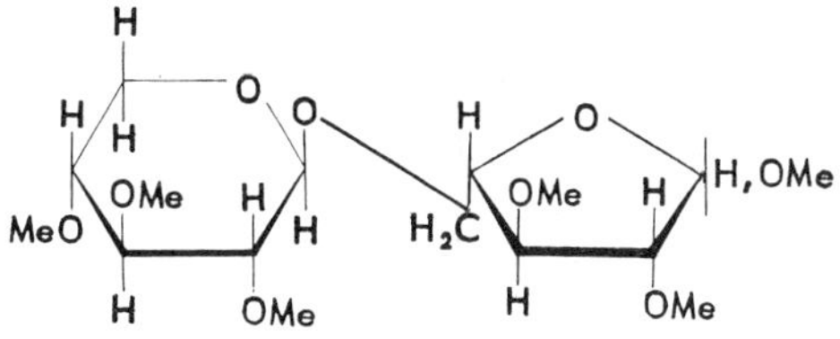

(CCXXI)

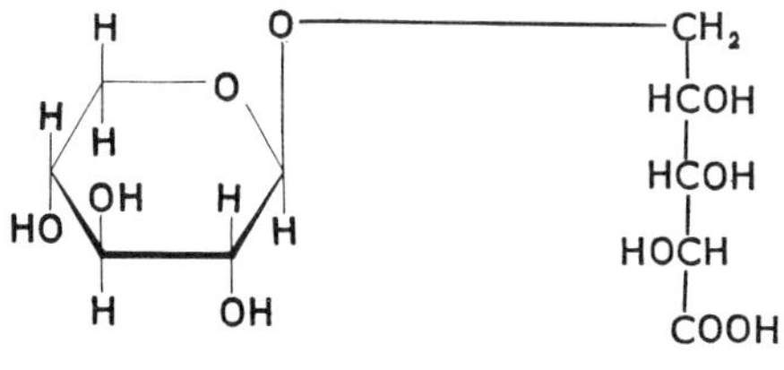

(CCXXII)

H   O————CH₂   COOH

H   HCOMe   HCOMe

  H   HCOMe   MeOCH

  OMe   H   MeOCH   MeOCH

MeO   H   MeOCH

H   OMe   COOH   CH₂OH

(CCXXIII)   (CCXXIV)

Periodate oxidation of peach gum leads to the consumption of 10 moles of periodate and the formation of two moles of formic acid per equivalent of gum (2040). During this oxidation all the D-xylose, approximately two-thirds of the L-arabinose, and two-fifths of the D-galactose undergo scission. The resistance of some of the L-arabinose residues is to be expected in view of the isolation of the disaccharide (CLXLVI) in which the reducing moiety is linked at C_3 with the resulting exclusion of adjacent free hydroxyl groups. Since the gum does not continue to liberate formic acid slowly upon periodate oxidation under the conditions of the reaction (57), it is unlikely that the D-glucuronic acid is an end-group and it is probably linked through C_4 as in egg-plum gum. The liberation of two moles of formic acid requires the consumption of four moles of periodate and it follows, therefore, that six sugar residues per equivalent of gum are cleaved without the production of formic acid. From the analysis of the periodate-oxidized gum it is seen that four moles of L-arabinose, one mole of D-xylose and two moles of D-galactose are cleaved which would account for at least seven moles of periodate. It follows that if the D-xylopyranose unit of the side chain represented by the isolation of disaccharide CCXX is an end-group and the D-galactopyranose unit of the aldobiouronic acid-containing side chains is linked in the gum through C_1 and C_6, then periodate oxidation of these residues would give rise to two moles of formic acid and all the end-groups must be L-arabofuranose residues which would not liberate formic acid upon oxidation. Alternatively, if the D-galactose units occupy terminal positions or if they are linked only through C_1 and C_6 then the two end-groups must be the D-xylopyranose and L-arabofuranose residues represented in the disaccharides CCXX and CLXLVI, respectively. It may also be inferred that the D-galactose main chain is linked through C_1 and C_3 and probably through other positions, as is the case in all other gums of the order *Prunus,* and that the labile L-arabinose residues in the side chains, in view of the high proportion of L-arabinose in the gum, resemble those in egg-plum gum. However, these speculations concerning the structure of the gum can only be more definitely decided by application of the classical methylation techniques.

Almond Gum

The gum exudes abundantly from old almond trees, *Prunus amygdalus*, in the autumn (66), most abundantly from the trunk and larger branches. The production of gum reduces the number of leaves and flowers and otherwise injures the tree. At the time of collection and for several months afterward the gum gives the usual reaction for oxidases as do other gums. The gum exudes first as a colorless or pale yellow material which is soluble in water to an extent of only 10 per cent (66).

The gum is the salt of an acidic polysaccharide whose acid groups are neutralized with calcium, iron and potassium. The free acid of the almond gum, having an equivalent weight of 1470, is obtained by precipitation of the gum from an acidified aqueous solution with alcohol (47,67). Upon heating an aqueous solution of the gum acid, autohydrolysis is effected and all the L-arabinose and D-xylose residues are liberated leaving a degraded gum nucleus that is relatively stable to acid. Hydrolysis of the degraded gum with 0.1N sulfuric acid affords D-galactose (2 moles) and 6-O-(β-D-glucopyranosyluronic acid)-D-galactose (CLXXVII) (1 mole). The isolation of CLXXVII in high yield suggests that is is the only aldobiouronic acid present in the gum.

A preliminary study of the hydrolysis products of methylated almond gum has led to the identification of 2,3,5-tri-O-methyl-L-arabinose (CLXL), indicating that L-arabofuranose residues are present in the gum as end groups (68).

Purple Plum Gum

The gum exudate of the purple plum tree, *Prunus* sp., which resembles the gum of egg-plum and of almond and is composed of L-arabinose, (3 moles), D-xylose, (1 mole), D-galactose (3 moles) and D-glucuronic acid (1 mole) (47,71).

Lemon Gum

The gum exudate of the lemon tree, *Citrus limonia*, is a pale yellow, brittle solid possessing a characteristic aromatic odor (72÷76). By dissolution in water followed by precipitation with acidified alcohol, the ash-free lemon gum acid (76) is liberated from the metal cations among which calcium predominates (77). Purification by electrodialysis gives a product having $[\alpha]_D + 21°$ (water) and equivalent weight, 785 (78). The polysaccharide forms an insoluble copper complex with Fehling solution (76), but does not reduce this reagent. The gum is variously described as being composed of L-arabinose (2 parts), D-galactose (2 parts) and a mono-O-methyl-D-glucuronic acid (1 part) (78,79), and of L-arabinose (2 parts), D-galactose (5 parts) and D-glucuronic acid (2 parts). Analysis shows that the gum contains 4 per cent of methoxyl (76) and subsequent investigations proved that both D-glucuronic acid and 4-O-methyl-D-glucuronic acid are present. Hydrolysis of the lemon gum with N sulfuric acid at room temperature for 12 to 24 weeks liberates L-arabinose, a small amount of D-galactose, two neutral pentose-containing oligosaccharides, and two oligosaccharides containing 4-O-methyl-D-glucuronic acid (CCXXV) (80). The principal sugar acid, 4-O-(4-O-methyl-α-D-glucosyluronic acid)-L-arabinose (CCXXVI), which is very resistant to hydrolysis, has been shown chromatographically to be composed of 4-O-methyl-D-glucuronic acid (CCXXV) and L-arabinose. In order to elucidate the structure of the aldobiouronic acid (CCXXVI) it was methylated with methyl sulfate and alkali and corresponding the methyl ester (CCXXVII) was reduced to the corresponding D-glucopyranosyl-L-arabinose derivative (CCXXVIII) with lithium aluminum hydride (21,81). The newly formed primary alcoholic group was methylated with Purdie reagents and the resultant methylated neutral disac-

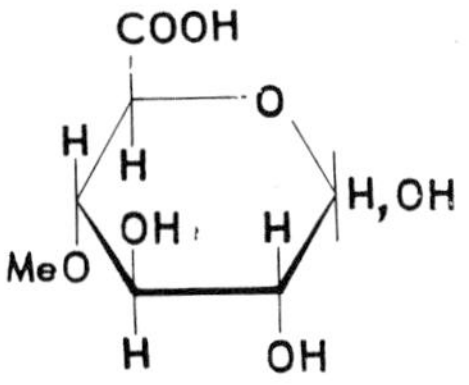

(CCXXV)

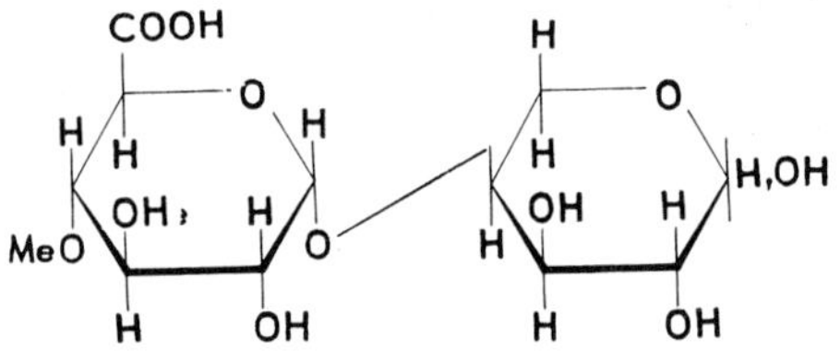

(CCXXVI)

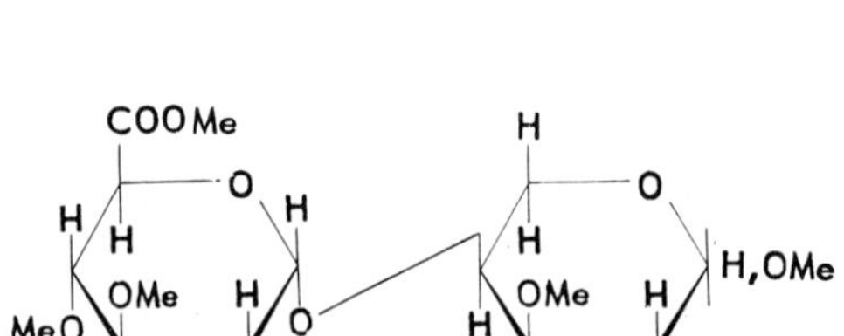

(CCXXVII)

charide (CCXXIX) hydrolyzed to give 2,3,4,6-tetra-O-methyl-D-glucose (CCXXX) and 2,3-di-O-methyl-L-arabinose (CCI). The high optical rotation, $[\alpha]_D + 134°$, of the aldobiouronic acid (CCXXVI) indicates that the L-arabinose has a pyranose structure and that the $1 \rightarrow$ 4-biose linkage has the α-D- and not the β-D-configuration (CCXXXIV).

The second sugar acid which is formed at the same time as CCXXVI discussed above, appears to be a trisaccharide. Chromatographic analysis of the hydrolyzate of this second acid revealed the presence of equimolecular proportions of the aldobiouronic acid (CCXXVI) and L-arabinose. A comparison of its optical rotation, $[\alpha]_D + 47°$, with that

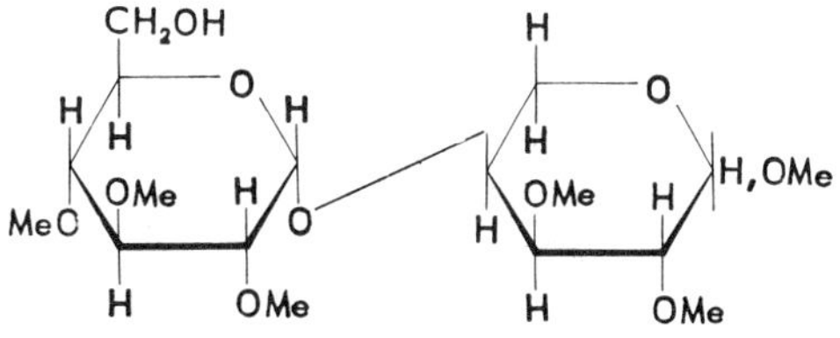

(CCXXVIII)

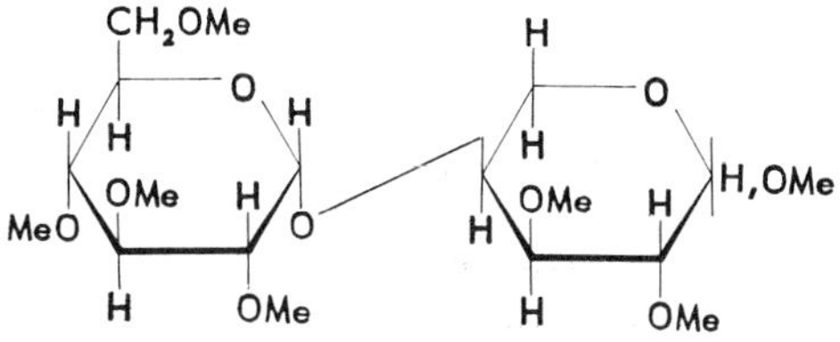

(CCXXIX)

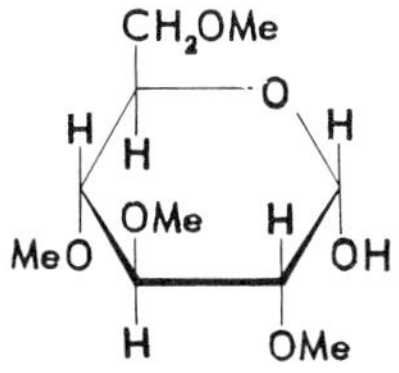

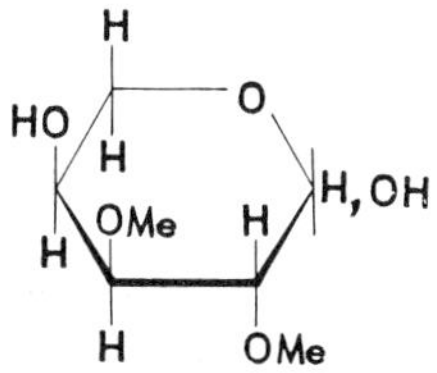

(CCXXX)   (CCI)

(+134°) of CCXXVI suggests that the L-arabinose unit joined to CCXXVI to give the aldotriouronic acid is in the furanose form.

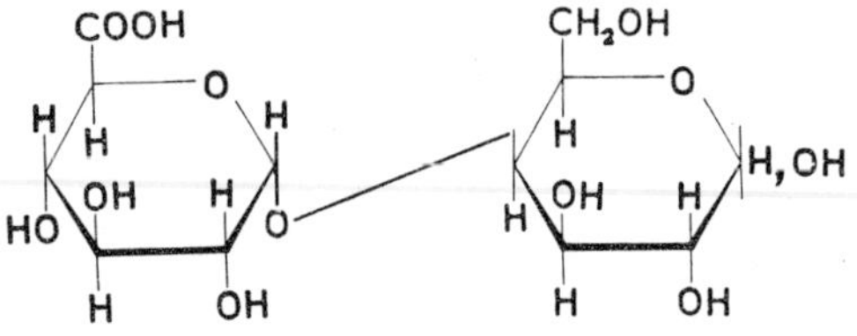

(CLXLVII)

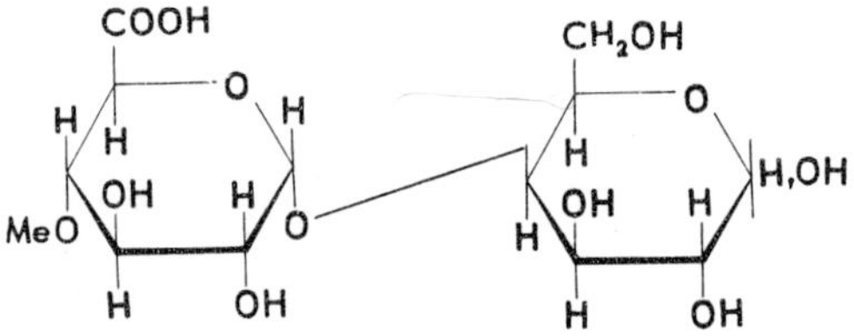

(CCXXXI)

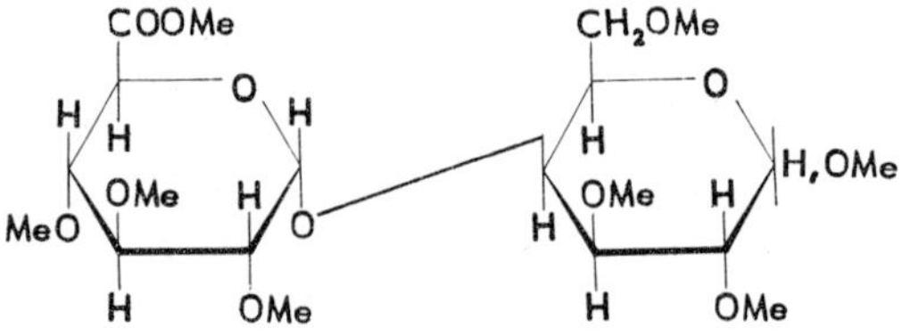

(CCXXXII)

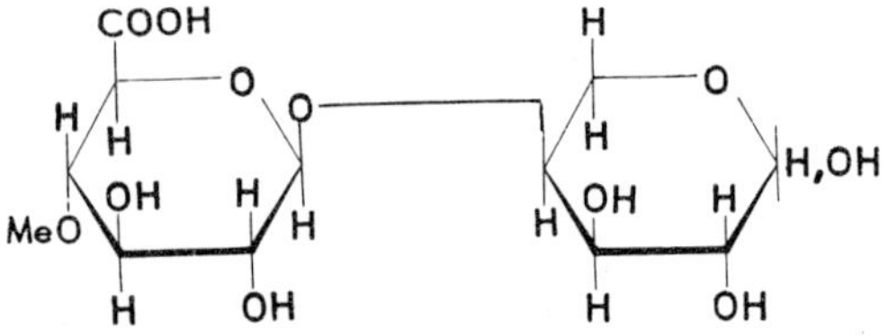

(CCXXXIV)

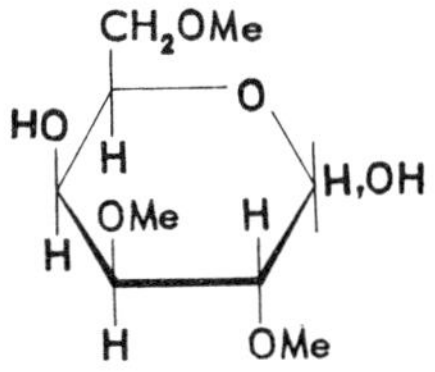

(CCXXXIII)

The ash-free gum, $[\alpha]_D$ (as sodium salt in water) $+ 19.5°$ to $+ 21.2°$ (c.f. $[\alpha]_D + 20.7°$ in water for gum containing mono-O-methyl-D-glucuronic acid (79), shows an equivalent weight 770–800 and an aqueous solution undergoes autohydrolysis with the liberation of all the L-arabinose residues. Further hydrolysis of the polysaccharide results in the formation of D-galactose and an aldobiouronic acid thought to be 4-O-(α-D-glucopyranosyluronic acid)-D-galactose, (CLXLVII), but from subsequent studies (78) this acid is more likely to be 4-O-(4-O-methyl-α-D-glucosyluronic acid)-D-galactose (CCXXXI).

The structure of the aldobiouronic acid was indicated by hydrolysis of the methylated derivative (CCXXXII) which afforded 2,3,4-tri-O-methyl-D-glucuronic acid (XV) and 2,3,6-tri-O-methyl-D-galactose (CCXXXIII). The pyranose structure assigned to the D-galactose moiety is based upon the high positive rotation of the aldobiouronic acid. The sugar acid, (CLXLVII) was isolated in poor yield from the degraded gum, but it was not detected at all after the mild hydrolysis of lemon gum (80) in which 4-O-(4-O-methyl-α-D-glucosyluronic acid)-L-arabinose CCXXVI was formed. It appears, therefore, that 4-O-β-D-glucopyranosyluronic acid-D-galactose (CLXLVII) is only associated with the nucleus of the gum that is relatively stable to acid hydrolysis.

Hydrolysis of the methylated lemon gum afforded 2,4-di-O-methyl-D-galactose (CLXXXII), 2,3-di-O-methyl-D-glucuronic acid (CLXLI), and 2,3,5-tri-O-methyl-L-arabinose (CLXL), together with other methylated sugars which have not been identified (68). Preliminary results of methylation data proved without doubt that this specimen of lemon gum contained D-glucuronic acid since there was no methoxyl group at C_4 of the dimethyl uronic acid cleavage fragment (CLXLI). It may also be inferred that the D-galactopyranose residues in the main chain are linked through C_1, C_3 and C_6. The L-arabinose residues which give rise to the 2,3,5-tri-O-methyl-L-arabinose are present in the gum as end groups in the furanose form. However, some of the L-arabinose residues are present in the pyranose form as evidenced by the recent isolation of 3-O-β-L-arabopyranosyl-L-arabinose (CLXLVI) from lemon gum (27). This disaccharide is identical with that isolated from the gums of cherry and peach.

Further information on the structure of lemon gum was obtained from a study of the oxidation with periodate, in which one mole of formic acid was produced per equivalent of gum with the consumption of 3.2 moles of periodate. Analysis of the oxidized lemon gum showed that both L-arabinose and D-galactose residues were present. The periodate oxidation studies therefore indicated that some L-arabinose residues are linked through C_1 and C_3 (or C_2) as would be expected from the isolation of 3-O-β-L-arabopyranosyl-L-arabinose (CLXLVI) from lemon gum. It is also clear that a considerable percentage of 1 → 3-linked D-galactose residues, such as are encountered in the *Acacia* and *Prunus* gums, occurs also in lemon gum.

Grapefruit Gum

The gum of the grapefruit tree, *Citrus maxima*, is similar to that from the lemon tree. Samples of gum obtained from trees growing in Florida and California and those from a *Phytophthora*-infected tree were found to be similar in their properties. The gum acid is characterized by its optical rotation, $[\alpha]_D + 56°$ in water, and equivalent weight, 590 (76). The ash-free gum, composed of L-arabinose (16 per cent), D-galactose (53 per cent), and D-glucuronic acid (31 per cent), undergoes auto-hydrolysis in aqueous solution at 100° with the facile liberation of all of its L-arabinose residues. Further hydrolysis of the polysaccharide with 0.1N sulfuric acid results in the formation of D-galactose and 4-O-(α-D-glucopyranosyluronic acid)-D-galactose (CLXLVII) identical with the aldobiouronic acid isolated from lemon gum. In the case of both the grapefruit and the lemon gum the aldobiouronic acid (CLXLVII) is obtained in poor yield.

Hydrolysis of methylated grapefruit gum affords 2,4-di-O-methyl-D-galactose (CLXXXII), 2,3-di-O-methyl-D-glucuronic acid (CLXLI), and 2,3,5-tri-O-methyl-L-arabinose (CLXL), together with other methylated sugars which have not yet been identified (68).

The periodate oxidation of grapefruit gum gives one mole of formic acid for two equivalent proportions of gum with the consumption of four moles of periodate on the same basis. Hydrolysis of the periodate-oxidized gum shows that some L-arabinose and D-galactose residues are resistant to oxidation by periodate.

It appears, therefore, that the general structural features of both grapefruit and lemon gums are the same, and it is most probable that grapefruit gum also contains both D-glucuronic acid and 4-O-methyl-D-glucuronic acid, the presence of the latter being suggested by the fact that the gum contains ethereal methyl groups (5.2 per cent) (76).

Orange Gum

The gum of the orange tree, *Citrus sinensis*, is composed of D-glucuronic acid, D-galactose, and L-arabinose (47). It is possible that the acid component may be 4-O-methyl-D-glucuronic acid.

Gum Tragacanth

Gum tragacanth is an exudation from various species of shrubs belonging to the genus *Astragalus* (of the order *Leguminosae*). The early work of Kraut (82) and O'Sullivan (83), who subjected the gum to fractionation, indicated that the gum is a complex mixture. It is only partially soluble in water, the insoluble fraction, termed "bassorin," comprising 60 to 70 per cent of the gum (84). The gum contains 3.8 to 4.6 per cent of methoxyl which appears to be partly associated with the "bassorin" fraction (85,89). It has been reported, however, that virtually all of the methoxyl is present as ester groups (88).

Hydrolysis of the crude gum with dilute mineral acid affords a mixture of sugars from which L-arabinose (86), D-xylose (86), L-fucose (87), and D-galactose (87) have been identified in the crystalline state or as crystalline derivatives. The gum also contains acid constituents and it was suggested by early workers (83) that the acid degradation products of the gum bear some relationship to the degradation products from gum arabic which had been previously studied; this suggestion did not prove to be correct.

The commercial gum is slightly acid to blue litmus and, when freed from ash by precipitation from an acidified aqueous solution with alcohol, it has an equivalent weight of 442 (89). The crude gum tragacanth is a mixture of the salt of a complex acid polysaccharide, a neutral polysaccharide composed principally of L-arabinose, and a small amount of a glycoside (89). A small amount of starch is also present in the gum (83). The neutral polysaccharide, a galacto-araban, may be separated from the crude gum by precipitation from an aqueous solution with ethanol, since it is soluble in 70 per cent aqueous alcohol. It is not yet certain whether the galacto-araban is in physical admixture with, or chemically bound to the polysaccharide acid, although its ease of separation favors the former view. The acid character of the gum is due to units of D-galacturonic acid and not to D-glucuronic acid. It is of interest to note that this is one of the few gum exudates which contain D-galacturonic acid and, in its ability to form gels, it resembles pectin and the mucilages extracted from seeds such as flaxseed mucilage, which also contain D-galacturonic acid (see Table 31).

The fractionation of the gum from aqueous solution by the addition of alcohol is made difficult by the physical properties of the gum. In structural studies, therefore, the fractionation has been carried out after methylation of the crude gum has been accomplished.

Gum tragacanth was methylated with methyl sulfate and sodium hydroxide at room temperature, six methylation treatments being applied (89). The methylated product is soluble in both alkaline and acid solutions and cannot be extracted from the reaction solution with chloroform. The inorganic salts may be removed from the methylated gum by dialysis and fractionation of the product was carried out as follows. The small fraction, corresponding to the glycoside, was removed first by virtue of its insolubility in cold water. The acid component was converted to its sodium salt and the mixture extracted with hot water in which the methylated galacto-araban was insoluble. The sodium salt of the methylated tragacanthic acid, was extracted with hot water and converted to the barium salt from whicn any residual methylated galacto-araban was extracted with acetone. The resulting methylated tragacanthic acid, liberated from its barium salt with oxalic acid, was essentially homogeneous as demonstrated by fractional precipitation from an acetone solution with light petroleum ether. In a similar manner, the homogeneity of the methylated galacto-araban was demonstrated.

Constitution of Tragacanthic Acid (89). Treatment of the methylated tragacanthic acid with methanolic hydrogen chloride afforded a mixture of methyl glycosides which were separated by fractional distillation. The following sugars were identified: 2,3,4-tri-O-methyl-L-fucose (CCXXXV), 2,3,4 - tri - O - methyl - D - xylose   (CCXII),   3,4 -di - O -methyl - D - xylose (CCXXXVI), 2,3-di-O-methyl-D-galacturonic acid (CCXXXVII), and a mono-O-methyl-D-galacturonic acid.   Another, unidentified cleavage fragment of the methylated tragacanthic acid was obtained which may be a di-O-methylpentose.

The complexity of the hydrolytic mixture and the difficulty experienced in the separation of the constituents of the mixture made it difficult to determine the relative proportions of the cleavage fragments. However, the mode of union of these fragments in the complex methylated tragacanthic acid is obvious from their identity.

The order in which they are joined is still obscure. The 2,3,4-tri-O-methyl-L-fucose (CCXXXV) and 2,3,4-tri-O-methyl-D-xylose (CCXII) must arise from terminal residues in the complex, whereas the 3,4-di-O-methyl-D-xylose (CCXXXVI) is involved in union at C_1 and C_2 with other residues. It is also clear that the 2,3-di-O-methyl-D-galacturonic acid

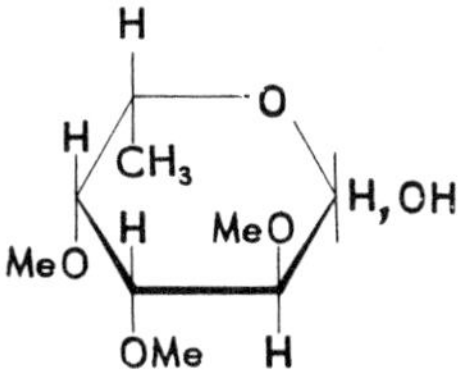

(CCXXXV) 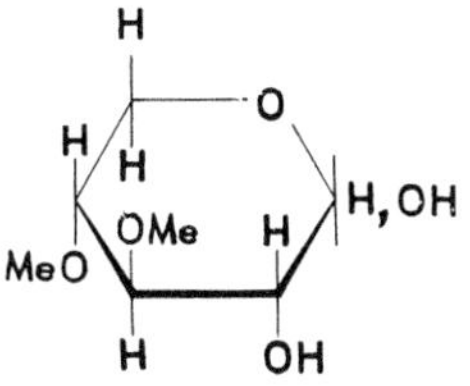   (CCXXXVI) 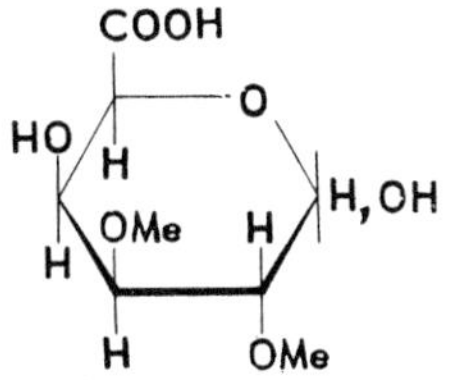   (CCXXXVII)

(CCXXXVII) is derived from D-galacturonic acid units of tragacanthic acid which are joined to other residues through C_1 and C_4 as they are in pectic acid (90,91). The mono-O-methyl-D-galacturonic acid, which gives a crystalline methyl ester methyl glycoside, arises from a D-galacturonic acid residue which is involved in the branching of the chains in the molecule and it is probably the residue to which the side chains of L-fucose and D-xylose are attached. The isolation of this monomethyl ether has the same constitutional significance as that already deduced from the liberation of 2,4-di-O-methyl-D-galactose (CLXXXII) from the methylated derivatives of gum arabic, damson gum, cherry gum, egg-plum gum and lemon gum. The 2,3-di-O-methyl-D-galacturonic acid was actually identified as the crystalline methyl (2,3-di-O-methyl-β-D-galactofuranosid) uronamide (CCXXXVIII), whereas the mono-O-methyl-D-galacturonic acid was obtained as a pyranoside. The difference in ring structure of these two uronic acid residues is not to be taken as an

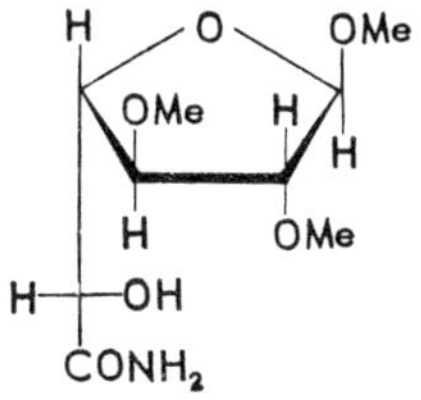

(CCXXXVIII) 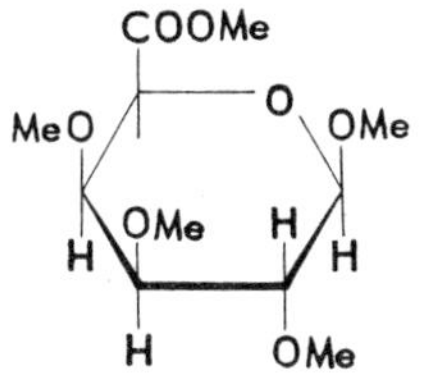   (CCXXXIX)

indication that pyranose and furanose forms of D-galacturonic acid pre-exist in the gum. In point of fact, the relatively high stability of tragacanthic acid and its methyl derivative and their high positive rotation indicate that the uronic acid residues present in the gum are all of the pyranose form.

Although the mono-O-methyl-D-galacturonic acid was not completely identified it must be the 2-, 3-, or 4-O-methyl derivative, since methylation gives the crystalline methyl (methyl 2,3,4-tri-O-methyl-β-D-galacto-sid)uronate (CCXXXIX).   Its isolation, together with the identifica-tion of the terminal residues as 2,3,4-tri-O-methyl-D-xylose (CCXII) and 2,3,4-tri-O-methyl-L-fucose (CCXXXV) (89,92), shows that this gum is probably similar to other plant gums in possessing a branched chain structure.

Constitution of the Galacto-Araban of Gum Tragacanth.   The methyl-ated galacto-araban, [α]D - 92° in methanol, undergoes rapid metha-nolysis when boiled with 2 per cent methanolic hydrogen chloride (89). The mixture of methyl glycosides so obtained was separated by fractional distillation and the cleavage fragments were identified as 2,3,5-tri-O-methyl-L-arabinose (CLXL), 2,3-di-O-methyl-L-arabinose (CCI), L-arabi-nose, and a di-O-methyl-D-galactose.   Evidence for the presence of a di-O-methyl-D-galactose is based upon the methoxyl content of a fraction which upon further methylation with Purdie reagents afforded 2,3,4,6-tetra-O-methyl-D-galactose (XXXIX).

From the above data, it is evident that the neutral polysaccharide con-tains end-groups of L-arabofuranose.   The facile hydrolysis of the meth-ylated polysaccharide suggests that all the L-arabinose residues are in the furanose form, although the identification of 2,3-di-O-methyl-L-arabi-nose (CCI) and L-arabinose in the cleavage fragments does not exclude the presence of L-arabopyranose units.   Assuming that all the arabinose units are of the furanose form, they are joined through C_1, C_1 and C_5, and C_1, C_2, C_3, and C_5 in accord with the identification of 2,3,5-tri-, 2,3-di-O-methyl-L-arabinose, and L-arabinose, respectively.   It would appear, however, that the polysaccharide is not of a simple araban variety since it contains galactose residues which are linked through C_1 and two other positions as yet undetermined.

Mesquite Gum

Mesquite gum, exuded by the mesquite tree (93,94) (*Prosopis juliflora* D.C. and related species) is the neutral salt of a complex acidic poly-saccharide (95).   The gum, which dissolves slowly in warm water, con-tains moisture (11 per cent), protein (0.7 per cent) and ash (2 to 4 per cent) (95,96).   The small amount of protein may arise from the enzyme which is responsible for the formation of the gum or from contact of the gum with protein material of the tree.   The composition of the ash indi-cates that mesquite gum is predominantly in the form of a calcium salt.

Hydrolysis of mesquite gum with dilute mineral acid affords L-arabi-nose and D-galactose, both of which can be isolated in the crystalline state (97,98), and 4-O-methyl-D-glucuronic acid (58,99,100), identified as the α- and β- anomers of methyl (4-O-methyl-D-glucosid)uronamide (58), in the molar ratios 4:2:1 (101). By virtue of its high L-arabinose content (approx. 50 per cent) which is easily removed, mesquite gum has proved to be an excellent source for the preparation of this sugar (97,98, 103).

The free acid, mesquitic acid, obtained by pouring an aqueous acidified solution of the gum into alcohol, has an equivalent weight of 1350, shows [α] D + 60° in water (102) and contains 2.9 per cent of methoxyl. The gum or its free acid undergoes ready hydrolysis when heated with 0.01N sulfuric acid and affords L-arabinose and a degraded mesquitic acid (102). The latter does not appear to contain L-arabinose and is composed of D-galactose and 4-O-methyl-D-glucuronic acid.

Prolonged hydrolysis of mesquitic acid or degraded mesquitic acid with dilute sulfuric acid (3 per cent) affords a mixture containing two aldobiouronic acids and the monosaccharide building units of the gum (102). The barium salts of the aldobiouronic acids are readily separated from the reducing sugars by precipitation with alcohol and their methoxyl content (7.3 per cent) demonstrates the presence of one methoxyl group. The two acids are 6-O-(4-O-methyl-β-D-glucosyluronic acid)-D-galactose (CCXL) and 4-O-(4-O-methyl-D-glucosyluronic acid)-D-galactose (CCXLI). The two acids (CCXL and CCXLI) were separated by first transforming them into their octa-O-methyl derivatives by methylation with methyl sulfate and then with Purdie reagents, and by converting the mixed methyl esters to the corresponding amides by treatment with methanolic ammonia. The amide (CCXLII) of methyl[6-O-(2,3,4-tri-O-methyl-β-D-glucosyluronic acid)]-tri-O-methyl-β-D-galactoside crystallizes from the mixture and is identical with that obtained from gum arabic in similar studies. The β-D-1 → 6 linkage between the 4-O-methyl-D-glucuronic acid and D-galactose moieties is established and the formula (CCXL) for this acid disaccharide therefore follows.

The structure of the second aldobiouronic acid (CCXLI) is demonstrated by the fact that hydrolysis of its octamethyl ether gives 2,3,6-tri-O-methyl-D-galactose (CCXXXIII) and 2,3,4-tri-O-methyl-D-glucuronic acid (XV). The tri-O-methylgalactose residue may arise of course from a D-galactose unit in the furanose or pyranose form. However, if the aldobiouronic acid exists in the complex as 4-O-methyl-D-glucosyluronic acid-D-galactofuranose, the linkage of such an aldobiouronic acid to the rest of the molecule in the mesquitic acid would be expected to be cleaved relatively easily by acid hydrolysis. In practice the liberation of the aldobiouronic acid is found to require prolonged hydrolysis and it is, therefore, designated as shown in CCXLI. The anomeric type of the glycosidic linkage is not certain.

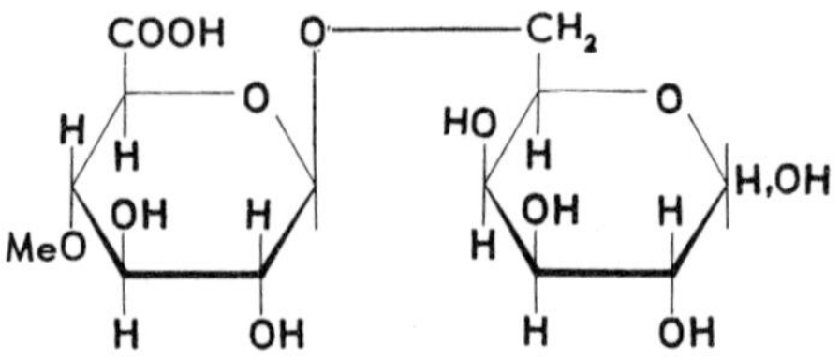

(CCXL)

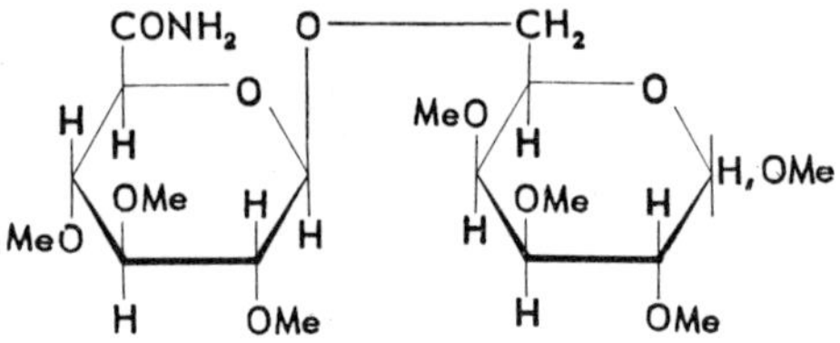

(CCXLII)

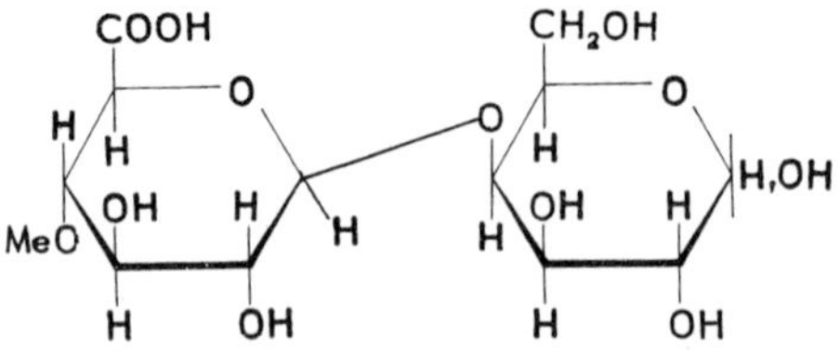

(CCXLI)

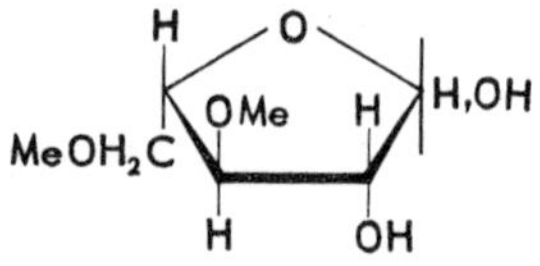

(CCXLIII)

An examination of the methanolysis products of methylated mesquite gum reveals the presence of five substances of which the following four have been identified: 2,3,5-tri-O-methyl-L-arabinose (CLXL, 3 moles), 3,5-di-O-methyl-L-arabinose (CCXLIII, 6 to 7 moles), 2,4-di-O-methyl-D-galactose (CLXXXII, 4 moles) and 2,3,4-tri-O-methyl-D-glucuronic acid (XV, 2 moles), together with an unidentified di-O-methyl-D-galactose (1 mole) (104). It is also reported that the methanolysis products are 2,3,5-tri-O-methyl-L-arabinose (1 mole), 3,5-di-O-methyl-L-arabinose (3 moles), 2,4-di-O-methyl-D-galactose (2 moles) and 2,3,4-tri-O-methyl-D-glucuronic acid (1 mole) (101).

The available evidence favors the former quantitative values for the relative proportions of the cleavage fragments. In the former case, mesquite gum is represented as having a repeating unit of 17 sugar residues with an equivalent weight of 1262 for the mesquitic acid (found

1350) and 1577 for the methylated substance (found 1550). The second analytical figures correspond to a repeating unit of 7 having an equivalent weight of 1042 for the mesquitic acid and 1252 for the methylated substance. Also, in this second case, no di-O-methyl galactose fragment is reported which might correspond, as does possibly the unknown di-O-methyl galactose in the first case, to the D-galactose residue which is linked through C_4 in 4-O-(4-O-methyl-D-glucosyluronic acid-D-galactose (CCXLI), the aldobiouronic acid isolated from mesquite gum by graded hydrolysis.

Partial methanolysis of the methylated mesquitic acid has resulted in the identification of 3-O-(2,3,4-tri-O-methyl-D-glucosyluronic acid)-2,4,6-tri-O-methyl-D-galactose, (CCXLIV), which upon further hydrolysis gives 2,3,4-tri-O-methyl-D-glucuronic acid (XV), and 2,4,6-tri-O-methyl-D-galactose (XLVI) (105). The aldobiouronic acid residue in the mesquitic acid from which the hexamethyl ether (CCXLIV) arises is therefore 3-O-(4-O-methyl-D-glucosyluronic acid)-D-galactose (CCXLV). It is not known whether the glycosidic linkage is of the α or β-D-type. The same aldobiouronic acid (CCXLIV) was identified in the partial hydrolyzate of methylated degraded mesquitic acid (105). This brings to three the number of aldobiouronic acids that are obtained by hydrolysis

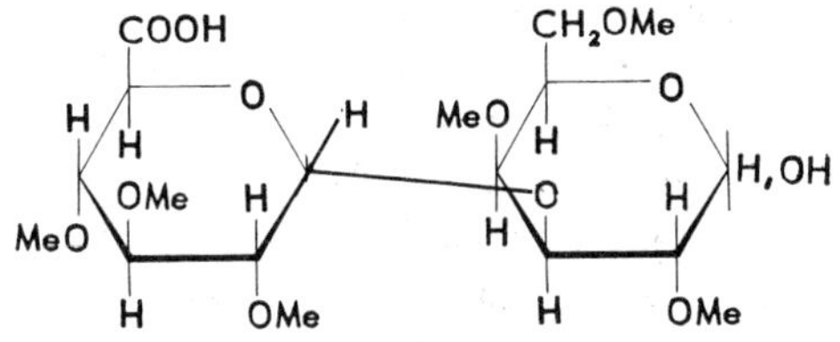

(CCXLIV)

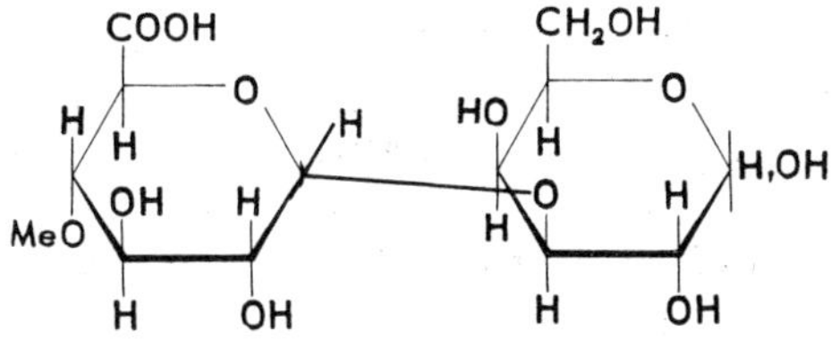

(CCXLV)

of mesquite gum. More vigorous hydrolysis of methylated degraded mesquitic acid (106) afforded 2,4-di-O-methyl-D-galactose (CLXXXII), 2,3,4-

tri-O-methyl-D-galactose (XVI), 2,4,6-tri-O-methyl-D-galactose (XLVI), and a small amount of 2,3,5-tri-O-methyl-L-arabinose (CLXL). The relative amounts of the two tri-O-methyl derivatives are 2,3,4-tri- (63 per cent) and 2,4,6-tri-O-methyl-D-galactose (37 per cent).

The accumulated methylation data, although not permitting the selection of any unique structure, enable the general features of mesquite gum to be deduced. Thus, the identification of 2,3,5-tri-O-methyl-L-arabinose (3 moles) and 2,3,4-tri-O-methyl-D-glucuronic acid (2 moles) prove that these units constitute end groups in a repeating unit of 17 sugar residues. This high proportion of end-groups can only arise from a highly branched structure; such a structure is further supported by the isolation of 2,4-di-O-methyl-D-galactose (4 moles) and an unidentified di-O-methyl-D-galactose (1 mole). It is to be noted that, as expected, the number of nonreducing end-groups equals the number of branch points. This unidentified di-O-methyl-D-galactose probably arises from that D-galactose unit linked at C_4 to 4-O-methyl-D-glucuronic acid and which gives rise to the 4-O-(4-O-methyl-D-glucosyluronic acid)-D-galactose (CCXLI). The D-galactose unit is also attached to another sugar residue through C_2, C_3 or C_6; the characterization of this unidentified di-O-methyl-D-galactose would clarify this point.

The isolation of 2,3,5-tri-O-methyl- and 3,5-di-O-methyl-L-arabinose shows that the pentose residues are present in the complex as furanose units, mutually linked through C_1 and C_2. It will be recalled that the arabofuranose units are linked by 1,3-glycosidic bonds in cherry and egg-plum gum and gum arabic whereas in damson gum the union is through a $1 \rightarrow 5$ link. Of the methylated arabofuranose units that are formed by cleavage of the methylated mesquitic acid, three are fully methylated and must constitute terminal units. The remaining L-arabinose units (6 to 7) appear as 3,5-di-O-methyl derivatives and must therefore be distributed as non-terminal units of three side chains which may contain one to eight arabinose units. These are represented in the general formula for mesquite gum (CCXLVI) as A. Since these L-arabinose side chains can be removed preferentially from the more acid stable nucleus by mild acid hydrolysis, the D-galactose units to which they are attached will acquire an additional hydroxyl group upon removal of the arabofuranose units. In other words, the hydrolyis of the methylated degraded mesquitic acid will give rise to tri-O-methyl-D-galactose residues in which the methyl group or the positions other than 2 and 4 will correspond to the points at which the arabinose side chains are attached in the mesquitic acid. It was found that 2,4,6-tri- and 2,3,4-tri-O-methyl-D-galactose were formed from methylated degraded mesquite gum in the proportions 37 per cent and 63 per cent, respectively. This indicates that two of the side chains are attached to a D-galactose residue through C_6 and the other side chain through C_3. It is also clear from the identification of the two tri-O-methyl derivatives that the main chains of D-galactose members are mutually joined by $1 \rightarrow 3$ as well as $1 \rightarrow 6$ linkages.

The identification of three aldobiouronic acid residues in mesquite gum, namely 6-O-, 4-O-, and 3-O- (4-O-methyl-D-glucosyluronic acid)-D-galactose, may be taken to indicate that these form side chains in the gum, as in the cases of all other gum exudates discussed above. However, the possibility exists that the D-galactose moieties of these aldobiouronic acids form part of the main chain. By analogy with the other gum exudates, however, this is not considered the most likely of the possibilities. If the aldobiouronic acid residues are side chains, the D-galactose units are substituted at other positions by arabinose side chains since only di-O-methyl galactose is identified in the hydrolysis products of the methylated mesquite gum. Further evidence is forthcoming from the observation (104) that a penta-O-methyl aldobiouronic acid is formed as a result of the cleavage of methylated mesquite gum which upon further hydrolysis affords 2,3,4-tri-O-methyl-D-glucuronic acid and 2,4-di-O-methyl-D-galactose. This penta-O-methyl derivative may arise from the 6-O- or 3-O- (4-O-methyl-D-glucosyluronic acid)-D-galactose

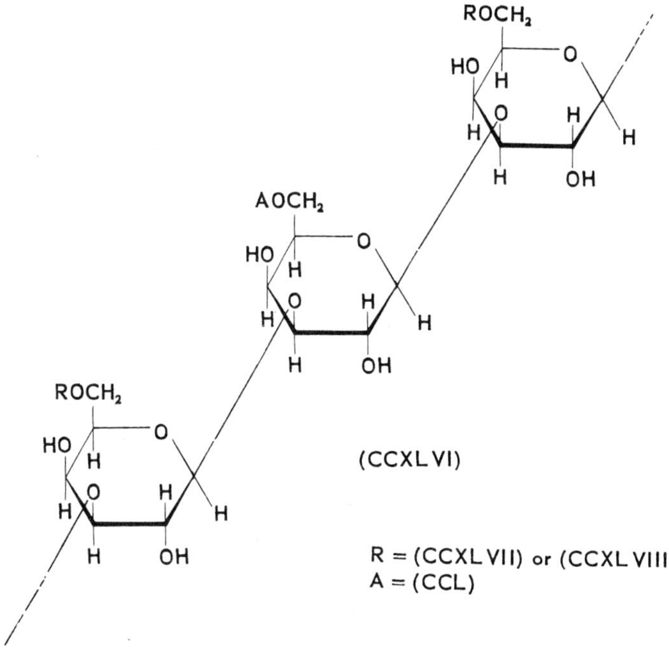

(CCXLVI)

R = (CCXLVII) or (CCXLVIII) or (CCXLIX)
A = (CCL)

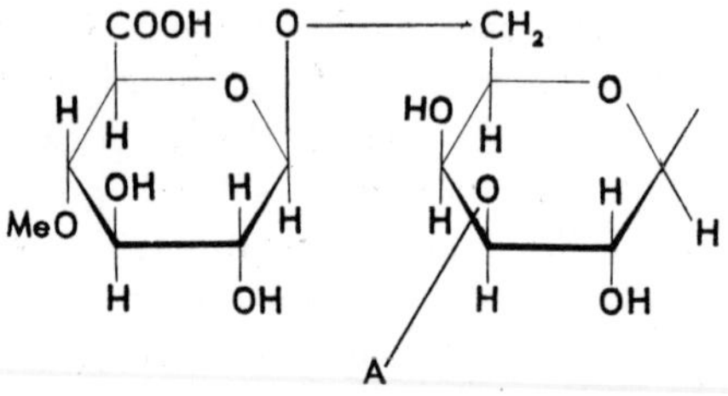

(CCXLVII)

residues, the side chain of arabinose units being attached to the D-galactose residues through C_3 or C_6, respectively.

The structure shown in CCXLVI is one of several which may be proposed for mesquite gum. It shows three D-galactopyranose units in the main chain united by $1 \rightarrow 3$ linkages and to C_6 of each of these units a side chain is attached. It will be apparent, however, that, as in the case of gum arabic, it is also possible for the three D-galactose units to be joined by $1 \rightarrow 6$ or by $1 \rightarrow 3$ and $1 \rightarrow 6$ linkages.

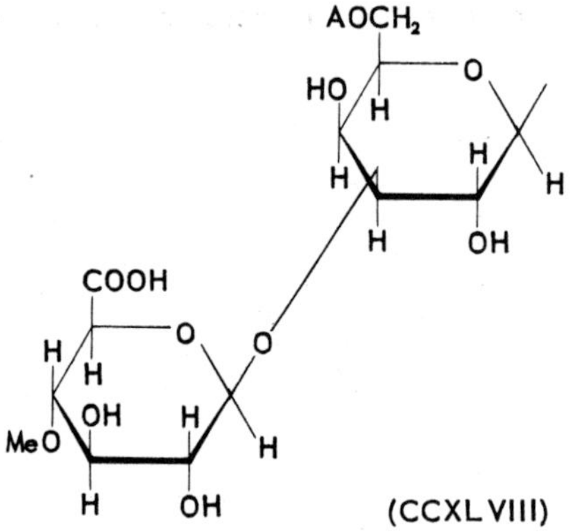

(CCXLVIII)

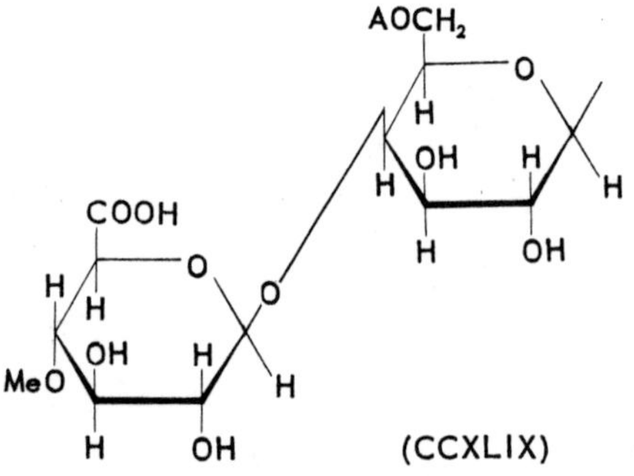

(CCXLIX)

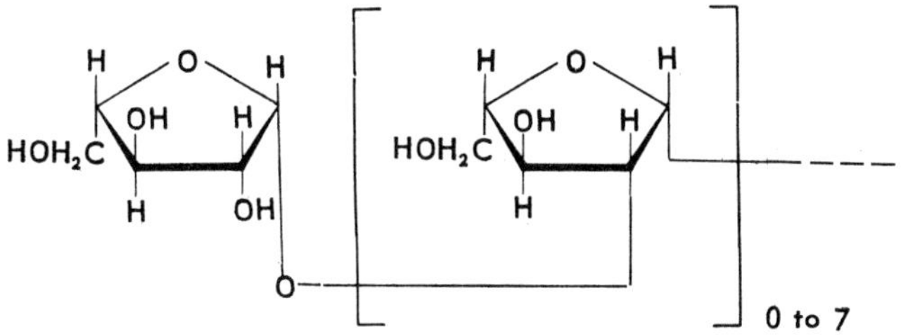

(CCL)

The choice must await further investigations along the lines described for gum arabic. Also the aldobiouronic acid residue (CCXLIX) may have the L-arabinose side chain, A, at C_2, C_3 or C_6 of the D-galactose unit.

Sterculia Setigera Gum

The cacao tree, *Sterculia setigera*, found in tropical West Africa, exudes a gum which is marketed in the form of hard brown amorphous nodules. This gum imbibes large proportions of water to give a gel. The gum occurs as the partly acetylated (AcO, 15.5%) derivative of the inorganic salt of an acidic polysaccharide (107,108), which is nonreducing to Fehling solution and forms an insoluble copper salt with copper sulfate. The smell of acetic acid can be detected when the gum is kept in a closed container. The gum, after being deacetylated with sodium hydroxide and freed from ash, has an equivalent weight of 370–400. The gum is resistant to acid hydrolysis for which reason quantitative analysis for the component sugars gives only the approximate result: D-galactose (5 parts), L-rhamnose (5 parts), D-tagatose (1 part), and D-galacturonic acid (8 parts), and traces of two other sugars which behave like D-xylose and a ketorhamnose upon paper chromatographic analysis (108). D-Tagatose had not hitherto been reported in Nature. Partial hydrolysis of the gum, by heating a solution of it in 0.05 N sulfuric acid for 15 hours, afforded D-galactose (7 parts), D-tagatose (2 parts), L-rhamnose (5 parts), a ketorhamnose (traces) together with a mixture of sugar acids. Certain components of the acidic mixture (equivalent weight, 234) were extremely resistant to acid hydrolysis and required prolonged heating (24 hours) with 2 N sulfuric acid for complete scission. The uronic acid was identified as D-galacturonic acid and in this respect *Sterculia setigera* gum resembles gum tragacanth.

The mixture of sugar acids produced by partial hydrolysis of the gum contains at least three aldobiouronic acids whose structures were shown by methylation data to be 2-O-(D-galactopyranosyluronic acid)-L-rhamnose (CCLI), 3-(or 2-)-O-(D-galactopyranosyluronic acid)-D-galacturonic acid (CCLII), and 4-O-(D-galactopyranosyluronic acid)-D-galactose (CCLIII), the latter being present in small proportion.

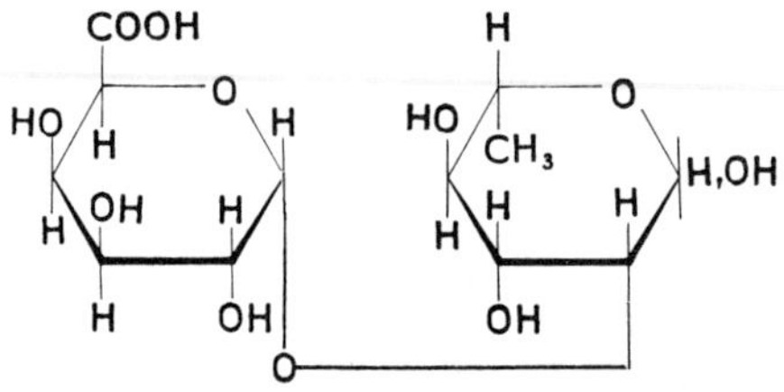

(CCLI)

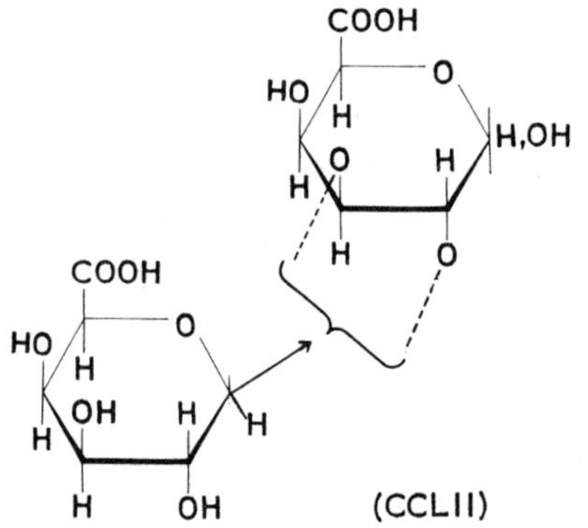

(CCLII) 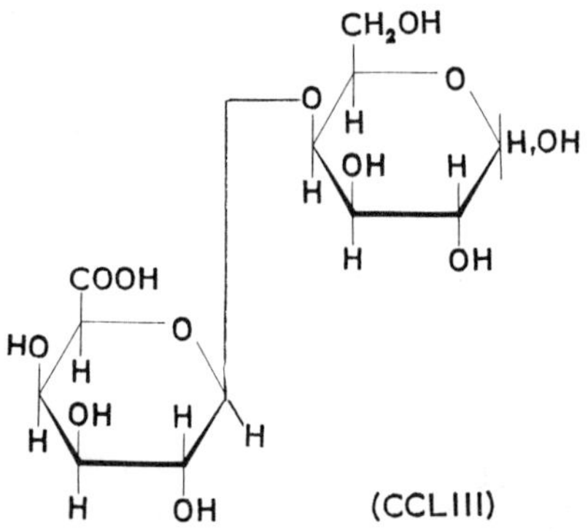   (CCLIII)

Methylated *Sterculia setigera* gum, prepared by treating the gum in the usual way with methyl sulfate and alkali, upon methanolysis followed by hydrolysis of the glycosides, afforded 2,3,4,6 tetra-O-methyl-D-galactose (XXXIX 6 parts), (?) 3,4-di-O-methyl-L-rhamnose (CCLIV, 4 parts), 2,3,6-tri-O-methyl-D-galactose (CCXXIII, 3 parts), 2-(CCLV), and/or 3-O-methyl-L-rhamnose (CCLVI, 3 parts), 2,6-di-O-methyl-D-galactose (CCXVII, trace), L-rhamnose (trace), and 2-O-methyl-D-galacturonic acid (CCLVII, 16 parts) (109). The presence of large proportions of 2,3,4,6-tetra-O-methyl-D-galactose and 2-O-methyl-D-galacturonic acid indicates that the gum is highly branched. It will be noted that no methyl derivatives of D-tagatose are detected in the cleavage fragments of the methylated gum probably because they are destroyed during methanolysis. A formula for the gum cannot be advanced until more information is accumulated.

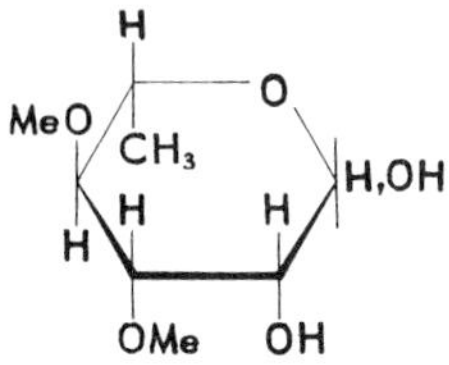

(CCLIV) 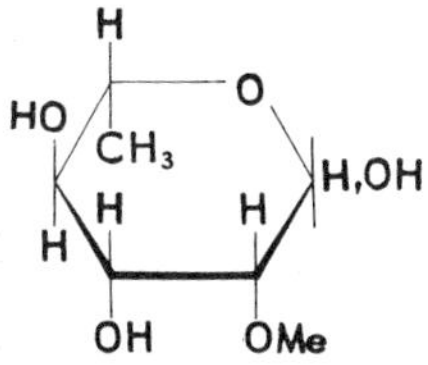   (CCLV)

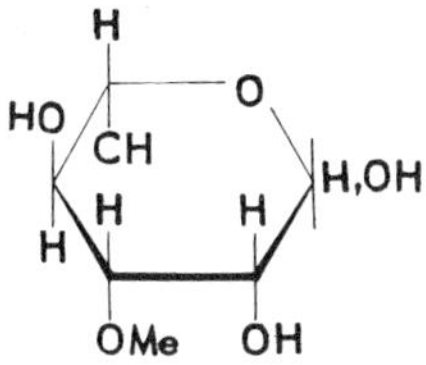

(CCLVI) 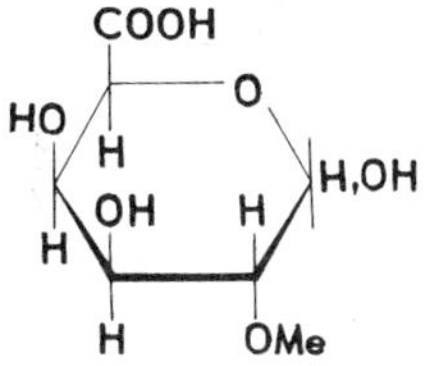   (CCLVII)

Karaya Gum

Exudates from the bark of *Cochlospermum gossypium* (family *Bixineae*), a small deciduous tree which grows in Northwest Himalaya, and *Sterculia urens*, a large tree found in India, have been termed karaya gum (110). In commerce, however, the gum from *Cochlospermum gossypium* is known as Indian gum and has little commercial value in comparison with other gums. Karaya gum, from *Sterculia urens*, is also known as kadaya gum, Indian tragacanth, India gum (not to be confused with Indian gum) and *Sterculia* gum (111). A gum similar to karaya is produced by other trees of the *Sterculiaceae* family, namely *S. foetida*, *S. tomentosa* and *S. cordifolia*, the last two varieties being found in West Africa (112).

The gums of the *Sterculiaceae* are chemically characterized by a high acetyl content (108,113), a high proportion of D-galacturonic acid and the presence of residues of L-rhamnose, D-galactose and a ketohexose (110). The gums from *S. setigera* and *S. urens* give D-tagatose on hydrolysis, the instability of which towards acid may account for its absence in an analysis of *S. tomentosa* in which there is found D-galacturonic acid (43 per cent), D-galactose (13 per cent) and L-rhamnose (15 per cent) (114). The gums give an acid reaction in aqueous solution and some samples evolve acetic acid on exposure to moist air. Karaya gum swells in water and the dispersions have a pH of 3.6 to 4.4 (115).

Cochlospermum Gossypium Gum

Cochlospermum gossypium gum closely resembles the *Sterculiaceae* gums (110). This gum, which swells in water to a bulky gel, occurs as the partially acetylated (OAc, 18.9 per cent) derivative of the inorganic salt of an acidic polysaccharide which, after deacetylation with sodium hydroxide and purification by precipitation from an acidified aqueous solution with alcohol, shows $[\alpha]_D + 64°$ in N sodium hydroxide and has an equivalent weight of 470. The sodium salt of the gum does not reduce Fehling solution. With copper sulfate it gives an insoluble copper complex through which it can be purified.

Hydrolysis of the gum with boiling N sulfuric acid for 18 hours afforded equimolecular amounts of L-rhamnose, D-galactose, and D-galacturonic acid, together with a trace of a labile ketohexose. It is likely that most of this ketohexose is destroyed even under mild conditions of hydrolysis. D-Xylose is also reported in some samples of the gum (116).

Partial hydrolysis of the gum gives a mixture of monosaccharides and acidic oligosaccharides, which include 2-O-(D-galactopyranosyluronic acid)-L-rhamnose (CCLI), and 4-O-(D-galactopyranosyluronic acid)-D-galactose (CCLIII). These acids are also found in a similar partial hydrolyzate of *Sterculia setigera* gum (108).

The gum undergoes methylation with methyl sulfate and alkali in the usual way and the methyl derivative upon hydrolysis affords 2,3,4-tri-O-methyl-L-rhamnose (CLXXXIX, 1 part), 2,3,4,6-tetra-O-methyl-D-galactose (XXXIX, 2 parts), 3,4-di-O-methyl-L-rhamnose (CCLIV, 1 part), 2,3,6-tri-O-methyl-D-galactose (CCXXXIII, 1 part), 3-O-methyl-L-rhamnose (CCLVI, 1 part), 2,6-di-O-methyl-D-galactose (CCXVII, 1 per cent approx.) and a mixture of methylated uronic acids. The mixture of methylated uronic acids contains four components as indicated by chromatographic analysis; the identity of these acid components is not known, but methoxyl and equivalent weight determinations suggest that the mixture contained mono-O-methyl- and di-O-methyl-D-galacturonic acids, the latter probably including the 2,4- or 3,4-di-O-methyl derivatives. These data further demonstrate the similarity of the gums from C. *gossypium* and S. *setigera*.

Ghatti Gum and Marike Gum

Ghatti gum, also known as Indian gum and ghati gum, is the exudate from the stems of *Anogeissus latifolia*, Wall., a tree widely distributed in India and Ceylon. The gum is the inorganic salt, principally the calcium salt, of a polysaccharide acid, ghattic acid. It is soluble in water to an extent of 90 per cent, the soluble portion having a molecular weight of 11,860 as determined by osmotic pressure measurements (117,

118). Ghattic acid, prepared by precipitation of the gum from an acidified aqueous solution with alcohol, has an equivalent weight of between 1340 and 1735 (117,118). One specimen of the free acid, with an equivalent weight of about 1600, is found to be composed of L-arabinose (5 moles), D-galactose (3 moles), D-mannose (1 mole), D-xylose (0.5 mole), D-glucuronic acid (1 mole) and traces (below 1 per cent) of 6-deoxyhexose (119). Partial hydrolysis of the gum with 0.16N acid resulted in the generation of two aldobiouronic acids, namely, 6-O-(β-D-glucopyranosyluronic acid)-D-galactose (CLXXVII), and 2-O-(β-D-glucopyranosyluronic acid)-D-mannose (CLXLVIII).

Gum ghatti, therefore, resembles damson gum (44) and particularly cherry gum (49,50) from the standpoint of its component sugars, but in that it also contains 6-O-(β-D-glucopyranosyluronic acid)-D-galactose residues it is similar to the *Acacia* gums.

Upon autohydrolysis of the gum acid, the specific rotation changes from $[\alpha]_D + 48°$ to $+6°$ and there is liberated 80 per cent of the L-arabinose of the gum, leaving a degraded gum containing 4 per cent of L-arabinose and having an equivalent weight of about 1000 (119). Upon oxidation with periodate, it is found that 3 moles of formic acid are liberated per equivalent of gum and 80 per cent of the arabinose residues are oxidized together with about 33 per cent of the galactose residues. These results can be explained if the labile L-arabinose residues are present in the furanose form with an α-L-type linkage and if most of the D-galactose residues are joined through C_1 and C_3 with the remainder joined by $1 \rightarrow 6$ linkages (119).

Further insight into the structure of gum ghatti has been obtained (154) by methylation studies of the gum and of its degraded derivative formed by autohydrolysis. Hydrolysis of the methylated degraded gum yielded the components listed in column 1 of Table 51 together with small amounts of 2,3,4-tri-O-methylxylose, 2,3,4-tri-O-methylrhamnose and 2,3,5-tri-O-methylarabinose.

The acid components of the hydrolyzate were separated largely as a mixture of methylated aldobiouronic acids (equiv. wt. 370). Upon further hydrolysis this mixture afforded 2,3,4-tri- and 2,3-di-O-methyl-D-glucuronic acid, 3,4,6-tri-O-methyl-D-mannose, 2,3-di-, and 2,3,4-tri-O-methyl-D-galactose. From these findings it was deduced that some of the glucuronic residues in the degraded gum were present in non-terminal positions linked through C_1 and C_4. It was also pointed out that since the main neutral products of hydrolysis of the methylated aldobiouronic acid were 2,3,4-tri-O-methyl-D-galactose and 3,4,6-tri-O-methyl-D-

TABLE 51. HYDROLYSIS PRODUCTS OF METHYLATED DEGRADED GUM
GHATTI AND METHYLATED GUM GHATTI

Methylated Degraded Gum Ghatti	Methylated Gum Ghatti
2,3,4,6-Tetra-O-methyl-D-galactose	2,3,4,6-Tetra-O-methyl-D-galactose
2,3,4,-Tri-O-methyl-D-galactose	2,3,4-Tri-O-methyl-D-galactose
2,3-Di-O-methyl-D-galactose	2-O-Methyl-D-galactose
2,4-Di-O-methyl-D-galactose	2,4-Di-O-methyl-D-galactose
3,4,6-Tri-O-methyl-D-mannose	4-O-Methyl-D-mannose
2,3,4-Tri-O-methyl-D-glucuronic acid	2,3,4-Tri-O-methyl-D-glucuronic acid
2,3-Di-O-methyl-D-glucuronic acid	2,3-Di-O-methyl-D-glucuronic acid
	2,3,4-Tri-O-methyl-L-rhamnose
	2,3,5-Tri-O-methyl-L-arabinose
	2,3-Di-O-methyl-L-arabinose
	2,4-Di-O-methyl-L-arabinose
	2,5-Di-O-methyl-L-arabinose
	3,5-Di-O-methyl-L-arabinose

mannose, the aldobiouronic acid groups, D-GpA-1 → 6-D-Galp and
D-GpA-1 → 2-D-Manp, are present in the degraded gum as terminal groups
(119). Inasmuch as the galactose framework of the degraded gum contains 1 → 6 linkages and since these appear in the hydrolyzate of the
methylated degraded gum as 2,3-di-O-methyl-D-galactose, it would
appear that the aldobiouronic acid side chains are probably attached to
C_4 of the galactose units in the main framework.

The origin of the 2,3,4,6-tetra-O-methyl-D-galactose is not clear but it
is likely that, together with some of the terminal units of rhamnose,
xylose and arabinose, they are attached to those units of glucuronic acid
that give rise to a not insignificant proportion of 2,3-di-O-methyl-D-
glucuronic acid. The galactose residues may terminate another type of
side chain as in the case of gum arabic (10) or they may form the nonreducing ends of the D-galactose framework and are generated by cleavage of the main chain during autohydrolysis. Although most of the side
chains are attached to C_4 of the galactose residues of the main chain
some appear to be attached to C_3 since the 2,3-di-O-methyl-D-galactose
is accompanied by some 2,4-di-O-methyl-D-galactose.

Hydrolysis of the methylated undegraded gum ghatti gave the components listed in column 2 of Table 51. The acid components consisted
of 2,3-di- and 2,3,4-tri-O-methyl-D-glucuronic acid thus showing that
some of the uronic acid residues formed terminal units and others non-
terminal units joined through C_1 and C_4. The D-galactose residue of the
side chain of aldobiouronic acid, DGpA-1 → 6-DGal, gave rise to 2,4-di-
O-methyl-D-galactose whereas the mannose containing aldobiouronic

acid side chains, D-GpA-1 → 2-D-Man$p$, furnished 4-O-methyl-D-mannose. It would appear, therefore, that arabinose side chains are attached to these sugars through C_3 of D-galactose and through C_3 and C_6 of D-mannose. Side chains of L-arabinose, D-galactose, D-xylose or L-rhamnose may be attached to C_4 of some of the D-glucuronic acid units as in the case of the degraded gum.

Because the D-galactose units of the methylated degraded gum, which gave rise to the 2,3-dimethyl ether, appear in the hydrolyzate of the methylated undegraded gum as 2-mono-O-methyl-D-galactose, it is clear that side chains, probably of arabinose, must be joined to C_3 of those 1 → 6 linked D-galactose units of the main chain to which the side chain aldobiouronic acids are also attached.

The 2,3,5-tri-O-methyl-L-arabinose, which is one of the major components of the hydrolyzate of the methylated undegraded gum, represents 80 per cent of the arabinose content of the gum. The remaining 20 per cent appears in the hydrolyzate of the methylated gum as a mixture of about equal parts of 2,3-, 2,4-, 2,5- and 3,5-di-O-methyl-L-arabinose. Of these four dimethyl ethers of L-arabinose only the first arises from residues that would be susceptible to periodate oxidation. This agrees with the finding (119) that 20 per cent of the L-arabinose residues in the gum are not affected by periodate. It is also likely that, except for the 2,4-dimethyl ether, the rest arise from arabinose units which have a furanose structure and which are readily removed during autohydrolysis. The structural significance of the 2,4-di-O-methyl-L-arabinose is not yet clear but it may arise from arabopyranose units that are interposed in the main 1 → 6-linked D-galactose framework as suggested for gum arabic (see above).

Gum ghatti resembles acacia, damson, cherry, egg plum and mesquite gums in containing a high proportion of terminal L-arabofuranose units but it appears to differ from them in possessing a 1 → 6-linked galactose framework. It is apparent that further work is required to clarify the structure of gum ghatti.

Another tree of the genus *Anogeissus*, *A. schimperi*, found in Northern Nigeria and the eastern parts of the Sudan, provides a gum exudate which is known as marike gum. The gum may be yellow or light brown in color and forms a viscous solution in water. After precipitation from aqueous solution with acidified alcohol, the gum shows $[\alpha]_D -64°$ (approx.) in water. It does not reduce Fehling solution and neither contains protein, nor methoxyl groups. When the gum is hydrolyzed with N-sulfuric acid for 11 hours on a boiling water bath, the rotation changes from $[\alpha]_D$ $-64°$ to $+25°$ and there are formed L-arabinose, D-galactose, and a degraded acidic polysaccharide (120). The latter has an equivalent weight of approximately 343 and upon further hydrolysis with 2N sulfuric acid, there is produced L-arabinose, D-galactose, and an acid which is probably glucuronic acid. The identification of the neutral sugars is based upon paper chromatographic analysis and is probably correct but the characterization of the acid component depends upon a color reaction with basic lead acetate and needs confirmation.

Neem Gum

Neem gum, obtained from *Melia azadirachta* (*Azadirachta indica*) by tapping, has been in pharmaceutical use in India for many centuries. It is found in the form of pale yellow to light brown nodules and is the neutral salt of a polysaccharide acid. The gum acid, obtained by precipitation of the gum from an acidified aqueous solution with alcohol, shows $[\alpha]_D -70°$ in water, is nonreducing to Fehling solution and has an equivalent weight of 1080. It is composed of L-arabinose, L-fucose, D-galactose, and D-glucuronic acid, the ratio of D-galactose to L-arabinose being 3:2 (121). Mild hydrolysis of the gum readily liberates L-arabinose and L-fucose, leaving a more stable acid nucleus. Hydrolysis of the degraded gum acid affords D-galactose and 4-O-(D-glucopyranosyluronic acid)-D-galactose (CLXLVII). The latter, isolated in good yield directly from the gum, is the same as that obtained from lemon and grapefruit gums. The periodate-oxidized gum upon acid hydrolysis is found to contain D-galactose residues together with traces of L-arabinose thus indicating that the gum is highly branched.

Sapote Gum

Sapote gum forms slowly in the wounds of the sapote trees, such as *Sapota achras* found growing in Peru. The gum exudation occurs after the collection of chicle. It finds use as a sizing agent for cloth and felt and as a glue. The gum is composed of D-xylose, L-arabinose, and D-glucuronic acid, and contains 2.5 per cent methoxyl (122). Precipitation of the gum from an acidic aqueous solution with alcohol gives the free acid which has an equivalent weight of 679.

The structure of the gum has been investigated using methylation techniques. Methylation was effected with methyl sulfate and alkali to give a methylated derivative which is resistant to complete methanolysis (52). Upon treatment with boiling 3.4 per cent methanolic hydrogen chloride for eight hours, methylated sapote gum yields as the glycosides, 2,3,4-tri-O-methyl-D-xylose (CCXII), 2,3,4-tri-O-methyl-L-arabinose

(CCXV), 3-O-methyl-D-xylose (CCLVIII), and an acid fraction (123). The latter contains 3,4-di-O-methyl-D-glucuronic acid (CCLIX), identified by the reduction of its methyl ester methyl glycoside with lithium aluminum hydride to the methyl glycoside of 3,4-di-O-methyl-D-glucose (CCLX), and a mixture of two partially methylated aldobiouronic acids. This mixture upon prolonged hydrolysis yields 3-O-methyl-D-xylose (CCLVIII), but the hydrolytic conditions cause extensive degradation of the uronic acid residues. The resistance of the methylated aldobiouronic acids to hydrolysis is decreased by the reduction of their methyl esters with lithium aluminum hydride. The resulting neutral disaccharides are hydrolyzed for 5 hours with boiling N-sulfuric acid and there is formed 3-O-methyl-D-xylose (CCLVIII), 3,4-di-O-methyl-D-glucose (CCLX), and 2,3,4-tri-O-methyl-D-glucose (CCLXI) (124). The 3,4-di-O-methyl-D-glucose (CCLX) is derived from 3,4-di-O-methyl-D-glucuronic acid (CCLIX) and the 2,3,4-tri-O-methyl-D-glucose (CCLXI) from 2,3,4-tri-O-methyl-D-glucuronic acid (XV). These two methylated derivatives of D-glucuronic acid are therefore each glycosidically linked in the two partially methylated aldobiouronic acids to 3-O-methyl-D-xylose.

A quantitative analysis of the composition of methylated sapote gum is achieved by combining the methods employed in the identification of the component methyl sugar residues (123, 124). The methylated gum is subjected to partial methanolysis after which the resulting mixture of glycosidic products is reduced with lithium aluminum hydride and finally hydrolyzed without difficulty to the corresponding reducing sugars. The mixture of methyl sugars was quantitatively analyzed by paper chromatographic techniques; the molar ratio of the component sugars of the methylated gum was found to be: 3-O-methyl-D-xylose (CCLVIII, 3 moles), 3,4-di-O-methyl-D-glucuronic acid (CCLIX), determined as 3,4-di-O-methyl-D-glucose (CCLX, 1 mole), 2,3,4-tri-O-methyl-D-glucuronic acid (XV), determined as 2,3,4-tri-O-methyl-D-glucose (CCLXI, 1 mole), 2,3,4-tri-O-methyl-D-xylose (CCXII, 1 mole), and 2,3,4-tri-O-methyl-L-arabinose (CCXV, 1 mole).

The main structural features of the gum are apparent from the above data. In an average repeating unit of the seven sugar residues there are three end-groups represented by 2,3,4-tri-O-methyl-L-arabinose, 2,3,4-tri-O-methyl-D-xylose, and 2,3,4-tri-O-methyl-D-glucuronic acid. The three branch points in this unit are supported by the characterization of the three 3-O-methyl-D-xylose residues, which probably also form part of the main chain. These D-xylose residues are linked through C_1, C_2 and C_4. The 3,4-di-O-methyl-D-glucuronic acid is uniquely linked through

C_1 and C_2 in a side chain of the repeating unit, and attached to it at C_2 is either an L-arabopyranose or a D-xylopyranose residue. The other two side chains are composed of either L-arabopyranose or D-xylopyranose and the uronic acid. If this general structure is correct, the D-xylose moieties of the two aldobiouronic acid residues must arise from the main xylan chain and two of the three side chains would be composed of single sugar residues, the other side chain having two sugar residues. Such a structure would account for the tough, transparent films which can be formed from methylated sapote gum.

The structure (CCLXII) assigned to sapote gum is one of several which can explain the experimental facts. The xylose units in the main chain may be joined to each other by $1 \rightarrow 4$ (as in CCLXII), $1 \rightarrow 2$, or $1 \rightarrow 4$ and $1 \rightarrow 2$ linkages. From the methoxyl value of the gum about half of the D-glucuronic acid residues contain a methyl group which by analogy with other gums so constituted, for example mesquite gum, is probably at C_4. The isolation of an aldobiouronic acid, composed of a methoxyuronic acid and xylose, supports the view that the methyl group is attached to some of the D-glucuronic acid residues (122).

It is of interest to note that all the L-arabinose residues are of the pyranose form. Although L-arabopyranose residues have also been reported in gum arabic and in peach, cherry and cholla gums, these gums have also contained L-arabofuranose residues.

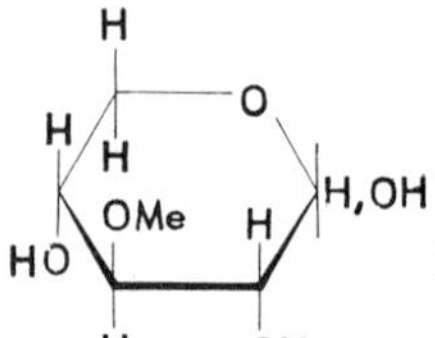

(CCLVIII) 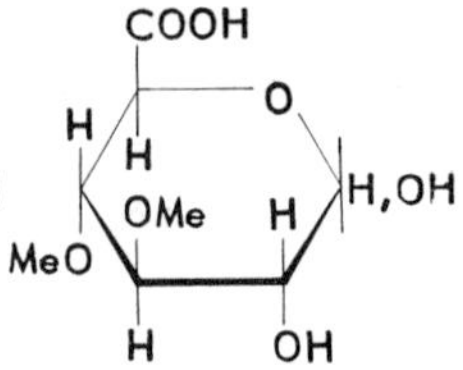   (CCLIX)

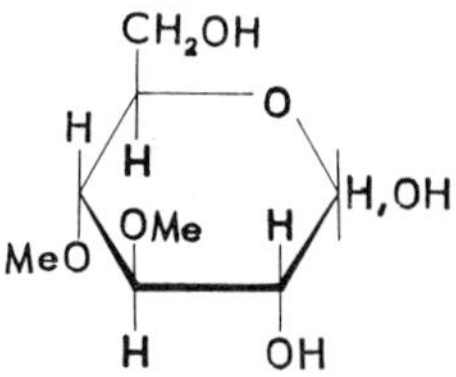

(CCLX) 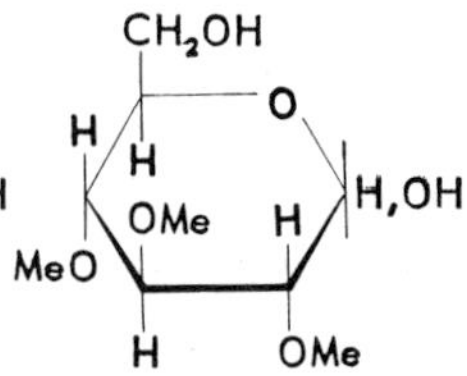   (CCLXI)

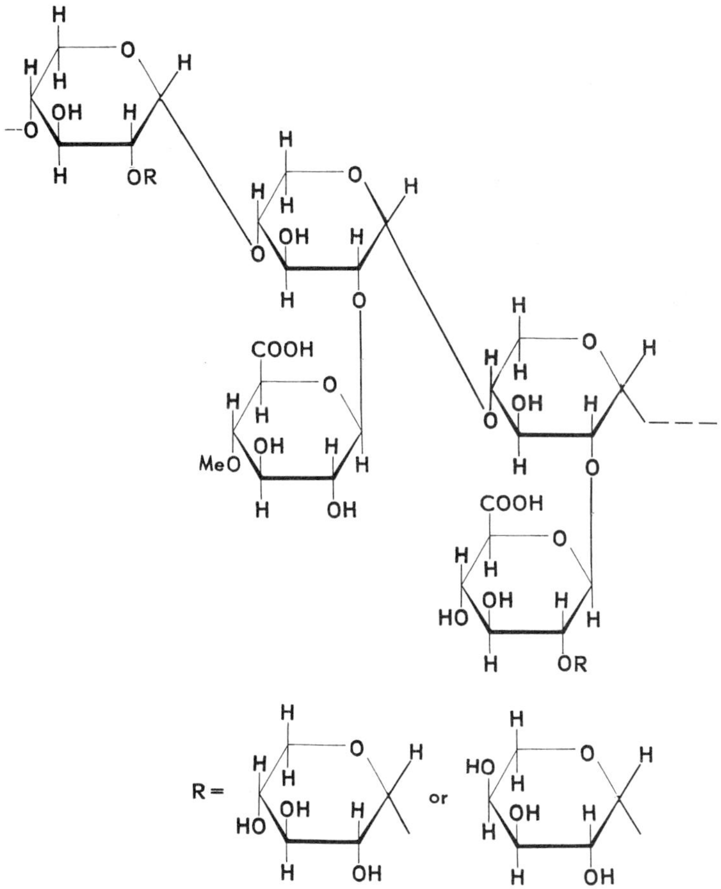

(CCL XII)

A sample of gum obtained through commercial channels from Peru and sold as sapote gum was found to be completely different from that described above (125). The gum had a much higher viscosity than sapote gum and was composed of L-arabinose (25.1 per cent), D-galactose (45.5 per cent), L-rhamnose (6.8 per cent), D-xylose (5.2 per cent) and D-glucuronic acid (17 per cent), together with 2 per cent of methoxyl. The purified gum showed $[\alpha]_D +57°$ in water and it had an equivalent weight of 1095 compared to the sapote gum with $[\alpha]_D -6°$ in water and equivalent weight of 679. A preliminary study of the structure of the gum by methylation techniques indicates a highly branched structure with a backbone composed largely of D-galactopyranose residues and end groups of L-rhamnopyranose, D-xylopyranose, L-arabofuranose and D-glucuronic or mono-*O*-methyl-D-glucuronic acid. It is apparent that this sample of gum is entirely different from those described above for sapote gum, (52,122–124) and it may well be that one of these gums has been incorrectly named. The above findings on the so-called sapote gums clearly demonstrate the vital importance of working with samples of known source and history.

Cholla Gum

Cholla gum is of tropical origin and is exuded by the white cactus, *Opuntia fulgida*, which is native to Mexico and the Southern States of North America. The formation of the gum seems to be favored by prolonged hot dry spells and occurs most frequently on large, old, or diseased plants.

The gum is partially soluble (approx. 50 per cent) in water; the soluble part does not reduce Fehling solution. The composition of the gum seems to vary. In one case (95,126) the crude gum was reported to be composed of ash (8.4 per cent), nitrogen (0.4 per cent), D-galacturonic acid (11.5 per cent), L-arabinose (53.2 per cent), L-rhamnose (5.5 per cent) and D-galactose (8.4 per cent). Mild hydrolysis preferentially removed the L-arabinose leaving a stable nucleus which upon further hydrolysis afforded an aldobiouronic acid composed of L-rhamnose and D-galacturonic acid.

Other workers (127) record the following analysis for a sample of cholla gum: D-galacturonic acid (1 part), L-arabinose (6 parts), D-xylose (2 parts), D-galactose (3 parts) and L-rhamnose (trace). This result was obtained for cholla gum after purification by precipitation from an acidified aqueous solution with alcohol. The gum acid which showed, $[\alpha]_D$ $-83°$ in water, was said to be homogeneous electrophoretically.

A solution of the gum in boiling 0.01N sulfuric acid underwent a change in optical rotation, from $[\alpha]_D$ $-82°$ to $+53°$ in 10 hours, during which time there was a rapid diminution of viscosity. The mixture of sugars so formed contained L-arabinose, D-xylose, D-galactose, and neutral oligosaccharides, the total neutral sugars being present in the relative proportions: L-arabinose (6 parts), D-xylose (2 parts), and D-galactose (1 part). The acids produced by the mild hydrolysis, which corresponded to a trisaccharide, gave upon further hydrolysis D-galactose and D-galacturonic acid.

An alternative procedure for the partial hydrolysis of cholla gum (42), involving solution of the gum in 6N sulfuric acid and allowing the solution to stand for 2 to 3 weeks at room temperature gave L-arabinose, D-xylose, D-galactose, a disaccharide composed of D-galactose, oligosaccharides composed of L-arabinose and the disaccharide, 5-O-β-D-xylopyranosyl-L-arabinose (CCXX). This disaccharide (CCXX) which can be obtained from peach gum in a similar manner has also been synthesized (152).

The ash-free gum underwent methylation with methyl sulfate and alkali to give a methyl derivative which upon methanolysis and fractional distillation gave the glycosides of: 2,3,5-tri-O-methyl-L-arabinose (CLXL, 4 parts), 2,3,4-tri-O-methyl-D-xylose (CCXII, 2 parts), 2,3-di-O-methyl-L-arabinose (CCI, 1 part), 2,4-di-O-methyl-D-galactose (CLXXXII, 3 parts), L-arabinose (1 part) and 2-O-methyl-D-galacturonic acid (CCLVII, 1 part). In view of the difficulties experienced in the separation of such a complex mixture of sugars, the quantitative analysis of the proportions of the cleavage fragments of the methylated gum is only approximate. However, the data indicated that all the D-xylose residues are present in the gum as end-groups in the pyranose form whereas the greater part of the L-arabinose units are end-groups of the furanose form. The ease with which the L-arabinose units are liberated from the gum by mineral acids lends support to the suggestion that they are probably all in the furanose form and in the side-chains of the gum. Cholla gum, like damson gum, contains L-arabofuranose residues linked through C_1 and C_5 but it is unique in having some of these residues linked through C_1, C_2, C_3 and C_5. This type of structure in which every hydroxyl group, other than that concerned with ring-formation, is combined with another sugar, has been encountered in the field of plant gums and mucilages only in the cases of the galactoaraban of gum tragacanth and in slippery-elm mucilage; it is a fairly common structural feature of the cereal grain gums of the pentosan type. The highly branched character of cholla gum is further supported by the isolation of 2-O-methyl-D-galacturonic acid (CCLVII) from the cleavage fragments of the methylated gum which shows that the D-galacturonic acid units are joined through C_1, C_3 and

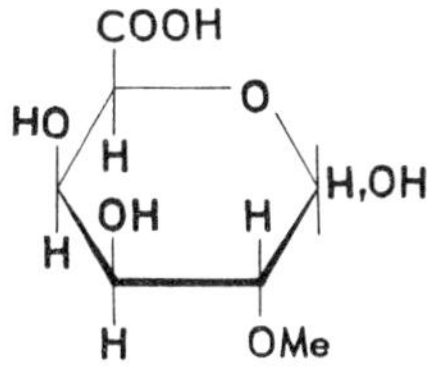

COOH
|
HO————O
  H   \
   OH   H   H,OH
H   /
|
H   OMe

(CCLVII)

C_4. The D-galactose units, all of which are probably in the main chain, are linked through C_1, C_3 and C_6, once again demonstrating that D-galactose units favor the $1 \rightarrow 3$ and $1 \rightarrow 6$ type of linkage that is typical of many of the gums.

Chagual Gum

Chagual gum is obtained from species of *Puya*, especially *P. chilensis* and also *P. lanuginosa*, *P. lanata* and possibly others. The large trees are found growing on the slopes of the Andes in Chile and in other parts of South America. Chagual gum is produced by the tree as a result of damage by the larvae of *Kastnia (Castnia) elegans*.

The gum is partially soluble in water and does not reduce Fehling solution. In an early study Winterstein reported (128) that the gum was slightly dextrorotatory and that it contains xylose (45 per cent) and galactose (21 per cent); the latter was believed to be present as the L-enantiomorph.

In other studies (129), chagual gum, purified by precipitation from an aqueous solution with alcohol, showed $[\alpha]_D - 30°$ in N-sodium hydroxide and thus differed from the sample studied before (128). The polysaccharide acid, chagualic acid, prepared by passing an aqueous solution of the gum through Amberlite IR-120 cation exchange resin showed $[\alpha]_D -31°$ in water, and had an equivalent weight of 1030. Upon hydrolysis of the gum with boiling N sulfuric acid there was produced L-arabinose (7 per cent), D-xylose (31 per cent), D-galactose (36 per cent) and an aldobiouronic acid (27 per cent).

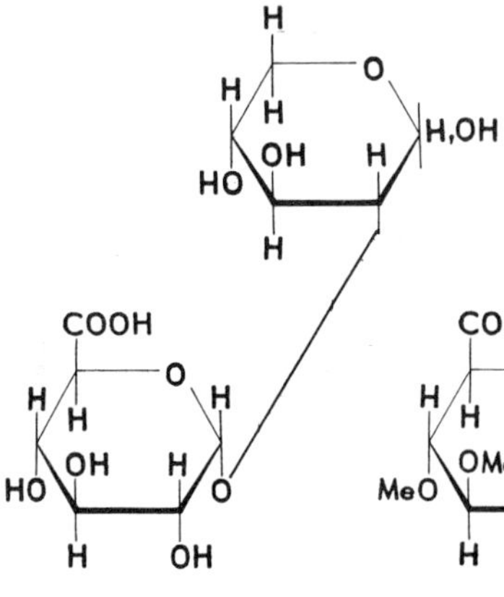

(CCLXV)

(CCLXIII)   (CCLXIV)   (CCLXVI)

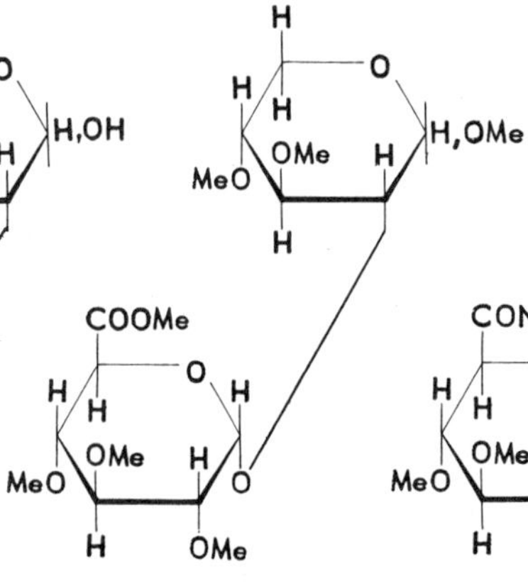

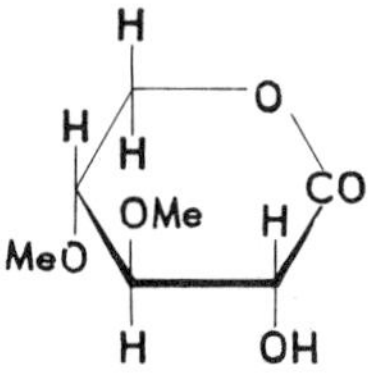

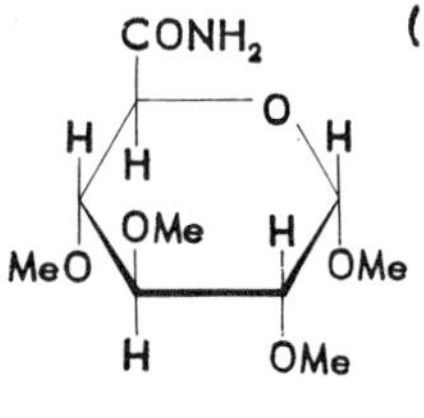

The aldobiouronic acid, $[\alpha]_D$ +95° in water, proved to be 2-O-(D-glucopyranosyluronic acid)-D-xylose (CCLXIII). Its structure was established by methylation to the hepta-O-methyl derivative (CCLXIV) which upon hydrolysis afforded 2,3,4-tri-O-methyl-D-glucuronic acid (XV) and 3,4-di-O-methyl-D-xylose (CCXXXVI), the first of which was identified as the crystalline methyl 2,3,4-tri-O-methyl-D-glucosiduron-amide (CCLXVI) whereas the second cleavage product was characterized as the crystalline 3,4-di-O-methyl-D-xylonolactone (CCLXV).

Hakea acicularis Gum

This gum which exudes infrequently from the bark of the tree *Hakea acicularis* (family *Proteaceae*) is an acid polysaccharide. Freshly exuded material is soluble in water but the gum hardens on keeping and its solubility in water decreases until it becomes insoluble (150). The gum acid shows $[\alpha]_D$ −13° (NaOH) and it has an equivalent weight of 2000. Periodate oxidation shows that 11 moles of periodate are consumed per equivalent of the gum with the liberation of 4 moles of formic acid.

Chromatography on a cellulose column using 1-butanol:water (10:1) of the hydrolyzate of the gum showed that it consisted of L-arabinose (19 per cent), D-xylose (8 per cent), D-galactose (58 per cent), D-mannose (7 per cent) and D-glucuronic acid (8 per cent). Most of the L-arabinose of the gum appears to be present in the furanose form since it is preferentially removed from the gum by hydrolysis with 0.01N sulfuric acid at 96°, a view supported by the fact that during the hydrolysis there is an upward change in rotation.

Further hydrolysis of the gum leads to the formation of an aldobiouronic acid (CLXLVIII), recognized as 2-O-(β-D-glucopyranosyluronic acid)-D-mannose. The structure of this aldobiouronic acid was established by methylation, first with methyl sulfate and alkali, and then with silver oxide and methyl iodide, by which means there was obtained methyl 2-O-[methyl (2,3,4-tri-O-methyl-β-D-glucopyranosyluronate)]-3,4,6-tri-O-methyl-D-mannoside. Hydrolysis of the latter afforded 2,3,4-tri-O-methyl-D-glucuronic acid, recognized as the characteristic amide methyl glycoside, and 3,4,6-tri-O-methyl-D-mannose which crystallized directly.

Since the proportions of D-glucuronic acid and D-mannose were approximately the same and since only one aldobiouronic acid was produced from the gum, it is suggested that all of the D-mannose units are joined through C_2 to a unit of D-glucuronic acid. On the assumption that the arabinose units are present in the gum in the furanose form, the liberation of formic acid from the gum by periodate oxidation and from the

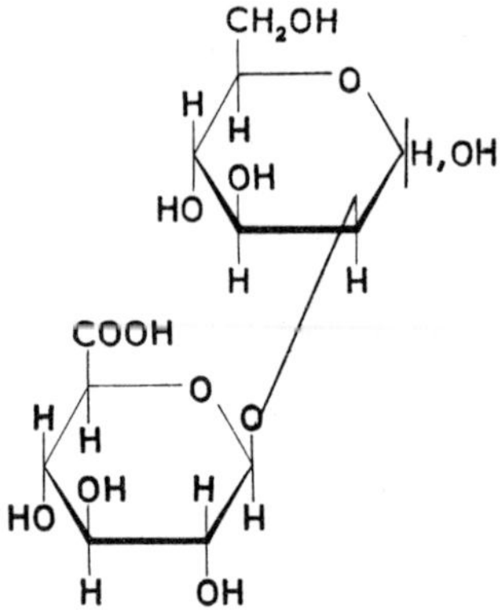

(CLXLVIII)

degraded gum after the arabinose has been removed, lends support to the view that a considerable number of the D-galactose building units, presumed to be of the pyranose type from their stability to acid hydrolysis, are joined by 1 → 6 glycosidic bonds. Further support for these structural predictions will no doubt be forthcoming from methylation studies.

Structure of Khaya Grandifolia Gum

Khaya gum is an exudate of the West African mahogany tree *Khaya grandifolia.* It softens and swells in cold water and dissolves with difficulty in hot water to give a clear neutral solution (120). The crude gum dissolves in 4 per cent sodium hydroxide and after purification by precipitation from an acidified aqueous solution with alcohol shows $[\alpha]_D$ + 104° in 4 per cent sodium hydroxide. Hydrolysis of the gum with mineral acids results in a decrease in optical rotation, indicating α-D-linkages in the polysaccharide, and in the liberation of D-galactose, L-rhamnose, and a uronic acid which is probably D-galacturonic acid. *Khaya grandifolia* gum was later shown to be composed of D-galactose, L-rhamnose, D-galacturonic acid, 4-O-methyl-D-glucuronic acid, and traces of L-arabinose (120,155). This is the only gum so far examined that contains two different uronic acids.

The crude gum examined in these later experiments did not dissolve completely in water, but after dissolution in alkali followed by acidification and precipitation with acetone it readily dissolved in water (155). Chagual gum has been found to behave in the same way (129). The treatment with alkali may have removed ester groupings since several gums are known to contain acetyl residues (108–110). The purified gum has a high uronic acid content in which particular it resembles tragacanthic acid (156). It is extremely resistant to hydrolysis even with 2 N sulfuric acid. Hydrolysis does not appear to liberate any of the neutral sugars preferentially for after hydrolysis for 6 hours at 100°, which liberated L-rhamnose (3.7 per cent), L-arabinose (0.2 per cent), and D-galactose (18 per cent), the incompletely hydrolyzed acidic residue (52 per cent of the original weight) gave, after reduction of the uronic acid groups with potassium borohydride and subsequent hydrolysis, L-rhamnose (10.1 per cent), 4-O-methyl-D-glucose (2.0 per cent), D-glucose (trace), and D-galactose (26.6 per cent). Since 4-O-methyl-D-glucose was not present in the gum residue before reduction, it could only have arisen from the reduction of the residues of 4-O-methyl-D-glucuronic acid. The trace of glucose found in the hydrolyzate of the reduced portion of the partially hydrolyzed gum was believed to be produced by demethylation of 4-O-methyl-D-glucose. Evidence for the presence in the gum of D-galacturonic acid residues came from the nitric acid oxidation by which more galactaric acid was produced than could have arisen from the total amount of galactose in the gum. The gradual liberation of acid residues during hydrolysis indicated that all of the uronic acid units were not joined to each other.

Treatment of the gum with methyl sulfate and alkali followed by silver oxide and methyl iodide gave methylated *Khaya* gum (OMe, 40.2 per cent) which, like the parent gum, was resistant to hydrolysis, a behavior that may be related to the presence of galacturonic acid units. From the hydrolyzate of the methylated gum there were obtained 2,3,4,6-tetra-O-methyl-D-galactose, 2,3,6-tri-O-methyl-D-galactose, 3-O-methyl-L-rhamnose, a trace of an unidentified di-O-methyl galactose (said to be of no structural significance), and a mixture of methylated oligosaccharides containing uronic acid units.

These acidic components could not be separated directly, but after reduction of the corresponding ester glycosides with lithium aluminum hydride to give neutral products, hydrolysis gave a mixture of methylated sugars which was resolved by column partition chromatography on cellulose into 2,3,6-tri-O-methyl-D-galactose, 3-O-methyl-L-rhamnose, 2,3,4-tri-O-methyl-D-glucose, and 2,3-di-O-methyl-D-galactose. Since these last two components were not present in the mixture of neutral sugars isolated after hydrolysis of the methylated gum, they must have been formed from the uronic acid components of the gum, namely 2,3,4-tri-O-methyl-D-glucuronic acid and 2,3-di-O-methyl-D-galacturonic acid.

In the mixture of acidic oligosaccharides obtained by partial hydrolysis of the gum there was identified D-galacturonic acid (CCLXVII),

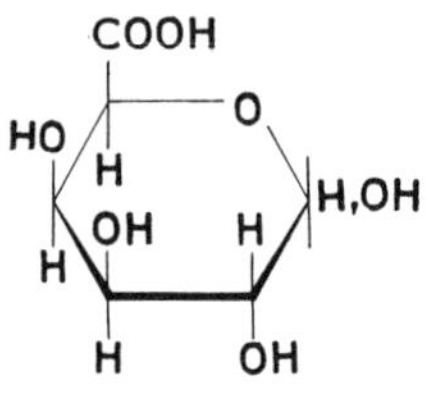

(CCLXVII) 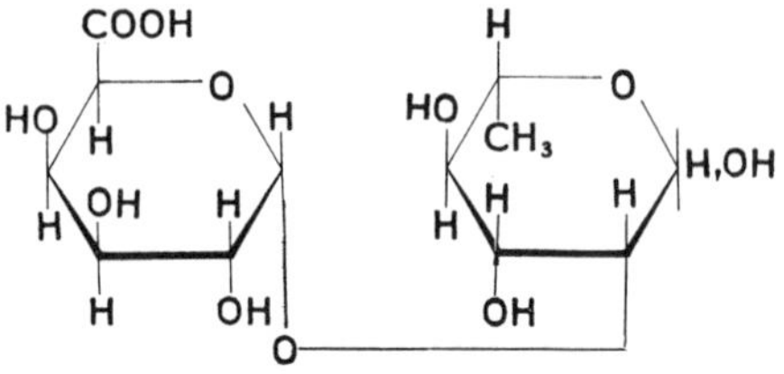   (CCLI)

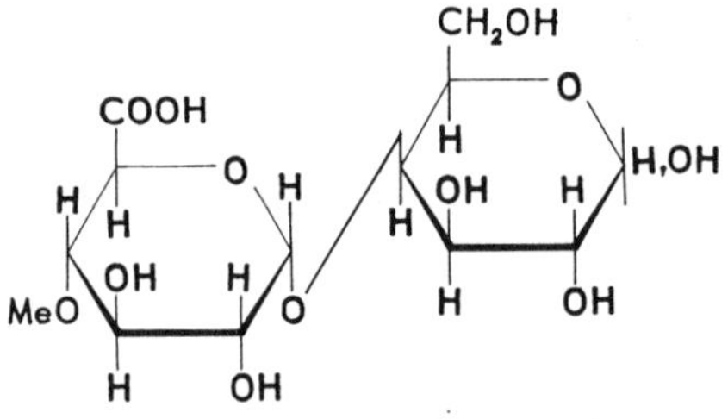

(CCXXXI)

2-O-(D-galactopyranosyluronic acid)-L-rhamnose (CCLI), and 4-O-(4-O-methyl-D-glucosyluronic acid)-D-galactose (CCXXXI).

Although these two aldobiouronic acids could not be separated since they had the same R_F values when examined by paper partition chromatography and almost the same M_G values by paper electrophoresis, it was possible to deduce their structures from the following experimental facts. Hydrolysis of the mixture of the two aldobiouronic acids gave 4-O-methyl-D-glucuronic acid, D-galacturonic acid, D-galactose, and L-rhamnose whereas after oxidation with bromine neither D-galactose nor L-rhamnose could be detected. Reduction of the mixture of the methylated derivatives of the aldobiouronic acids with lithium aluminum hydride followed by methylation, gave two fully methylated neutral disaccharides which upon hydrolysis yielded 2,3,4,6-tetra-O-methyl-D-glucose, 2,3,4,6-tetra-O-methyl-D-galactose, 3,4-di-O-methyl-L-rhamnose, and 2,3,6-tri-O-methyl-D-galactose. The above evidence established that the L-rhamnose unit was joined through C_2 and that the D-galactose unit was combined through C_4 but it was not possible to say which uronic acid unit was joined to which neutral sugar residue. Certain evidence enabled the structures CCLI and CCXXXI to be chosen for the two aldobiouronic acids. Thus, since the two aldobiouronic acids had the same R_F value it was unlikely that the 4-O-methyl-D-glucuronic acid unit was combined with L-rhamnose for both these components travel faster than either D-galacturonic acid or D-galactose and it would be expected that an aldo-biouronic acid formed from 4-*O*-methyl-D-glucuronic acid and L-rhamnose would move faster on a chromatogram than one formed from D-galactu-ronic acid and D-galactose, providing that all the residues had pyranose structures. The similar electrophoretic mobilities of the two aldobio-uronic acids pointed to the structures CCLI and CCXXXI for the pair of acids rather than the alternative pair, 4-*O*-(D-galactopyranosyluronic acid)-D-galactose and 2-*O*-(4-*O*-methyl-D-glucosyluronic acid)-L-rham-nose, because the former contains two *cis* glycol groupings, whereas the latter contains none and hence in a borate buffer their electro-phoretic mobilities would be expected to be quite different (157–159). The aldobiouronic acid (CCLI) has been isolated before from karaya gum (108) exuded by *Sterculia setigera*, and from the gum exuded by *Coch-lospermum gossypium* (110), while CCXXXI has been obtained from gum myrrh (160).

Further information concerning the structure of *Khaya* gum was afforded by an examination of the aldotriouronic acid obtained by graded hydroly-sis of the gum. This acid gave D-galactose and L-rhamnose upon further hydrolysis. After oxidation with bromine and hydrolysis only rhamnose was detected, thus showing that the rhamnose unit was not located at the reducing end of the trisaccharide. Reduction of the acid unit in the aldotriouronic acid with potassium borohydride followed by hydrolysis yielded galactose and rhamnose from which it was deduced that the acid component was galacturonic acid. The aldotriouronic acid was trans-formed into a fully methylated trisaccharide, the hydrolysis products of which were found by paper chromatography to correspond to 2,3,4,6-tetra-*O*-methyl-D-galactose, 3,4-di-*O*-methyl-L-rhamnose and 2,3,6-tri-*O*-methyl-D-galactose. It was evident from this that the rhamnose unit occupied the central position in the aldotriouronic acid and whereas the results could be explained by assigning to the aldotriouronic acid the structure *O*-D-galactosyl-(1 → 2)-*O*-L-rhamnosyl-(1 → 4)-D-galacturonic acid it is much more likely that the alternative structure *O*-D-galactosyluronic acid-(1 → 2)-*O*-L-rhamnosyl-(1 → 4)-D-galactose is the correct one; this is supported not only by the general chemistry of uronosides, but also by the fact that one of the two aldobiouronic acids (CCLI) was shown to have the structure, 2-*O*-(D-galactosyluronic acid)-L-rhamnose. A decision between the two structures could have been reached by examining the hydrolysis products of the methylated aldotriouronic acid for if the uronic acid occupied the reducing position it would appear as the 2,3-di-*O*-methyl derivative whereas the galactose unit would give 2,3,4,6-tetra-*O*-methyl-D-galactose; if the uronic acid was located at the nonreducing end of the molecule, it would furnish

2,3,4-tri-O-methyl-D-galacturonic acid and the galactose unit residing at the reducing end of the molecule would give rise to 2,3,6-tri-O-methyl-D-galactose.

The main structural features of the *Khaya* gum as deduced from the above findings are as follows: The identification of 2,3,4,6-tetra-O-methyl-D-galactose and 2,3,4-tri-O-methyl-D-glucuronic acid shows that end groups of D-galactose and 4-O-methyl-D-glucuronic acid occur in the gum. The characterization of 3-O-methyl-L-rhamnose proves that L-rhamnose residues constitute branch points in the molecule. Assuming that the small amount of unidentified di-O-methyl-D-galactose is of no significance, the identification of 2,3-di-O-methyl-D-galactose after reduction of the methyl galacturonic acid residues demonstrates that $1 \rightarrow 4$ linked D-galacturonic acid units are also present in the gum molecule. Since the aldobiouronic acid (CCLI) obtained by graded hydrolysis of the gum, was shown to have a $1 \rightarrow 2$ glycosidic linkage it is clear that branching of the molecule occurs at C_4 of the rhamnose units. Inasmuch as the linkages of all aldobiouronic acids so far examined are highly resistant to acid hydrolysis, the formation of galactose (together with a small proportion of arabinose) and no oligosaccharides, suggests that the galactose nonreducing end groups are joined directly to the rhamnose residues. The formation of 4-O-(4-O-methyl-D-glucosyluronic acid)-D-galactose (CCXXXI) by graded acid hydrolysis shows that the terminal units of 4-O-methyl-D-glucuronic acid are joined to the main chain through at least one galactose unit by a $1 \rightarrow 4$ glycosidic bond. The characterization of the aldotriouronic acid, D-GalpA-$(1 \rightarrow 2)$-L-Rhap-$(1 \rightarrow 4)$-D-Gal, shows that $1 \rightarrow 4$ linked D-galactose units are present in the main chains. In addition, since all of the D-galacturonic acid units give rise to the 2,3-di-O-methyl derivative, recognized as the corresponding 2,3-di-O-methyl-D-galactose, and since not all of the galacturonic acid residues could be accounted for by the aldobio- and trio-uronic acids, it is evident that D-galacturonic acid units must be present in the main chain of the molecule. In this respect *Khaya* gum resembles gum tragacanth (156). Since decomposition occurs during the hydrolysis of the methylated gum before and after reduction with lithium aluminum hydride (21), an accurate analysis of the hydrolyzate was not possible, but assuming all of the above structural features are present in each molecule of the gum, a structure (CCLXVIII) may be tentatively advanced. This structure is composed of D-galactose (3 parts), L-rhamnose (2 parts), D-galacturonic acid (4 parts), and 4-O-methyl-D-glucuronic acid (1 part); it was reported that this was consistent with the quantitative results after allowing for decomposition during hydrolysis.

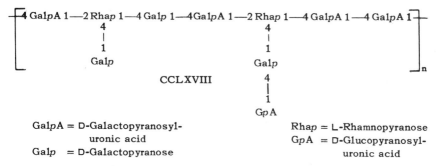

GalpA = D-Galactopyranosyl-
       uronic acid
Galp = D-Galactopyranose

Rhap = L-Rhamnopyranose
GpA = D-Glucopyranosyl-
       uronic acid

This formula does not include any units of arabinose, although this sugar was produced in trace amounts by hydrolysis of the gum, because hydrolysis of the methyl gum gave no derivative of arabinose.

The striking feature of the above gum is that it is the only one investigated thus far which contains two different uronic acids. Other gums have been shown to give rise to two or even three aldobiouronic acids, but in these cases the two acids have contained the same uronic acid united to different sugars or to the same sugar through a different linkage.

The gum resembles gum tragacanth (156) and pectic acid (161,162) in that it contains a large proportion of $1 \rightarrow 4$ linked galacturonic acid units, and, like gum tragacanth, it contains a 6-deoxyhexose (86,156). It also resembles the gums from *Sterculia setigera* (108,109) and *Cochlospermum gossypium* (110) which likewise contain D-galactose, L-rhamnose, and D-galacturonic acid; and, as with these two gums the galactose units of *Khaya* gum are joined by $1 \rightarrow 4$ bonds. In comparison, galactose units in acacia (10,20), cherry (51), damson (46) and egg-plum (64) gums are joined through C_1 and C_3 and C_1 and C_6 though in the case of gum arabic it is more likely that the major proportion of the galactose units are joined through C_3 (23,30). In *Khaya grandifolia* gum, the L-rhamnose units serve as branch points whereas in the *Sterculia* and *Cochlospermum* gums, the L-rhamnose units are joined through C_1 and C_2 and thus occur only in the chains and not at branch points or as terminal units as in the case of gum arabic. Unlike the *Setigera* gum and gum tragacanth in which branching occurs at the D-galacturonic acid units, the D-galacturonic acid components of *Khaya* gum do not form branch points in the molecule.

Another gum of a related species, *Khaya senegalensis*, was also examined and preliminary results indicated that it was similar to the *Khaya grandifolia* gum in its general structure although different from it in detail as is the case with the various species of *Acacia* gums.

The exudate from *Khaya madagascariensis* is a pale yellow, odorless gum which is partially soluble in water and upon hydrolysis with 6 per cent sulfuric acid gives a mixture of sugars in which L-arabinose and D-galactose are present (138).

Gum Olibanum (Frankincense)

Trees or shrubs of the genus *Boswellia* are the source of frankincense or gum olibanum. One specie of this genus, *B. serrata*, is a deciduous tree common on dry hills in northern India and is the source of the so-called Indian olibanum.

On extraction with 90 per cent ethanol, the resin is removed from the gum and a polysaccharide residue (68) having acidic groups (69) remains. The carbohydrate component can be obtained from other gum resins, such as gum asafoetida, gum galbani and gum cambogia (68) in a similar manner.

Hydrolysis of the carbohydrate component of Indian olibanum from *B. serrata* with 3 per cent sulfuric acid for 8 hours gives L-arabinose, D-xylose, D-galactose, and an acidic fragment which is insoluble in alcohol (130).

More recently the carbohydrate component having $[\alpha]_D - 8°$, and an equivalent weight, 545 obtained from the frankincense-gum of *Boswellia carterii*, has been shown (131) to give upon hydrolysis with N-sulfuric acid D-galactose (7 moles), L-arabinose (1 mole), and 4-O-methyl-D-glucuronic acid (4 moles). Traces of two other sugars suspected from chromatographic analysis to be fucose and rhamnose were also detected. Controlled hydrolysis of the carbohydrate component of frankincense gum appears to give rise to 6-O-(4-O-methyl-β-D-glucosyluronic acid)-D-galactose.

When an aqueous solution of the polysaccharide components of the gum was deionized with a cation resin and treated with three volumes of ethanol, a neutral polysaccharide gum, A, was precipitated. Further addition of three volumes of acetone yielded a polysaccharide acid component, B (70).

The neutral polysaccharide gum A which had $[\alpha]_D^{20} - 14.7°$ in pyridine : water (1 : 3) and underwent complete hydrolysis with 0.5N mineral acid in 6 hours to give D-galactose and L-arabinose in equimolecular proportions. Treatment of polysaccharide A first with methyl-iodide and sodium in liquid ammonia and then with methyl sulfate and alkali, gave a methyl derivative (OMe, 41.2 per cent). Hydrolysis of the latter furnished 2,3,4,6-tetra-O-methyl-D-galactose (identified as its aniline derivative), 2,3,4-tri-O-methyl-D-galactose (identified as its aniline derivative and as the phenylhydrazide of the corresponding 2,3,4-tri-O-methyl-D-galactonic acid), and 2,4-di-O-methyl-D-galactose (identified also as the aniline derivative). The fate of the arabinose component of the methyl polysaccharide A was not determined and hence structural deductions must await further study. The yield of the methylated polysaccharide falls off during the methylation experiments suggesting that the polysaccharide A is a mixture of a galactan and an araban and that the latter is lost during dialysis of the methylation reaction mixture to remove inorganic impurity. It is clear, however, that this galactan component A of the olibanum gum forms part of a highly branched structure. Although the isolation of 2,4-di-O-methyl-D-galactose reveals the presence of 1 → 3 glycosidic bonds this is not the only type of linkage involved in the complex, since periodate oxidation shows that all the other residues are split except the galactose units at which branching occurs.

Polysaccharide B, which constitutes the acid component of the gum, showed $[\alpha]_D - 9°$ (water). The gum B could not be precipitated from a 5 per cent aqueous solution with three volumes of ethanol, but it was rendered insoluble upon the addition of a further five volumes of acetone. Hydrolysis of polysaccharide B furnished D-galactose and D-galacturonic acid in the molecular ratio of 2 : 1. Periodate oxidation studies showed that for a repeating unit of 2 residues of galactose and 1 of galacturonic acid, three molecular proportions of periodate were consumed with the formation of about 0.5 mole of formic acid.

Methylation of the polysaccharide B, using the same methods as described for component A, gave a methylated derivative which had OMe 45.9 per cent, thus indicating that methylation was complete. After hydrolysis of the methyl derivative, three components were identified, namely, 2,3,4,6-tetra-O-, 2,3,4-tri-O-, and 2,4-di-O-methyl-D-galactose. A derivative of the D-galacturonic acid component of the gum was not encountered perhaps because it was present as a silver salt in the final hydrolyzate submitted to resolution by paper chromatography.

The evidence on the chemistry of frankincense gum is conflicting as well as incomplete indicating that further investigations on material of known origin are necessary.

Gum Myrrh

Gum myrrh exudes from cracks and fissures in the bark of *Commiphora myrrha*, Holmes (fam. *Burseraceae*) found in Northeast Africa and in Arabia, forming nodules composed of a red oily resin and white streaks of gum. The substance has been used as incense for many centuries and in more recent times it has been employed, as an antiseptic.

The crude gum contains carbohydrate, protein, and terpenoid resins (68). On extraction with 90 percent alcohol, the resins are largely removed and the crude polysaccharide, left as an insoluble residue, yield approximately 40 percent is purified further by precipitation from an acidified 20 percent aqueous alcohol solution with a large excess of alcohol (132). The crude acidic polysaccharide, having equivalent weight 547 and methoxyl 6.1 percent, contains approximately 18 percent of protein and is precipitated in part (70 percent) from an aqueous solution by copper sulfate, leaving a soluble polysaccharide (19 percent) that is precipitated with alcohol. Both fractions contain protein, that part forming an insoluble copper complex had an equivalent weight of 500 and contained 15 percent of protein whereas that fraction which was not precipitated as a copper complex had an equivalent weight of 680 and contained 20 percent of protein. Hydrolysis of each fraction gives L-arabinose (5 percent), D-galactose (20 percent) and 4-O-methyl-D-glucuronic acid (15 percent).

The 4-O-methyl-D-glucuronic acid was identified by the reduction of its methyl ester methyl glycoside with lithium aluminum hydride to 4-O-methyl-D-glucose as in the case of mesquite gum (58).

In a later communication (160), the removal of protein from the carbohydrate component of myrrh gum has been described. The process involved treatment first with cadmium hydroxide (133) and then with chloroform (134,135) and 1-butanol and yielded a polysaccharide acid having $[\alpha]_D$ + 32° (water) and an equivalent weight of 460. Hydrolysis of the purified polysaccharide gum acid afforded D-galactose (8 moles), L-arabinose (2 moles), and 4-O-methyl-D-glucuronic acid (7 moles).

Hydrolysis of the polysaccharide acid component of gum myrrh with N sulfuric acid gave a mixture of 6-O-(4-O-methyl-β-D-glucosyluronic acid)-D-galactose and 4-O-(4-O-methyl-β-D-glucosyluronic acid)-D-galactose in the proportions of 1:6. It was pointed out that gum myrrh resembles mesquite gum (58,100) and lemon gum (76) since these also give rise to the same two aldobiouronic acids.

Cashew Gum

Cashew gum exudes from the bark of trees belonging to the family *Anacardiaceae*, particularly *A. occidentale*. The gum finds local application for many pharmaceutical purposes and as a substitute for gum arabic. However, the gum is only partially soluble in cold water for which reason it is not a competitor of gum arabic.

Solutions of the gum are dextrorotatory. The polysaccharide contains 5.2 percent pentosan and 33.6 percent galactose residues, and upon hydrolysis with mineral acid liberates a mixture of sugars in which L-arabinose and D-galactose have been identified (136).

Paper chromatographic analysis of the hydrolyzate of a different sample of cashew gum reveals the presence of glucose, arabinose and xylose (137).

Ketha Gum

Ketha gum, an exudate of *Feronia elephantum*, has properties similar to those of the *Acacia* gums and is recognized as a good substitute for them. Upon hydrolysis it gives L-arabinose, D-xylose, D-galactose, a trace of L-rhamnose, an unidentified sugar which gives a *N*-methylphenylhydrazone, m.p. 213–215°, and an aldobiouronic acid (139). The latter is isolated as the barium salt and forms a methyl derivative, when treated first with methyl sulfate and alkali and then with Purdie reagents, which has b.p., 1 mm., 140–160° (bath temp.), m.p. 97–97.5° and gives a crystalline amide m.p. 187–187.5° (140). Methanolysis followed by hydrolysis of the fully methylated aldobiouronic acid yields 2,4,6-tri-O-methyl-D-galactose and an unidentified O-methyl-uronic acid which is probably 2,3,4-tri-O-methyl-D-glucuronic acid. If this assumption is correct, then the aldobiouronic acid component of *Ketha* gum is 3-O-(D-glucopyranosyluronic acid)-D-galactopyranose, and represents a new type of aldobiouronic acid linkage.

Jeol Gum

Jeol gum is an exudate of the gingan tree, *Lannea grandis* (*Odina wodier*) which is found in the forests of Burma, Ceylon, India, Indo-China, and Siam. Aqueous solutions of this gum are similar in their properties to solutions of gum arabic (141). However, the ease with which the gum dissolves in water decreases with its age (144). The gum finds use as an adhesive, in paper sizing and in calico printing.

The gum undergoes hydrolysis with dilute acid to give some reducing sugars and a degraded gum jeolic acid, which has an equivalent weight of 1200 (142). The treatment of jeolic acid for 20 hours with 1.5*N*-sulfuric acid gives an aldobiouronic acid composed of D-galactose and D-galacturonic acid (143,145), together with L-arabinose, D-galactose, and perhaps other sugars (144).

The aldobiouronic acid upon complete methylation gives a methylated derivative which is shown by hydrolysis to be composed of 2,4,6-tri-O-methyl-D-galactose and a methyl ether of D-galacturonic acid (146). It is seen, therefore, that this aldobiouronic acid has a 1,3-linkage as in the case of the aldobiouronic acid from *Ketha* gum.

It is reported (147) that jeol gum upon electrodialysis undergoes hydrolysis with the production of reducing sugars, whereas under the same conditions, gum arabic gives only traces of reducing sugar. The degraded gum produced by electrodialysis appears to be the same as that formed by the mild hydrolysis with mineral acid.

Phormium Gum

The leaves of New Zealand flax (*Phormium tenax*) exude a gum which is the neutral salt of a polysaccharide acid composed of D-xylose and D-glucuronic acid (148). Purification of the gum is achieved by precipitation from an acidified aqueous solution with alcohol. It is nonreducing to Fehling solution, shows $[\alpha]_D$ $-63°$, and contains 45 percent of pentosan and 42.4 percent of uronic acid. The gum is reported to have an equivalent weight of 880 which is inconsistent with the high (42.4 percent uronic acid content.

On periodate oxidation the gum consumes 1.7 moles of periodate per xylose residue, but due to the high uronic acid content of the gum, little concerning the structure of the gum can be inferred from this result.

Phormium gum is found to be extremely resistant to methylation by methyl sulfate and alkali, a result that is not too unexpected in view of its high uronic acid content, and no improvement is effected by applying the thallium salt—methyl iodide method. Six successive methylations of the gum with methyl sulfate and alkali gave a product containing 28.6 percent methoxyl in only 6 percent yield.

Golden-Apple Gum

In the dry season, the Golden-apple (*Spondias cytheria*), a tree occurring in the West Indies, exudes a gum composed of D-galactose, L-arabinose, D-xylose, a mono-O-methyl glucuronic acid, and traces of L-rhamnose and L-fucose (43). The ash-free acidic polysaccharide, prepared by deionization with ion-exchange resins, undergoes autohydrolysis and after 24 hours at 90° there is formed a mixture of L-arabinose, traces of D-galactose, and L-rhamnose, together with a number of neutral pentose-containing oligosaccharides, traces of several acidic oligosaccharides and a degraded gum which still contains L-arabinose, D-xylose, D-galactose and mono-O-methyl glucuronic acid residues.

Two of the neutral oligosaccharides were formed in relatively large proportions. One was 3-O-β-L-arabopyranosyl-L-arabinose, (CLXLVI), which is also isolated from cherry and peach gums. The other was 3-O-α-D-xylopyranosyl-L-arabinose (CCLXIX), the structure of which was deduced from the following evidence. Hydrolysis gave L-arabinose and D-xylose, but after oxidation with bromine water to the corresponding disaccharide acid the only reducing sugar in its hydrolyzate was xylose thus showing that the reducing moiety in CCLXIX is arabinose. The hexa-O-methyl derivative (CCLXX) of the disaccharide afforded equimolecular amounts of 2,3,4-tri-O-methyl-D-xylose (CCXII) and 2,4-di-O-methyl-L-arabinose (XL) together with a trace of 2,5-di-O-methyl-L-arabinose (XLIII) which indicated that the L-arabinose residue can exist in the furanose form. In view of the ease with which this disaccharide is hydrolyzed from the gum, it is probable that the L-arabinose residue is present in the polysaccharide in the furanose form. From the cleavage fragments, CCXII and XL, it follows that the D-xylopyranose residue is linked through C_1 to C_3 of the L-arabinose moiety and the glycosidic linkage is believed to be of the α-D-type on the basis of the high positive rotation, $[\alpha]_D + 173°$, of the disaccharide.

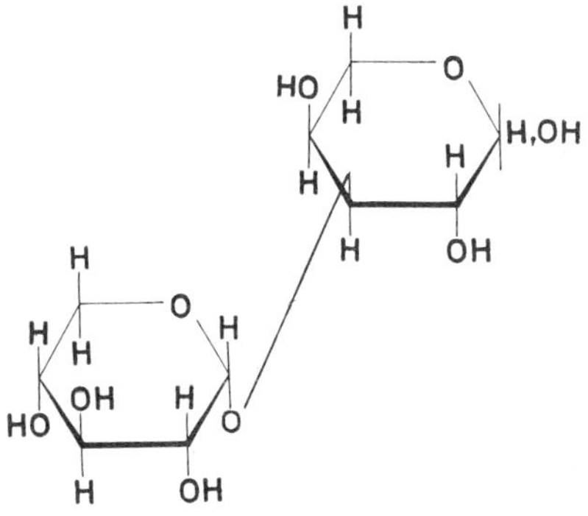

(CCLXIX)

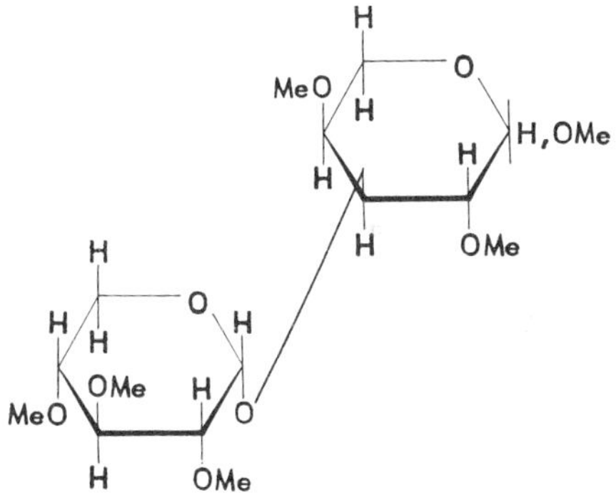

(CCLXX)

There were also obtained from the autohydrolyzate of the gum two other disaccharides, which gave only arabinose upon hydrolysis, and three oligosaccharides were isolated which appeared to be trisaccharides. One gave arabinose and 3-O-β-L-arabopyranosyl-L-arabinose (CLXLVI) upon partial hydrolysis. The other two are composed of one xylose and two arabinose units and appear to have arabinose units at the reducing ends. The structures of these oligosaccharides have not yet been elucidated.

Silk Oak Gum

The gum produced by the silk oak tree (*Grevillea robusta*) is the neutral salt, principally of calcium and of magnesium, of a complex polysaccharide acid (149). The gum is composed of L-arabinose, D-galactose, and D-glucuronic acid. Upon mild hydrolysis, all of the L-arabinose and some of the D-galactose is liberated leaving an acidic degraded polysaccharide. Prolonged hydrolysis of the gum yields an aldobiouronic acid which is composed of D-galactose and D-glucuronic acid.

Drum Stick Gum (Moringa Pterygosperma)

The drum stick plant or Shewga tree (*Moringa pterygosperma*), which is cultivated in all parts of India and Burma, exudes a gum which is initially white, but generally changes to a mahogany color on the surface. The gum swells in water and gives a highly viscous solution from which the gum is precipitated with alcohol to give a pink colored powder. The ash-free gum, equivalent weight approximately 1500, upon treatment with 10 percent sulfuric acid precipitates a fibrous material, which is said to be cellulose, amounting to 5.3 percent of the gum (163). In this respect, it resembles the mucilages from the seeds of flax, white mustard, cress and quince. Further hydrolysis of the gum produces L-arabinose, D-galactose and D-glucuronic acid in the ratio 10 : 7 : 2 together with traces of L-rhamnose.

Gums of Virgilia oroboides and V. divaricata

The gum exudate of *V. oroboides*, collected in S. Africa, was transformed into the corresponding polysaccharide acid (equiv. wt., 2100, $[\alpha]_D - 38°$ (water)) by precipitation of an aqueous solution of the gum with acidified ethanol (153). Hydrolysis of gum acid with 0.01N sulfuric acid at 95° for 6 hours effected graded hydrolysis to give L-arabinose, which was crystallized, together with rhamnose and galactose, identified chromatographically. There was also formed an arabinose disaccharide (CCLXXa) mp 142° (164) which showed $[\alpha]_D - 14°$ (water) and gave a crystalline osazone. Methylation of CCLXXa first with methyl sulfate and alkali and then with silver oxide and methyl iodide yielded the fully methylated disaccharide (CCLXXb). Hydrolysis of the latter with N hydrochloric acid gave 2,3,4-tri-O-methyl-L-arabinose, characterized after bromine oxidation as the phenylhydrazide of 2,3,4-tri-O-methyl-L-arabonic acid, and 2,3-di-O-methyl-L-arabinose, which was identified after bromine oxidation as the lactone and amide of 2,3-di-O-methyl-L-arabonic acid. The low rotation of the disaccharide indicated that the biose linkage was of the α-L-type. That it engaged C_5 of the reducing arabinose residue followed from the observation that the osazone of the disaccharide afforded the *bis*phenylhydrazone of mesoxaldehyde upon oxidation with periodate. The formation of the disaccharide by mild acid hydrolysis shows that the disaccharide is present in the gum as 5-O-α-L-arabopyranosyl-L-arabofuranose as in (CCLXXa). This disaccharide is the second L-arabopyran-

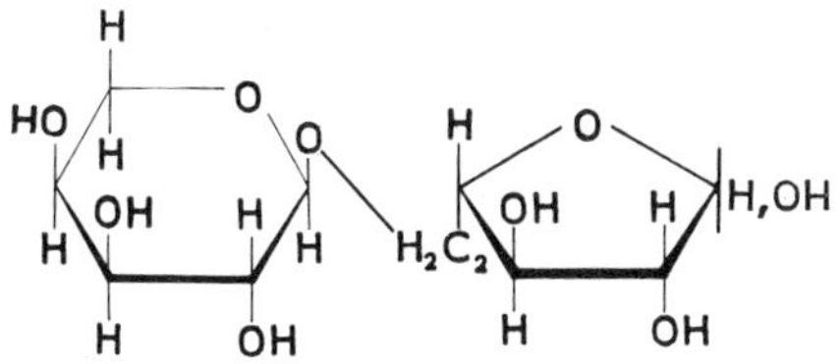

(CCLXXa)

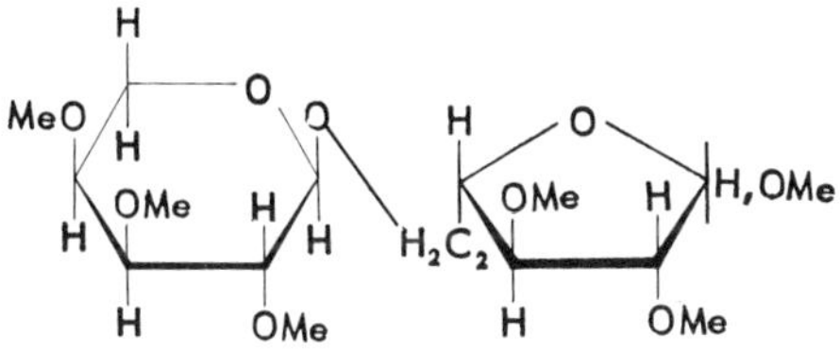

(CCLXXb)

osyl-L-arabinose isolated from natural sources, the β-L-1,3-linked isomer having been obtained from larch galactan (122), peach (42), cherry (142), golden-apple (43), lemon (27), and *Acacia karroo* (40) gums.

Controlled hydrolysis of the gum acid with 0.01 N sulfuric acid yields arabinose-containing disaccharides as well as a xylosyl-arabinose and galactose oligosaccharides. Continued hydrolysis of the residual degraded gum acid with 0.1 N sulfuric acid affords a series of galactose oligosaccharides and subsequent treatment with more concentrated acid (0.5 N) produces two acids that correspond to 6-O-(β-D-glucosyluronic acid)-D-galactose and 2-O-(β-D-glucosyluronic acid)-D-mannose, together with several other acidic components in relatively small amount.

Virgilia divaricata gum acid, prepared similarly (164), has $[\alpha]_D - 29°$ (water) and equiv. wt., 2600. Upon hydrolysis this gum acid furnishes products that are similar to those from *V. oroboides*.

REFERENCES

1. Neubauer, C., *J. prakt. Chem.*, 62, 193 (1854).
2. Adriaens, L., *Inst. roy. colonial Belge, Sect. sci. nat. méd., Mein.*, 8, 1 (1939); Chem. Abstracts, **37**, 4926 (1943).
3. Scheibler, C., *Ber.*, **6**, 612 (1873).
4. O'Sullivan, C., *J. Chem. Soc.*, **45**, 41 (1884).
5. Kiliani, H., *Ber.*, **13**, 2304 (1880).
6. Claesson, P., *Ber.*, **14**, 1270 (1881).
7. Butler, C. L., and Cretcher, L. H., *J. Am. Chem. Soc.*, **51**, 1519 (1929).
8. Hirst, E. L., and Perlin, A. S., *J. Chem. Soc.*, 2622 (1954).

9. Norman, A. G., *Biochem. J.*, 23, 524 (1929).
10. Smith, F., *J. Chem. Soc.*, 1035 (1940).
11. Smith, F., *J. Chem. Soc.*, 744 (1939).
12. Butler, C. L., and Cretcher, L. H., *J. Am. Chem. Soc.*, 52, 4509 (1930).
13. Heidelberger, M., and Adams, J., *J. Exptl. Med.*, 103, 189 (1956).
14. Joubert, F. J., *J. S. African Chem. Inst.*, 7, 107 (1954).
15. Lewis, Bertha A., and Smith, F., *J. Am. Chem. Soc.*, 79, 3929 (1957).
16. Carrington, H. C., Haworth, W. N., and Hirst, E. L., *J. Chem. Soc.*, 1653 (1934).
17. Jackson, J., and Smith, F., *J. Chem. Soc.*, 79 (1940).
18. Challinor, S. W., Haworth, W. N., and Hirst, E. L., *J. Chem. Soc.*, 258 (1931).
19. Hotchkiss, R. D., and Goebel, W. F., *J. Am. Chem. Soc.*, 58, 858 (1936).
20. Smith, F., *J. Chem. Soc.*, 1724 (1939).
21. Abdel-Akher, M., and Smith, F., *Nature*, 166, 1037 (1950).
22. Jackson, J., and Smith, F., *J. Chem. Soc.*, 74 (1940).
23. Dillon, T., O'Ceallachain, D. F., and O'Colla, P., *Proc. Roy. Irish Acad.*, 55B, 331 (1953).
24. Barry, V. C., *Nature*, 152, 537 (1943).
25. Barry, V. C., *J. Chem. Soc.*, 578 (1942).
26. Dillon, T., O'Ceallachain, D. F., and O'Colla, P., *Proc. Roy. Irish Acad.*, 57B, 31 (1954).
27. Andrews, P., and Jones, J. K. N., *J. Chem. Soc.*, 583 (1955).
28. Abdel-Akher, M., Hamilton, J. K., Montgomery, R., and Smith, F., *J. Am. Chem. Soc.*, 74, 4970 (1952).
29. Barry, V. C., and Mitchell, P. W. D., *J. Chem. Soc.*, 3610 (1953).
30. Smith, F., and Spriestersbach, D. R., *Abstracts 128th A. C. S. Meeting, Minneapolis* 1955, p. 15D.
31. Barker, G. R., and Smith, D. C. C., *Chemistry and Industry*, 1035 (1952).
32. Huffman, G. W., Lewis, Bertha A., and Smith, F., and Spriestersbach, D. R., *J. Am. Chem. Soc.*, 77, 4346 (1955).
33. Fean, Christina M., and Menzies, R. C., *J. Chem. Soc.*, 937 (1926).
34. Oakley, H. B., *Trans. Faraday Soc.*, 32, 1360 (1936); 33, 372 (1937).
35. Briggs, D. R., Spriestersbach, D. R., and Smith, F., unpublished.
36. Stephen, A. M., *J. Chem. Soc.*, 646 (1951).
37. Gutheil, N. C., and Formoso, M., *Anais assoc. brasil. quím.*, 10, 335 (1951); *Chem. Abstracts*, 47, 11782 (1953).
38. Harding, T. S., *Sugar*, 24, 656 (1922); *Chem. Abstracts*, 17, 1164 (1923).
39. Charlson, A. J., Nunn, J. R., and Stephen, A. M., *J. Chem. Soc.*, 269 (1955).
40. Charlson, A. J., Nunn, J. R., and Stephen, A. M., *J. Chem. Soc.*, 1428 (1955).
41. Jones, J. K. N., *J. Chem. Soc.*, 1672 (1953).
42. Andrews, P., Ball, D. H., and Jones, J. K. N., *J. Chem. Soc.*, 4090 (1953).
43. Andrews, P., and Jones, J. K. N., *J. Chem. Soc.*, 4134 (1954).
44. Hirst, E. L., and Jones, J. K. N., *J. Chem. Soc.*, 1174 (1938).
45. Hirst, E. L., and Jones, J. K. N., *J. Chem. Soc.*, 1482 (1939).
46. Hirst, E. L., and Jones, J. K. N., *J. Chem. Soc.*, 506 (1946).
47. Hirst, E. L., *J. Chem. Soc.*, 70 (1942).
48. Butler, C. L., and Cretcher, L. H., *J. Am. Chem. Soc.*, 53, 4160 (1931).
49. Jones, J. K. N., *J. Chem. Soc.*, 558 (1939).
50. Jones, J. K. N., *J. Chem. Soc.*, 3141 (1949).

51. Hirst, E. L., and Jones, J. K. N., *J. Chem. Soc.*, 496 (1938).
52. White, E. V., *J. Am. Chem. Soc.*, **75**, 257 (1953).
53. Jones, J. K. N., *J. Chem. Soc.*, 1055 (1947).
54. Hough, L., Jones, J. K. N., and Wadman, W. H., *J. Chem. Soc.*, 2511 (1949).
55. Hirst, E. L., and Jones, J. K. N., *J. Chem. Soc.*, 1064 (1947).
56. Hirst, E. L., and Jones, J. K. N., *J. Chem. Soc.*, 120 (1948).
57. Brown, F., Dunstan, Sonia, Halsall, T. G., Hirst, E. L., and Jones, J. K. N., *Nature*, **156**, 785 (1945).
58. Smith, F., *J. Chem. Soc.*, 2646 (1951).
59. Huebner, C. F., Lohmar, R., Dimler, R. J., Moore, S., and Link, K. P., *J. Biol. chem.*, **159**, 503 (1945).
60. Sprinson, D. B., and Chargaff, E., *J. Biol. Chem.*, **164**, 433 (1946).
61. Grangaard, D. H., Gladding, E. K., and Purves, C. B., *Paper Trade J.*, **115**, No. 7, 41 (1942).
62. Halsall, T. G., Hirst, E. L., and Jones, J. K. N., *J. Chem. Soc.*, 1427 (1947).
63. Lindstedt, G., *Arkiv. Kemi, Mineral.*, *Geol.*, **20A**, No. 13 (1945); *Chem. Abstracts*, **41**, 1209 (1947).
64. Brown, F., Hirst, E. L., and Jones, J. K. N., *J. Chem. Soc.*, 1757 (1949).
65. Jones, J. K. N., *J. Chem. Soc.*, 534 (1950).
66. Huerre, R., *J. pharm. chim.*, [6] **27**, 561 (1908); *Chem. Abstracts*, **2**, 2970 (1908).
67. Brown, F., Hirst, E. L., and Jones, J. K. N., *J. Chem. Soc.*, 1677 (1948).
68. Hirst, E. L., and Jones, J. K. N., *Research*, **4**, 411 (1951).
69. Tschirch, A., and Halbey, *Arch. Pharm.*, **236**, 487 (1898).
70. El-Khadein, H., and Megahed, M. M., *J. Chem. Soc.*, 3953 (1956).
71. Hirst, E. L., *J. Chem. Soc.*, 522 (1949).
72. Fawcett, H. S., *Univ. Calif. Agr. Expt. Sta. Bull.*, No. 395 (1925); *J. Agr. Research*, **24**, 191 (1923).
73. Savastano, L., *Gommosi degli agrumi in Patologia Arborea Applicata*, Lezione **20**, 127, Napoli, 1910.
74. Swingle, W. T., and Webber, H. J., U. S. Dept. Agr. Div. Veg. Phys. & Path., Bull. No. **8**, 1 (1896).
75. Butler, O., *Ann. Bot.*, **25**, 107 (1911).
76. Connell, J. J., Hainsworth, Ruth M., Hirst, E. L., and Jones, J. K. N., *J. Chem. Soc.*, 1696 (1950).
77. Parisi, E., *Ann. chim. applicata*, **25**, 230 (1935); *Chem. Abstracts*, **29**, 6790 (1935).
78. Dutton, G. G. S., *Can. J. Chem.*, **34**, 406 (1956).
79. Anderson, E., Russell, F. H., and Seigle, L. W., *J. Biol. Chem.*, **113**, 683 (1936).
80. Andrews, P., and Jones, J. K. N., *J. Chem. Soc.*, 1724 (1954).
81. Lythgoe, B., and Trippett, S., *J. Chem. Soc.*, 1983 (1950).
82. Gmelin-*Kraut*, **4**, 650 (1862).
83. O'Sullivan, C., *J. Chem. Soc.*, **79**, 1164 (1901).
84. Rowson, J. M., Quart. *J. Pharm. Pharmacol.*, **10**, 161 (1937).
85. Fellenberg, T. von., Mitt. Lebensm. *Hyg.*, **5**, 256 (1914); *Chem. Abstracts*, **9**, 624 (1915).
86. Widtsoe, J. A., and Tollens, B., *Ber.*, **33**, 132 (1900).
87. Hilger, A., and Dreyfus, W. E., *Ber.*, **33**, 1178)1900).

88. Selby, K., *J. Chem. Soc.*, 2504 (1953).
89. James, Sybil P., and Smith, F., *J. Chem. Soc.*, 749 (1945).
90. Luckett, S., and Smith, F., *J. Chem. Soc.*, 1506 (1940).
91. James, Sybil P., and Smith, F., *J. Chem. Soc.*, 746 (1945).
92. Schmidt, O. T., Mayer, W., and Distelmaier, A., *Ann.*, **555**, 26 (1943).
93. Procter, W., *Am. J. Pharm.*, **27**, 14, 223 (1855).
94. Morfit, C., *Am. J. sci.*, **69**, 263 (1855).
95. Anderson, E., Sands, Lila, Sturgis, N., *Am. J. Pharm.*, **97**, 589 (1925).
96. Diaz. H., *Rev. quim.*, **6**, No. 11, 8 (1931); *Chem. Abstracts*, **25**, 5588 (1931).
97. Anderson, E., and Sands, Lila, *J. Am. Chem. Soc.*, **48**, 3172 (1926).
98. White, E. V., *J. Am. Chem. Soc.*, **69**, 715 (1947).
99. Anderson, E., and Otis, Louise, *J. Am. Chem. Soc.*, **52**, 4461 (1930).
100. White, E. V., *J. Am. Chem. Soc.*, **70**, 367 (1948).
101. White, E. V., *J. Am. Chem. Soc.*, **68**, 272 (1946).
102. Cunneen, J. I., and Smith, F., *J. Chem. Soc.*, 1141 (1948).
103. Hudson, C. L., *J. Am. Chem. Soc.*, **73**, 4038 (1951).
104. Cunneen, J. I., and Smith, F., *J. Chem. Soc.*, 1146 (1948).
105. White, E. V., *J. Am. Chem. Soc.*, **69**, 2264 (1947).
106. White, E. V., *J. Am. Chem. Soc.*, **69**, 622 (1947).
107. Beauquesne, L., *Bull. soc. chim. biol.*, **28**, 895 (1946).
108. Hirst, E. L., Hough, L., and Jones, J. K. N., *J. Chem. Soc.*, 3145 (1949).
109. Hough, L., and Jones, J. K. N., *J. Chem. Soc.*, 199 (1950).
110. Hirst, E. L., and Dunstan, Sonia, *J. Chem. Soc.*, 2332 (1953).
111. Martell, C. L., *The Water-Soluble Gums*, Reinhold Publishing Corp., New York, 1947, p. 50.
112. Toothaker, C. R., *The Soluble Gums, No. 4, Handbooks to the Exhibits to the Commercial Museum of the Philadelphia Museums*, Philadelphia, Pa., 1921.
113. Tschirch, A., and Flück, H., *Pharm. Acta Helv.*, **3**, 151 (1928).
114. Beauquesne, L., *Compt. rend.*, **222**, 1056 (1946).
115. Mason, C. F., *Chem. Industries*, **53**, 858 (1943).
116. Robinson, H. H., *J. Chem. Soc.*, **89**, 1496 (1906).
117. Hanna, D., and Shaw, Jr., E. H., *Proc. S. Dakota, Acad. Sci.*, **21**, 78 (1941); *Chem. Abstracts*, **36**, 3386 (1942).
118. Hanna, D., McReynolds, L., and Shaw, Jr., E. H., Proc. S. Dakota Acad. Sci., **19**, 130 (1939); [Chem. Abstracts, **34**, 3123 (1940)].
119. Aspinall, G. O., Hirst, E. L., and Wickstrøm, A., *J. Chem. Soc.*, 1160 (1955).
120. McIlroy, R. J., *J. Chem. Soc.*, 1918 (1952).
121. Mukherjee, S., and Srivastava, H. C., *J. Am. Chem. Soc.*, **77**, 422 (1955).
122. Anderson, E., and Ledbetter, H. D., *J. Am. Pharm. Assoc.*, **40**, 623 (1951).
123. White, E. V., *J. Am. Chem. Soc.*, **75**, 4692 (1953).
124. White, E. V., *J. Am. Chem. Soc.*, **76**, 4906 (1954).
125. Dutton, G. G. S., Kilgour, G. L., Merler, E., and Snyder, J. L., private communication.
126. Sands, Lila, and Klaas, Rosalind, *J. Am. Chem. Soc.*, **51**, 3441 (1929).
127. Brown, F., Hirst, E. L., and Jones, J. K. N., *J. Chem. Soc.*, 1761 (1949).
128. Winterstein, E., *Ber.*, **31**, 1571 (1898).
129. Hamilton, J. K., Spriestersbach, D. R., and Smith, F., *J. Am. Chem. Soc.*, **79**, 443 (1957).

130. Malandkar, M. A., *J. Indian Inst. Sci.*, 8A, 240 (1925); *Chem. Abstracts*, 20, 837 (1926).
131. Jones, J. K. N., and Nunn, J. R., *J. Am. Chem. Soc.*, 77, 5745 (1955).
132. Hough, L., Jones, J. K. N., and Wadman, W. H., *J. Chem. Soc.*, 796 (1952).
133. Laidlaw, R. A., and Reid, S. G., *J. Sci. Food Agric.*, 3, 19,(1952).
134. Sevag, M. G., Lackman, D. B., and Smolens, J., *J. Biol. Chem.*, 124, 425 (1938).
135. Sevag, M. G., *Biochem. Z.*, 273, 419 (1934).
136. Tiomno, F. R., *Rev. quim. ind* (Rio de Janeiro), 15, No. 168, 23 (1946); 15, No. 172, 19 (1946); *Chem. Abstracts*, 41, 2921 (1947).
137. Smith, F., unpublished.
138. Gerard, A., Bull. sci. pharmacolog., 18, 148 (1912); Chem. Abstracts, 6, 307 (1912).
139. Mathur, G. P., and Mukherjee, S., *J. Sci. Ind. Research* (India) 11B, 544 (1952); *Chem. Abstracts*, 47, 10881 (1953).
140. Mathur, G. P., and Mukherjee, S., *J. Sci. Ind. Research.* (India), 13B, 452 (1954); *Chem. Abstracts*, 49, 12309 (1955).
141. Mukherjee, S. N., and Chaudhury, R. N. R., *J. Indian Chem. Soc.*, 30, 198 (1953).
142. Mukherjee, S. N., *J. Indian Chem. Soc.*, 30, 201 (1953).
143. Mukherjee, S. N., and Chakravarti, S. C., *J. Indian. Chem. Soc.*, 25, 113 (1948).
144. Mukherjee, S. N., and Banerjee, G., *J. Indian Chem. Soc.*, 25, 59, 63 (1948).
145. Mukherjee, S. N., Chakravarti, S. C., and Choudhury, R. N. R., *J. Indian Chem. Soc.* , 30, 851 (1953).
146. Mukherjee, S., and Dhar, P. K., private communication.
147. Mukherjee, S. N., *J. Indian Chem. Soc.*, 25, 333 (1948).
148. McIlroy, R. J., *J. Chem. Soc.*, 1372 (1951).
149. Anderson, E., and Harris, L., *J. Am. Pharm. Assoc.*, 41, 529 (1952).
150. Stephen, A. M., *J. Chem. Soc.*, 4487 (1946).
151. Hamilton, J. K., and Thompson, N. S., private communication.
152. Ball, D. H., and Jones, J. K. N., *J. Chem. Soc.*, 4871 (1957).
153. Stephen, A. M., *J. Chem. Soc.*, 1919 (1957).
154. Aspinall, G. O., Auret, Barbara J., and Hirst, E. L., *J. Chem. Soc.*, 221 (1958).
155. Aspinall, G. O., Hirst, E. L., and Matheson, N. K., *J. Chem. Soc.*, 989 (1956).
156. James, Sybil, and Smith, F., *J. Chem. Soc.*, 739 (1952).
157. Consden, R., and Stanier, Winifred M., *Nature*, 169, 783 (1952).
158. Foster, A. B., *J. Chem. Soc.*, 892 (1953).
159. Foster, A. B., and Stacey, M., *J. Chem. Soc.*, 1778 (1955).
160. Jones, J. K. N., and Nunn, J. R., *J. Chem. Soc.*, 3001 (1955).
161. Beaven, G. H., and Jones, J. K. N., *Chemistry and Industry*, 363 (1939).
162. Smith, F., *Chemistry and Industry*, 363 (1939).
163. Ingle, T. R., and Bhide, B. V., *J. Indian Chem. Soc.*, 31, 939 (1954).
164. Stephen, A. M., private communication.

CHAPTER 12

THE STRUCTURE OF GUMS AND MUCILAGES FROM SEEDS, ROOTS AND LEAVES

Galactomannans

Polysaccharides composed of D-mannose and D-galactose are most commonly found in the seeds of the *Leguminosae*, particularly in the endosperm. They are also found in the seeds of African oil palm, (*Elaeis guinensis*), date palm (*Phoenix dactylifera*) (1), *Cocus nucifera*, *Coffea arabia* and in the seeds of clovers, for example, *Trifolium pratense*, *Lotus corniculatus*, *Melilotus* species, and alfalfa (*Medicago sativa*), sometimes called lucerne and purple medic.

In a study of the endosperm of leguminous seeds Anderson (2) examined 163 species and by visual inspection found that about three fourths of these contained mucilage-yielding endosperms in amounts up to 60 per cent of the seed. The galactomannan was isolated from the endosperm of several species by aqueous extraction and its composition determined by hydrolysis with 2 per cent sulfuric acid followed by analysis of the D-mannose as its phenylhydrazone and D-galactose by a fermentation technique (8) or as a phenylhydrazone derivative (3). These methods of quantitative analysis, although now superseded by chromatographic procedures, gave results which are summarized in Table 29 (see page 105) from which it will be seen that the relative amounts of D-mannose and D-galactose vary from 81 per cent mannose and 16 per cent galactose in *Sophora japonica* to 59 per cent mannose and 38 per cent galactose in guar. The physical properties of the different polysaccharides are similar and are characterized by being soluble in water to form thick highly viscous solutions which are usually gelled by the addition of such inorganic salts as borax and, like the mannans, they form complexes with Fehling solution. It is interesting, therefore, to compare the chemical structures of these various galactomannans and to search for common structural features which may account for the similarity in physical properties. Whereas the galactomannans possess similarities in structure it is becoming apparent that they must also have differences in structure because they display different physical properties, especially in their behavior with water, in electrophoretic studies and in molecular weight. These differences are put to good use in industry where it is well known that the two gums, guar and locust bean, cannot be used interchangeably.

Guar (*Cyamopsis Tetragonolobus*)

The polysaccharide in guar flour, as the crude, powdered gum is sometimes called, contains 84 per cent of D-mannose and 16 per cent D-galactose (4,5). The crude guar gum which may contain 1 to 5 per cent protein is a greyish-white powder 90 per cent of which dissolves in water (6). The insoluble residue, containing D-mannose and D-galactose, together with protein, dissolves slowly when kept in prolonged contact with water. An aqueous solution of the gum gives an insoluble complex with Fehling solution, but does not reduce it even on prolonged boiling. The purified gum, $[\alpha]_D^{23} + 60°$ in 0.6N sodium hydroxide, is essentially homogeneous (6,7) and contains D-mannose and D-galactose in the ratio of 2 : 1 (2,6–10).

Partial hydrolysis of guar gum by heating a solution in 0.5N hydrochloric acid for 3.5 hours affords 4-O-β-D-mannopyranosyl-β-D-mannose (CCLXXI) (11), 6-O-α-D-galactopyranosyl-β-D-mannose (CCLXXII) (11), and 4-O-(6-O-α-D-galactopyranosyl-β-D-mannopyranosyl)-β-D-mannose (CCLXXIII) (12), all of which were obtained crystalline.

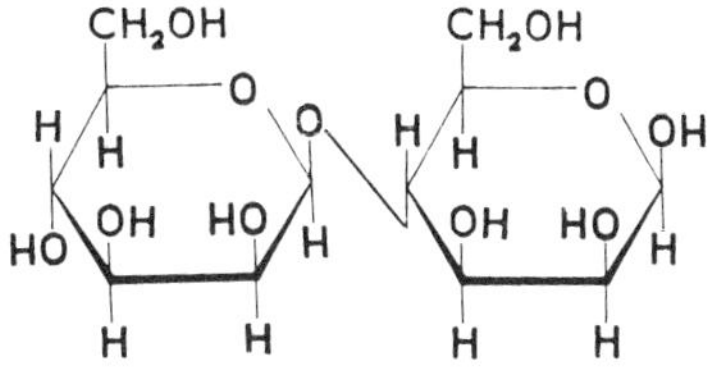

(CCLXXI) 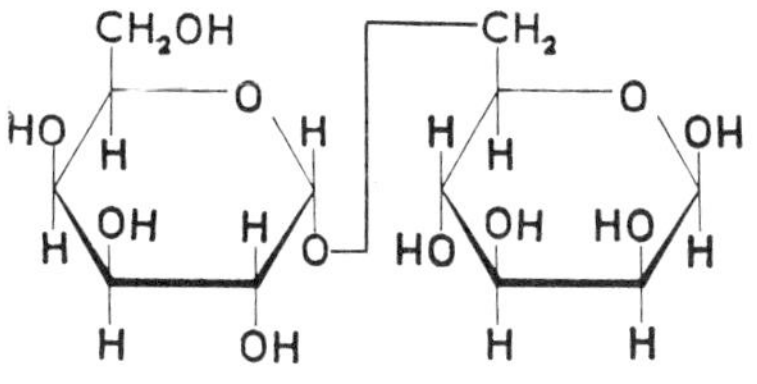   (CCLXXII)

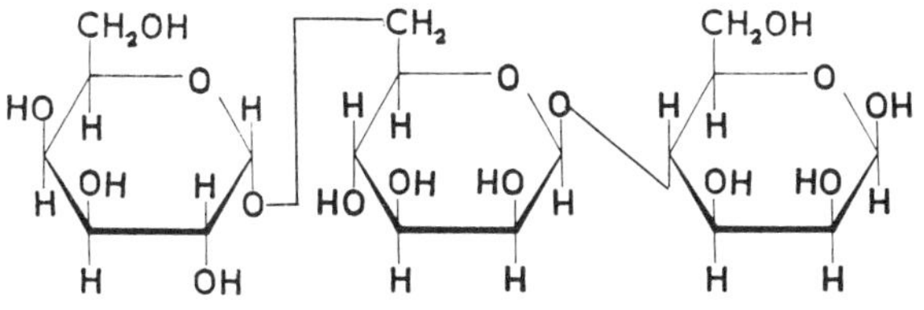

(CCLXXIII)

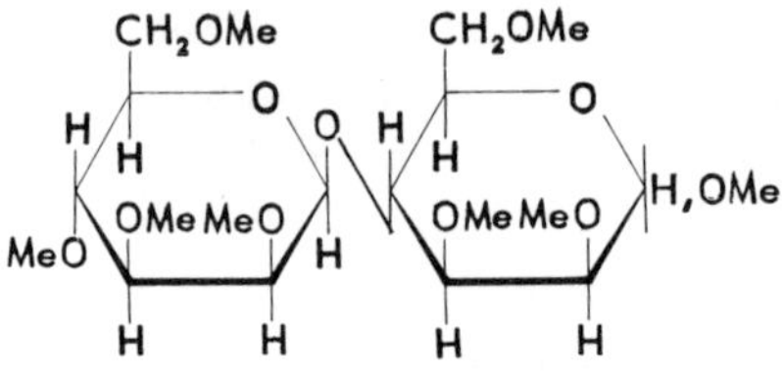

(CCLXXIV)

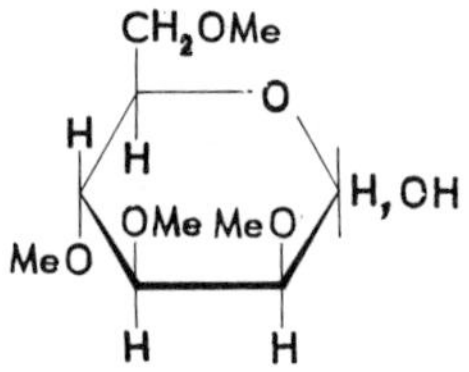

(CCLXXV)

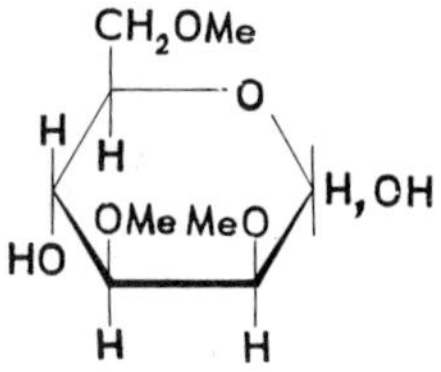

(CCLXXVI)

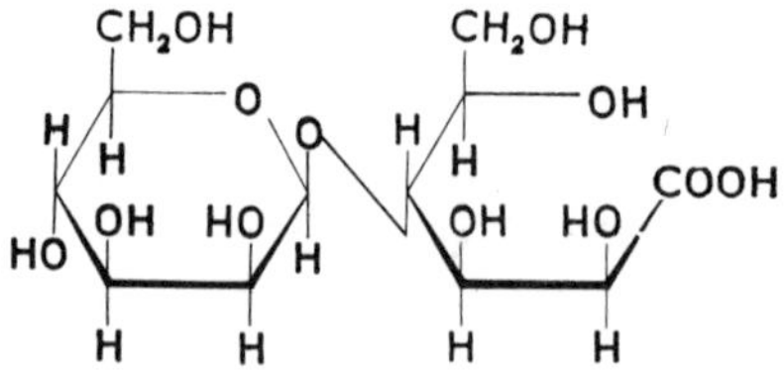

(CCLXXVII)

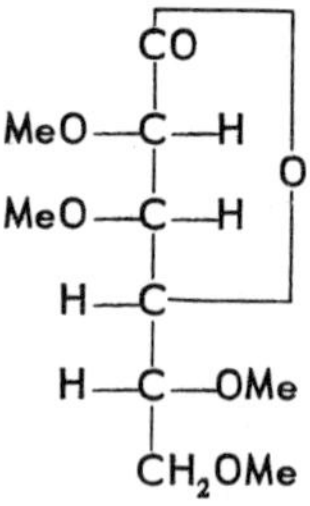

(CCLXXVIII)

The structure of CCLXXI was proved (13) by its methylation with methyl sulfate to the octamethyl ether (CCLXXIV), which upon hydrolysis gave 2,3,4,6-tetra-O-methyl-D-mannose (CCLXXV) and 2,3,6-tri-O-methyl-D-mannose (CCLXXVI). Also, oxidation of CCLXXI with bromine to the corresponding acid (CCLXXVII), followed by methylation and hydrolysis as before, yielded 2,3,4,6-tetra-O-methyl-D-mannose (CCLXXV), and 2,3,5,6-tetra-O-methyl-D-mannono-γ-lactone (CCLXXVIII). The two mannose units in the disaccharide (CCLXXI) are therefore linked through C_1 and C_4 as shown in formula CCLXXI. The presence of a β-D-glycosidic linkage is suggested by the fact that the sugar is not hydrolyzed by emulsin which is a known source of α-D-mannosidase (14). Mutarotation in a positive direction when the sugar is dissolved in water also indicates that it crystallizes in the β-D-form.

The second disaccharide (CCLXXII) gave a phenylosazone identical with that from melibiose (CCLXXIX), thus proving that the D-galactose moiety is linked through C_1 to C_6 of the D-mannose unit (11).

The structure (CCLXXIII) assigned to the trisaccharide is based upon periodate oxidation studies and partial hydrolysis. Upon oxidation with periodate one mole of the trisaccharide consumed 7.08 moles of periodate with the production of 4.04 moles of formic acid and 0.98 mole of formaldehyde. Partial hydrolysis of one mole of the trisaccharide (CCLXXIII) by heating a solution in 0.5N-hydrochloric acid at 80° for 2 hours resulted in the formation of D-galactose (0.137 mole), D-mannose (1.091 moles), mannobiose (CCLXXI) (0.234 moles), galactosylmannose (CCLXXII) (0.163 mole), and unhydrolyzed trisaccharide (CCLXXIII) (0.355 mole). The identification of 4-O-β-D-mannopyranosyl-β-D-mannose (CCLXXI), establishes that the two D-mannose units are joined by a β-1 → 4 linkage. The α-D-galactose residue is linked to one of these mannose units through C_6 as evidenced by the isolation of 6-O-α-D-galactopyranosyl-β-D-mannopyranose CCLXXII, and it is suggested that the periodate oxidation studies indicate that the nonreducing D-mannose unit is linked to D-galactose.

Following an enzymic degradation procedure employed many years ago in the study of the galactomannan of carob bean gum (15,16), guar gum is likewise found to undergo hydrolysis when subjected to the action of an enzyme present in the germinating guar seed (17). The crude enzyme is obtained by extracting the germinating guar seeds with water in a Waring Blender and fractionating the extract with ammonium sulfate. Most of the enzyme activity is found in the 20 to 30 per cent ammonium sulfate fraction. When an aqueous solution of the guar gum is treated with the enzyme preparation, hydrolysis proceeds to about 65 per cent of completion (17). Monosaccharides constitute about 65 per cent of the hydrolyzate and most of the D-galactose is found as the free sugar. However, there are also obtained 4-O-β-D-mannopyranosyl-β-D-mannose

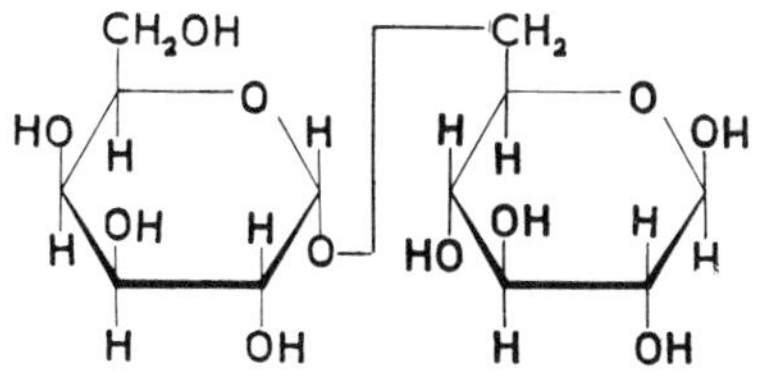

(CCLXXIX)

(CCLXXI) (13), 6-*O*-α-D-galactopyranosyl-β-D-mannopyranose (CCLXXII) (11,18), and 4-*O*-(4-*O*-β-D-mannopyranosyl-β-D-mannosyl-)-β-D-mannose (CCLXXX). The disaccharides, CCLXXI and CCLXXII, are also produced by acid hydrolysis of guar gum but the D-mannose trisaccharide has only been reported in the enzymic hydrolyzates.

The trisaccharide (CCLXXX) upon partial hydrolysis with 0.5*N*-hydrochloric acid affords D-mannose and 4-*O*-β-D-mannopyranosyl-β-D-mannose (CCLXXI). Reduction of the trisaccharide with hydrogen and platinum catalyst affords the corresponding alditol (CCLXXXI), the dodecaacetate of which has a molecular weight of 1010 (calcd. 1070). These data support the structure (CCLXXX), assigned to the trisaccharide.

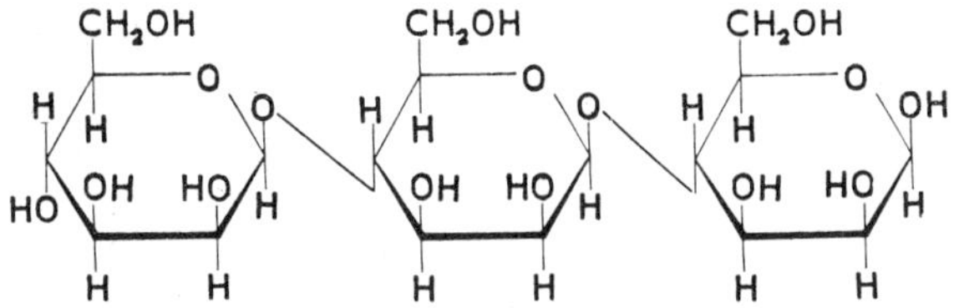

(CCLXXX)

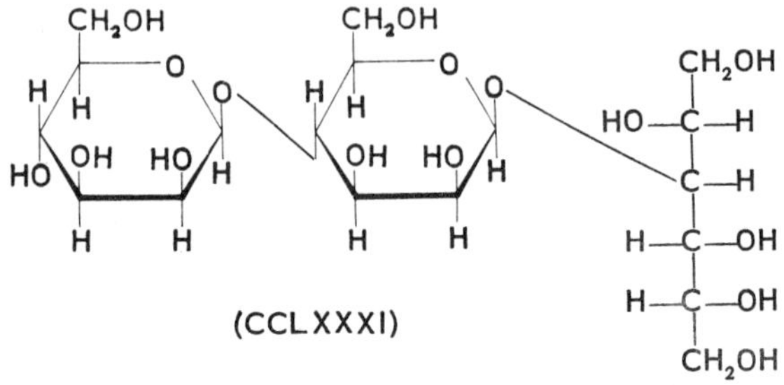

(CCLXXXI)

The data obtained from the partial hydrolysis of guar gum indicate the probable occurrence of the residue (CCLXXXII) in the gum molecule.

Further information concerning the structure is forthcoming from methylation studies (6,19,20). The guar gum is methylated with methyl sulfate and alkali and fractional precipitation of the methylated gum indicates the essential homogeneity of the polysaccharide. When the methylated gum is subjected to methanolysis and the cleavage products separated by fractional distillation, it is found that these cleavage fragments consist of approximately equimolecular amounts of 2,3,4,6-tetra-*O*-methyl-D-galactose (XXXIX), 2,3,6-tri-*O*-methyl-D-mannopyranose (CCLXXVI), and 2,3-di-*O*-methyl-D-mannopyranose (CCLXXXIII). Four average repeating units for guar can be suggested from the methylation

data (6). All these formulae derive support from the evidence of periodate oxidation in which four moles of periodate ar˙ consumed per hexose
unit with the concomitant formation of one mole of formic acid (6). The
periodate oxidation results of other workers (20,21) are at variance with
any structure for guar gum based on methylation or partial hydrolysis
data.

Further limitations in the possible structures for guar gum are found
in a study of the tosyl derivative of the gum (22), which indicates that

(XXXIX)   (CCLXXXIII)

the branching in the molecule takes place through a 1 → 6-linkage.
Also, stress-strain measurements on films of guar gum acetate (23)
reveal that the molecules are highly anisodimensional and X-ray investigations (24) on films of crude gum show that the branches must be
very short in length.

The accumulation of evidence, therefore, indicates that the general
structure for guar gum is best represented by structure CCLXXXII. However, it was shown chromatographically that the cleavage fragments of
the methylated gum contain small amounts of two unknown methylated
sugars (6) and consequently it is possible that a small percentage of
additional branching is present in the molecule.

(CCLXXXII)

Carob or Locust Bean (*Ceratonia Siliqua L.*) Gum

The carob gum of commerce is usually a white powder which, in addition to the galactomannan (88 per cent), contains pentosan (3 to 4 per cent), protein (5 to 6 per cent), cellular tissue (1 to 4 per cent) and ash (1 per cent) (25,26). The material dissolves in water to give a neutral mucilaginous solution containing some insoluble particles (27). The purified gum is obtained either by dialysis of an acidified aqueous solution against distilled water followed by precipitation of the gum with alcohol (27), or by precipitation of an alkaline (sodium hydroxide) solution of the gum by pouring the filtered solution into alcohol acidified with hydrochloric acid (28). The gum forms an insoluble copper complex when treated with Fehling solution and is sensitive to borates (29,30).

The two sugars, D-galactose and D-mannose, found as the building units of carob gum long ago (4,5,31,32), are variously reported to be present in the ratio of 27:73 (33), 20:80 (8,27), 18:82 (34) and 14:86 (28). These differences may result from the decomposition of the sugars during hydrolysis which will vary with the concentration of acid and time of heating (28); they may also be due to different analytical procedures or they may reflect varietal or geographical differences in gum origin.

Compared to ivory nut mannan, carob gum is relatively easy to hydrolyze with mineral acid and is recommended as a source of D-mannose (35). Graded hydrolysis of the gum with $0.2N$ sulfuric acid affords D-galactose and a mixture of oligosaccharides of different molecular size (27). Contrary to the behavior of many of the plant gum exudates upon treatment with acid, there is no arrest point in the hydrolysis of carob gum, the hexose residues being randomly cleaved. The gum is also slowly and incompletely hydrolyzed by the commercial mixture of enzymes known as "Pectinol 10 M" (28). The enzymic hydrolyzate contains D-mannose but no D-galactose was detected.

Oxidation of carob gum with potassium periodate results in the liberation of formic acid, indicating one terminal or $1 \longrightarrow 6$ linked hexose residue for every six hexose units.

More detailed information about the structure of the polysaccharide is obtained from an examination of its methyl derivative. Methylation of the gum with methyl sulfate and alkali can be effected directly (27,28) or through its acetate (27). The resulting methylated gum, $[\alpha]_D^{18} -4°$ in acetone (27), $[\alpha]_D -11°$ in water (28), is essentially homogeneous and when subjected to methanolysis it yields a mixture consisting of the methyl glycosides of 2,3,4,6-tetra-O-methyl-D-galactose, (XXXIX), 2,3,6-tri-O-methyl-D-mannose (CCLXXVI), and 2,3-di-O-methyl-D-mannose (CCLXXXIII). The molecular proportions of these cleavage fragments are reported to be 1:2–3:1 (27) and 1:4:1 (28).

The relative stability of the polysaccharide to treatment with dilute mineral acids indicates that the sugars are in the pyranose form. The 2,3,4,6-tetra-O-methyl-D-galactose arises from D-galactose units which constitute the terminal units of the side chains present in what must be a highly branched structure. The 2,3-di-O-methyl-D-mannose will be formed from those D-mannose units of the main mannose chain to which are attached the side chains. On the basis of the methylation data, the simplest structure for the average repeating unit of carob gum is shown in formula CCLXXXIV. The glycosidic bonds are believed to be mainly of the β-D-variety in view of the low specific rotation of the polysaccharide, $[\alpha]_D^{20}$ +9° in N sodium hydroxide, and its methylated derivative. It will be seen that the structures proposed for carob and guar gum differ only in the number of the D-galactose side chains.

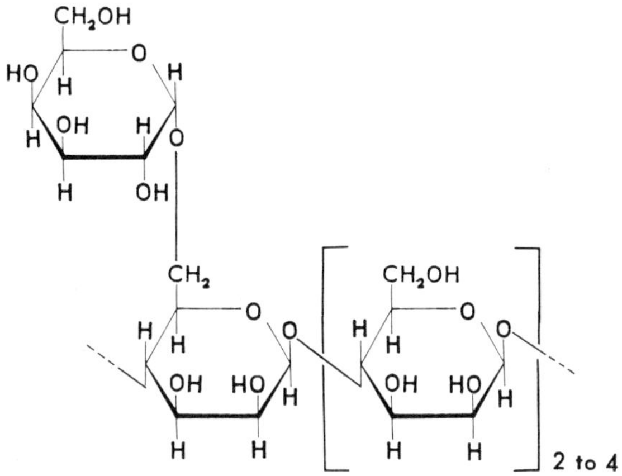

(CCLXXXIV)

Kentucky Coffee Bean (*Gymnocladus Dioica.*)

The Kentucky coffee bean seed contains a galactomannan gum which forms the hard vitreous inner layer of the seed coat (2,8,36). The composition of the gum is reported to be 26 per cent D-galactose and 71 per cent D-mannose in one case (2) and 20 per cent D-galactose and 80 per cent D-mannose in another (36). The differences may be due to the various analytical techniques employed rather than to actual differences in the samples of the gums.

The gum forms highly viscous solutions in water and alkali which give a precipitate with Fehling solution but do not reduce it (36). Solutions of the galactomannan are gelled by small amounts of borax.

Methylation of the polysaccharide with methyl sulfate and alkali yields the corresponding methyl derivative which appears from fractional precipitation data to be essentially homogeneous (36). Upon hydrolysis, the methylated galactomannan gives rise to a mixture of methyl sugars which after separation by column and paper chromatography is found to contain 2,3,4,6-tetra-O-methyl-D-galactose (XXXIX, 1 mole), 2,3,6-tri-O-methyl-D-mannose (CCLXXVI, 3 moles), 2,3-di-O-methyl-D-mannose (CCLXXXIII, 1 mole), and 2,3,4,6-tetra-O-methyl-D-mannose (CCLXXV, 0.17 mole).

The presence of the 2,3,4,6-tetra-O-methyl-derivatives of D-galactose and D-mannose shows that these must have arisen from D-galactose and D-mannose units which are endgroups in the side chains of the molecule. The ratio of D-galactose to D-mannose endgroups is 6 : 1. For each side chain galactose unit there are four mannose residues, one of which affords the 2,3-di-O-methyl-D-mannose cleavage fragment of the methylated gum and hence must represent the branching point in the molecule, being linked through C_1, C_4 and C_6; the other three mannose units occupy positions in a chain of residues joined by $1 \longrightarrow 4$ glycosidic bonds.

A probable structure for Kentucky coffee bean gum is shown in formula CCLXXXV, support for which is forthcoming from the fact that the gum consumes 6 moles of periodate for every 5 sugar residues with the liberation of one mole of formic acid, the latter arising from the terminal non-reducing galactose and mannose residues. Moreover, the periodate-oxidized gum contains no residues of D-mannose or D-galactose which are resistant to cleavage by the periodate.

Inasmuch as the gum shows a relatively low rotation $[\alpha]_D + 29°$ in water, as does its acetate, $[\alpha]_D +20°$ in acetone, and methyl ether $[\alpha]_D \pm 0°$ in acetone, it is believed that most of the glycosidic bonds joining

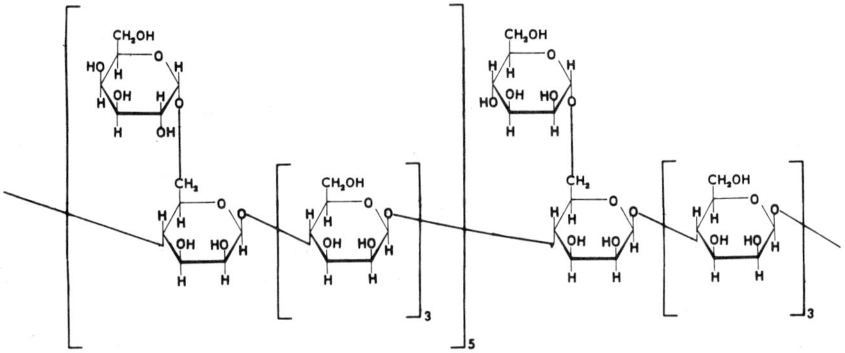

(CCLXXXV)

the mannose units of the polysaccharide are of the β-D-type. The terminal units of D-galactose may be joined by α-D-glycosidic bonds, as is the case with guar (11) and carob gum (34).

It is seen that the structures for carob gum and Kentucky coffee bean gum are very similar, differing only in the presence of terminal D-mannose units in certain of the sidechains of the Kentucky coffee bean gum. It is even possible that these may be detected in carob gum if sought by the more precise chromatographic procedures employed in the examination of Kentucky coffee bean gum.

Fenugreek (*Trigonella Foenum-Graecum*)

The fenugreek (*Trigonella foenum-graecum*) is a leguminous plant, very similar to clover in appearance, which is grown in North Africa, Asia Minor, India and Pakistan. The small brown seeds, which are found in long pods, are used for various medicinal purposes.

Extraction of the milled seed with cold water affords a thick mucilaginous solution from which a galactomannan (2,37) can be isolated in 14 to 15 per cent yield either by precipitation with alcohol or as an insoluble copper complex.   The polysaccharide, reported to contain D-galactose and D-mannose in the ratios of 1 : 1 (38) and 1 : 1.2 (37), is incompletely soluble in water and shows $[\alpha]_D$ + 70 ± 10° in 2N sodium hydroxide.

The polysaccharide undergoes smooth methylation with methyl sulfate and alkali in the usual way and the methyl derivative, $[\alpha]_D$ + 50° in chloroform, gives upon hydrolysis a mixture of methyl sugars which are separated chromatographically (37).   The cleavage fragments are found to be 2,3,4,6-tetra-O-methyl-D-galactose (XXXIX, 5 parts), 2,3,6-tri-O-methyl-D-mannose (CCLXXVI, 1 part), and 2,3-di-O-methyl-D-mannose (CCLXXXIII, 5 parts), together with traces of a mono-O-methyl hexose.

The structure of fenugreek galactomannan is therefore based upon a chain of six 1 → 4 linked D-mannopyranose units and to C_6 of five of these are attached D-galactopyranose residues. Clearly, the galactomannan is very highly branched, but the basic linkages are the same as those in the guar, carob and Kentucky coffee bean gums. Formula CCLXXXVI, where $y = 1$ and $(x + z) = 3$, is therefore proposed for the fenugreek galactomannan, the 1 → 4 and 1 → 6 linkages being of the β-D- and α-D-type, respectively. The two types of glycosidic linkages are present in formula CCLXXXVI to about the same extent which might be expected from the optical rotation of the polysaccharide ($[\alpha]_D$ + 70° in water) and its methylated derivative ($[\alpha]_D$ + 50° in chloroform).

Support for the structure shown in formula CCLXXXVI is found in the fact that upon periodate oxidation 5 moles of formic acid are formed for every 11 hexose residues with the consumption of 16.4 moles of periodate. Also, the periodate-oxidized gum contains no intact D-galactose or D-mannose units. However, as suggested in the case of carob gum, the indications of mono-O-methyl hexose residues during the chromatographic analysis of the cleavage fragments of the methylated galactomannan may signify additional branching in the molecule.

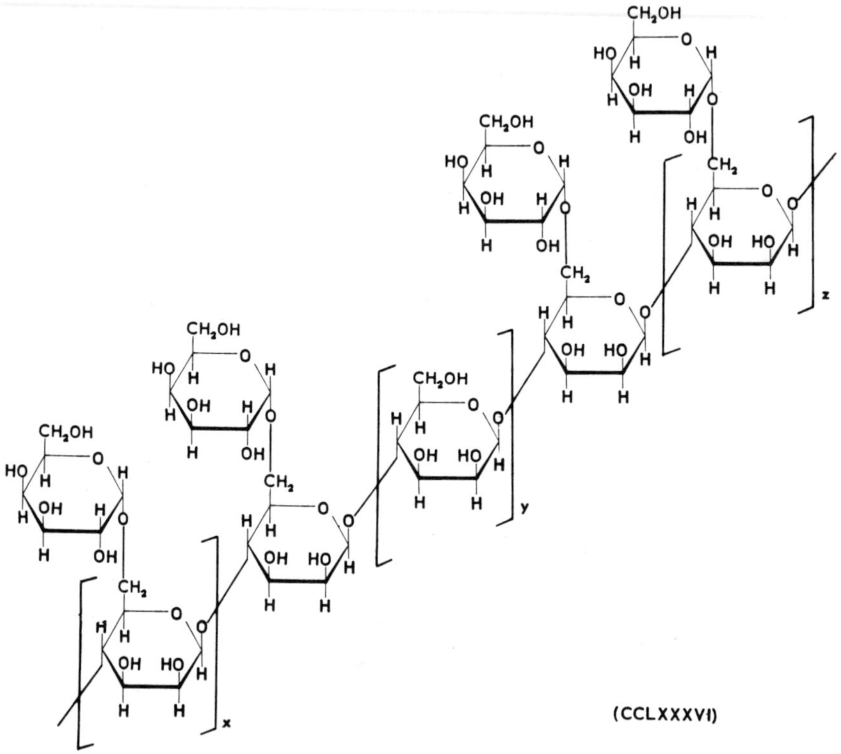

(CCLXXXVI)

Clover (*Trifolium Pratense*)

A galactomannan, isolated in 3.5 per cent yield from clover seeds by extraction with cold water and purification *via* the copper complex, shows $[\alpha]_D$ +78 ± 11 ° in water and contains D-galactose and D-mannose in the ratio of 7 : 9 (39). It is only 63 per cent soluble in water and incompletely soluble in 2N sodium hydroxide.

Methylation of the polysaccharide with methyl sulfate and alkali afforded a methyl derivative, $[\alpha]_D$ + 76 °in chloroform, which was hydrolyzed to give 2,3,4,6-tetra-O-methyl-D-galactose (XXXIX, 7 moles), 2,3,6-tri-O-methyl-D-mannose (CCLXXVI, 2 moles), and 2,3-di-O-methyl-D-mannose (CCLXXXIII, 7 moles). These data suggest that the structure of the clover galactomannan is similar to that from Fenugreek seed and can be represented by formula CCLXXXVI, where $y = 2$ and $(x + z) = 5$, support for which is found in the periodate oxidation of the polysaccharide where 7 moles of formic acid are produced for every 16 hexose residues.   The completely periodate-oxidized polysaccharide is found to contain no intact D-galactose or D-mannose residues.

Lucerne (*Medicago Sativa*)

The seeds of lucerne (*Medicago sativa*) when milled and extracted with hot potassium hydroxide yield a galactomannan showing $[\alpha]_D + 89°$ in water and containing D-galactose and D-mannose in the ratio 2:1 (44). By extraction with hot water the seeds afford a galactomannan, $[\alpha]_D + 118 \pm 11°$ in water, containing D-galactose and D-mannose in the proportions 4:5 (39), respectively. (Further extraction of the seeds with alkali gives another 1 per cent of material which contains some xylan.) Both products are obtained in about 6 per cent yield and when purified through their insoluble copper complexes they appeared to be differently constituted.

The polysaccharide, which is extracted from the lucerne seeds (*var. Provence*) with hot water, is only 62 per cent soluble in water after an aqueous solution of it had been concentrated to dryness; the desiccated product is also incompletely soluble in $2N$ sodium hydroxide.

The methylated galactomannan, prepared like that from the clover galactomannan, affords upon methanolysis and hydrolysis, 2,3,4,6-tetra-*O*-methyl-D-galactose (XXXIX, 4 moles), 2,3,6-tri-*O*-methyl-D-mannose (CCLXXVI, 1 mole), and 2,3-di-*O*-methyl-D-mannose (CCLXXXIII, 4 moles).   The oxidation of this galactomannan with periodate gives 4 moles of formic acid for every 9 hexose residues. It is clear that it conforms to the general type of structure which has been formulated for the fenugreek   and   clover   polysaccharides   and   consequently   formula CCLXXXVI, where $y = 1$ and $(x + z) = 2$, may be assigned to this lucerne galactomannan fraction.

The galactomannan extracted from lucerne seeds with 10 per cent potassium hydroxide (44) following a procedure given by Schultz and May (40), who first described a galactomannan from this source, had quite a different structure from that extracted with water.   This polysaccharide, $[\alpha]_D + 89°$ in water, did not reduce Fehling solution and gave aqueous solutions of comparitively high viscosity. The fully methylated galactomannan was obtained by reaction with methyl sulfate and alkali followed by further treatment of the thallium hydroxide complex of the partially methylated derivative with methyl iodide.   The methylated polysaccharide was essentially homogeneous and was resistant to hydrolysis by methanolic hydrogen chloride. Hydrolysis was effected by the use of a mixture of hydrochloric and acetic acids (41). The cleavage fragments were not completely identified but included 2,3,4,6-tetra-O-methyl-D-galactose (XXXIX), 2,4,6-tri-O-methyl-D-galactose (XLVI), and 3,4-di-O-methyl-D-mannose (CCLXXXVII). It was also shown that the molecular ratios of 2,3,4,6-tetra-O-methyl-D-galactose, tri-O-methyl hexose and di-O-methyl hexose were 1:1:1. At least one third of the tri-O-methyl hexose was known to be 2,4,6-tri-O-methyl-D-galactose and at least one-third of the di-O-methyl hexose was 3,4-di-O-methyl-D-mannose.

Although the incomplete methylation data do not permit structural formulae to be proposed it is seen that all the end groups in the galactomannan are D-galactopyranose residues while the remainder of the molecule contains D-galactose residues linked through C_1 and C_3 and D-mannose residues linked through C_1, C_2 and C_6. This galactomannan differs, therefore, from that which is extracted with hot water and resembles more closely the plant gum exudates in having $1 \rightarrow 3$ linked galactose units and $1 \rightarrow 6$ and $1 \rightarrow 2$ linked D-mannose residues.

The constitutional studies of the galactomannans have shown that all of them possess a $1 \rightarrow 4$ linked D-mannopyranose backbone and to C_6 of certain of these mannose units are attached side chains terminated by D-galactopyranose residues. In all cases the mannose residues have free hydroxyl groups at C_2 and C_3 accounting, therefore, for the gelling properties of these mucilages with borax and their ability to form insoluble copper complexes.

In the case of the guar galactomannan it is known that the D-mannose residues are joined by β-D-1 $\rightarrow$ 4 linkages and that the D-galactose residues are linked through α-D-glycosidic bonds. In general the optical

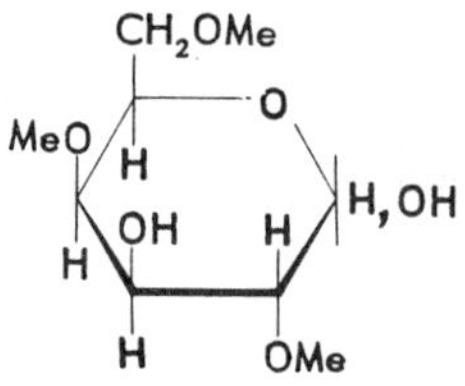

(XLVI) 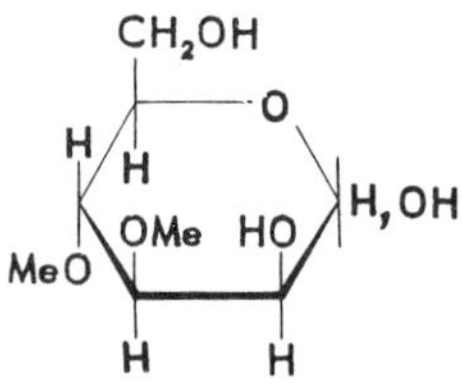   (CCLXXXVII)

rotations of the other free polysaccharides and their methylated derivatives become increasingly positive as the ratio of D-galactose to D-mannose nears unity (see Table 52). (This does not hold for the galactomannan extracted with hot alkali (44) which has quite a different structure from the other galactomannans in Table 52). It appears, therefore, that the proportion of α-D-glycosidic linkages is increasing, which would be the case if in all of these galactomannans the D-galactose residues were linked in this way. Confirmation of this postulation must await partial hydrolysis of these mucilages and identification of the oligosaccharides so formed.

TABLE 52. OPTICAL ROTATIONS OF THE GALACTOMANNANS AND THEIR METHYL DERIVATIVES

Galactomannan	Ratio of D-galactose to D-Mannose	Approximate specific rotation $([\alpha]_D)^a$	
		Polysaccharide	Methylated Derivative
Carob	1 : 4 to 1 : 5	+ 9 (N NaOH)	− 4 (A)
Kentucky coffee	1 : 4	+ 29 (W)	± 0 (A)
Guar	1 : 2	+ 60 (0.6N NaOH)	+ 42 (C)
Soybean	1 : 1.5	+ 65 (W)	+ 58 (C)
Fenugreek	1 : 1.2	+ 70 (W)	+ 50 (C)
Clover	1 : 1.3	+ 78 (W)	+ 76 (C)
Lucerne (Var. *Provence*)	1 : 1.3	+ 118 (W)	+ 66 (C)

[a]A = acetone, C = chloroform, and W = water.

The Galactomannan of Soy Bean Hulls

When soy bean hulls are extracted with water at 4° a galactomannan is obtained in 2 per cent yield (195). The polysaccharide which is precipitated with ethanol shows $[\alpha]_D + 65°$ in water and it is composed of D-galactose and D-mannose in a ratio of 2 : 3. The way in which these building units are mutually formed has been ascertained by methylation studies. The fully methylated polysaccharide was produced by treating the polysaccharide with methyl sulfate and alkali followed by methyl iodide and silver oxide in dimethyl formamide (196). Upon hydrolysis the methylated galactomannan ($[\alpha]_D + 58°$ in chloroform) yielded 2,3,4,6-tetra-O-methyl-D-galactose (2 moles), 2,3,6-tri-O-methyl-D-mannose (1 mole), and 2,3-di-O-methyl-D-mannose (2 moles). It is apparent, therefore, that the D-galactose is located only in terminal positions in the molecule and that these D-galactopyranose units are connected to C_6 of the D-mannose units of the main structural framework. One formulation that may be suggested for this soybean hull galactomannan is as follows:

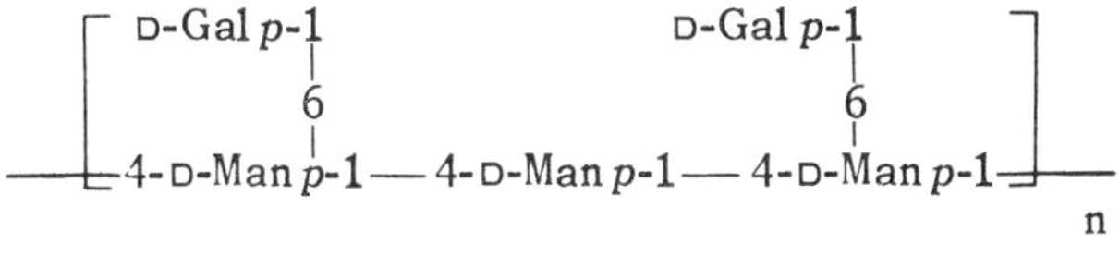

$$
\begin{bmatrix}
\text{D-Gal } p\text{-1} & & \text{D-Gal } p\text{-1} \\
\big| & & \big| \\
6 & & 6 \\
\big| & & \big| \\
\text{---4-D-Man } p\text{-1 --- 4-D-Man } p\text{-1 --- 4-D-Man } p\text{-1---}
\end{bmatrix}_n
$$

Such a formula is analogous to those proposed for other galactomannan polysaccharides (see above) and it is supported by the results of periodate oxidation which showed that 1.2 (theory requires 1.4) moles of periodate were consumed per hexose unit and at the same time 0.37 (theory 0.4) mole of formic acid was liberated.

In the case of this galactomannan it will be noted that the apparent relationship between the ratio of D-mannose to D-galactose and the specific rotation of the polysaccharide and of its methylated derivative agrees reasonably well with those recorded in Table 52.

Glucomannans

Mucilaginous polysaccharides composed of glucose and mannose are found in the tubers of various species of *Amorphophallus*, (*A. oncophyllus, A. variabilis, A. konjak*) the seeds of some species of *Iris* (*I. ochroleuca, I. sibirica*) and *Ruscus aculeatus*, some orchid bulbs (*Cremastra variabilis, Bletilla striata*) and the leaves of one member of the lily family, (*Aloe vera*). Until recently very little was known of the structure or homogeneity of this class of polysaccharides and in the case of *Bletilla* mannan (*B. striata*) (42) and the glucomannan from *Lycoris radiata* bulbs (43), knowledge is still limited to its composition, the ratio of mannose to glucose being 4 : 1. The same composition is reported for Japanese salep (*Cremastra variabilis*) (45). The molecular weight of this glucomannan, from studies on its acetyl and methyl derivatives, is about 3000. The polysaccharide is said to be slightly hydrolyzed by pancreatin and takadiastase enzymes but very rapidly hydrolyzed by the intestinal juices of the snail (*Helix sp.*). Such enzymic degradations may find use in the future for constitutional studies on this polysaccharide.

Iles Mannan (*Amorphophallus oncophyllus* and *A. variabilis*). Iles mannan meal is prepared from the tubers of the *Amorphophallus oncophyllus* and *A. variabilis* plants which are native to and cultivated in Indonesia. Cellulose, protein, lignin, and minerals are present in the meal composed principally of a glucomannan and a smaller amount of a glucan (46). The mannose content is reported to vary from 43 to 76 per cent, depending upon the species and growing conditions (47,48).

The Iles mannan polysaccharide can be extracted from the flour with water, but complete extraction by this procedure is very difficult (48). During the course of constitutional studies on this material, it was found that the gum is completely gelled by the action of a 50 per cent aqueous solution of sodium xylenesulfonate so that the resulting gel becomes soluble in 30 per cent sodium hydroxide (46). This solution is stable to dilution with water and to neutralization with acetic acid. Treatment of a dilute alkaline solution of Iles mannan with Fehling solution effects a partial separation, the glucomannan being precipitated while the polyglucosan remains in solution. Aqueous solutions of the glucomannan purified in this way are stable, but the polysaccharide is precipitated when the solutions are boiled.

Separation of the Iles mannan polysaccharides can be effected by methylation with methyl sulfate and alkali followed by fractional precipitation of the mixture of methylated polysaccharides. The pure methylated glucan component shows $[\alpha]_D + 163°$ in ethanol and the methylated glucomannan shows $[\alpha]_D - 41°$ in ethanol. Since the methylated polysaccharide before fractional precipitation shows $[\alpha]_D - 12°$ in ethanol, the ratio of the glucomannan to the glucan in the original methyl Iles mannan is approximately 6:1.

The glucan and its methyl derivative produce a blue color with iodine similar to that given by the linear starch fraction, amulose. Cleavage of the methyl derivative with 1 per cent methanolic hydrogen chloride under reflux requires 6 to 8 hours for completion, during which time the rotation of the solution decreases indicating that α-D-type glycosidic linkages are present in the gum. The only sugar present in the hydrolyzate is 2,3,6-tri-O-methyl-D-glucose (CCLXXXVIII). Since the methylated glucan is comparatively stable to hydrolysis, the glucose residues are most probably of the pyranose type and from the isolation of CCLXXXVIII, the glucose units must be linked through C_1 and C_4. Since no tetra-O-methyl or di-O-methyl-glucose is formed by cleavage of the methyl polysaccharide the latter must be a linear molecule of large chain length. It was suggested that the glucan is very similar to, if not identical with, the amylose of starch. This finding is rather surprising since heretofore amylose has been found only in association with amylopectin.

The methylated derivative of the glucomannan component undergoes cleavage with 3 per cent methanolic hydrogen chloride at a rate which suggests the sugar units in the polysaccharide are of the pyranose type, and since the change in rotation is towards a more positive direction it is believed that a large proportion of the glycosidic bonds are of the β-D-type. The cleavage fragments consisted of 2,3,6-tri-O-methyl-D-mannose (CCLXXVI), and 2,3,6-tri-O-methyl-D-glucose (CCLXXXVIII), in the molecular ratio 2:1. The D-glucopyranose and D-mannopyranose

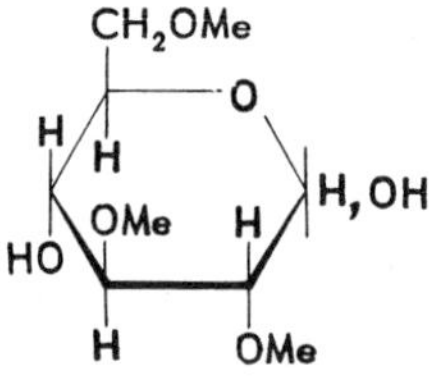

(CCLXXXVIII) 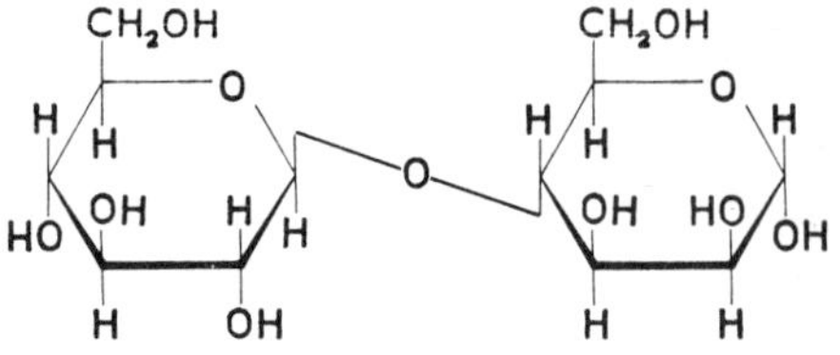   (CCLXXXIX)

residues in the polysaccharide are, therefore, linked to each other through C_1 and C_4 thus giving a linear molecule. The order in which the units are joined is clarified by a study of the acetolysis degradation products of the glucomannan (49).

Graded acetolysis of Iles glucomannan gives a mixture of sugar acetates which can be separated after deacetylation by column chromatography, first on charcoal (50,52) and then on cellulose (51).

D-Glucose and D-mannose first emerge from the column, followed by three disaccharides which proved to be 4-O-β-D-glucopyranosyl-α-D-mannose (CCLXXXIX), 4-O-β-D-glucopyranosyl-β-D-glucose (cellobiose) (CCXC), and 4-O-β-D-mannopyranosyl-α-D-glucose (CCXCI). The first of these gives equal parts of D-glucose and D-mannose upon hydrolysis and when oxidized before hydrolysis there is formed D-glucose and D-mannonic acid. This evidence shows that the disaccharide is a D-glucosyl → D-mannose and since methylation proves (49) that the linkages in the polysaccharide are of the 1 → 4-type, the disaccharide must be a 4-O-D-glucosyl-D-mannose. Final proof of the structure (CCLXXXIX) is forthcoming from the fact that this disaccharide proved to be identical with the disaccharide, 4-O-β-D-glucopyranosyl-D-mannose, previously synthesized (53,54), and moreover it affords the characteristic crystalline octaacetate (55).

The cellobiose (CCXC) was readily recognized as its octaacetate while the third disaccharide (CCXCI), which contained glucose and mannose, proved to be mannosyl-glucose because oxidation with bromine followed

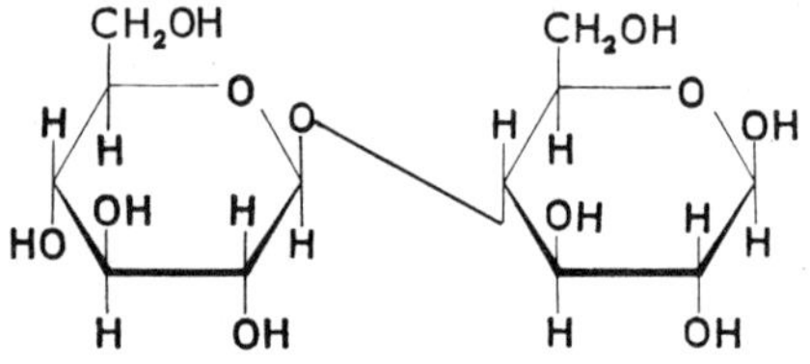

(CCXC)

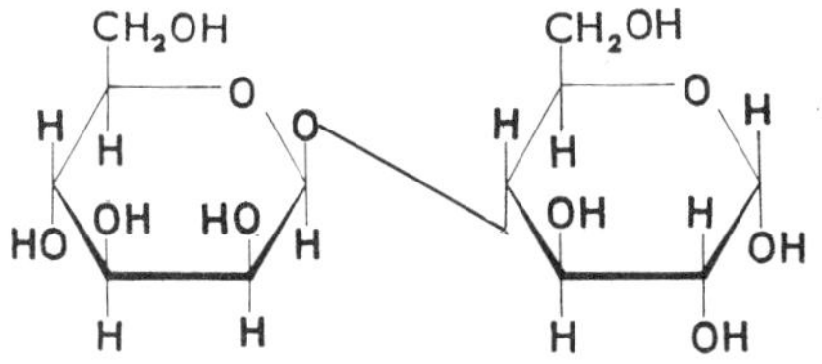

(CCXCI)

by hydrolysis afforded mannose and gluconic acid. Methylation studies on the polysaccharide show that it contains only $1 \rightarrow 4$ bonds so that this disaccharide must also possess a $1 \rightarrow 4$ glycosidic linkage and it is designated 4-O-D-mannosyl-D-glucose. Final proof of this follows from the fact that methylation followed by hydrolysis gives 2,3,4,6-tetra-O-methyl-D-mannose, identified as its aniline derivative and 2,3,6-tri-O-methyl-D-glucose, identified as the 1,4-*bis*-p-nitrobenzoate. Inasmuch as the oligosaccharide shows downward mutarotation, it is an α-D-anomer and since the disaccharide displays a low rotation ($[\alpha]_D + 30°$, water) it must possess a β-D-biose linkage. The disaccharide is therefore designated 4-O-β-D-mannopyranosyl-α-D-glucose.

Although the identification of other oligosaccharides containing more than two hexose residues, which are produced on graded acetolysis of the glucomannan polysaccharide, would greatly simplify the structural problem, certain deductions may still be made from the above findings. It has already been established (46) by methylation techniques that the Iles glucomannan has a linear structure in which the units are joined by $1 \rightarrow 4$ glycosidic bonds and that the ratio of D-mannose to D-glucose is $2 : 1$. Now if it be assumed that the structural pattern is repeated throughout the whole molecule the isolation of cellobiose only and none of its related homologs, such as cellotriose or cellotetraose, requires that the structural pattern of the repeating unit of the glucomannan polysaccharide be formulated as follows:

$$-4\text{-}\beta\text{-}D\text{-}Gp\,1-4\text{-}\beta\text{-}D\text{-}Gp\,1-(4\text{-}\beta\text{-}D\text{-}Manp\,1)_4-$$

This formulation (49) explains the formation of 4-O-β-D-glucopyranosyl-D-glucose (cellobiose) and of 4-O-β-D-glucopyranosyl-D-mannose and if two or more of these units are joined together, an explanation of 4-O-β-D-mannopyranosyl-D-glucose also follows.

Since neither mannobiose nor mannotriose was isolated, it appears that the linkages between the mannose units are cleared more readily than the others during acetolysis.

Konjak Glucomannan. The bulbs of *Amorphophallus konjak* C. Koch (syn. *Conophallus konjak* Schott), a member of the family *Araceae* are the source of the so-called konjak (konjaku) flour.

A careful study of the whole plant has revealed that mannan is present in the leaves and stalk as well as the root (see Table 53). It is also clear that the mature root contains the highest concentration of glucomannan. In the dormant state, the tuber contains glucomannan (58.8 per cent), starch (18.85 per cent), and smaller amounts of glucose (0.57 per cent) and fructose (1.2 per cent).

TABLE 53. CARBOHYDRATE COMPOSITION OF VARIOUS PARTS
OF A. KONJAK (61)

	Carbohydrate			
Material	Glucomannan	Starch	Glucose	Fructose
Leaves (a)	19.22	2.93	7.68	6.63
(b)	25.05	1.89	4.34	2.98
Stalk (a)	18.79	0.42	15.56	9.60
(b)	23.49	0.0	17.42	16.56
New Tuber (a)	39.75	8.29	6.50	6.08
(b)	50.38	18.60	9.58	5.60
Old Tuber (b)	36.24	6.91	2.82	2.31

(a) Plant examined in full growth.
(b) Old tuber withered, leaves going yellow, new tuber reaching maturity.

The flour is prepared (59) by cutting the bulbs of the three-year old plants into thin slices followed by drying and grinding. Although the crude glucomannan polysaccharide can be extracted from the flour with hot water, the purified polysaccharide is insoluble in water (56,61) and it is said to be precipitated from aqueous alkaline solutions on heating (57). Films formed by evaporation of aqueous solutions of the glucomannan by warming are insoluble in water (57).

The polysaccharide was originally thought to be composed only of mannose (60), but later found to contain glucose, the mannose : glucose ratio being recorded as 2 : 1 (62, cf. 63), and 5 : 2 (61). Acid hydrolysis and also enzymic hydrolysis shows that the konjak glucomannan contains only glucose and mannose (65). Fructose is also said to be present with mannose and glucose in a ratio of 1 : 3 : 2 respectively (64), but it is more than likely that the fructose arises from free sugars present in the crude konjak flour.

More recently konjak mannan is said to be composed of D-glucose, D-mannose, and D-glucuronic acid with an average of one acetyl group and one phosphate group for every 9 and 70 hexose units, respectively, and in which the ratio of hexose to uronic acid is about 20–30 (57).

By extraction with water under a pressure of 1.0–1.5 atmospheres or by treatment with a 10 per cent pancreatin extract a polysaccharide is obtained from konjak flour which can be purified by formation of the insoluble copper complex with Fehling solution, as in the case of Iles mannan, to give a glucomannan which contains D-mannose (2 moles) and D-glucose (1 mole) (62) and shows $[\alpha]_D - 43°$ in water (65).

The most recent analysis of the konjak glucomannan, $[\alpha]_D - 38°$ in 20 per cent NaOH, purified via its copper complex, shows that it is composed only of D-mannose and D-glucose in the ratio 3 : 2 (66).

Acetylation of konjak mannan with acetic anhydride in pyridine gives an acetyl derivative in which there is only one acetyl group per anhydrohexose unit (62). Complete acetylation, however, is achieved by the use of acetic anhydride with either stannous chloride or zinc chloride. The triacetate, $[\alpha]_D - 22°$ (in a mixture of alcohol and chloroform, 1 : 9), has a molecular weight of 2300–2400 when determined cryoscopically in tribromomethane.

Degradation of konjak glucomannan by a sporulating bacteria isolated from crude konjak powder is said to produce a trisaccharide "Laevidulin," $[\alpha]_D - 11.5°$ (67). A similar oligosaccharide, "Laevidulinose," $[\alpha]_D - 15.2°$, results from the prolonged action of takadiastase on the konjak polysaccharide (65).

Acetolysis of konjak glucomannan with a mixture of acetic anhydride, acetic acid and sulfuric acid leads to the formation of (A), a trisaccharide acetate, mp. 95–110°, $[\alpha]_D + 18°$ in chloroform, which affords the free trisaccharide, mp. 216–217°, $[\alpha]_D - 16°$, (water), and (B), two disaccharide acetates; one of the disaccharides is composed of glucose and mannose while the other, mp. 125–140°, $[\alpha]_D - 79°$ (water), contains only mannose (62).

A trisaccharide, $[\alpha]_D + 15°$ in water, which was not crystalline, however, is obtained by an enzymic hydrolysis of konjak glucomannan (65).

Another oligosaccharide is obtained in low yield from the glucomannan by the action of takadiastase (68). This oligosaccharide has a molecular weight of 1000 and corresponds therefore to a hexasaccharide for which a composition of D-mannose (4 moles) and D-glucose (2 moles) is given.

The structure of these oligosaccharides is not known and as a consequence this evidence cannot yet be utilized in ascertaining the structure of the konjak glucomannan, with the exception that it shows the poly-saccharide to be a glucomannan and also that some of the mannose units are joined to each other.

The methyl derivative of konjac mannan is prepared by the action of methyl sulfate and alkali followed by methyl iodide and silver oxide reagents (62,64). Methanolysis of the methyl derivative gives principally the methyl glycosides of trimethyl hexoses (62), but although these were reported by the authors to be the glycosides of 2,3,4-tri-O-methyl-D-glucose and 2,3,6-tri-O-methyl-D-mannose, the conclusions reached are based largely upon negative evidence and they do not correspond to those carried out more recently (66) on the glucomannan from a com-mercial sample of konjak flour. This glucomannan, purified through its copper complex, undergoes smooth methylation with methyl sulfate and alkali followed by silver oxide and methyl iodide to give a methyl derivative ($[\alpha]_D - 20°$ ($CHCl_3$), OMe, 44 per cent). Hydrolysis of the methylated polysaccharide affords a mixture of tetra-, tri-, and di-O-methyl sugars which can be resolved by chromatography on a cellulose-hydrocellulose column using butanone: water azetrope as the solvent. The tetra-O-methyl-hexose fraction was found to consist of 2,3,4,6-tetra-O-methyl-D-glucose (CCXXX, 2 parts), and 2,3,4,6-tetra-O-methyl-D-mannose (CCLXXV, 1 part). The tri-O-methyl hexose fraction con-sists of a mixture of 2,3,6-tri-O-methyl-D-glucose (CCLXXXVIII), recognized chromatographically and as its crystalline 1,4-di-p-nitro-benzoate, and 2,3,6-tri-O-methyl-D-mannose (CCLXXVI), which also gives a characteristic crystalline p-nitrobenzoate. These two sugars may be distinguished by the fact that their relative mobilities on paper chromatograms using benzene: ethanol: water, R_F 0.35 for the glucose derivative and 0.43 for the mannose derivative, are reversed when butanone: water azeotrope is the solvent, when the R_F values are 0.68 for the glucose derivative and 0.60 for the mannose derivative; the two 2,3,6-tri-O-methyl derivatives of D-glucose and D-mannose are also distinguishable by the fact that the former readily forms a methyl fu-ranoside, whereas the latter does not (46).

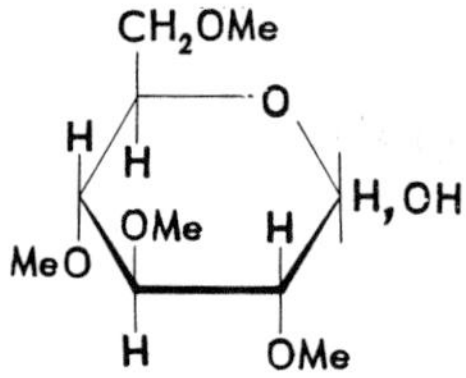

(CCXXX) 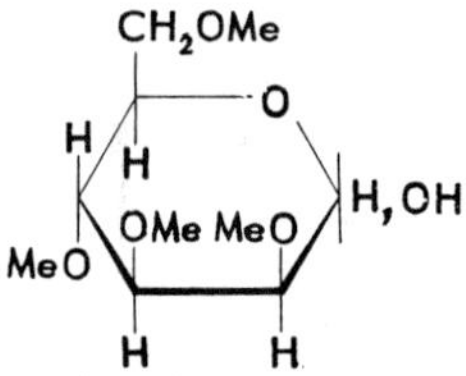   (CCLXXV) 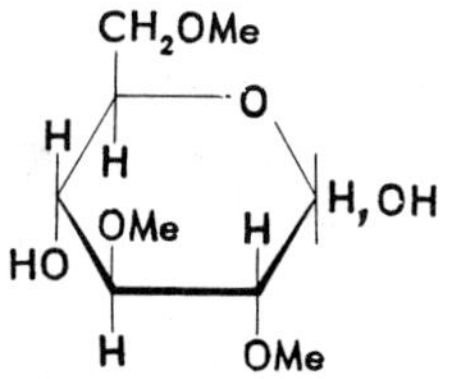   (CCLXXXVIII)

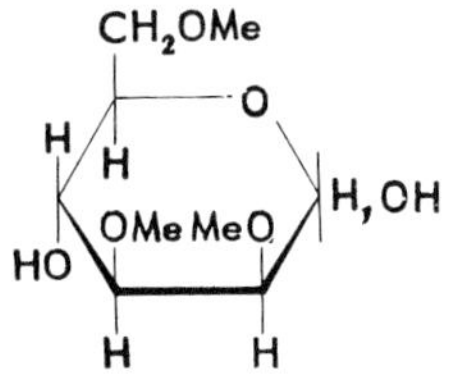

CH₂OMe structures:

(CCLXXVI) 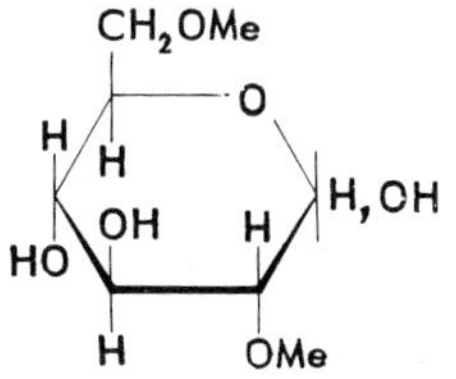   (CCXCII) 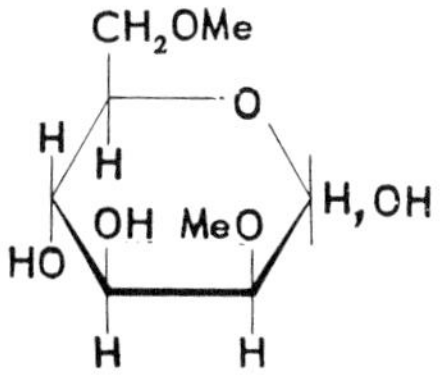   (CCXCIII)

The di-O-methyl hexose component of the hydrolyzate consists of 2,6-di-O-methyl-D-glucose (CCXCII) readily recognizable as its 1,3,4-tri-O-p-phenylazobenzoyl derivative (69), and 2,6-di-O-methyl-D-mannose, (CCXCIII). The latter is not known as a crystalline derivative but since it differs chromatographically from all the possible di-O-methyl-D-glucoses and corresponds to the epimerization product (70) of 2,6-di-O-methyl-D-glucose there is little doubt that the second di-O-methyl hexose is indeed 2,6-di-O-methyl-D-mannose. That these 2,6-di-O-methyl derivatives of D-glucose and D-mannose arise from glucose and mannose residues that are linked in the complex through C_1, C_3 and C_4 is proved by the fact that the periodate-oxidized glucomannan polysaccharide after reduction with sodium borohydride gives upon hydrolysis both D-glucose and D-mannose.

The relative amounts of tetra-O-methyl-, tri-O-methyl-, and di-O-methyl hexose derivatives in the hydrolyzate of the methylated polysaccharide are found to be 3:26:3 respectively, thus indicating that the average repeating unit consists of about 32 hexose units. The isolation of 2,3,4,6-tetra-O-methyl-D-glucose and 2,3,4,6-tetra-O-methyl-D-mannose shows that these units are located in terminal positions and it is estimated from rotational data that there are twice as many glucose as mannose terminal residues. The 2,3,6-tri-O-methyl derivatives of D-glucose and D-mannose arise from 1 → 4-linked units of D-glucose and D-mannose while the 2,6-di-O-methyl derivatives of D-glucose and D-mannose arise from the branch points in the polysaccharide.

The molecular ratios of the cleavage fragments of the methylated konjak glucomannan are given in Table 54.

Thus, for an average of every 32 hexose units consisting of D-glucose and D-mannose there are three branch points, terminated by two glucopyranose units and one mannopyranose unit. It is not possible to say how many sugar units are interposed between the terminating side-chain residues and the branch points, but the physical properties, and especially the solubility characteristics of the glucomannan, suggest that

TABLE 54. COMPOSITION OF THE HYDROLYZATE FROM METHYLATED
KONJAK GLUCOMANNAN (66)

Methylated Sugar	Mole proportions (approx.)
2,3,4,6-Tetra-O-methyl-D-glucose	2
2,3,4,6-Tetra-O-methyl-D-mannose	1
2,3,6-Tri-O-methyl-D-glucose	10
2,3,6-Tri-O-methyl-D-mannose	16
2,6-Di-O-methyl-D-glucose	2
2,6-Di-O-methyl-D-mannose	1

few if any are located in such positions for this would most likely result in the polysaccharide being soluble in water whereas it is insoluble when pure. An examination of the properties of methyl mannose and methyl glucose derivatives shows that the ratio of D-mannose to D-glucose is about 3 : 2 which is in accord with the results obtained by analysis of the hydrolyzate of the original glucomannan. It is also seen that the ratio of terminal to non-terminal units is about 1 : 10–11, which agrees well with the finding that 1 mole proportion of formic acid is produced for every 10 hexose units by periodate oxidation. The structure deduced from the methylation data requires that of the 32 hexose residues in an average repeating unit, three will be immune to periodate, three will each consume two moles of periodate, and the remaining 26 hexose units will each consume one mole of periodate; this will lead to the consumption of one mole proportion of periodate for each hexose unit which agrees with experimental findings.

One possible formula (CCXCIV) for the structure of the average repeating unit of the glucomannan, based on the above results, consists of a linear chain of about 29 hexose units, 12 of D-glucose and 17 of D-mannose, joined by 1,4-β-D-glycosidic bonds—the negative rotation of the polysaccharide in alkali indicates β-glycosidic bonds—

$$— (H)a — \underset{\underset{S}{|}}{H} — (H)b — \underset{\underset{S}{|}}{H} — (H)c — \underset{\underset{S}{|}}{H} — (H)d — \qquad \text{CCXCIV}$$

where H = D-glucose or D-mannose and $a + b + c + d = 26$ (10 glucose + 16 mannose units)

$$3S = 2 \text{ glucose} + 1 \text{ mannose}$$

and to C_3 of two of the D-glucose and one of the D-mannose units are attached single side chain units, two of them being D-glucose and one D-mannose unit. This type of structure is preferred to that in which the side chains are attached to C_4 of the branching units for the reason that this latter type of structure would display considerable irregularity and this is not supported by the fact that the polysaccharide is insoluble in water. Consequently the konjak glucomannan must have structural regularity so that the molecular chains can approach and associate through hydrogen bonds that are numerous enough to prevent the chains being forced apart not only by water, but to a large extent by dilute alkali. In other words, the glucomannan possesses certain features in common with the linear Iles glucomannan and with cellulose both of which are 1 → 4 linked polymers. This deduction is supported by the observation that the amorphous glucomannan polysaccharide can be cast into films which are not only insoluble in water, but exhibit a certain amount of crystallinity as revealed by X-ray crystallography (57,71,72). Moreover, the nitro derivative of konjak glucomannan resembles nitro-cellulose in its solubility characteristics (58,73).

Iris (*Iris Ochroleuca* and *I. Sibirica*). The endosperms of the ripe seeds of three species, *I. germanica, I. pseudacorus,* and *I. foetidissima,* are said to contain an arabomannan consisting of 82 per cent of D-man-nose and 18 per cent of L-arabinose (75,78). Two other species of iris, *I. ochroleuca,* and *I. sibirica,* contain glucomannans in their seed endo-sperms (79). It is of interest to note that the rhizomes of species of iris contain either starch or fructan (71–77).

The glucomannans of *I. ochroleuca* and *I. sibirica* are isolated by ex-traction of the endosperm of the two species of iris with 10 per cent sodium hydroxide and the polysaccharides are precipitated from the thick mucilaginous extract with alcohol. The glucomannans, which can be purified through the insoluble copper complexes, show a striking similar-ity and they were investigated in an identical manner. The following discussion is applied to the glucomannan from the seeds of *I. ochroleuca* and the results of the investigations on both polysaccharides are sum-marized in Table 55.

The glucomannan of *I. ochroleuca,* isolated in 20 per cent yield from the whole seed shows $[\alpha]_D - 25°$ in $2N$ sodium hydroxide and contains approximately equal amounts of D-glucose and D-mannose, and D-galac-tose (3 per cent).

Methylation of the polysaccharide with methyl sulfate and alkali gave the methyl derivative which upon methanolysis with 2 per cent methanolic hydrogen chloride yielded a mixture of the methyl glycosides of the cleavage fragments. Hydrolysis of the glycosides followed by chroma-tographic separation of the methyl sugars afforded 2,3,4,6-tetra-O-methyl-D-galactose (XXXIX, 3.7 per cent), and equal amounts of 2,3,6-tri-O-methyl-D-mannose (CCLXXVI), and 2,3,6-tri-O-methyl-D-glucose

(CCLXXXVIII), together with trace amounts of 2,3,4,6-tetra-O-methyl-D-glucose (CCXXX). Di-O-methyl hexoses (3 per cent approx.), probably the 2,3-di-O-methyl derivatives of D-mannose (CCLXXXIII), and of D-glucose (CCXCV) were also formed but not definitely identified.

The glucomannan is, therefore, composed of a chain of D-mannose and D-glucose residues linked through C_1 and C_4. The relative stability of the polysaccharide to hydrolysis with mineral acids suggests that all the hexose residues are in a pyranose form and the low optical rotation of

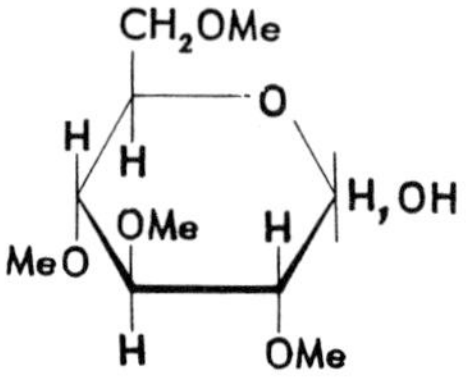

(CCXXX)

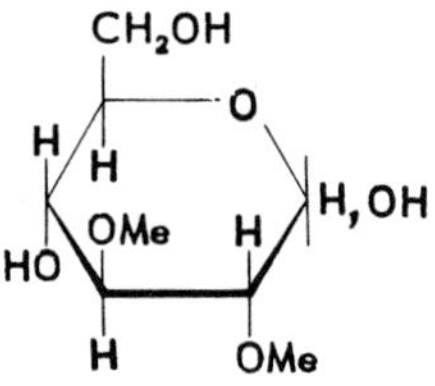

(CCXCV)

the polysaccharide and of its acetylated and methylated derivatives (see Table 55) indicate that the majority of the glycosidic bonds are of the β-D-type. Attached to the glucose-mannose main chain, either as end groups or side chains, are principally D-galactose residues, together with some D-glucose and D-mannose units. The side chains are probably linked to C_6 of either D-mannose or D-glucose units in the main chain, in

TABLE 55. POLYSACCHARIDES FROM *I. OCHROLEUCA* AND *I. SIBIRICA*

	I. ochroleuca	*I. sibirica*
Per cent yield from whole seed	20	18
$[\alpha]_D$ in 2N-NaOH	$-25 \pm 2°$	$-26 \pm 3°$
Component sugars (mole proportions)		
D-mannose	15	22–23
D-glucose	14	21–22
D-galactose	1	1
Acetyl derivative, $[\alpha]_D$ in acetone	$-14°$	$-13°$
Methyl derivative, $[\alpha]_D$ in chloroform	$-9°$	$-11°$
Mole ratio of cleavage fragments:		
Tetra-O-methyl	1.0	1.0
Tri-O-methyl	23–26	27–33
Di-O-methyl	1.3–1.4	0.8–0.9
Periodate oxidation		
Hexose residues per mole formic acid	19	12
Intact sugars present in oxidized polysaccharide	glucose (trace) mannose (trace)	(?) glucose (trace)

view of the tentative identification of the 2,3-di-O-methyl derivatives of these sugars in the cleavage fragments of the methylated polysaccharide . It is suggested that the di-O-methyl sugars may be due to incomplete methylation of the polysaccharide, but in view of the fact that the amounts of di-O-methyl and tetra-O-methyl sugars are about the same, the view is taken that the residues giving rise to the di-O-methyl derivatives are branch points in the polysaccharide.

The amount of end-group as determined by the methylation procedure corresponds to a repeating unit of 25 to 28 hexose residues whereas by periodate oxidation one mole of formic acid is produced from 19 hexose residues.   Assuming that periodate oxidation proceeds normally and furnishes formic acid from reducing and nonreducing terminal units, these results suggest that the *I. ochroleuca* polysaccharide has a degree of polymerization of 150 to 175 hexose units with an average of 5 to 6 branches.

The periodate-oxidized polysaccharide contains traces of intact glucose and mannose.   If periodate oxidation proceeds to completion, this finding is at variance with the methylation results unless di-O-methyl derivatives other than the suspected 2,3-di-O-methyl compounds are also formed from the methylated polysaccharide.   It is also conceivable that some other tri-O-methyl derivatives of D-mannose and D-glucose remain to be identified.

In the case of *I. sibirica*, the amount of end-group as determined by the methylation procedure corresponds to 29 to 35 hexose units and by periodate oxidation one mole of formic acid is produced from 12 hexose residues.   These results are most consistent with an essentially linear molecule of small molecular weight.   This difference in molecular size of the *I. ochroleuca* and *I. sibirica* glucomannans may be related to the fact that, although both are soluble in dilute alkali, the *I. ochroleuca* polysaccharide is precipitated when the solution is neutralized whereas the other is not.   However, in view of the difficulty of determining the end point of the periodate oxidation of the polysaccharides, especially that from *I. sibirica*, and the unreliable estimates of the degree of polymerization by reducing power determinations, together with the unknown effects of the alkaline conditions of extraction upon the molecular size, it is evident that determinations of molecular size by these chemical means is still open to question.

Aloe (Aloe Vera) Mucilage.   Large plantations of *Aloe vera* are cultivated in Hawaii for the latex obtained from the leaves which, when dried, gives the product known to the pharmacist as commercial aloes.   The leaf contains about 45 per cent of a mucilaginous layer which can be scraped from the dissected leaf.   Extraction of the dried, mucilaginous or assimilatory tissue with 50 per cent ethanol gives a viscous solution from which a glucomannan is precipitated by the addition of four volumes of 95 per cent ethanol (80). The polysaccharide is purified by precipitation from an aqueous solution with alcohol and shows $[\alpha]_D \pm 0°$ in water. The mucilage gave approximately equal amounts of D-glucose and D-mannose upon hydrolysis with 4 per cent sulfuric acid on a boiling water bath for 7 hours. A small amount (2.4 per cent) of uronic acid was also present.

Salep Mannan. Salep, the dried tubers of several species of *Orchis* and *Eulophia*, contains a water-soluble reserve polysaccharide which is composed of D-mannose. The polysaccharide, called salep mannan, and first prepared by Pringsheim and Genin (151), constitutes about 27 to 34 per cent of salep (152). In order to obtain the mannan in the least state of degradation it was necessary to inactivate any enzymes by treating the salep first with boiling alcohol (153). The powdered salep was extracted with water at room temperature for about 15 hours and the polysaccharide precipitated from the extract with methanol. The mannan so obtained had a viscosity about 350 times greater than that isolated (154) without previous enzyme inactivation, and it was found that whereas an undegraded product had a degree of polymerization, DP, of 1340, the product isolated from an aqueous extract after it had stood for 9 days had a DP of 164.

Salep mannan shows $[\alpha]_D - 44°$ in 6 per cent sodium hydroxide (153), $[\alpha]_D - 35°$ in water (154) and gives a triacetate with $[\alpha]_D - 28.9°$ in chloroform (152).

The methylated mannan affords 2,3,6-tri-*O*-methyl-D-mannose (CCLXXVI), and 2,3,4,6-tetra-*O*-methyl-D-mannose (CCLXXV, 1.7 per cent), upon acid hydrolysis, the amount of the latter being a maximal value since the original mannan had undergone enzymic degradation (154) during isolation. Salep mannan appears, therefore, to be constituted of $1 \rightarrow 4$-β-D-mannopyranose units, similar to the linear component of ivory nut mannan (155). The close similarity of these two mannans is further exemplified by their hydrolysis with malt extract (156).

Okra Mucilage

Aqueous extraction of the seed pods of the okra plant (*Hibiscus esculentus* syn. *Abelmoschus esculentus*) grown in the United States of America, followed by precipitation with alcohol provides a white amorphous polysaccharide acid which is reported to consist largely of D-galactose, L-rhamnose and D-galacturonic acid (157). This mucilage has been suggested as a blood volume expander (158). The same plant, *Bamia fellahi*, growing in Egypt, gave a similar polysaccharide which showed $[\alpha]_D + 26°$ in 0.6 N sodium hydroxide and was composed of D-galactose (80 per cent), L-rhamnose (10 per cent), L-arabinose (3 per cent) and D-galacturonic acid (6 per cent) (191).

Controlled hydrolysis of the okra mucilage with 5 per cent sulfuric acid at 80° has provided two oligosaccharides of constitutional significance, namely, 4-O-D-galactopyranosyl-D-galactose (CCXCVI) (157) and 2-O-(D-galactopyranosyluronic acid)-L-rhamnose (CCLI) (159). The galactose disaccharide (CCXCVI) has not been previously encountered whereas the aldobiouronic acid (CCLI) has been obtained from the mucilages of flax seed (176), slippery elm (104), *Plantago arenaria* (85), *Plantago ovata* (83), from the gum of *Khaya grandifolia* (192) and also from a polysaccharide in grapes (*Vitis vinifera*) (194).

The structure of the galactose disaccharide (CCXCVI) was proved (157) by the fact that after methylation to give CCXCVII, acid hydrolysis afforded 2,3,4,6-tetra-O-methyl-D-galactose, characterized as the aniline derivative, and 2,3,6-tri-O-methyl-D-galactose which was transformed by bromine oxidation into the corresponding crystalline γ-lactone. Inasmuch as periodate oxidation in alkaline solution afforded formaldehyde (193) it was concluded (157) that the biose linkage was of the $1 \rightarrow 4$ type. While the mechanism of the oxidation of oligosaccharides

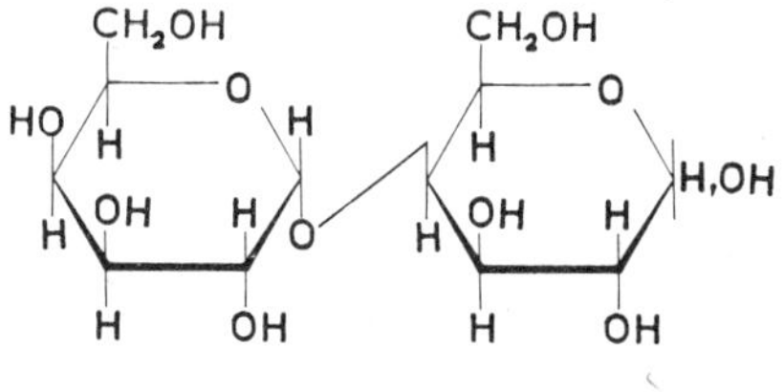

(CCXCVI)

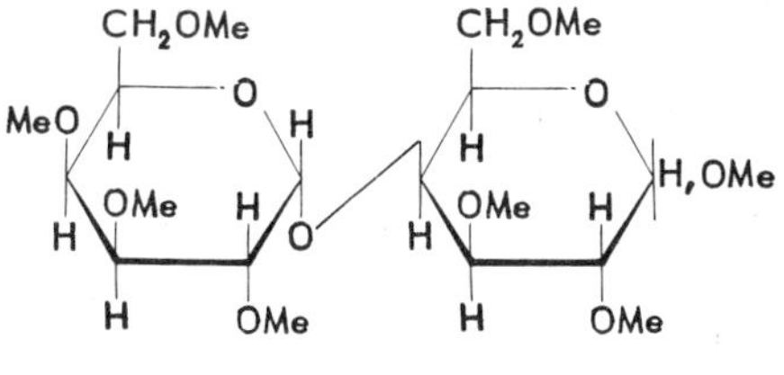

(CCXCVII)

2,3,4,6-Tetra-O-methyl-D-galactose
2,3,6-Tri-O-methyl-D-galactose

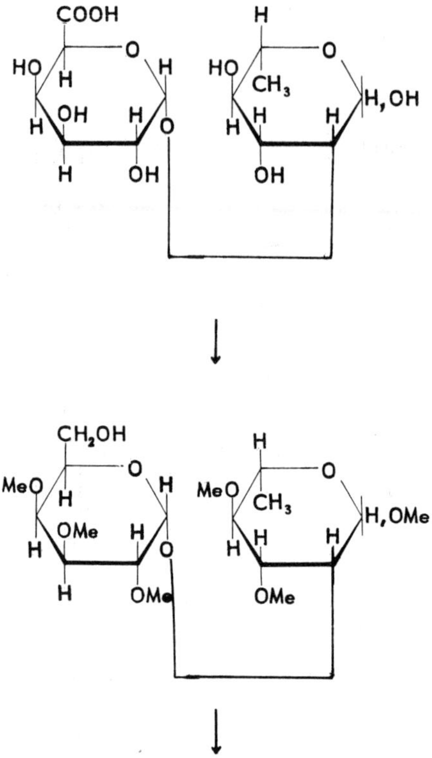

(CCLI)

(CCXCVIII)

2,3,4-Tri-O-methyl-D-galactose
3,4-Di-O-methyl-L-rhamnose

with alkaline periodate is not completely understood, it was pointed out that such compounds as maltose, lactose and melibiose behaved as expected the first two giving formaldehyde whereas the third did not. The presence of a $1 \to 5$ biose linkage, not ruled out by the methylation results, would require that the reducing galactose residue of the disaccharide be present in the polysaccharide as a furanose unit; this is an unlikely possibility when the relative stability of the polysaccharide to hydrolysis is taken into consideration. Since the galactose disaccharide displays a high positive rotation, $[\alpha]_D + 177°$ (water), it follows that the disaccharide must be 4-O-α-D-galactopyranosyl-D-galactose as shown in formula CCXCVI. Two other galactose disaccharides were isolated, but their structures remain to be established (157).

Resolution of the acid components present in the hydrolyzate of the okra mucilage on a cellulose column in the usual way has yielded (159) the aldobiouronic acid (CCLI) referred to above which is composed of D-galacturonic acid and L-rhamnose.   In addition, two aldotriouronic acids composed of D-galacturonic acid, D-galactose and L-rhamnose were obtained.

The structure of the aldobiouronic acid followed from the observation that methylation of CCLI and reduction with lithium aluminum hydride gave the neutral methylated disaccharide (CCXCVIII).   Hydrolysis of CCXCVIII then furnished 2,3,4-tri-O-methyl-D-galactose (from the uronic acid moiety of the aldobiouronic acid) and 3,4-di-O-methyl-L-rhamnose. The former was identified as its characteristic aniline derivative while the latter was characterized as its δ-lactone. It was clear, therefore, that the aldobiouronic acid was indeed 2-O-(D-galactopyranosyluronic acid)-L-rhamnose as shown in CCLI; the rotation of the aldobiouronic acid suggests that the biose linkage is of the α-D-type.

Although the two aldotriouronic acids were not completely identified, it was possible to deduce that one of them (A) was O-D-galactosyl → O-(D-galactosyluronic acid) → L-rhamnose and the other (B) O-(D-galactosyluronic acid) → O-L-rhamnosyl → D-galactose (159).

The identity of the reducing end in A and B was established by comparing chromatograms of the hydrolyzates of A and B before and after bromine oxidation.   In the case of A, L-rhamnose failed to show up on the chromatogram of the hydrolyzate of the bromine-oxidized trisaccharide whereas in the case of B it was the D-galactose component of the trisaccharide which was oxidized by bromine.   The relative positions of the two other units in B was deduced from the successive application of methylation, reduction with lithium aluminum hydride, and hydrolysis, which afforded two tri-O-methyl-galactose derivatives and a di-O-methyl-rhamnose.   Methylation of A followed by hydrolysis yielded, what appeared to be from chromatographic evidence, tetra-O-methyl-galactose, a di-O-methyl-galacturonic acid and a di-O-methyl-rhamnose.

It is of interest to note that the tentative identification of the aldotriouronic acid A reveals that some at least of the D-galacturonic acid units do not form terminal units in the polysaccharide.

Methylation studies of the mucilage from Egyptian okra (*Bamia fellahi*) revealed (191) that the methyl polysaccharide, $[\alpha]_D + 52°$ (chloroform), affords upon hydrolysis 2,3,4,6-tetra-O-methyl-D-galactose (XXXIX, 12 per cent, identified as the aniline derivative), 2,3,6-tri-O-methyl-D-galactose (CCXXXIII, 60 per cent, identified as the γ-lactone), 2,6-di-O-methyl-D-galactose (CCXVII, 6 per cent, identified chromatographically), 3,4-di-O-methyl-L-rhamnose (CCLIV, 8 per cent, identified as the lactone), and a mono-O-methyl derivative of L-rhamnose, whose identity was deduced from chromatographic evidence.   The fate of the L-arabinose and of the D-galacturonic acid component of the original mucilage was not established, but it seems likely that the uronic acid derivative was eliminated on the anion exchange resin. However, it is clear that as far as the D-galactose units are concerned some of them occupy terminal nonreducing positions in the molecule, whereas others are joined by 1 → 4 and 1 → 3 bonds since they give rise to the 2,6-di-O-methyl derivative (CCXVII). The major portion of the galactose forms a 1 → 4 linked polymeric chain. L-Rhamnose also forms part of the main structural framework of doubly linked units since these residues yield the 3,4-dimethyl ether (CCLIV); the mono-O-methyl derivative probably arises from L-rhamnose units that serve as branch points in the molecule.

Although fractional extraction failed to furnish a product with a higher methoxyl content than that of the crude methylated mucilage (OMe, 37.5 per cent), the structural deductions that were made from the nature and amounts of the hydrolysis products of the methylated mucilage were advanced with the reservation that methylation may not have been completed even though the mucilage had been methylated six times with methyl sulfate and alkali and twice with Purdie reagents.

Mucilage of Corchorus olitorius (Mulukhia)

This mucilage which is extracted from the leaves of the plant with 0.1 N hydrochloric acid at room temperature (yield 2 per cent) was purified via its copper complex. Like the okra mucilage it proved to be a polysaccharide acid; it had $[\alpha]_D + 39°$ in 0.6 N sodium hydroxide and analysis showed that it contained D-galactose (60 per cent), L-rhamnose (20 per cent), arabinose (12 per cent), xylose (6 per cent), and uronic acid (3 per cent) (191).

The methylated Corchorus mucilage ($[\alpha]_D + 58°$ (CHCl₃); OMe, 36 per cent) gave upon hydrolysis, first with boiling methanolic hydrogen chloride and then with 4 per cent dilute hydrochloric acid, a mixture of products reported to consist of 2,3,4,6-tetra-O-methyl-D-galactose (XXXIX) and 3,4-di-O-methyl-L-rhamnose (CCLIV) (17.5 per cent), 2,3,6-tri-(CCXXXIII, 58 per cent), 2,6-di-O-methyl-D-galactose (CCXVII, 6 per cent), and (?) O-methyl rhamnose (10 per cent). Of these the first three components were identified as crystalline derivatives.

The author suggested that the results indicated that there was a similarity between the structures of the Corchorus and the okra mucilages. There was no evidence concerning the fate of the arabinose, xylose, and uronic acid components which together make up 21 per cent of the original mucilage, although it is very likely that the uronic acid component of the hydrolyzate of the methylated mucilage was removed by the anion resin during the deionization steps.

Tororo-Aoi Mucilage

The Tororo-aoi plant, *Abelmoschus manihot*, is native to China and is also cultivated in Japan for the mucilage which is present in the roots and under the bark. It is used in paper manufacture (160) and its colloidal properties are said to resemble those of sodium alginate. The crude mucilage upon hydrolysis with acid is shown by chromatographic analysis to be composed of xylose, arabinose, glucose, rhamnose, and galacturonic acid (161), although earlier investigations had indicated D-galactose, L-arabinose and L-rhamnose as the component sugars (162). However, when the mucilage is treated with boiling water under pressure a polysaccharide was precipitated which is composed of xylose, arabinose and glucose while a polyglycosiduronic acid containing rhamnose and galacturonic acid can be obtained from the aqueous solution (161). Fractionation may also be effected through the acetylated derivative (163). By a partial hydrolysis of the mucilage an aldobiouronic acid composed of galacturonic acid and rhamnose is reported (164) to be formed but it is not known whether this corresponds to the aldobiouronic acid, 2-O-(α-D-galactopyranosyluronic acid)-L-rhamnose (CCLI) from okra (*Abelmoschus esculentus*).

Cellulose-containing Mucilages

The mucilages extracted from the seeds of flax (171), white mustard (165), cress (171) and quince (166,167) have the unique characteristic of containing an associated polysaccharide which in all its properties resembles cellulose. The solubilization of the cellulose is not understood and infra-red absorption spectra of some of these mucilages has been interpreted to show the absence of cellulose *per se*. However, such mucilages as those above and the noriasa mucilage (*Abelmoschus glutiotextilis*) (168) when treated with dilute acid yield a glucan which separates in fibrous form and which is in all respects similar to cellulose. The elucidation of the nature of its solubilization by the mucilage may have important industrial application and it might well further the understanding of the uses of mucilages in the improvement of paper quality.

Flax Seed Mucilage. Commercial flax (*Linum usitatissimum*) has been cultivated for centuries, flax fibers being used by the Egyptians and the Greeks. It is also grown for the oil (linseed oil) which is expressed from the seeds and used in the paint and varnish industries. In addition, the seeds are the source of a mucilage which finds use to a limited extent in the cosmetic and pharmaceutical fields and the linseed oil meal cake has been suggested as a commercial source of this mucilage (169). Such material, being a by-product, would be inexpensive, though probably seasonal. The mucilage gives solutions of high viscosity, 1.8 to 2.0

centipoises for a 1 per cent solution at 25°, and this property, together with others, has suggested its use in the food industries as a water-soluble emulsifying agent, thickener or binder (169).

The mucilage is isolated from the cleaned flax seed by extraction with cold water for about 24 hours and precipitated from the extract with 4 to 5 volumes of alcohol (170). The water-soluble powder, which is obtained in 5 to 7 per cent yield, shows $[\alpha]_D$ + 10.8° in water and is the calcium salt of a polysaccharide acid, equivalent weight 731 (170), complexed with about 0.5 per cent of cellulose (171).

An ash-free polysaccharide, known as linseed acid, is prepared (172, 173) by soaking the seeds in four times their weight of cold water for 24 hours after which time the mixture is heated to 80° when hydrochloric acid is added to 2 per cent concentration and the temperature maintained at 80° for three minutes. The hot solution is rapidly filtered and the filtrate immediately added to five volumes of alcohol. The precipitate is washed and dried to give a colorless product in 5.8 per cent yield, showing $[\alpha]_D$ + 11.90° in water and having an equivalent weight of 639. The linseed acid so prepared does not form the highly viscous solutions as does the mucilage and is probably degraded to varying extents which depend upon the acid treatment.

The linseed (flax seed) acid is composed of D-xylose, L-galactose, L-rhamnose, L-arabinose, and D-galacturonic acid, together with a sugar which may be either ribose or fucose (174).

The presence of an aldobiouronic acid in the hydrolyzate of flax seed mucilage was recognized quite early (170,176), later isolated as the calcium or barium salt (176), and shown to be a D-galactosyluronic acid-L-rhamnose (176,177). The aldobiouronic acid was identified as 2-O-(α-D-galactopyranosyluronic acid)-L-rhamnose (CCLI), by the identification of equimolecular amounts of 2, 3, 4-tri-O-methyl-D-galacturonic acid (CCXCIX), and 3,4-di-O-methyl-L-rhamnose (CCLIV), as the products of hydrolysis of its hexa-O-methyl derivative (CCC) (172). One of the anomeric forms of the methylated aldobiouronic acid was obtained crystalline, m.p. 93 to 94°, $[\alpha]_D$ + 129.8° in water. The same aldobiouronic acid was subsequently obtained from the mucilages of slippery elm, *Plantago ovata* Forsk., and common okra.

Upon treatment of the linseed acid with 2 per cent hydrochloric acid at 80° for one hour there were produced D-xylose, D-galactose and an aldotriouronic acid composed of L-galactose, L-rhamnose, and D-galacturonic acid. The aldotriouronic acid was isolated as its strontium salt, $[\alpha]_D$ + 60° in water, and it was suggested (173) that this intermediate is more suitable for the preparation of L-galactose than is the undegraded mucilage (178). Two aldotriouronic acids of similar composition have been isolated from okra mucilage (see above), except that in these cases the galactose is the D-isomer.   It will be of interest, therefore, to compare the structures of these acidic oligosaccharides, particularly since both mucilages have been shown to give the same aldobiouronic acid.

The ash-free flax seed mucilage was originally thought to be composed of approximately equimolecular proportions of D-xylose, L-galactose, L-rhamnose and D-galacturonic acid.   However, the presence also of L-arabinose was demonstrated by the use of chromatographic methods of analysis (174). Also, the homogeneity of the mucilage was questioned by fractionation studies (174).   The addition of copper acetate to an aqueous solution of the mucilage resulted in the formation of an insoluble copper salt (45 per cent), which gave upon hydrolysis L-galactose (8 per cent), L-arabinose (9 per cent), D-xylose (25 per cent), L-rhamnose (13 per cent), and an undetermined amount of an aldobiouronic acid. The water-soluble fraction, not precipitated by copper acetate, was composed of L-galactose (12 per cent), L-arabinose (12 per cent), D-xylose (27 per cent), L-rhamnose (29 per cent), and either ribose or fucose, together with an aldobiouronic acid which is probably 2-O-(α-D-galactopyranosyluronic acid)-L-rhamnose (CCLI).

White Mustard Seed Mucilage. The seeds of white mustard (*Brassica alba*) contain a mucilage which is obtained by extraction with cold water (165).   The mucilage is composed of a mixture of acidic polysaccharides and cellulose from which the latter is obtained as a fibrous gel by treating the mucilage with 1 to 4 per cent sulfuric acid on a boiling water bath for 2 hours.   The cellulose amounts to about 43 per cent of the mucilage (171).

By continuing the hydrolysis for a further 16 hours after removing the cellulose there is obtained a mixture of aldobiouronic acids which from proximate analysis is probably composed of two disaccharides, one a uronic acid $\longrightarrow$ hexose and the other a uronic acid $\longrightarrow$ 6-deoxyhexose, in the proportion of $2:1$.

The mucilage may be fractionated by adding an equal volume of saturated barium hydroxide solution to a solution of the mucilage in water when a gel is precipitated.   There remains in solution a polysaccharide ($[\alpha]_D$ +10° in water) which does not reduce Fehling solution and a proximate analysis of this fraction of the mucilage indicates 7 per cent pentosan, 10 per cent 6-deoxyhexosan, 24 per cent uronic acid, 45 per cent hexosan and 5 per cent methoxyl. Upon hydrolysis it affords L-arabinose, D-galactose and an aldobiouronic acid composed of L-rhamnose and D-galacturonic acid.

The gel from the barium hydroxide precipitation contains the cellulose and acidic polysaccharides from which the latter are extracted with 4 per cent sodium hydroxide. The material, which is soluble in the alkali and does not reduce Fehling solution, contains 9 per cent pentosan, 15 per cent uronic acid, 72 per cent hexosan and 3.4 per cent methoxyl. The hydrolysis of this fraction with mineral acid gives a mixture of sugars in which are identified L-arabinose, D-galactose, D-galacturonic acid, and D-glucuronic acid.

It is apparent, therefore, that the mucilage of white mustard seed contains a mixture of at least two acidic polysaccharides which in some way solubilize an equal amount of cellulose.

Cress Seed Mucilage. When the seeds of the cress plant (*Lepidium sativum*) are allowed to soak in water the mucilaginous layer swells, but does not disperse (171). It is not possible, therefore, as in the case of mustard seed, to obtain the mucilage simply by soaking, and mechanical agitation during extraction is required. In this way, the swelled mucilaginous layer of the seed is broken away and appears as an upper layer after centrifugation of the extraction mixture. The mucilaginous layer is squeezed through muslin to remove solid impurities and poured into ethanol. The material so obtained is reprecipitated from an acidified aqueous solution with alcohol in order to reduce the ash-content. The yield of mucilage is about 3 per cent of the weight of the original seed.

The mucilage contains 25.5 per cent of uronic acid and pentosan equivalent to 18.6 per cent furfuraldehyde. Some methoxyl groups (1.4 per cent) are also present. A partial fractionation appears to be obtained by precipitation with barium hydroxide solution.

Hydrolysis of the mucilage at 80° with 2 per cent sulfuric acid causes the associated cellulose to separate as an insoluble residue, which amounts to 18.3 per cent. More prolonged hydrolysis results in the formation of L-arabinose, D-galactose, L-rhamnose, and D-galacturonic acid, all of which have been obtained crystalline. Hydrolysis of the cellulose component of the gum afforded D-glucose. The barium salt of an aldobiouronic acid composed of D-galacturonic acid and L-rhamnose, probably the same as that from flax seed mucilage, is also produced.

Quince Seed Mucilage. The quince tree, of the genus *Cydonia*, is native to the Near East and is cultivated in America, Asia, Europe and South Africa. The fruit of the tree contains seeds which are the source of a commercially important mucilage. The quince seed mucilage, used in cosmetic and medicinal preparations as well as in foods, is obtained largely from Iran. The indigenous specie, *Cydonia vulgaris*, gives seeds surrounded by a membrane which contains a high proportion of mucilage; these seeds are said to be the best source of mucilage.

The mucilage is extracted from the quince seeds with water, either at room temperature for about 24 hours or at 100° for about 30 minutes.

The mucilaginous extract is drained from the seeds and filtered through muslin. Precipitation from the aqueous extract with alcohol gives a neutral material which can be freed to a large extent from ash by reprecipitation from an acidified aqueous solution, containing 1 per cent hydrochloric acid, with alcohol. However, it was found that the mother liquors from such reprecipitation contain L-arabinose and a more soluble gum fraction which has about 30 per cent uronic acid and 52 per cent pentose (83). The original neutral material contained 26 per cent uronic acid, 31 per cent pentose, and 2.9 per cent of methoxyl while the reprecipitated acidic gum had 28 per cent uronic acid, 33 per cent pentoses and 3.3 per cent of methoxyl. It would appear, therefore, that the arabinose residues in the mucilage are quite labile and probably in the furanose form.

It was shown (166), as previously suggested (179), that the quince seed mucilage is composed of cellulose combined with a more readily hydrolyzed polysaccharide. Hydrolysis of the mucilage causes the cellulose to separate in a fibrous form which amounts to about 33 per cent of the crude mucilage (167). After hydrolysis of the mucilage with boiling $0.5N$-sulfuric acid has continued for 10 hours, there is obtained L-arabinose and a mixture of aldobiouronic acids which contain 5.5 per cent of methoxyl and which give D-xylose on prolonged hydrolysis. It is suggested therefore, from the methoxyl content, that this mixture of acids consists of about 72 per cent of a (mono-O-methyl-hexosyluronic acid) $\longrightarrow$ xylose and 28 per cent of an unmethylated aldobiouronic acid. The nature of acidic moieties of the aldobiuronic acids is still unknown.

Mucilages of the Asparagus Family

Asparagus Adscendens Mucilage. The root of the shrub, *Asparagus adscendens* Roxb., which is abundant in Afghanistan, the Punjab and West Himalayan areas of India, contains a mucilage extractable from the dried root powder with warm water in 2.3 per cent yield on a dry weight basis (180). The polysaccharide is precipitated from the aqueous extract with alcohol acidified with hydrochloric acid and is obtained as a colorless material which gives viscous solutions in water, is nonreducing to Fehling solution and shows $[\alpha]_D + 21°$ in water. It is composed of D-glucose (4 parts), D-mannose (4 parts), D-xylose (1 part), and glucuronic acid (1 part), but its structure and homogeneity are not known.

Asparagus Filicinus Mucilage. *Asparagus filicinus* Buch.-Harn. ex D. Don. is an undershrub occurring widely in tropical and temperate regions of the Himalayas, the Punjab, and Kashmir. The powdered root of this plant, called *Chirya musli* or *Nari musli*, swells when treated with water.

In 2 per cent solution the viscosity is 9 times that of gum tragacanth. Aqueous solutions of the root powder leave continuous elastic and transparent films and preliminary experiments on its use in bulk-sizing of textiles are promising (181).

The main constituent of the root powder extracted with water is the neutral salt of an acidic polysaccharide. The mucilage is isolated in 60 per cent yield by pouring the aqueous extract into acidified ethanol. Its solution does not reduce Fehling solution even on boiling, but an insoluble copper complex is formed. The purified polysaccharide, $[\alpha]_D$ −12.4° in water, contains D-fructose (2 moles), D-glucose (8 moles), and D-mannose (10 moles), together with a uronic acid (1 mole) which is probably D-glucuronic acid since its barium salt, $[\alpha]_D$ + 12.2°, gives no galactaric acid upon oxidation with nitric acid.

The polysaccharide undergoes partial hydrolysis when treated with 4 per cent sulfuric acid at 80° for 3 hours and amongst the products of hydrolysis there have been isolated an aldobiouronic acid, composed of glucuronic acid and mannose, and a degraded polysaccharide which is composed of D-mannose (9 moles), D-glucose (8 moles), and D-fructose (2 moles) (182).

Asparagus Racemosus Mucilage. *Asparagus racemosus* Willd. is a tall climbing undershrub found in many parts of India. It has a stout creeping rootstock from which a cluster of elongated tuberous roots arises annually. The roots find application in indigenous medicine.

The powdered roots of *A. racemosus* when extracted with warm water yield a viscous solution from which a mucilage (yield 2 per cent) is precipitated with alcohol (183). The mucilage shows $[\alpha]_D$ + 27.5° in water, does not reduce Fehling solution, and upon complete hydrolysis affords D-glucose and D-galacturonic acid in the ratio of 3 : 2. By heating the polysaccharide at 80° for 3 hours with 4 per cent sulfuric acid a partial hydrolysis is achieved in which there are formed D-glucose, and an aldobiouronic acid composed of D-glucose and D-galacturonic acid (184).

Curculigo Orchioides Mucilage. The tuberous roots of *Curculigo orchioides*, a small herbaceous plant indigenous to the hotter regions of India and Ceylon, contain about 8 per cent of a mucilage (185) which gives a viscous, nonreducing, aqueous solution. The polysaccharide, $[\alpha]_D$ + 99.6° in water, is composed of mannose (6 moles), glucose (9 moles), and glucuronic acid (10 moles).

Plantago Seed Mucilages

The seeds of the plantain family (*Plantago*) upon extraction with water, yield mucilages which are composed of D-xylose, L-arabinose, D-galacturonic acid, and in some cases L-rhamnose or D-galactose.

The mucilages appear to be mixtures of at least two polysaccharides differing in their uronic acid content.   They may be compared with gum tragacanth which contains a polyuronide and a neutral polysaccharide, and with pectin, which is a complex mixture of pectic acid associated with an araban and a galactan.

Constitutional studies have been limited to the neutral polysaccharide components since application of the usual methylation techniques result in eliminating at some point in the experimental procedures, the uronide-containing carbohydrates.

Of the several commercially or agriculturally important members of this family, including *Plantago psyllium*, which produces the psyllium seed of commerce, *P. fastigiata*, T., known as Indian wheat, *P. loeflingii*, *P. lanceolata*, or ribgrass, *P. arenaria* and *P. ovata* Forsk, producing the dark and light "Psyllium" seeds respectively, only three have received any careful structural study.   These are *Plantago ovata* Forsk, *P. arenaria* and *P. lanceolata*, although the mucilage content of others, *P. inflexa*, *P. helleri*, and *P. rhodo-sperma* has been investigated (82).

Plantago Ovata Forsk Seed Mucilage. In an early study (81) of the composition of a *Plantago* seed mucilage from *P. psyllium*, it was reported that the composition of the mucilage varies with the conditions of extraction.   This observation was confirmed later in studies (83,84) on the mucilage of *P. ovata* Forsk.   Extraction of the seeds with cold water gives a product having a higher uronic acid content (20 per cent) and a lower pentosan content (52 per cent) than the polysaccharide isolated by extracting the residue with water at 90 to 95°C.   The latter polysaccharide contained approximately 3 per cent uronic acid and 90 per cent pentosan.

Extraction of *P. ovata* seeds with water at 15° gives a highly viscous solution from which the polysaccharide is precipitated with alcohol in about 1.5 per cent yield.   Reprecipitation of the product from aqueous solution with acidified alcohol yields an almost ash-free polysaccharide with an equivalent weight of approximately 700.   Hydrolysis of the purified polysaccharide gave D-xylose (46 per cent), L-arabinose (7 per cent), an aldobiouronic acid (40 per cent), 2-O-(α-D-galactopyranosyluronic acid)-L-rhamnose (CCLI) and an insoluble residue (2 per cent).

The structure of the aldobiouronic acid is proved by methylation to the hepta-O-methyl derivative (CCC) which undergoes hydrolysis to give 3,4-di-O-methyl-L-rhamnose (CCLIV) and 2,3,4-tri-O-methyl-D-galacturonic acid (CCXCIX).   The high positive rotation of the barium salt ($[\alpha]_D$ +70° in water) of the acid (CCLI) and of its methyl derivative (CCC) ($[\alpha]_D$ + 107°) indicates that the glycosidic linkage of the aldobiuronic acid is of the α-type.

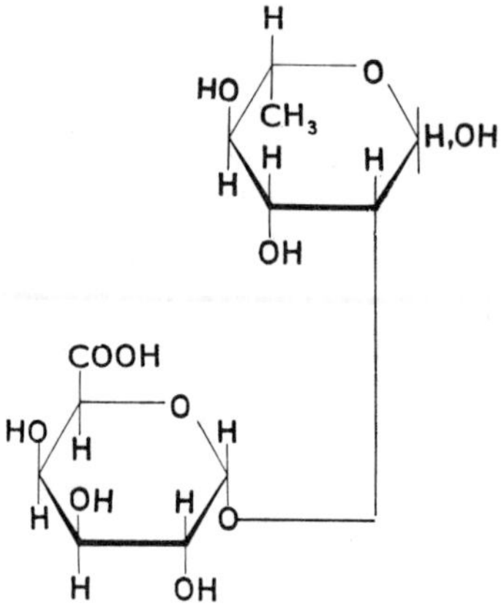

(CCLI)

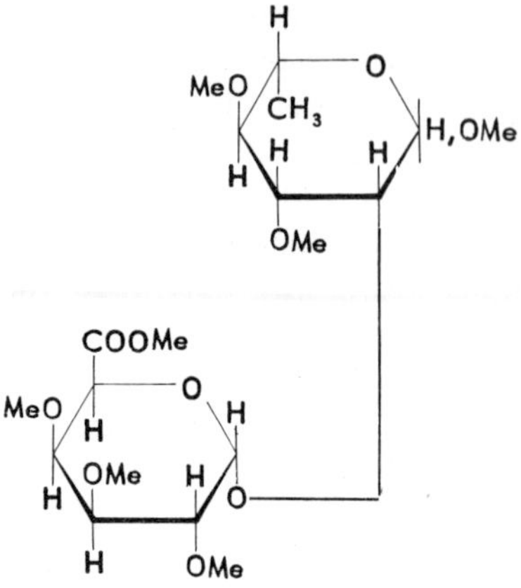

(CCC)

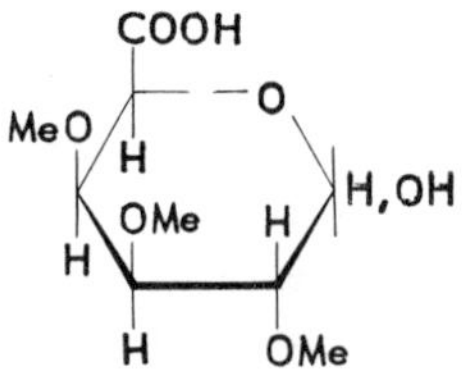

(CCXCIX)

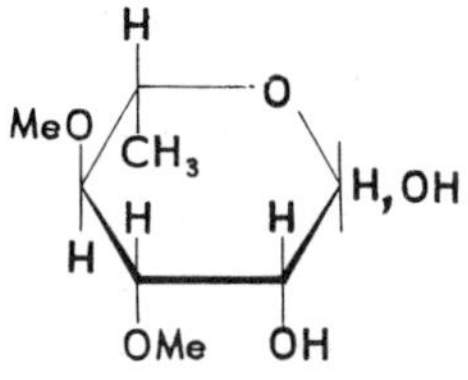

(CCLIV)

Acetylation of the polysaccharide with acetic anhydride in pyridine gave an acetyl derivative which was fractionated by extraction with boiling acetone-chloroform (1:1) into a soluble fraction (60 per cent) and an insoluble fraction (40 per cent) which appeared to differ only in molecular size. However, the uronic acid content (2.5 per cent) indicated that there was a considerable loss of uronic acid units during acetylation. Also, an examination of the polysaccharide regenerated from the acetates showed that only D-xylose and L-arabinose were present, L-rhamnose having been removed.

Methylation of the polysaccharide with methyl sulfate and alkali gives a methyl derivative, $[\alpha]_D - 114°$ in chloroform, which is insoluble in the methylation mixture and contains no uronic acid units, together with a fraction which is soluble in the methylation mixture having $[\alpha]_D + 78°$ in chloroform and 15 per cent of uronic anhydride. The "insoluble" methylated derivative appears to correspond to the methyl derivatives, $[\alpha]_D - 121°$ in chloroform, obtained by the methylation of either the acetone-chloroform soluble or acetone-chloroform insoluble fractions of the acetate noted above. From the hydrolysis of the "insoluble" methyl derivative the cleavage fragments shown in Table 56, column 1, were identified.

It will be seen that no methyl derivatives of D-galacturonic acid or L-rhamnose are present in the cleavage products of the methylated polysaccharide. Since aldobiouronic acid residues are stable to alkali and methylation, it was suggested (85) that in the mucilage either (a) the aldobiouronic acid is attached to the rest of the molecule by an alkalisensitive linkage of the ester type, or (b) the mucilage consists of a neutral portion with an associated short chain polyuronide. An investigation of the soluble methyl derivative described above would probably aid in deciding between the various possibilities.

It is clear from the cleavage fragments of the methyl derivative (Table 56, column 1) that the neutral portion of the *P. ovata* mucilage is highly branched and that it is similar to the corresponding fraction of the material extracted with hot water following exhaustive cold water extraction. This hot water extraction gives a highly viscous solution which sets to a gel on cooling. The polysaccharide is precipitated from the extract with acidified alcohol as a fibrous product with an equivalent weight of approximately 4000 (a value of 700 was noted for the cold water extracted polysaccharide). Hydrolysis of the polysaccharide with 3 per cent aqueous oxalic acid gives D-xylose (80 per cent), L-arabinose (14 per cent) D-galactose (trace) and a small amount (0.3 per cent) of a substance which appeared to be the barium salt of an aldobiouronic acid that did not correspond to 2-O-(α-D-galactopyranosyluronic acid)-L-rhamnose (CCLI).

TABLE 56. CLEAVAGE FRAGMENTS IDENTIFIED IN THE HYDROLYZATE OF THE METHYL DERIVATIVES OF P. OVATA MUCILAGES EXTRACTED BY COLD AND HOT WATER (85)

Cold Water Extract	Hot Water Extract
2,3,4-Tri-O-methyl-D-xylose (CCXII, 6 parts)	2,3,4-Tri-O-methyl-D-xylose (CCXII, 8 parts)
2,3,5-Tri-O-methyl-L-arabinose (CLXL, 1 part)	2,3,5-Tri-O-methyl-L-arabinose (CLXL, 3 parts)
2,4-Di-O-methyl-D-xylose (CCXVI, 1 part)	2,4-Di-O-methyl-D-xylose (CCXVI, 4 parts)
3-O-Methyl-D-xylose (CCLVIII, 4 parts)	2,3-Di-O-methyl-D-xylose (CCCI, 1 part)
2-O-Methyl-D-xylose (CCCII, 1 part)	3-O-Methyl-D-xylose (CCLVIII, 8 parts)
D-Xylose (2 parts)	2,5-Di-O-methyl-L-arabinose (XLIII, 1 part)
	D-Xylose (1 part)
	2,3,4,6-Tetra-O-methyl-D-galactose (XXXIX, 1.3 per cent)

The polysaccharide, methylated *via* its acetate, gives the methyl derivative, $[\alpha]_D$ −121° in chloroform, which, upon methanolysis and hydrolysis gives the cleavage fragments shown in Table 56, column 2. It is apparent that though there is a highly branched structure there are several differences in detail between the two extracts of *P. ovata* seeds. Approximately the same proportion of end-groups is present in each case, but in the hot water fraction the amount of 2,3,5-tri-*O*-methyl-L-arabinose (CLXL) is doubled at the expense of the 2,3,4-tri-*O*-methyl-D-xylose (CCXII). Also, the hot water fraction contains D-galactopyranose end groups, L-arabofuranose residues linked through C_1 and C_3, and D-xylopyranose units linked through C_1 and C_4, none of which is found in the cold water fraction. The latter, however, contains D-xylose units linked through C_1, C_3 and C_4, and C_1, C_2 and C_4 whereas only the hot water fraction has D-xylose units triply-linked through C_1, C_2 and C_4. Again, the hot water fraction appears to contain a much higher proportion of doubly-linked D-xylose units and a smaller proportion of D-xylose units linked through all four positions than the cold water fraction. The two fractions are, therefore, to be regarded as distinct polysaccharides.

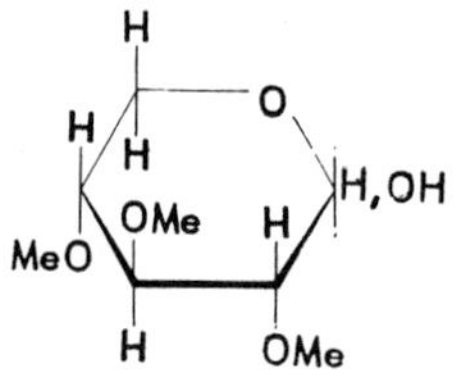

(CCXII) 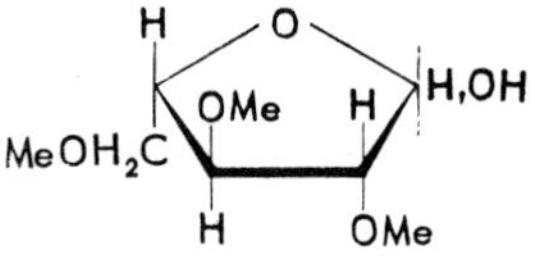   (CLXL) 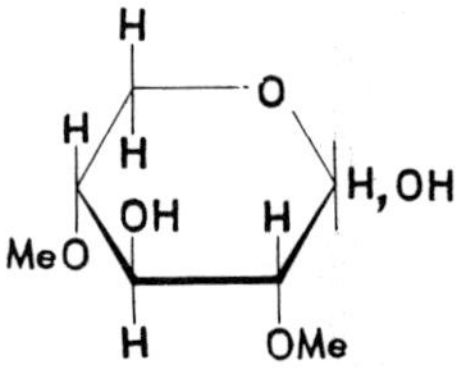   (CCXVI)

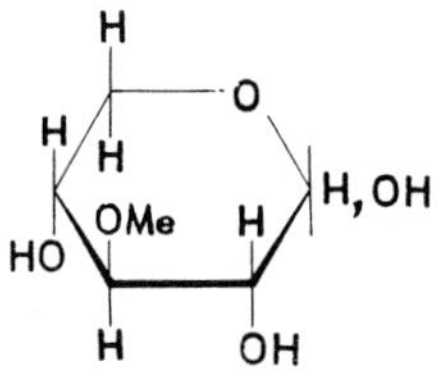

(CCLVIII) 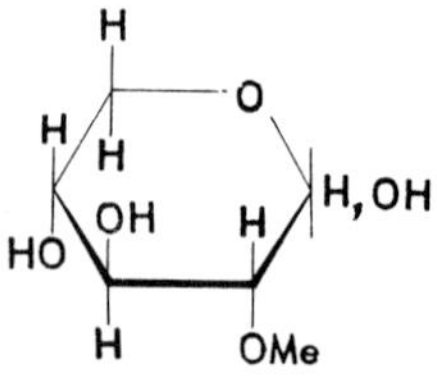   (CCCII) 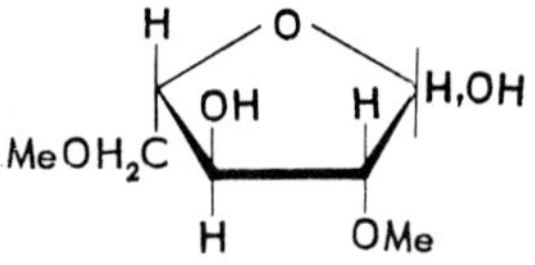   (XLIII)

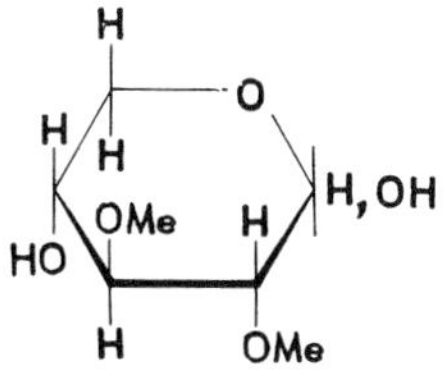

(CCCI)

Plantago Lanceolata **Seed Mucilage.** Extraction of ribgrass (*Plantago lanceolata*) seeds with water at room temperature gives a viscous solution from which a polysaccharide is precipitated with acidified alcohol in 5 per cent yield. The stringy product, $[\alpha]_D - 60°$ in water, has an equivalent weight of 1100 and contains 15.2 per cent uronic acid, 72 per cent pentosan, and 11 per cent methyl pentosan (86). Hydrolysis of the polysaccharide with 3 per cent oxalic acid gives D-xylose, a small amount of D-galactose and a degraded acid which contains D-galacturonic acid, L-arabinose, D-xylose, L-rhamnose, and D-galactose (87). Further hydrolysis of the acidic oligosaccharide results in the isolation of an aldobiouronic acid derived from D-galacturonic acid and either a pentose or a 6-deoxyhexose (87).

The acetyl derivative of the rib-grass polysaccharide is partially soluble (40 per cent) in acetone. Methylation of the crude polysaccharide acetate, or its soluble and insoluble fractions, yields methyl derivatives which appear to differ only in molecular size. The methylated polysaccharide, $[\alpha]_D - 105°$ in chloroform, contains no uronic acid residues and upon cleavage with methanolic hydrogen chloride followed by fractionation of the glycosides using a combination of distillation, extraction and chromatographic techniques, the following methyl sugars are identified (87): 2,3,4-tri-*O*-methyl-D-xylose (CCXII, 37 per cent), 2,3,4,6-tetra-*O*-methyl-D-galactose (XXXIX, 2.4 per cent), 2,4-di-*O*-methyl-D-xylose (CCXVI, 16 per cent), 2,3-di-*O*-methyl-D-xylose (CCCI, 16 per cent), 2,4,6-tri-*O*-methyl-D-galactose (XLVI, 1.2 per cent), 2-*O*-methyl-D-xylose (CCCII, 8 per cent), 3-*O*-methyl-D-xylose (CCLVIII, 5 per cent), and D-xylose (7 per cent). It was originally thought that 3,4-di-*O*-methyl-D-xylose (CCXXXVI) was one of the cleavage fragments of the methylated polysaccharide (86), but it could not be substantiated (87).

It is apparent from the methylated sugars derived from the methylated rib-grass polysaccharide that the latter has structural features which resemble the cold and hot water fractions of *P. ovata* in part, with the exception that the *P. lanceolata* polysaccharide has no L-arabofuranose residues, but does have a small number of D-galactopyranose residues linked through C_1 and C_3.

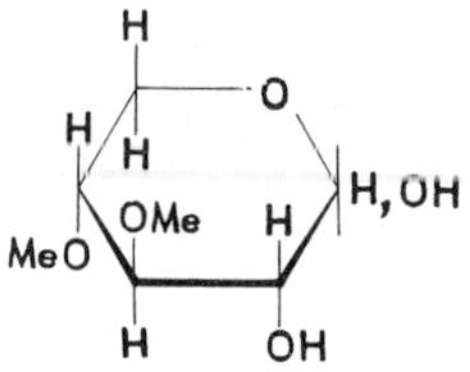

(CCXXXVI)

Plantago Arenaria Seed Mucilage. The mucilage from dark "Psyllium" (*Plantago arenaria*) seeds is extracted with cold water and no further material is obtained by extraction of the seeds with hot water (85). The acidic polysaccharide is obtained by precipitation from the viscous aqueous extract with acidified alcohol. It contains 80 per cent of pentose and 7.2 per cent of uronic acid and has an equivalent weight of about 2000 (88). Hydrolysis with 3 per cent oxalic acid yields D-xylose (62 per cent), L-arabinose (17 per cent), D-galactose (6 per cent), 2-O-(α-D-galactopyranosyluronic acid)-L-rhamnose (CCLI, 13 per cent), and an insoluble residue which appeared to be a mixture of cellulose and lignin. This aldobiouronic acid was formerly isolated by Hostettler and Deuel (89).

Acetylation of the mucilage gives a derivative which is fractionated with acetone-chloroform (1:1) to give a soluble portion (20 per cent) and an insoluble portion (80 per cent). The uronic acid contents of these products, 2.3 per cent and 3.9 per cent respectively, showed that, as in the cases of *P. ovata* and *P. lanceolata*, a partial loss of uronic acid had taken place during acetylation. The corresponding methyl derivatives prepared from both acetate fractions yield a complex mixture of the same methyl sugars upon hydrolysis. These are identified as follows: 2,3,4-tri-O-methyl-D-xylose (CCXII, 10 parts), 2,3,5-tri-O-methyl-L-arabinose (CLXL, 1 part), 2,3,4,6-tetra-O-methyl-D-galactose (XXXIX, 2 parts), 2,3-di-O-methyl-D-xylose (CCCI, 6 parts), 2,4-di-O-methyl-D-xylose (CCXVI, 3 parts), 2,5-di-O-methyl-L-arabinose (XLIII, 2 parts), 2-O-methyl-D-xylose (CCCII, 8 parts), D-xylose (1 part), and unidentified derivatives (2 parts).

From the high proportion of 2-O-methyl-D-xylose and end groups, it is clear that the mucilage possesses a highly branched structure similar to that of *P. ovata* and *P. lanceolata*.

Additional evidence is forthcoming from a study of the *P. arenaria* mucilage concerning the nature of the uronide components in the complex. The acetylated mucilage upon deacetylation gives a product which can be separated by sedimentation in alcohol into a fibrous material, containing little or no uronic acid, and a gelatinous precipitate, giving a positive naphthoresorcinol test for uronic acid. Furthermore, the action of $2N$ sodium hydroxide on the mucilage itself, followed by electrodialysis, was found to reduce the uronic acid content from 7.2 per cent to 2.5 per cent, and in the process an anion was removed which gave a positive naphthoresorcinol test. On the other hand, electrodialysis of the untreated mucilage failed to remove any uronic acid. These results lend support to the hypothesis that the D-galacturonic acid residue is attached to another residue in the molecule by a linkage of the ester type. Glycosidically linked to the D-galacturonic residues are the L-rhamnose units, as evidenced by the isolation from the mucilages of 2-O-(α-D-galacto-pyranosyluronic acid)-L-rhamnose.

In general, therefore, it appears that the *Plantago* mucilages are composed of an alkali stable nucleus attached through an alkali-sensitive linkage to, or closely associated with a polyuronide containing a 2-O-(α-D-galactopyranosyluronic acid)-L-rhamnose residue. The alkali-stable nucleus consists of a D-xylopyranose main chain linked through C_1 and C_3 and/or C_1 and C_4. Side-chains with D-xylopyranose, D-galactopyranose and in the cases of *P. ovata* and *P. arenaria* L-arabofuranose end groups are attached to D-xylopyranose units in the main chain such that these units are linked through C_1, C_2 and C_4 and/or C_1, C_3 and C_4 and also through C_1, C_2, C_3 and C_4. Also, in the cases of *P. arenaria* and the hot water fraction of *P. ovata* some L-arabofuranose residues are linked through C_1 and C_3. In *P. lanceolata* some D-galactose units are doubly-linked through positions 1 and 3. In view of the high negative rotations some of the mucilages and their acetyl and methyl derivatives it is probable that the majority of the glycosidic linkages are of the β-D-type. At present, it is impossible to put forward a unique molecular formula for any of the alkali-stable polymers from the *Plantago* mucilages.

Plantago Psyllium. The seed coats of psyllium seed are composed of about 98 per cent of a mucilage which can be extracted with cold water, either from the whole seed or the separated seed coat; the mucilage is contained entirely in the seed coat (81). It forms viscous solutions in water and does not reduce Fehling solution. The composition of the polysaccharide is dependent upon the method of extraction and it appears therefore to be a mixture; the proximate analysis gave uronic acid (6.7 to 13.6 per cent) and pentosan (78 to 91 per cent). The mucilage is composed of L-arabinose, D-xylose, and D-galacturonic acid, graded acid hydrolysis affording an aldobiouronic acid consisting of L-arabinose and D-galacturonic acid and an aldotriouronic acid containing all three sugars. Although the relative amounts of the monosaccharide components of the mucilage are not known, it is reported that D-xylose is the principal sugar and that the ratio of D-galacturonic acid to pentose varies from 1 : 9 to 1 : 36 with a corresponding variation in equivalent weight of 1300 to 1800.

Plantago Fastigiata. Indian wheat, *P. fastigiata*, contains about 19 per cent of a mucilage which is extracted from the seeds with cold water and appears to be very similar to the mucilage from *P. psyllium* (90). Extraction of the seeds with 25 per cent ethanol gives a mucilage containing uronic acid residues 13.6 per cent, pentosan (86.9 per cent) and the free acid has an equivalent weight of 1294. The residue from this extraction when soaked in cold water gives a product having uronic acid (4.2 per cent), pentosan (92.6 per cent) and an equivalent weight of 2444.

As in the case of *P. psyllium* this mucilage is therefore a mixture, but, from complete acid hydrolysis all fractions studied contained D-xylose as the principal component together with smaller amounts of L-arabinose and D-galacturonic acid. A partial acid hydrolysis affords the same aldobiouronic acid, O-(D-galactopyranosyluronic acid)-L-arabinose, as is obtained from *P. psyllium*, the barium salt of which shows $[\alpha]_D + 58.2°$ in water. From the resistance of the L-arabinose residues to hydrolysis it is possible that some of them occur in the pyranose form, as in the cases of some of the plant exudates. These mucilages like gum arabic and sapote gum may therefore be another source of oligosaccharides containing an L-arabopyranose unit.

Tamarind Seed Polysaccharide. The flour produced from the seed kernel of the tamarind tree (*Tamarindus indica*, Linn) has been used in India as a sizing agent for cotton and jute. Extraction of the flour with hot water removes a polysaccharide (91) which is isolated from the extract by precipitation with alcohol (92). The polysaccharide forms gels with sugar concentrates under diverse conditions of hydrogen ion concentration (93), a property which may have commercial significance.

The products of aqueous acid hydrolysis of the tamarind seed polysaccharide are D-glucose (3 moles), D-xylose (2 moles), and D-galactose (1 mole) (94, cf. 95–99). The mode of union of these sugar residues in the molecule has been investigated by application of methylation techniques. The methylated derivative of the polysaccharide, prepared in the usual way with methyl sulfate and alkali, gives upon methanolysis a mixture of methyl sugar glycosides (100). These are separated by a combination of fractional distillation and chromatographic methods and the following methyl sugars identified: 2,3,4-tri-O-methyl-D-xylose (CCXII, 1 part), 3,4-di-O-methyl-D-xylose (CCXXXVI, 1 part), 2,3,4,6-tetra-O-methyl-D-galactose (XXXIX, 1 part), 2,3,6-tri-O-methyl-D-glucose (CCLXXXVIII, 0.9 part), and 2,3-di-O-methyl-D-glucose (CCXCV, 2 parts). In view of the relative resistance of the methylated polysaccharide to cleavage it is probable that all the component sugar residues are in the pyranose form.

Although no unique structure could be assigned to the molecule on the basis of present knowledge, it is clear from the above cleavage fragments that the polysaccharide is composed of D-xylose and D-glucose residues linked through C_1 and C_2 and C_1 and C_4, respectively, with two side chains joined to two other D-glucose units which are linked through C_1, C_4 and C_6. The two end-groups in this average repeating unit are D-xylose and D-galactose.

Recent investigations into tamarind gum have shown (186) that the crude tamarind flour consists of three materials: A (2 to 4 per cent) the component soluble in water within 2 to 3 minutes at 5°; B (20 to 22 per cent) the component soluble at room temperature after 35 minutes stirring; and C (30 to 35 per cent) which consists of the material insoluble in cold but soluble in boiling water. While this classification may be only approximate and dependent to some extent on the grinding of the seed material it is reported that component A has no gelling properties while the other two (B and C) have excellent gelling and sizing properties.

Extraction (187) of component C with 4 per cent aqueous sodium hydroxide at room temperature followed by acidification with acetic acid and precipitation with acetone, afforded a product which, upon purification through its copper complex (Fehling solution), and washing with water, appeared to be a xylan. Upon hydrolysis it gave only xylose, recognized as its dibenzylidene dimethylacetal derivative.

Treatment of the xylan complex with methyl sulfate and 40% sodium hydroxide afforded a methyl derivative, $[\alpha]_D$ − 84° (?chloroform), having a methoxyl content of 36.8 per cent. This low value (theory, OMe 38.75) may be due to solvent (?water) impurity or to incomplete methylation, since xylans are notoriously difficult to methylate completely with methyl sulfate and sodium hydroxide; perhaps 45 per cent potassium hydroxide might have been more effective (188,189).

Hydrolysis of the methylated xylan component yielded 2,3,4-tri-O-methyl-D-xylose (CCXII), 2,3-di-O-methyl-D-xylose (CCCI), and 2-O-methyl-D-xylose (CCCII). The quantitative results are not entirely clear, the values from paper chromatography differing from those by column chromatography, but the author reports that "the polysaccharide consists of about 80 ± 5 β-D-xylopyranose units, linked through 1,4-positions and disposed in a singly branched structure with bifurcation involving the 3-hydroxyl group of one of the xylopyranose residues." The reducing power determined by means of the alkaline-iodine method and periodate oxidation studies was reported to support this structure (187).

While this estimate of the general structural character of the xylan component of tamarind gum may be true it is not easy to reconcile it with the fact that a polysaccharide with such linear character displays gelling properties.

It would appear that more work is necessary to clarify the exact nature of this so-called xylan component of tamarind gum and also the crude gum itself. This work (187) does, however, cast some doubt on the previous investigations (100) discussed above from which it was concluded that the gum was composed of glucose and galactose as well as xylose. It would appear that the gum is a complex mixture of polysaccharides.

Slippery Elm Mucilage. "Slippery Elm Bark" is obtained from *Ulmus fulva*, a tree native to North America. The inner bark, which forms the commercial drug, is marketed in the form of broad flat strips and contains about 16 per cent of a mucilage that is used as a demulcent. On stirring the bark with boiling water for about 24 hours, the mucilage, together with resins, oils and calcium oxalate, is extracted and from this extract the crude polysaccharide is precipitated by alcohol (101,102). It is purified by re-precipitation from dilute hydrochloric acid with alcohol. The resulting ash-free acidic polysaccharide gives a viscous solution in water which does not reduce Fehling solution.

The hydrolysis of the slippery elm mucilage gives D-galactose, L-rhamnose, D-galacturonic acid, and an aldobiouronic acid (102), shown to be 2-O-(α-D-galactopyranosyluronic acid)-L-rhamnose (CCLI) (101), which is also found in the *Plantago* mucilages and flax-seed mucilage. The earlier indication for the presence of a partially methylated aldose in slippery elm mucilage (102) was later confirmed when 3-O-methyl-D-galactose (CCCIII) was identified in the hydrolyzate (103). Quantitative analytical data indicate the mucilage to be composed of D-galactose (1 part), 3-O-methyl-D-galactose (1 part) L-rhamnose (2 parts), and D-galacturonic acid (2 parts) (103).

The purified ash-free polysaccharide contains nitrogen and sulfur. On boiling in aqueous solution it undergoes autohydrolysis with considerable reduction in viscosity and the precipitation of a brown solid which contains all the sulfur and nitrogen and represents about 10 per cent of the undegraded polysaccharide. The degraded polysaccharide is precipitated from the autohydrolyzate solution with alcohol and is found to be slightly reducing to Fehling solution (101,104).   It shows $[\alpha]_D + 68°$ in water and has an equivalent weight of approximately 480.

Treatment of the ash-free polysaccharide with methyl sulfate and alkali removes the protein-like nitrogen and sulfur-containing portion of the mucilage and gives a partially methylated degraded polysaccharide. Methylation of the degraded mucilage by treatment of its thallous salt with methyl iodide gives an essentially homogeneous methylated derivative (104).   The isolation, estimation, and identification of the sugars present in the methylated polysaccharide is complicated by the fact that complete hydrolysis is accompanied by considerable decomposition. Also separation of the methyl glycosides at that time (prior to the advent of partition chromatography) could not be accomplished by fractional distillation due to the formation of constant-boiling mixtures.   However, the following cleavage fragments were identified: 2,3,4,6-tetra-O-methyl-D-galactose (XXXIX, 2 parts), 2,3,6-tri-O-methyl-D-galactose (CCXXXIII, 1 part), 2,4,6-tri-O-methyl-D-galactose (XLVI, 1 part), 3,4-di-O-methyl-L-rhamnose (CCLIV, 2 parts), 4-O-methyl-L-rhamnose (CCCIV, 2 parts), 2,3-di-O-methyl-D-galacturonic acid (CCXXXVII, 4 parts), and 2,3,4-tri-O-methyl-D-galacturonic acid (CCXCIX, trace).   Some unmethylated L-rhamnose has also been reported (105) as a cleavage fragment of the methylated mucilage.

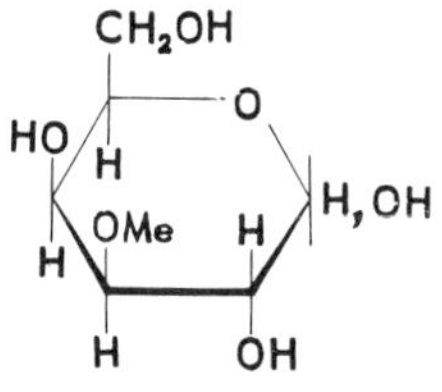

(CCCIII)

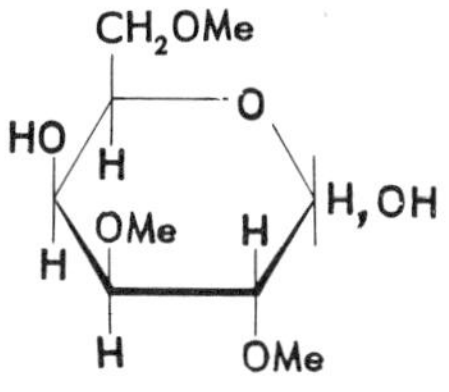

(CCXXXIII)

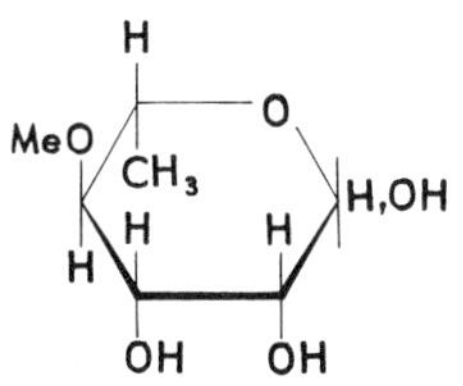

(CCCIV)

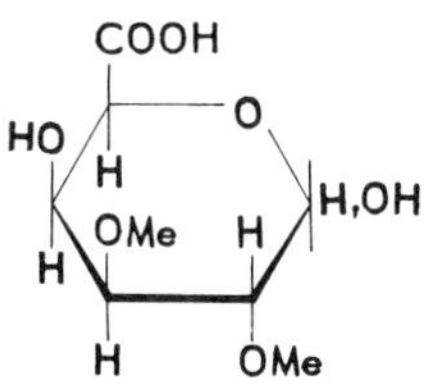

(CCXXXVII)

Although the above evidence indicates the principal linkages in the slippery elm mucilage, the picture is complicated by the fact that half of the D-galactose residues in the untreated polysaccharide are methylated at C_3. Except for the D-galactose units which are linked through

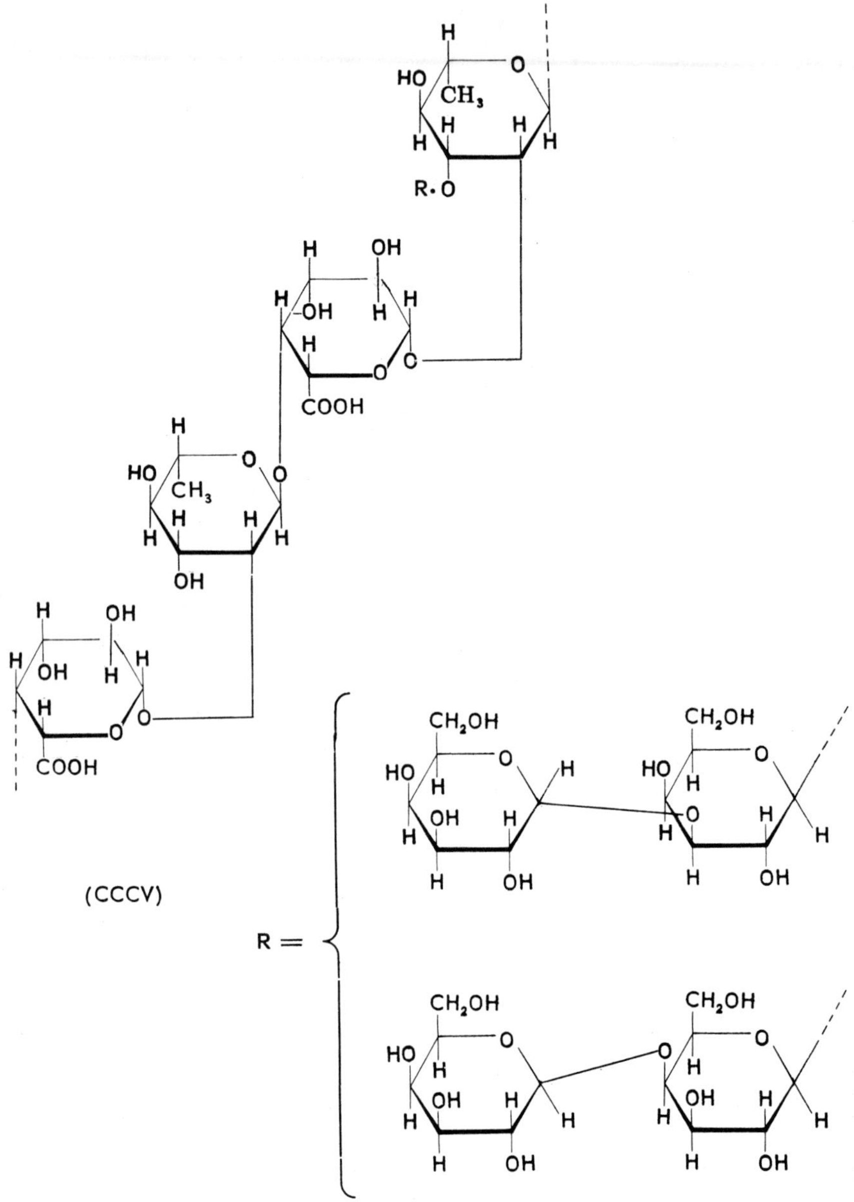

(CCCV)

$R =$

C_1 and C_3 and give rise to 2,3,6-tri-O-methyl-D-galactose upon methylation, the other three methyl D-galactose derivatives may have arisen from D-galactose or 3-O-methyl-D-galactose residues in the polysaccharide. These include the two end groups and that unit which affords 2,3,6-tri-O-methyl-D-galactose and is linked through C_1 and C_4.

Since the only branch points in the average repeating unit of the polysaccharide are the two L-rhamnose residues giving rise to 4-O-methyl-L-rhamnose, it is apparent that there must be L-rhamnose units in the main chain of the molecule. However, the isolation of the aldobiouronic acid, 2-O-(α-D-galactopyranosyluronic acid)-L-rhamnose (CCLI), in good yield from the degraded mucilage indicates that D-galacturonic acid is probably linked to each L-rhamnose unit at C_2.

These features are illustrated by the structure given in formula CCCV of which there are obviously many variants (106).

Cereal Gums

The cereal gums are the non-starchy water-soluble polysaccharides found in seeds of the *Gramineae*. Although finding no use as yet in industry, they are important in the fields of malting and brewing, starch technology, baking and in preparation of all cereal foods. The presence of water-soluble gums in cereals has been known for years, but it is only recently that structural studies of these materials have been made. Such studies have been complicated by the presence of several carbohydrate components, particularly starch, in the cereal grain, and consequently the aqueous extracts of these seeds require careful fractionation before any constitutional work can be commenced. In general, it may be stated that fractionation of the mixture of free polysaccharides into the component polysaccharides is rarely complete and for structural studies most success is achieved by fractionation of the polysaccharide mixture after acetylation and/or methylation. Also, in view of the presence of enzymic systems in the cereal grains it is always imperative that the enzymes be destroyed, usually by heating with 80–85% aqueous ethanol, before the water-soluble materials are extracted. It follows that, since all seeds contain degradative enzymes which become active when the water content and temperature reach certain values, all mucilages extracted from seeds with water may become modified, frequently with resulting loss in viscosity, unless precautions are taken to prevent enzymic breakdown. This has been well-demonstrated in the case of barley gum (107) and it is probably for this reason that the U. S. Dispensatory recommends that the mucilage of quince seeds be freshly prepared as needed and it may explain why aqueous dispersions of guar and locust bean gums will not keep.

Gums of Barley (*Hordeum Vulgare*). In 1882 O'Sullivan described the isolation and properties of *alpha* and *beta* amylan, polysaccharides extracted from barley flour with water (108). Apart from a few investigations (109–112) little additional information about these substances became available until the isolation of a β-D-glucan, $[\alpha]_D - 12.5°$ in water, from fractionation of the aqueous extract of barley by the addition of ammonium sulfate (113,190) (see Table 57). The structure of this glucan was elucidated by methylation studies, the methylated polysaccharide, $[\alpha]_D - 5°$ in chloroform, giving upon hydrolysis equimolecu-

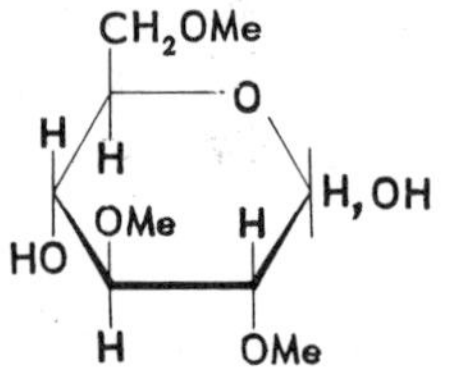

(CCLXXXVIII) 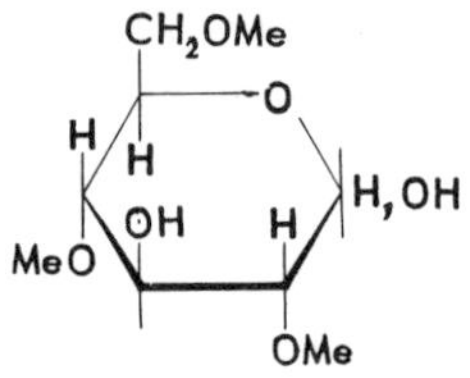   (CCCVI)

lar amounts of 2,3,6-tri-O-methyl-D-glucose (CCLXXXVIII), and 2,4,6-tri-O-methyl-D-glucose (CCCVI), together with a small amount of a mixture of a di-O-methyl and mono-O-methyl glucose (114). Since no tetra-O-methyl-D-glucose (CCXXX), was present in the cleavage fragments it would appear that the polysaccharide has a large average repeating unit and also that the formation of mono-O- and di-O-methyl-glucose may not be of any structural significance. Molecular weight determinations by osmotic pressure measurements on the methylated polysaccharide indicate a DP of about 100, which, if correct, would mean that the β-D-glucan had a cyclic structure, since one part in a hundred is not too difficult to detect by chromatographic analysis. Other methylation studies (115) show that the hydrolyzate of the methylated β-D-glucan contains only 2,3,6-tri-O-methyl-D-glucose and 2,4,6-tri-O-methyl-D-glucose. These methylation data (114,115) suggest that the polysaccharide is an essentially linear chain of D-glucopyranose units with approximately equal proportions of 1 → 3 and 1 → 4 linkages. A study of the glucan by ultracentrifuge techniques had shown that it is not composed of two components while the levorotation of the polysaccharide and its methylated derivative is in keeping with a predominance of β-D-type glycosidic linkages. The presence of 1 → 3 linked D-glucose residues in barley β-D-glucan is also supported by the fact that the periodate-oxidized glucan contains periodate-stable glucose residues

TABLE 57. COMPOSITION OF THE PRINCIPAL
CEREAL GUM FRACTIONS (190)

(Results shown are the approximate percentage compositions of the fractions)

$(NH_4)_2SO_4$ precipitation level %	Sugar unit	Rye	Wheat	Barley	Oats	Maize
20	Glucose	...	...	100	100	...
30	Glucose	17	11	96	93	...
	Xylose	45	64	2	1	...
	Arabinose	38	25	2	6	...
40	Glucose	0	6	12	88	40
	Xylose	61	61	56	8	40
	Arabinose	39	33	32	4	19[a]
50	Glucose	0	23	7	...	92
	Xylose	55	47	65	...	0
	Arabinose	45	30	28	...	6[b]
60	Glucose	2	56	...	...	...
	Xylose	68	24	...	...	...
	Arabinose	30	20	...	...	...
Saturation..	Glucose	...	...	17	61	...
	Xylose	...	...	61	20	...
	Arabinose	...	...	9	19	...
	Mannose	...	...	13	0	...
Mother liquor	Glucose	25	18	15	15	66
	Xylose	9	9	10	14	7
	Arabinose	42	47	62	40	19
	Galactose	22	26	13	31	8

[a] Contains 1 per cent galactose (approx.).
[b] Contains 2 per cent galactose (approx.).

because after reduction with sodium borohydride followed by hydrolysis, a considerable proportion of D-glucose was formed (116).

In addition to the β-D-glucan described above, barley gum contains an α-D-glucan and an araboxylan composed of L-arabofuranose units and D-xylopyranose units (117,118). The three polysaccharides were separated as their methyl derivatives by fractional precipitation of the methylated crude barley gum. The methylated α-D-glucan, $[\alpha]_D + 158°$ in acetone, gives upon hydrolysis tetra-O-methyl-D-glucopyranose (CCXXX, 1 mole), 2,3,6-tri-O-methyl-D-glucopyranose (CCLXXXVIII, 6 moles), and 2,3-di-O-methyl-D-glucopyranose (CCXCV, 1 mole). The α-D-glucan is therefore similar in structure to the amylopectin fraction of starch, but having an average repeating unit of 8 as compared with 18 to 25 for amylopectin.

Hydrolysis of the methylated araboxylan, $[\alpha]_D - 160°$ in acetone, affords 2,3,5-tri-O-methyl-L-arabofuranose (CLXL), 2,3-di-O-methyl-D-xylopyranose (CCCI), 2-O-methyl-D-xylopyranose (CCCII), and D-xylopyranose. The arabo-xylan is therefore composed of a branched-chain of D-xylopyranose units having L-arabofuranose residue as the end groups. It resembles very closely the arabo-xylan of wheat flour.

Oat Gum. Oat gum sometimes referred to as oat lichenin (197,198) has been isolated from oat flour and from oat bran which had been extracted with methanol and with acetone to inactivate the hydrolytic enzymes. The oat gum was extracted with water at room temperature and purified by acetylation (197,198). Oat gum prepared in this manner was found (199) to be homogeneous (ultracentrifuge), it showed $[\alpha]_D + 6°$ (N NaOH) and gave only D-glucose upon hydrolysis. Like the gum from barley flour, oat gum thus appears to be a β-D-glucan.

The methylated oat gum, $[\alpha]_D - 13°$ (acetone), obtained by treatment of the gum with sodium and methyl iodide in liquid ammonia, afforded upon hydrolysis a mixture of 2,3,6-tri- and 2,4,6-tri-O-methyl-D-glucose together with trace amounts of 2,3-di- and 2,3,4,6-tetra-O-methyl-D-glucose which indicated a low degree of branching (199). The ratio of of 1 → 4 to 1 → 3 linkages, deduced from the molar ratio of the 2,3,6-tri- and 2,4,6-tri-O-methyl sugars was 1.77 : 1.00 a result in good agreement with that from periodate studies; these results may be compared with those from previous periodate oxidation studies which indicated values of 3.18 : 1.00 (198) and 1.86 : 1.00 (200) for the ratio of 1 → 4 to 1 → 3 linkages.

The average degree of polymerization (DP), calculated from the amount of formaldehyde liberated upon treating the reduced (NaBH$_4$) gum with periodate (201), was about 1000, a result in fairly good agreement with the value (920) from ultracentrifuge experiments (199).

Failure to destroy the enzymes in the oat flour before cold aqueous extraction results in the production of a degraded oat gum, specimens with a DP of 20 and 120 having been isolated (199). Methylation studies showed that in the degraded gums the ratio of 1 → 4 to 1 → 3 linkages was higher than that found for the so-called undegraded gum. In general it appears that the lower the DP the higher the ratio of 1 → 4 to 1 → 3 linkages. Thus for the gum with DP 1000 the ratio of 1 → 4 to 1 → 3 linkages was 1.77 : 1.00, for the degraded gum, DP 120, the ratio was 2.24 : 1.00 and for a specimen with DP 20 the ratio was 2.54 : 1.00.

That enzymes in the oat grain are indeed capable of hydrolyzing the oat gum has been shown by the observation that the viscosity of an aqueous solution of undegraded gum decreased rapidly when treated with the enzyme system extracted with water from untreated oat flour. The increase in the ratio of $1 \rightarrow 4$ to $1 \rightarrow 3$ bonds during enzymic breakdown of the oat gum indicated that the $1 \rightarrow 3$ linkages were preferentially attacked.

Evidence concerning the presence of contiguous $1 \rightarrow 4$ linkages in the oat gum has been obtained from the results of graded hydrolysis of the gum (198). When oat gum was heated on a boiling-water bath for 1 hr. with 0.33 N sulfuric acid until the apparent conversion to D-glucose was 27 per cent, there were produced in addition to D-glucose, cellobiose, laminaribiose, cellotriose, 4-O-β-laminaribiosylglucose and 3-O-β-cellobiosylglucose. The identification of these products indicated that contiguous $1 \rightarrow 4$ linkages were present in the oat gum and, as the authors pointed out (198), the oat gum was "similar in structure to if not identical with (Iceland) moss lichenin" concerning which they reported (198) that "there is thus some justification for the view that the lichenin (oat gum) molecule is constituted of cellotriose units joined by $1 \rightarrow 3$ links i.e. a repeating pattern of the link sequence, $(1 \rightarrow 4)$ $(1 \rightarrow 4)$ $(1 \rightarrow 3)$.

When a sugar residue of a polysaccharide is cleaved by periodate and then reduced, the resulting alcoholic derivative, being a true acetal, is extremely sensitive to acid. On the other hand a sugar residue which escapes periodate oxidation still carries a true glycosidic grouping which is relatively stable to acid. Because of the difference in stability between the acetal and glycosidic groups it is now possible to obtain from a wide variety of polysaccharides, oligosaccharide glycosides of constitutional significance (202). Thus for example a periodate-stable residue joined by a $1 \rightarrow 4$ bond to a D-glucopyranose unit gives rise to an erythrityl glycoside whereas if the stable residue is joined by a $1 \rightarrow 6$ bond a glyceryl glycoside is formed. The application of this new prodedure has indicated the presence of contiguous $1 \rightarrow 3$ linkages in oat gum. Thus periodate oxidation of oat gum followed by reduction and mild acid hydrolysis of the resulting polyalcohol afforded a mixture of erythritol which arises from two or more contiguous $1 \rightarrow 4$ linkages, D-(2-O-β-D-glucopyranosyl-erythritol) from alternating $1 \rightarrow 4$ and $1 \rightarrow 3$ linked D-glucose units, D-(2-O-β-D-laminaribiosyl-erythritol) from a sequence of two $1 \rightarrow 3$ linked glucose units flanked by $1 \rightarrow 4$ linkages, D-(2-O-β-laminaritriosyl-erythritol) from a sequence of three $1 \rightarrow 3$ linked glucose units flanked by $1 \rightarrow 4$ bonds and D-(2-O-β-laminaritetraosyl erythritol) from a sequence of four $1 \rightarrow 3$ linked glucose units flanked by $1 \rightarrow 4$ bonds (199,202). Confirmation that these fragments, which arose from $1 \rightarrow 3$ linked units, contained only β-linkages was provided by the observation that the fragments were all hydrolyzed by β-D-glucosidase to give D-glucose and erythritol.

The above experimental data indicated that the oat gum contains sequences of two 1 → 4 β links (198) and sequences of two to four 1 → 3 β linkages (202). The remainder and major portion of the oat gum molecule is made up of D-glucopyranose units joined by alternating 1 → 4 and 1 → 3 linkages (198–200,202). The oat gum molecule (DP 1000 approx.) appears to be largely linear in character although methylation studies on both the degraded (199,200) and undegraded oat gum (199) indicate the presence of a low degree of branching.

Gums of Wheat (*Triticum Vulgare*). Wheat flour, previously treated with 82 per cent aqueous alcohol to inactivate enzymes and extracted with 70 per cent aqueous alcohol to remove free sugars and oligosaccharides (120), gives a mixture of glucans and an arabo-xylan when extracted with water (119). A similar mixture is obtained from wheat flour by direct extraction with water without previous enzyme inactivation (121). By the fractional extraction (121) or precipitation (119) of the acetylated product, the acetylated pentosan component is obtained. Methylation of this acetylated pentosan fraction with methyl sulfate and alkali, followed by fractional precipitation of the methyl derivative gives the methylated arabo-xylan ($[\alpha]_D - 175°$ in acetone) free from associated methyl glucans. Hydrolysis of the methyl arabo-xylan affords 2,3,5-tri-*O*-methyl-L-arabofuranose (CLXL, 13 moles), 2,3-di-*O*-methyl-D-xylopyranose (CCCI, 19 moles), 2-*O*-methyl-D-xylopyranose (CCCII, 6 moles), D-xylose (4 moles) and a trace of 3-*O*-methyl-D-xylopyranose (CCLVIII) (119). The methylated derivative of an arabo-xylan, which was originally extracted from wheat flour without previous inactivation of the enzymes present in the flour, gives upon hydrolysis 2,3,5-tri-*O*-methyl-L-arabofuranose (CLXL, 3 moles), 2,3-di-*O*-methyl-D-xylopyranose (CCCI, 3 moles), 2-*O*-methyl-D-xylopyranose (CCCII, 1 mole), and D-xylose (1 mole) (121). Both arabo-xylans appear to have similar general structural features, being highly branched and having end-groups of L-arabofuranose residues.

When wheat flour, freed from gluten, is suspended in water and centrifuged, it separates into a tightly packed lower layer of wheat starch above which is a mucilaginous layer. The latter, which has been variously called the "amylodextrin" (122), "squeegee" (123) or "tailings" (124) of wheat flour, plays an important role in the starch-gluten separation process. Prolonged hydrolysis of the "squeegee" material with pancreatin, gives a water-insoluble product (125). Acetylation of the latter, followed by extraction with acetone leaves 70 per cent of the material as an insoluble acetate which upon deacetylation gives a water-soluble arabo-xylan, $[\alpha]_D - 108°$ in 0.5N sodium hydroxide (126). The methyl derivative of this pentosan has the striking property of giving highly viscous solutions in acetone, a physical characteristic of aqueous solutions of gums from barley, wheat and rye. Hydrolysis of the methylated pentosan affords 2,3,5-tri-O-methyl-L-arabofuranose (CLXL, 14 moles), 2,3-di-O-methyl-D-xylose (CCCI, 24 moles), 2-O-methyl-D-xylose (CCCII, 7 moles), D-xylose (4 moles), and small amounts of two unknown products. The general structure of this hemicellulose is, therefore, similar to that which is extracted from wheat flour with water and it is probable that the pentosan in the "squeegee" fraction of the flour is bound in some way to protein.

Reference should be made to the presence of a water-soluble polysaccharide, associated with the β-amylase in wheat flour, which may be isolated by extraction in the cold with 20 per cent aqueous alcohol (127). The crude polysaccharide is separated from the enzyme by the formation of its acetate derivative, $[\alpha]_D - 57.7°$ in chloroform, from which the nitrogen-free polysaccharide, $[\alpha]_D - 78.5°$ in water, is regenerated by deacetylation with potassium hydroxide. It shows no amylytic activity, gives no color with iodine thereby demonstrating the absence of starch or starch dextrins, and is composed of units of L-arabinose, D-xylose, and D-galactose. The presence of D-galactose differentiates this polysaccharide from the other water-soluble gums which have been isolated from wheat flour, for although this sugar has been reported (121) to be present in the crude products isolated by aqueous extraction of the flour it is not present in the purified pentosans isolated therefrom.

The structural features of the β-amylase polysaccharide are revealed by the fact that its methyl derivative (127) gives upon hydrolysis, 2,3,5-tri-O-methyl-L-arabinose (CLXL, 6 moles), 2,3-di-O-methyl-D-xylose (CCCI, 6 moles), 2-O-methyl-D-xylose (CCCII, 1 mole), D-xylose (1 mole) and 2,4-di-O-methyl-D-galactose (CLXXXII). The cleavage fragments, separated by the fractional distillation of the corresponding methyl glycosides, demonstrate that all the end-groups of the molecule are composed of L-arabofuranose residues while the D-galactopyranose units constitute branch points that are linked through C_1, C_3 and C_6. Other branch points are found in some of the D-xylopyranose residues, linked through C_1, C_3 and C_4, and C_1, C_2, C_3 and C_4, the remaining D-xylopyranose units being linked through C_1 and C_4. The branched structure of this polysaccharide, which is indicated by the high proportion of end groups, conforms to the general type of hemicellulose present in the Gramineae, differing, however, in the presence of D-galactopyranose residues in the molecule.

The Gum of Rye (Secale Cereale). The flour of rye, when extracted with water, gives a highly viscous gum-like product which after removal of the starch is composed of equimolecular amounts of L-arabinose, D-xylose and D-glucose (128). This so-called rye gum, said to give more viscous solutions than gum tragacanth, is largely responsible for the fact that it is difficult to isolate a gluten from rye flour. The gum probably consists of a mixture of glucans, an arabo-xylan, and possibly some protein.

Corn Hull Gum or Hemicellulose. A hemicellulose is extracted from the hulls of corn (Zea mays) kernels which are a by-product of the industrial wet-milling of corn. Aqueous solutions of the corn hull gum have a solution viscosity considerably higher than that of gum arabic, but lower than that of such gums as karaya and tragacanth (129). It is suggested that the material may prove useful as a thickener and as an adhesive.

The corn hulls are ground and, after a pre-treatment at pH 10.5 to 11.5 in sodium hydroxide solution, extracted with hot water. The product which is precipitated from aqueous extract after acidification with alcohol shows $[\alpha]_D - 81°$ in water and upon hydrolysis gives D-xylose (129), L-arabinose (129), D-galactose (129) and D-glucuronic acid (130).

The neutral sugars are in the proportion, D-xylose (7 parts), L-arabinose (5 parts), and D-galactose (1 part) and the uronic acid constitutes 7 to 12 per cent of the polysaccharide. The presence of D-galactose in the molecule suggests that it may resemble the polysaccharide associated with β-amylase in wheat flour (see above).

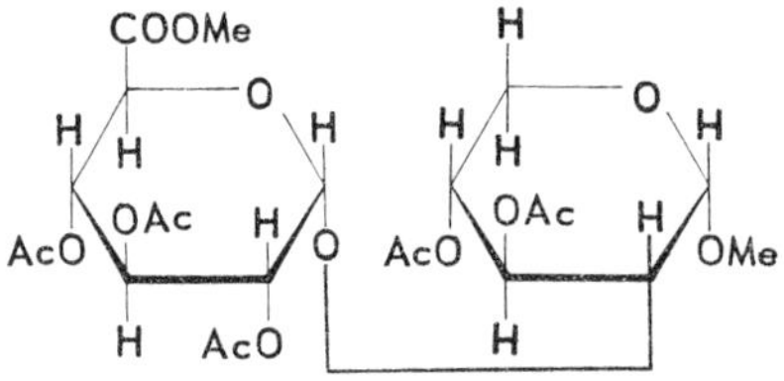

(CCCVII)

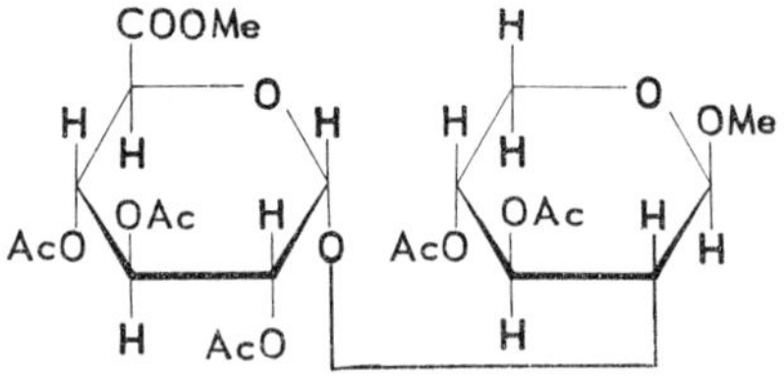

(CCCVIII)

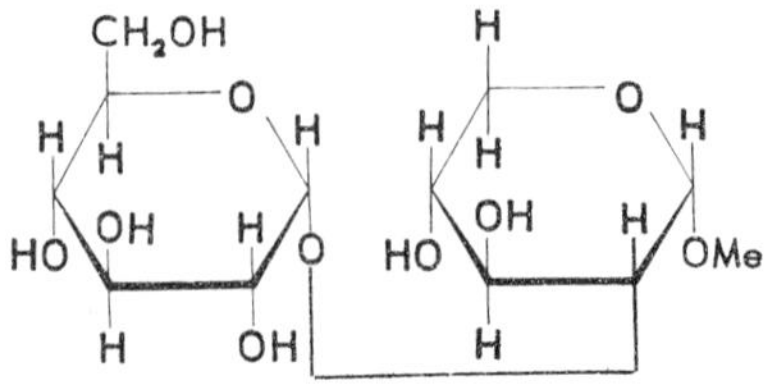

(CCCIX)

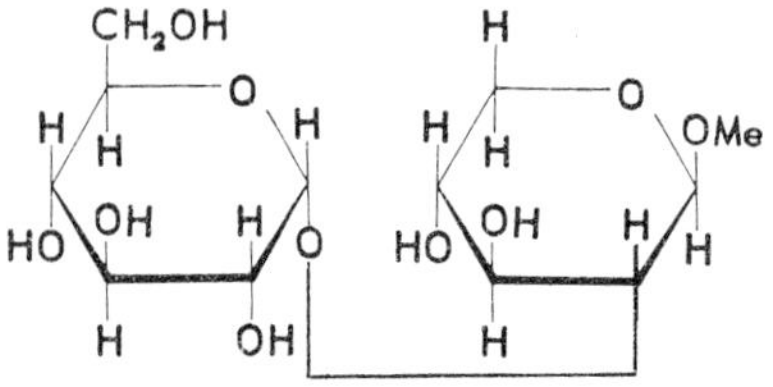

(CCCX)

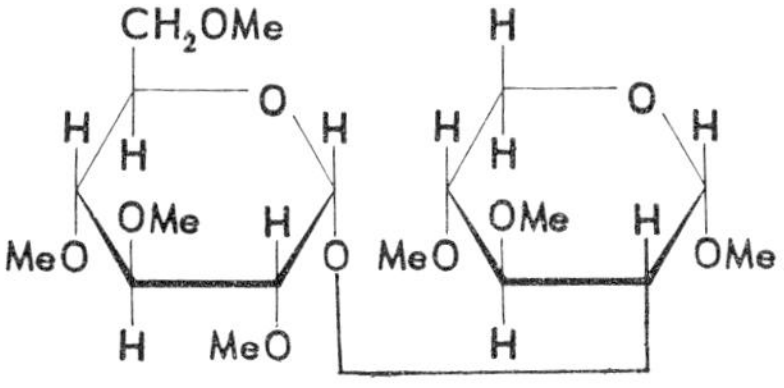

(CCCXI)

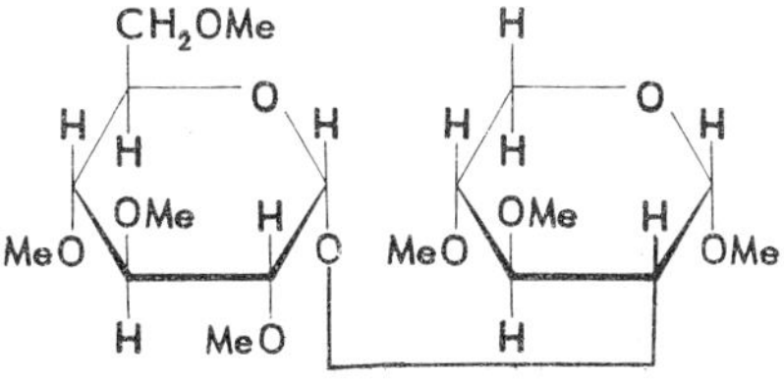

(CCCXII)

The structure of the corn hull gum has been investigated by graded hydrolysis to give oligosaccharides and by methylation studies.

Hydrolysis of the corn hull gum with N sulfuric acid produces L-arabinose, D- and L-galactose, D-xylose and an aldobiouronic acid. When the aldobiouronic acid, which can be readily separated as a barium salt from the sugars by precipitation from aqueous solution with alcohol, is boiled with methanolic hydrogen chloride and then acetylated, it is obtained in its crystalline anomeric forms (CCCVII) and (CCCVIII).

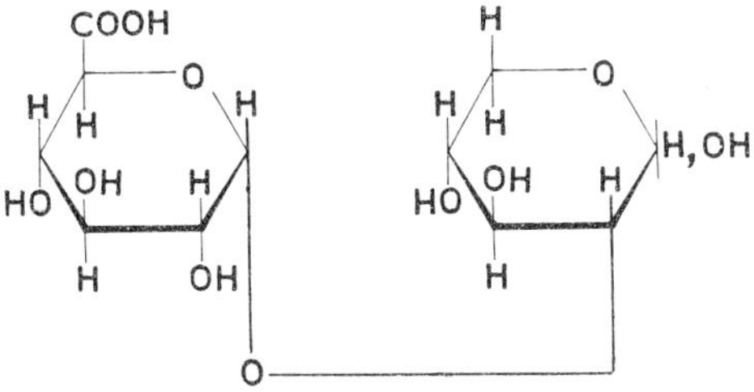

(CCLXIII)

Methylation of CCCVII and CCCVIII followed by reduction with lithium aluminum hydride (130–132) and re-methylation gives the corresponding anomers of the fully methylated neutral disaccharide CCCXI and CCCXII. Hydrolysis of either CCCXI or CCCXII gives 2,3,4,6-tetra-O-methyl-D-glucose recognized as its N-phenyl-glycosylamine and 3,4-di-O-methyl-D-xylose recognized as the corresponding crystalline lactone, thus proving the presence of a 1 → 2 biose linkage in the aldobiouronic acid; it is also clear that the aldobiouronic acid must be composed of D-glucuronic acid and D-xylose. Reduction of the anomers CCCVII and CCCVIII with lithium aluminum hydride gives the two neutral disaccharide glycosides CCCIX and CCCX both of which upon treatment with α-D-glucosidase furnish D-glucose; at the same time CCCVII gives methyl-α-D-xylopyranoside and CCCVIII gives methyl β-D-xylopyranoside as revealed by electrophoresis on glass paper (131,133). It is apparent, therefore, that the biose linkage in both CCCVII and CCCVIII is of the α-D-type and hence the aldobiouronic acid in question is designated 2-O-(α-D-glucopyranosyluronic acid)-D-xylose (CCLXIII). This same aldobiouronic acid has also been obtained from chagual gum (137) and there is evidence for it in a certain fraction of oat hull hemicellulose (138,139).

Graded acid hydrolysis of the corn hull gum has provided a variety of neutral oligosaccharides amongst which the following have been identified: 3-O-α-D-xylopyranosyl-L-arabinose (CCLXIX) (134,135), 4-O-β-D-xylopyranosyl-D-xylose (CCCXIII) (136), 5-O-β-D-galactopyranosyl-L-arabinose (CCCXIV) (136), 4-O-β-D-galactopyranosyl-D-xylose (CCCXV) (135), and O-L-galactopyranosyl-(1 → 4)-O-D-xylopyranosyl-(1 → 2)-L-arabinose (CCCXVI) (134).

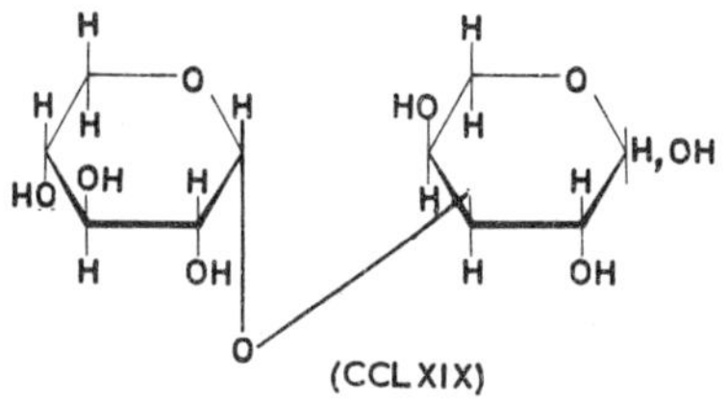

(CCLXIX)

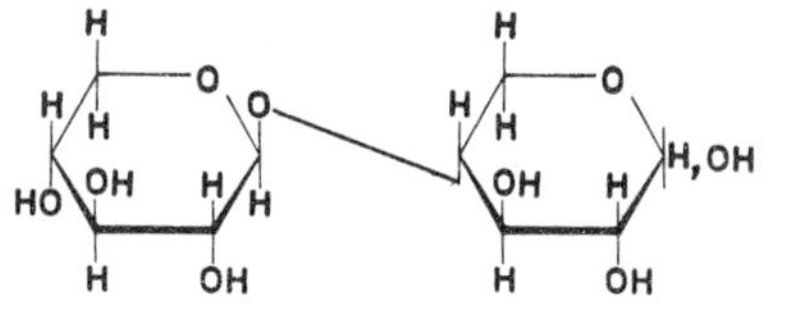

(CCCXIII)

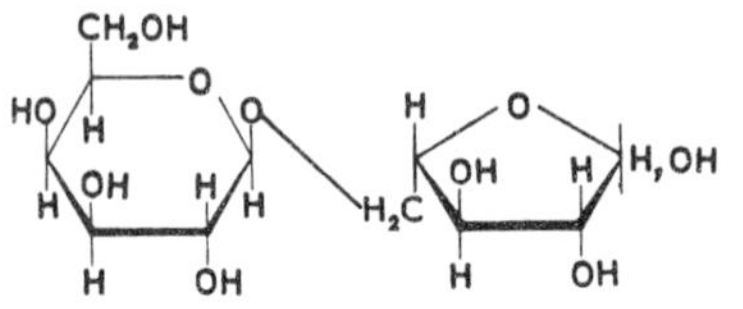

(CCCXIV)

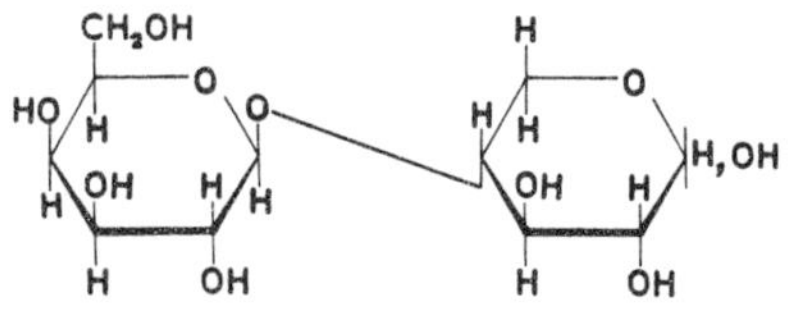

(CCCXV)

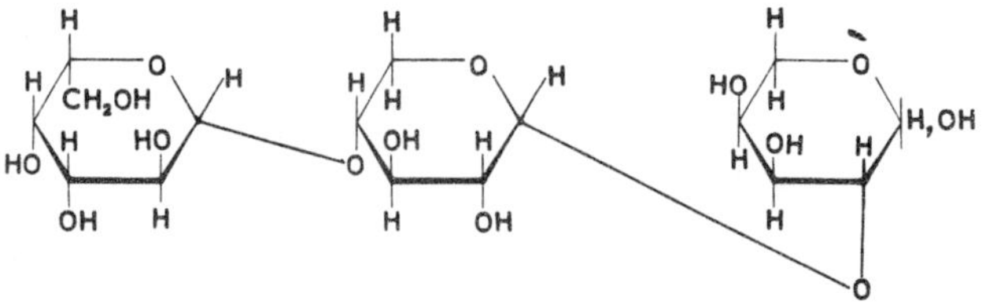

(CCCXVI)

The structure of the 3-O-α-D-xylopyranosyl-L-arabinose (CCL XIX), which is best characterized as its hexaacetate, is based upon the following evidence. The melting point and rotation of this disaccharide agreed with those quoted for the 3-O-α-D-xylopyranosyl-L-arabinose obtained from golden apple gum (140). Upon hydrolysis it affords xylose and arabinose and after oxidation with bromine to the corresponding aldobionic acid followed by hydrolysis it yields xylose, but no arabinose; likewise hydrolysis of the osazone of the disaccharide gave xylose and not arabinose. Both these observations show that the xylose moiety occupies the nonreducing end in the molecule. Methylation of CCL XIX followed by hydrolysis yields (134) 2,3,4-tri-O-methyl-D-xylose and 2,4-di-O-methyl-L-arabinose, a compound first obtained and characterized as its aniline derivative during studies on gum arabic (141); both fragments were characterized as their aniline derivatives. The isolation of 2,4-di-O-methyl-L-arabinose established the presence of the presence of the 1 → 3 biose linkage and since the disaccharide shows a high positive rotation, $[\alpha]_D$ + 175° → 183° (water), the biose linkage must be of the α type. Hence CCLXIX is designated 3-O-α-D-xylopyranosyl-L-arabinose.

The structure of the second oligosaccharide (CCCXIII) was shown to be 4-O-β-D-xylopyranosyl-D-xylose by the fact that upon hydrolysis it gave only xylose. Moreover, it afforded a characteristic crystalline osazone and had properties that were in agreement with that previously quoted for a sample of 4-O-β-D-xylopyranosyl-D-xylose obtained (142) from corn cob hemicellulose, the structure of which was ascertained in the usual classical manner. Methylation of the disaccharide (CCCXIII) followed by hydrolysis gave 2,3,4-tri-O- and 2,3-di-O-methyl-D-xylose, whereas successive bromine oxidation, methylation and hydrolysis gave 2,3,4-tri-O-methyl-D-xylose and 2,3,5-tri-O-methyl-D-xylonic acid. This evidence proved the presence of the biose linkage and since the original disaccharide had a low rotation ($[\alpha]_D$ − 30° → − 23° (water)), it was clear that the linkage was of the β-D-type.

The structure of the disaccharide 5-O-β-D-galactopyranosyl-L-arabofuranose (CCCXIV), rests on the following facts (136). Upon hydrolysis CCCXIV furnished D-galactose and L-arabinose, whereas hydrolysis of the osazone of CCCXIV yielded D-galactose, but no arabinose. This evidence showed that the disaccharide was composed of D-galactose and L-arabinose and that the L-arabinose constitutes the reducing end of the molecule; it was also apparent that the biose linkage did not engage C_2 of the L-arabinose residue since osazone formation would therefore have been prevented. Methylation of CCCXIV first with methyl sulfate and alkali and then with silver oxide and methyl iodide gave the fully methylated derivative which upon hydrolysis yielded approximately equimolecular amounts of 2,3,4,6-tetra-O-methyl-D-galactose and 2,3-di-O-methyl-L-arabinose. The former was identified as N-phenyl-D-galactopyranosylamino 2,3,4,6-tetramethyl ether and the latter was converted to the characteristic 2,3-di-O-methyl-L-arabinose 1,4-di-p-nitrobenzoate.

The facts thus far led to the deduction that the disaccharide was either 5-O-D-galactopyranosyl-L-arabofuranose, or 4-O-D-galactopyranosyl-L-arabopyranose. That CCCXIV contained a 1 → 5 and not a 1 → 4 biose linkage was proved by synthesizing CCCXIV by an unambiguous procedure. Thus interaction of 2,3,4,6-tetra-O-acetyl-α-D-galactosyl bromide with ethyl 2,3-di-O-acetyl-α-L-arabofuranoside in the presence of silver oxide afforded ethyl 5-O-(2,3,4,6-tetra-O-acetyl-β-D-galactosyl) 2,3-di-O-acetyl-α-L-arabofuranoside, which, upon deacetylation and hydrolysis with dilute sulfuric acid, gave rise to 5-O-β-D-galactopyranosyl-L-arabofuranose. This synthetic disaccharide had the same rotation and mobility on paper chromatograms as the disaccharide (CCCXIV) from corn hull gum, and, furthermore, upon methylation and hydrolysis it also furnished 2,3,4,6-tetra-O-methyl-D-galactose and 2,3-di-O-methyl-L-arabinose. There is little doubt, therefore, that CCCXIV is correctly designated as 5-O-β-D-galactopyranosyl-L-arabinose.

The structure of the fourth neutral oligosaccharide (CCCXV) was shown (135) to be 4-O-D-galactopyranosyl-D-xylose in the following way. Hydrolysis of CCCXV afforded D-galactose and D-xylose while hydrolysis of the aldobionic acid derived from CCCXV by bromine oxidation gave D-galactose but no D-xylose, thus proving that CCCXV was a D-galactosyl-D-xylose. Treatment of CCCXV with 0.5 per cent methanolic hydrogen chloride at room temperature furnished a crystalline glycoside, methyl 4-O-(β-D-galactopyranosyl)-D-xylopyranoside, which was completely methylated with silver oxide and methyl iodide and subsequently hydrolyzed. In this way there was obtained 2,3,4,6-tetra-O-methyl-D-galactose and 2,3-di-O-methyl-D-xylose, both of which were characterized as their crystalline aniline derivatives. It was deduced, therefore, that CCCXV contained a 1 → 4 linkage and from its low rotation this linkage is of the β-D-type and consequently it is designated 4-O-β-D-galactopyranosyl-D-xylose. The above experimental findings could be explained on the basis of a 1 → 5 linked disaccharide, but the relative slow rate of liberating the disaccharide from the gum by hydrolysis favors a pyranose structure for the xylose moiety and hence a 1 → 4 biose link.

The constitution of the trisaccharide (CCCXVI) obtained (134) from corn hull gum by graded hydrolysis rests upon the following evidence. Upon hydrolysis CCCXVI gives L-galactose, D-xylose and L-arabinose. The isolation of L-galactose shows that the corn hull gum is relatively rare among gums and mucilages for this far, only flaxseed mucilage and agar have been found to contain the L-form of this sugar (see Chapter 7, Tables 31 and 32). The location of the L-arabinose as the terminal reducing unit was established by showing that bromine oxidation of CCCXVI to the corresponding aldotrionic acid followed by hydrolysis yielded L-galactose and D-xylose, but no L-arabinose. The manner of the union of the residue in CCCXVI was established by methylation of the corresponding aldotrionic acid, and subsequent hydrolysis when there were obtained 2,3,4,6-tetra-O-methyl-L-galactose, 2,3-di-O-methyl-D-xylose and 3,4,5-tri-O-methyl-L-arabonic acid. The structure of this last compound was based on the fact that upon periodate oxidation it yielded one molecular proportion of carbon dioxide, thus indicating cleavage between C_1 and C_2. This revealed the presence of a hydroxyl group at C_2 and hence established that the methyl groups were located at C_3, C_4 and C_5. Although the possibility of the D-xylose existing as a furanose unit was not ruled out, the relative stability of CCCXVI towards acidic reagents favors the pyranose structure and hence it is designated O-L-galactopyranosyl-(1 $\rightarrow$ 4)-O-D-xylopyranosyl-(1 $\rightarrow$ 2)-L-arabinose (134).

Further evidence concerning the structure of corn hull gum is provided by methylation studies (143,144,147). The polysaccharide gum was methylated in the usual way, with methyl sulfate and 45 per cent potassium hydroxide and isolated as the methylated polysaccharide acid by precipitation from a solution in 1,4-dioxane with N hydrochloric acid. Like many methylated polysaccharides the methylated corn hull gum acid readily absorbed solvent and vigorous drying was required to remove it. Fractional precipitation of the methylated polysaccharide and the acetate from which it was prepared indicated that the polysaccharide was essentially homogeneous.

Methanolysis of the methylated gum with 3 per cent methanolic hydrogen chloride in the usual manner yielded a mixture of methylated sugar glycosides and the methyl ester glycoside of a methylated aldobiouronic acid. Treatment of this mixture of glycosides with dilute barium hydroxide to saponify the ester grouping of the methylated aldobiouronic acid enabled the latter to be separated on an anion-exchange resin from the neutral methylated sugar glycosides (145).

After displacement of the methylated aldobiouronic acid (CCCXVII) from the anion-exchange resin with alkali, it was freed from inorganic ions by passing a solution of it through a cation-exchange resin. Thereafter it was esterified and the resulting methylated methyl ester methyl glycoside reduced with lithium aluminum hydride (132) to give the

characteristic crystalline methyl 2-O-(2,3,4-tri-O-methyl-α- D-glucosyl)-
3-O-methyl-β-D-xylopyranoside (CCCXVIII) previously obtained (146) in
studies on the pentosan from Western Hemlock wood.

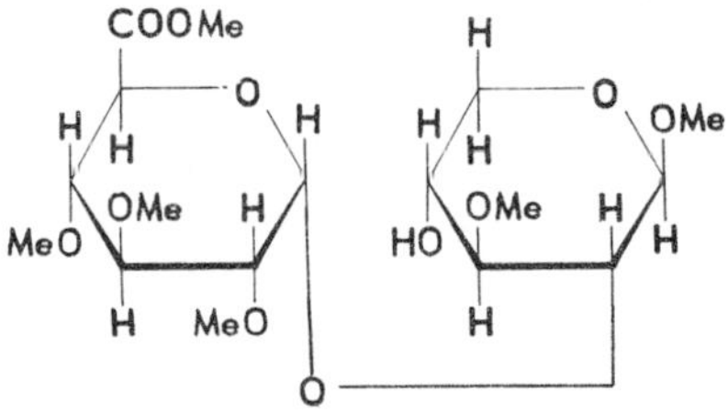

(CCCXVII) 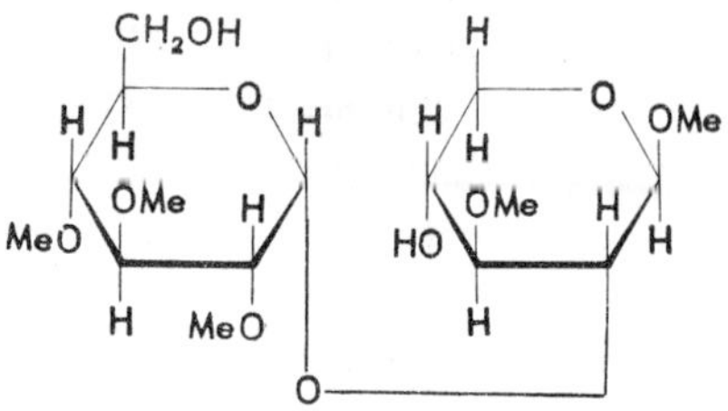   (CCCXVIII)

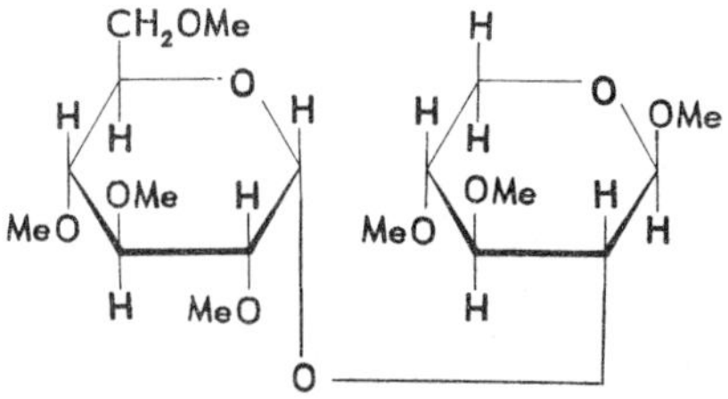

(CCCXIX)

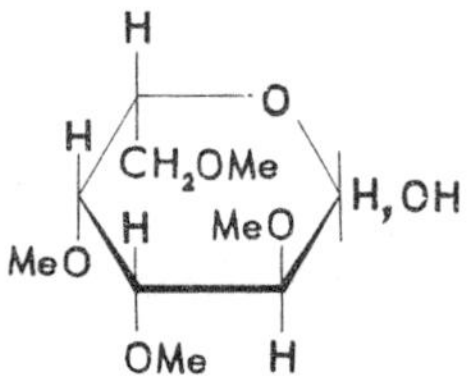

(CCCXX) 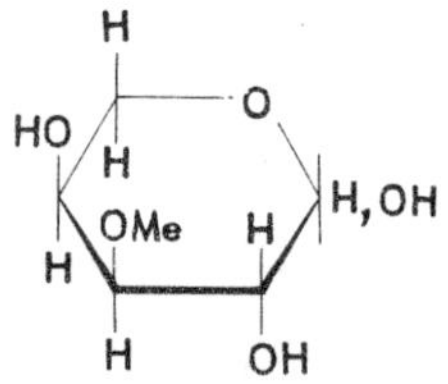   (CCCXXI)

The structure of CCCXVIII was proved by the fact that hydrolysis
afforded 2,3,4-tri-O-methyl-D-glucose, characterized as its N-phenyl-
glycosylamine, and 3-O-methyl-D-xylose, which crystallized directly.
Methylation of CCCXVIII to give CCCXIX followed by hydrolysis furnished 2,3,4,6-tetra-O-methyl-D-glucose (CCXXX) and 3,4-di-O-methyl-
D-xylose (CCXXXVI), the former crystallizing directly whereas the latter
was identified after bromine oxidation as the crystalline 3,4-di-O-methyl-
D-xylonolactone; this observation proved that the biose linkage in
CCCXIX and therefore in CCCXVII engages C$_2$ of the D-xylose residue.
The characterization of CCCXVIII taken together with the previous
identification of 2-O-(α-D-glucopyranosyluronic adid)-D-xylose as one

of the products of hydrolysis of the gum itself proves that the methylated aldobiouronic fragment present in the methylated gum is 2-O-(2,3,4-tri-O-methyl-D-glucosyluronic acid)-3-O-methyl-D-xylose and, in addition, it is also clear that the units of D-glucopyranuronic acid occupy terminal positions in the corn hull gum molecule and are linked directly to D-xylopyranose units which constitute branch points in the molecule (145,147).

Examination of the mixture of neutral methylated sugars obtained from methylated corn hull gum by partition chromatography on a hydrocellulose:cellulose column and on paper showed (143,144,147) that there were present 2,3,4,6-tetra-O-methyl-D-galactose (XXXIX), 2,3,4,6-tetra-O-methyl-L-galactose (CCCXX), 2,3,5-tri-O-methyl-L-arabinose (CLXL), 2,3,4-tri-O-methyl-D-xylose (CCXII), 2,5-di-O-methyl-L-arabinose (XLIII), 2,3-di-O-methyl-D-xylose (CCCI), 3-O-methyl-L-arabinose (CCCXXI), 2-O-methyl-D-xylose (CCCII), and D-xylose.

The presence of both the D- and the L-forms of 2,3,4,6-tetra-O-methyl-galactose was established by the isolation of the optically inactive anilide (148), while the 2,3,5-tri-O-methyl-L-arabinose was characterized after bromine oxidation as the corresponding amide. The 2,3,4-tri- and 2,3-di-O-methyl-D-xylose were identified as their aniline derivatives and the 2,5-di-O-methyl-L-arabinose as the amide of the corresponding aldonic acid. The 3-O-methyl-L-arabinose gave a crystalline aniline derivative also did the crystalline 2-O-methyl-D-xylose and the unsubstituted D-xylose crystallized directly.

The methylation results reveal (143–145) that the corn hull gum has a highly branched structure. This follows from the characterization of the 2,3,4,6-tetra-O-methyl-D- and L-galactose, 2,3,5-tri-O-methyl-L-arabinose, 2,3,4-tri-O-methyl-D-xylose and 2,3,4-tri-O-methyl-D-glucuronic acid, which arise from terminal nonreducing ends in the molecular complex. The same deduction is to be made from the isolation of 3-O-methyl-L-arabinose, 2-O-methyl-D-xylose and D-xylose, which are derived from sugar residues at which branching occurs.

The main structural framework is constructed of D-xylose units, probably of the pyranose type, and to this framework are attached some, if not all of the relatively labile oligosaccharides, produced by graded acid hydrolysis as well as units of glucuronic acid. Support for the view that the main structural pattern is a xylan polymer is forthcoming from the fact that methylation of that portion of the corn hull gum remaining after the oligosaccharides (CCLXIX, CCCXIII, CCCXV and CCCXVI) have been removed by graded hydrolysis affords only O-methyl derivatives of D-xylose as the neutral components (149), namely 2,3,4-tri-O-(CCXII, 14 parts), 2,3-di-O-(CCCI, 47 parts), 2-O-methyl-D-xylose (CCCII,

19 parts) and D-xylose (2 parts). It is very probable that the units of D-glucuronic acid that give rise to the 2-O-(D-glucopyranosyluronic acid)-D-xylose upon prolonged acid hydrolysis are also present in this degraded gum molecule which still retained the acid character of the original gum. On the assumption that the main structural framework of the stable nucleus is a glucurono-xylan it follows, from the characterization of 3-O-methyl-L-arabinose (CCCXXI) as one of the cleavage products of the methylated gum, that some L-arabinose units in the side chains are involved in branching.

The interesting feature of this particular gum is that the main structural framework is a glycurono-pentosan whereas many other gums are based upon a stable nucleus or collection of nuclei that are essentially glycurono-hexosans (150, cf. 100).

REFERENCES

1. Schultz, E., Steiger, E., and Maxwell, W., Z. physiol. Chem., **14,** 227 (1890).
2. Anderson, E., Ind. Eng. Chem., **41,** 2887 (1949).
3. Van der Haar, A. W., "Anleitung zum Nachweis, zur Trennung und Bestimmung der reinen und aus Glucosiden usw. erhaltenen Monosaccharide und Aldehydsäuren," Gebruder Borntraeger, Berlin (1920).
4. Bourquelot, E., and Hérissey, H., Compt. rend., **129,** 228, 391 (1899).
5. Iglesias, G., Anales soc. espan. fís. y quím., **33,** 114 (1935); Chem. Abstracts, **29,** 4044 (1935).
6. Rafique, C. M., and Smith, F., J. Am. Chem. Soc., **72,** 4634 (1950).
7. Heyne, Eileen, and Whistler, R. L., J. Am. Chem. Soc., **70,** 2249 (1948).
8. Wise, L. E., and Appling, J. W., Ind. Eng. Chem., Anal. Ed., **16,** 28 (1944).
9. Rowland, B. W., Chemurgic Digest, **4,** No. 23, 369 (1945); Chem. Abstracts, **40,** 1655 (1946).
10. Wise, L. E., Green, J. W., and Rittenhouse, Ruth C., Tappi, **32,** 335 (1949).
11. Whistler, R. L., and Durso, D. F., J. Am. Chem. Soc., **73,** 4189 (1951).
12. Whistler, R. L., and Durso, D. F., J. Am. Chem. Soc., **74,** 5140 (1952).
13. Whistler, R. L., and Stein, Joan Z., J. Am. Chem. Soc., **73,** 4187 (1951).
14. Adams, Mildred, Richtmyer, N. K., and Hudson, C. S., J. Am. Chem. Soc., **65,** 1369 (1943).
15. Effront, J., Compt. rend., **125,** 116 (1897).
16. Bourquelot, E., and Hérissey, H., Compt. rend., **129,** 614 (1899).
17. Whistler, R. L., Eoff, W. H., and Doty, A. M., J. Am. Chem. Soc., **72,** 4938 (1950).
18. Whistler, R. L., and Smith, C. G., J. Am. Chem. Soc., **74,** 3795 (1952).
19. Swanson, J., J. Am. Chem. Soc., **71,** 1510 (1949).
20. Ahmed, Z. F., and Whistler, R. L., J. Am. Chem. Soc., **72,** 2524 (1950).
21. Moe, O. A., Miller, S. E., and Iwen, Marjorie, H., J. Am. Chem. Soc., **69,** 2621 (1947).
22. Carson, J. F., and Maclay, W. D., J. Am. Chem. Soc., **70,** 2220 (1948).
23. Smart, C. L., and Whistler, R. L., J. Polymer. Sci., **4,** 87 (1949).
24. Palmer, K. J., and Ballantyne, M., J. Am. Chem. Soc., **72,** 736 (1950).

25. Knight, W. A., and Dowsett, M. M., *Pharm. J.*, **136,** 35 (1936).
26. Griffith, C., *Mfg. Chemist*, **20,** 321 (1949).
27. Smith, F., *J. Am. Chem. Soc.*, **70,** 3249 (1948).
28. Hirst, E. L., and Jones, J. K. N., *J. Chem. Soc.*, 1278 (1948).
29. Hart, R., *Ind. Eng. Chem., Anal. Ed.*, **2,** 329 (1930).
30. Williams, A. L., *Analyst*, **53,** 411 (1928).
31. Effront, J., *Compt. rend.*, **125,** 38, 309 (1897).
32. Van Ekenstein, A., *Compt. rend.*, **125,** 719 (1897).
33. Spada, A., *Atti soc. nat. mat. Modena*, **70,** 20 (1939); *Chem. Abstracts*, **34,** 6118 (1940).
34. Lew, B. W., and Gortner, R. A., *Arch. Biochem.*, **1,** 325 (1943).
35. Smith, F., *J. Chem. Soc.*, 1989 (1948).
36. Larson, E. B., and Smith, F., *J. Am. Chem. Soc.*, **77,** 429 (1955).
37. Andrews, P., Hough, L., and Jones, J. K. N., *J. Chem. Soc.*, 2744 (1952).
38. Daoud, K. M., *Biochem. J.*, **26,** 255 (1932).
39. Andrews, P., Hough, L., and Jones, J. K. N., *J. Am. Chem. Soc.*, **74,** 4029 (1952).
40. May, F., and Schultz, A. S., *Z. Biol.*, **97,** 201 (1936).
41. Bell, D. J., *Biochem., J.*, **29,** 2031 (1935).
42. Otsuki, T., *Acta Phytochim.* (Japan), **10,** 29 (1937); *Chem. Abstracts*, **31,** 8610 (1937).
43. Hayashi, K., Nagata, Y., and Mizuno, T., *J. Agr. Chem. Soc.* (Japan), **27,** 234 (1953); *Chem. Abstracts*, **49,** 4802 (1955).
44. Hirst, E. L., Jones, J. K. N., and Walder, Winifred, O., *J. Chem. Soc.*, 1443 (1947).
45. Otsuki, T., *Acta Phytochim.* (Japan), **10,** 1 (1937); *Chem. Abstracts*, **31,** 8610 (1937).
46. Rebers, P. A., and Smith, F., *J. Am. Chem. Soc.*, **76,** 6097 (1954).
47. van Hulssen, C. J., and Koolhaas, D. R., *Ing. Nederland-Indie*, **7,** 29 (1940); *Chem. Abstracts*, **35,** 4415 (1941).
48. Wise, L. E., *Arch. Biochem.*, **23,** 127 (1949).
49. Smith, F., and Srivastava, H. C., *J. Am. Chem. Soc.*, **78,** 1404 (1956).
50. Whistler, R. L., and Durso, D. F., *J. Am. Chem. Soc.*, **72,** 677 (1950).
51. Hough, L., Jones, J. K. N., and Wadman, W. H., *J. Chem. Soc.*, 2511 (1949).
52. Jeanes, Allene, Wilham, C. A., Jones, R. W., Tsuchiya, H. M., and Rist, C. E., *J. Am. Chem. Soc.*, **75,** 5911 (1953).
53. Bergmann, M., and Schotte, H., *Ber.*, **54,** 1564 (1921).
54. Haworth, W. N., Hirst, E. L., Streight, H. R. L., Thomas, H. A., and Webb, J. I., *J. Chem. Soc.*, 2636 (1930).
55. Brauns, D. H., *J. Am. Chem. Soc.*, **48,** 2776 (1926).
56. Sokurada, I., and Hutino, K., *Z. physik. Chem.*, **B21,** 18 (1938).
57. Torigata, H., *J. Chem. Soc. Japan, Pure Chem. Sect.*, **73,** 533 (1952).
58. Torigata, H., *J. Chem. Soc. Japan, Pure Chem. Sect.*, **73,** 157 (1952).
59. Torigata, H., *J. Chem. Soc. Japan, Pure Chem. Sect.*, **73,** 485 (1952).
60. Kinoshita, Y., *Bull. Coll. Agr. Imp. Univ. Tokyo*, **2,** 205 (1895).
61. Goto, K., *J. Biochem. Japan*, **1,** 201 (1922).
62. Nishida, K., and Hashima, H., *J. Dept. Agr. Kyushu Imp. Univ.*, **2,** 277 (1930); *Chem. Abstracts*, **25,** 498 (1931).
63. Mayeda, S., *Mitt. Med. Ges. Tokyo*, **29,** 57 (1915); **34,** 634, 728 (1920).
64. Miyake, S., *J. Coll. Agr. Hokkaido Imp. Univ. Sapporo*, **17,** 163 (1927); *Chem. Abstracts*, **21,** 3382 (1927).

65. Otsuki, T., *Acta Phytochim.* (Japan) **4,** No. 1, 1 (1928); *Chem. Abstracts,* **22,** 3682 (1928).
66. Srivastava, H. C., and Smith, F., unpublished.
67. Mayeda, M., *J. Biochem. Tokyo,* **1,** 131 (1922).
68. Otsuki, T., *Science* (Japan), **11,** 258 (1941); *Chem. Abstracts,* **35,** 5535 (1941).
69. Freudenberg, K., and Hüll, G., *Ber.,* **74B,** 237 (1941).
70. Prentice, N., Cuendet, L. S., and Smith, F., *J. Am. Chem. Soc.,* **78,** 4439 (1956).
71. Sakurada, I., and Fuchino, K., *J. Soc. Chem. Ind.* Japan, **36,** *Suppl. binding,* 90 (1933); *Chem. Abstracts,* **27,** 3139 (1933).
72. Sakurada, I., and Fuchino, K., *Sci. Papers Inst. Phys., Chem. Research (Tokyo),* **21,** 287 (1933); *Chem. Abstracts,* **28,** 947 (1934).
73. Hata, T., Ono, Y., and Maeda, K., *J. Chem. Soc. Japan, Ind. Chem. Section,* **54,** 532 (1951); *Chem. Abstracts,* **48,** 1969 (1954).
74. Colin, H., and Augem, A., *Compt. rend.,* **185,** 475 (1927).
75. Augem, A., *Rev. gén botan.,* **40,** 456, 537, 591 (1928); *Chem. Abstracts,* **23,** 634 (1929).
76. Schlubach, H. H., Knoop, H., and Liu, M. Y., *Ann.,* **504,** 30 (1933).
77. Colin, H., and Augem, A., *Bull. soc. chim. biol.,* **10,** 489 (1928).
78. Colin, H., and Augem, A., *Bull. soc. chim. biol.,* **10,** 822 (1928).
79. Andrews, P., Hough, L., and Jones, J. K. N., *J. Chem. Soc.,* 1186 (1953).
80. Roboz, Elizabeth, and Haagen-Smith, A. J., *J. Am. Chem. Soc.,* **70,** 3248 (1948).
81. Anderson, E., and Fireman, M., *J. Biol. Chem.,* **109,** 437 (1935).
82. Jones, Martha J., and Albers, C. C., *J. Am. Pharm. Assoc.,* **44,** 100 (1955).
83. Laidlaw, R. A., and Percival, E. G. V., *J. Chem. Soc.,* 1600 (1949).
84. Laidlaw, R. A., and Percival, E. G. V., *J. Chem. Soc.,* 528 (1950).
85. Hirst, E. L., Percival, E. G. V., and Wylam, Clare B., *J. Chem. Soc.,* 189 (1954).
86. Mullan, J., and Percival, E. G. V., *J. Chem. Soc.,* 1501 (1940).
87. Percival, E. G. V., and Willox, I. C., *J. Chem. Soc.,* 1608 (1949).
88. Nelson, W. A. G., and Percival, E. G. V., *J. Chem. Soc.,* 58 (1942).
89. Hostettler, F., and Deuel, H., *Helv. Chim. Acta,* **34,** 2440 (1951).
90. Anderson, E., Gillette, L. A., and Seeley, M. G., *J. Biol. Chem.,* **140,** 569 (1941).
91. Ghose, T. P., and Krishna, S., *J. Indian. Chem. Soc. Ind. and News Ed.,* **5,** 114 (1942); *Chem. Abstracts,* **37,** 1796 (1943).
92. Ghose, T. P., Krishna, S., and Rao, P. S., *J. Sci. Ind. Research (India),* **4,** 705 (1946); *Chem. Abstracts,* **40,** 6278 (1946).
93. Rao, P. S., *J. Sci. Ind. Research (India),* **7b,** 89 (1948); *Chem. Abstracts,* **42,** 7460 (1948).
94. Savur, G. R., and Sreenivasan, A., *J. Biol. Chem.,* **172,** 501 (1948).
95. Rao, P. S., and Dickey, E. E., *J. Textile Inst.,* **44,** T401 (1953).
96. Das, F. B., Chaudhuri, P. K. R., and Wareham, J. F., *J. Textile Inst.,* **44,** T402 (1953); *Chem. Abstracts,* **48,** 1719 (1954).
97. Damodaran, M., and Rangachari, P. N., *Current Sci.,* **14,** 203 (1945); **15,** 20 (1946); *Chem. Abstracts,* **40,** 411, 3839 (1946).
98. Rao, P. S., and Krishna, S., *Current Sci.,* **15,** 133, 168 (1946).
99. Sarkar, P. B., and Mazumdar, A. K., *J. Textile Inst.,* **43,** T453 (1952).
100. White, E. V., and Rao, P. S., *J. Am. Chem. Soc.,* **75,** 2617 (1953).

101. Gill, R. E., Hirst, E. L., and Jones, J. K. N., J. Chem. Soc., 1469 (1939).
102. Anderson, E., J. Biol. Chem., 104, 163 (1934).
103. Hirst, E. L., Hough, L. and Jones, J. K. N., J. Chem. Soc., 323 (1951).
104. Gill, R. E., Hirst, E. L., and Jones, J. K. N., J. Chem. Soc., 1025 (1946).
105. Hirst, E. L., J. Chem. Soc., 522 (1949).
106. Hirst, E. L., J. Chem. Soc., 70 (1942).
107. Bass, E. J., Meredith, W. O. S., and Anderson, J. A., Cereal Chem., 29, 262 (1952); 30, 313 (1953).
108. O'Sullivan, C., J. Chem. Soc., 41, 24 (1882).
109. Lindet, L., Compt. rend., 137, 73 (1903).
110. Piratsky, W. K., and Wiecha, G., Wochschr. Brau., 55, 97 (1938); Chem. Abstracts, 32, 8070 (1938).
111. Preece, I. A., Ashworth, A. S., and Hunter, A. D., J. Inst. Brewing, 56, 33 (1950).
112. Meredith, W. O. S., Bass, E. J., and Anderson, J. A., Cereal Chem., 28, 177 (1951).
113. Preece, I. A., and Mackenzie, K. G., J. Inst. Brewing, 58, 353 (1952).
114. Aspinall, G. O., and Telfer, R. G. J., J. Chem. Soc., 3519 (1954).
115. Gilles, K. A., Huffman, G. W., Meredith, W. O. S., and Smith, F., unpublished.
116. Abdel-Akher, M., Hamilton, J. K., Montgomery, R., and Smith, F., J. Am. Chem. Soc., 74, 4970 (1952).
117. Gilles, K. A., Meredith, W. O. S., and Smith, F., Cereal. Chem., 29, 314 (1952).
118. Gilles, K. A., Meredith, W. O. S., and Smith, F., unpublished.
119. Montgomery, R., and Smith, F., J. Am. Chem. Soc., 77, 3325 (1955).
120. Montgomery, R., and Smith, F., Cereal Chem., 31, 490 (1954).
121. Perlin, A. S., Cereal. Chem., 28, 370 (1951).
122. Sandstedt, R. M., Jolitz, C. E., and Blish, M. J., Cereal Chem., 16, 780 (1939).
123. Clendenning, K. A., and Wright, D. E., Can. J. Research, 28F, 390 (1950).
124. MacMasters, Majel M., and Hilbert, G. E., Cereal Chem., 21, 548 (1944).
125. Simpson, F. J., Can. J. Microbiol., 1, 131 (1954).
126. Montgomery, R., and Smith, F., J. Am. Chem. Soc., 77, 2834 (1955).
127. Ford, L. H., and Peat, S., J. Chem. Soc., 856 (1941).
128. Cuendet, L. S., Ph. D. Thesis, University of Minnesota (1950).
129. Wolf, M. J., MacMasters, M. M., Cannon, J. A., Rosewall, E. C., and Rist, C. E., Cereal Chem., 30, 451 (1953).
130. Montgomery, R., Smith, F., and Srivastava, H. C., J. Am. Chem. Soc., 78, 2837 (1956).
131. Montgomery, R., Smith, F., and Srivastava, H. C., J. Am. Chem. Soc., 78, 6169 (1956).
132. Abdel-Akher, M., and Smith, F., Nature, 166, 1037 (1950).
133. Briggs, D. R., Garner, E. F., and Smith, F., Nature, 178, 154 (1956).
134. Whistler, R. L., and Corbett, W. M., J. Am. Chem. Soc., 77, 6328 (1955).
135. Montgomery, R., Smith, F., and Srivastava, H. C., J. Am. Chem. Soc., 79, 698 (1957).
136. Srivastava, H. C., and Smith, F., J. Am. Chem. Soc., 79, 982 (1957).
137. Hamilton, J. K., Smith, F., and Spriestersbach, D. R., J. Am. Chem. Soc., 79, 443 (1957).
138. Falconer, E. L., and Adams, G. A., Can. J. Chem., 34, 338 (1956).

139. Hay, G., and Smith, F., unpublished.
140. Andrews, P., and Jones, J. K. N., *J. Chem. Soc.*, 4134 (1954).
141. Smith, F., *J. Chem. Soc.*, 744 (1939).
142. Whistler, R. L., and Tu, C. C., *J. Am. Chem. Soc.*, **74**, 3609 (1952).
143. Whistler, R. L., and BeMiller, J. N., *J. Am. Chem. Soc.*, **78**, 1163 (1956).
144. Goldstein, I. J., Montgomery, R., Srivastava, H. C., and Smith, F., unpublished.
145. Montgomery, R., and Smith, F., *J. Am. Chem. Soc.*, **79**, 695 (1957).
146. Dutton, G. G. S., and Smith, F., *J. Am. Chem. Soc.*, **78**, 2505 (1956).
147. Montgomery, R., and Smith, F., *Agr. and Food Chem.*, **4**, 716 (1956).
148. Bell, D. J., and Baldwin, E., *J. Chem. Soc.*, 125 (1941).
149. Whistler, R. L., and Corbett, W. M., *J. Org. Chem.*, **21**, 694 (1956).
150. Jones, J. K. N., and Smith, F., *Advances in Carbohydrate Chem.*, **4**, 243 (1949).
151. Pringsheim, H., and Genin, A., *Z. physiol. Chem.*, **140**, 299 (1924).
152. Pringsheim, H., and Liss, G., *Ann.*, **460**, 32 (1928).
153. Huseman, E., *J. prakt. Chem.*, **155**, 241 (1940).
154. Klages, F., and Niemann, R., *Ann.*, **523**, 224 (1936).
155. Klages, F., *Ann.*, **509**, 159 (1934); **512**, 185 (1934).
156. Klages, F., and Maurenbrecher, R., *Ann.*, **535**, 175 (1938).
157. Whistler, R. L., and Conrad, H. E., *J. Am. Chem. Soc.*, **76**, 1673 (1954).
158. Benjamin, H. B., Ihrig, H. K., and Roth, D. A., *Rev. Can. Biol.*, **10**, 215 (1951); *Chem. Abstracts*, **45**, 9805 (1951).
159. Whistler, R. L., and Conrad, H. E., *J. Am. Chem. Soc.*, **76**, 3544 (1954).
160. Machida, S., and Uchino, N., *J. Chem. Soc. Japan, Pure Chem. Sect.*, **74**, 183 (1953); *Chem. Abstracts*, **47**, 11782 (1953).
161. Machida, S., and Uchino, N., *J. Chem. Soc. Japan, Pure Chem. Sect.*, **72**, 917 (1951); *Chem. Abstracts*, **46**, 7351 (1952).
162. Ozawa, T., *J. Chem. Ind. (Japan)*, **25**, 389 (1922).
163. Machida, S., and Uchino, N., *J. Chem. Soc. Japan, Pure Chem. Sect.*, **74**, 615 (1953); *Chem. Abstracts*, **48**, 11357 (1954).
164. Mino, M., *Tech. Bull. Kagawa Agr. Coll. (Japan)*, **5**, 281 (1953–1954); *Chem. Abstracts*, **48**, 14264 (1954).
165. Bailey, K., and Norris, F. W., *Biochem. J.*, **26**, 1609 (1932).
166. Kirchner, W., and Tollens, B., *Ann.*, **175**, 205 (1874).
167. Renfrew, Alice G., and Cretcher, L. H., *J. Biol. Chem.*, **97**, 503 (1932).
168. Nodzu, R., and Tomita, T., *J. Chem. Soc. Japan*, **74**, 776 (1953); Chem. Abstracts, **48**, 8568 (1954).
169. Mason, C. T., and Hall, L. A., *Food Inds.*, **20**, 382 (1948).
170. Neville, A., *J. Agr. Sci.*, **5**, 113 (1913).
171. Bailey, K., *Biochem. J.*, **29**, 2477 (1935).
172. Tipson, R. S., Christman, C. C., and Levene, P. A., *J. Biol. Chem.*, **128**, 609 (1939).
173. Anderson, E., and Lowe, H. J., *J. Biol. Chem.*, **168**, 289 (1947).
174. Easterby, D. G., and Jones, J. K. N., *Nature*, **165**, 614 (1950).
175. Hilger, A., *Ber.*, **36**, 3197 (1903).
176. Anderson, E., and Crowder, J. A., *J. Am. Chem. Soc.*, **52**, 3711 (1930).
177. Niemann, C., and Link, K. P., *J. Biol. Chem.*, **104**, 205 (1934).
178. Anderson, E., *J. Biol. Chem.*, **100**, 249 (1933).
179. Schmidt, C., *Ann.*, **51**, 29 (1844).

180. Rao, P. S., Beri, R. M., and Budhiraya, R. P., *J. Sci. Ind. Research (India)*, 11B, 127 (1952); *Chem. Abstracts*, 47, 10882 (1953).
181. Rao, P. S., and Rozdon, O. N., *Proc. Indian Acad. Sci.*, 31A, 441 (1950); *Chem. Abstracts*, 45, 4070 (1951).
182. Rao, P. S., Rozdon, O. N., and Budhiraya, R. P., *Proc. Indian Acad. Sci.*, 32A, 264 (1950); *Chem. Abstracts*, 46, 1277 (1952).
183. Rao, P. S., Beri, R. M., and Budhiraya, R. P., *J. Sci. Ind. Research (India)*, 10B, 261 (1951); *Chem. Abstracts*, 47, 10882 (1953).
184. Rao, P. S., and Budhiraya, R. P., *J. Sci. Ind. Research (India)*, 11B, 209 (1952); *Chem. Abstracts*, 47, 10882 (1953).
185. Rao, P. S., and Beri, R. M., *Proc. Indian Acad. Sci.*, 34A, 27 (1951); *Chem. Abstracts*, 48, 1039 (1954).
186. Savur, G. R., *Current Sci.*, 24, 235 (1955); *Chem. Abstracts*, 50, 2763 (1956).
187. Savur, G. R., *J. Chem. Soc.*, 2600 (1956).
188. Hampton, H. A., Haworth, W. N., and Hirst, E. L., *J. Chem. Soc.*, 1739 (1929).
189. Montgomery, R., and Smith, F., *Methods of Biochem. Anal.*, Vol. 3 Ed. D Glick, Interscience Pub., New York (1956) 153.
190. Preece, I. A., and Hobkirk, R., *J. Inst. Brewing*, 59, 385 (1953).
191. Amin, El S., *J. Chem. Soc.*, 828 (1956).
192. Aspinall, G. O., Hirst, E. L., and Matheson, N. K., *J. Chem. Soc.*, 989 (1956).
193. Schryver, S. B., *Proc. Roy. Soc.* (London) B, 82, 226 (1910).
194. Büchi, W., and Deuel, H., *Helv. Chim. Acta*, 37, 1392 (1954).
195. Whistler, R. L., and Saarnio, J., *J. Am. Chem. Soc.*, 79, 6055 (1957).
196. Kuhn, R., Trischman, H., and Löw, I., *Angew. Chem.*, 67, 32 (1955).
197. Morris, D. L., *J. Biol. Chem.*, 142, 881 (1942).
198. Peat, S., Whelan, W. J., and Roberts, J. G., *J. Chem. Soc.*, 3916 (1957).
199. Briggs, D. R., Domenigg, H. S., Lewis, B. A., and Smith, F., unpublished.
200. Acker, L., Diemair, W., and Samhammer, E., *Z. Lebensm. Unters. u. Forsch*, 100, 180 (1955).
201. Unrau, A. M., and Smith, F., *Chemistry and Industry*, 330 (1957).
202. Goldstein, I. J., Hay, G. W., Lewis, B. A., and Smith, F., Abstracts 135th A. C. S. Meeting, Boston, Mass. (1959) 3 D.

CHAPTER 13

LICHEN POLYSACCHARIDES

Constitution of Lichen Algal Polysaccharides

The polysaccharide material of lichens, which consist of a symbiotic system of an alga and a fungus, is in most cases a mixture of at least two groups of glycans, one from the alga and one from the fungus. Evidence now indicates that the true algal polysaccharides are glucans whereas those materials containing mannose and sometimes galactose, as well as glucose, are probably derived from the fungus component of the lichen.

Polysaccharides have been isolated from the following lichens (1,24):

Cetraria islandica (2,3,5)
Umbilicaria pustulata (L.) Hoffm. (4)
Umbilicaria hirsuta Ach.
Cladonia rangiferina (L.) Web. mixed with C. silvatica (L.) Hoffm.
Cladonia alpestris (L.). Rabh.
Parmenlia furfuracea (L.) Ach.
Evernia prunastri (L.) Ach.
Usnea longissima (55)
Roccella montagnei (55)

The lichen glucans, or lichenins as they are sometimes called, have usually been isolated by extracting the lichens with boiling water. On cooling, a portion of the extracted polysaccharide is deposited and is referred to as lichenin. The cold water soluble polysaccharide recovered by alcoholic precipitation is often called iso-lichenin. This convenient classification into two groups (6) is generally adopted (7,8) but it is probably an oversimplification according to other work (1) in which a classification into four groups is proposed: (1) polysaccharides not extracted with boiling water; (2) polysaccharides extracted with boiling water, but not precipitated with tannin, for example, pustulin (1) (or pustulan (4)); (3) polysaccharides precipitated by tannin are then divided into two groups by reason of the fact that some, such as evernin (evernan), are soluble in cold water, $[\alpha]_D$ + 138° (H_2O), while others, such as lichenin (lichenan), $[\alpha]_D$ + 2° (dilute alkali), are soluble in hot, but not in cold water (1). Even this system has its limitations since the so-called iso-lichenins (iso-lichenans) have been separated into several components (9). Whereas one of the polysaccharides contains only D-glucose some of the iso-lichenin components contain galactose and mannose as well as glucose. These last named polymers are most likely derived from the fungus component of the lichens.

Thus far, two distinct lichen glucans have been recognized and subjected to constitutional study, namely, the lichen glucan, lichenin or lichenan, from *Cetraria islandica*, and the lichen glucan, pustulin, from *Umbilicaria pustulata.*

Constitution of Lichenin (Islandican) from *Cetraria islandica*. Iceland-moss lichenin, which is soluble in hot but insoluble in cold water, unlike the cold water-soluble iso-lichenin, gives no color with iodine (10). After purification by repeated precipitation from hot water, or as a copper complex (30), it shows $[\alpha]_D$ + 8 to + 10° (*N* sodium hydroxide) and gives only D-glucose upon hydrolysis either with acid (2,6,11–13) or with enzymes (14–16). The glucan composition is supported by the observation that acetolysis gives cellobiose octaacetate (3,17,15) though the yield of the latter is lower than that from cellulose. Partial degradation of lichenin to D-glucose and oligosaccharides composed of D-glucose is also achieved by enzymes from the germinating seeds of barley, maize, wheat, spinach, and oats (25).

Lichenin affords a triacetate (17,26–28), $[\alpha]_D$ – 34° (chloroform), thus showing the presence of three hydroxyl groups per D-glucose residue. Early studies (18) showed that hydrolysis of the methylated polysaccharide apparently gave only 2,3,6-tri-*O*-methyl-D-glucose (CCLXXXVIII). From this it was deduced that lichenin and cellulose had very similar structures and a similar observation made later (3), coupled with the fact that the derivatives of lichenin and cellulose had different rotations (28,29), prompted the interesting suggestion (3) that lichenin had the structure CCCXXII.

$$\left[\!-4\text{-G}p\text{-}1 \rightarrow 4\text{-G}p\text{-}1\right]\!\!\rightarrow 4\text{-G}p\text{-}1\!-\!\!1\text{-G}p\text{-}4 \leftarrow\!\!\left[1\text{-G}p\text{-}4 \leftarrow 1\text{-G}p\,4\!-\!\right]$$

CCCXXII

Methylation studies (20) on the potassium hydroxide addition complex also showed that there was a difference between lichenin and cellulose, the real reason for which was traced through the fact that the hydrolyzate of methylated lichenin was shown to contain 2,4,6-tri-*O*-methyl-D-glucose (CCCVI), characterized as the aniline derivative, as well as the crystalline 2,3,6-tri-O-methyl isomer (CCLXXXVIII) (9,19). Further quantitative methylation studies (21) showed that the proportions of 2,3,6-tri-O-methyl- and 2,4,6-tri-O-methyl-D-glucose were approximately 70 and 30 per cent, respectively, indicating a corresponding ratio of $1 \rightarrow 4$ to $1 \rightarrow 3$ linkage. Separation of the two tri-O-methyl sugars was effected also by reduction to the corresponding methyl glucitols, which were separated as their azoato esters on an alumina column (22); the relative proportions were confirmed. These findings were supported by periodate oxidation studies in which it was established (9) that 27 per cent of the D-glucose residues were immune to oxidation.

The earlier findings have been confirmed and extended (53). Chromatographic analysis on a cellulose column of a hydrolyzate of methylated lichenin (3) gave 2,3,4,6-tetra-O-methyl-D-glucose (CCXXX) in an amount equivalent to an average chain length of 62 glucose residues. The expected tri-O-methyl-D-glucose derivatives were found in the previously reported ratio and the di-O-methyl-D-glucoses were present in trace amounts only, indicating the virtual absence of branch points.

Added support for the linearity of the lichenin molecule came from the separation of the lower molecular weight components in the mixture resulting from partial acid hydrolysis (54). It was possible to identify, as their crystalline acetates, D-glucose, cellobiose and laminaribiose (the only disaccharides), cellotriose, 4-O-β-laminaribiosyl-D-glucose, and 3-O-β-cellobiosyl-D-glucose. No evidence was forthcoming for the presence of a branched trisaccharide which would be expected if the lichenin were not linear. Significant also was the absence of laminaritriose, suggesting that the $1 \rightarrow 3$ linkages are randomly distributed in the molecule but rarely, if ever, occurring consecutively. A similar conclusion was reached from the partial acid hydrolysis of the polyalcohol obtained from the reduction (56) of periodate-oxidized lichenin (53). Paper chromatography showed the presence of glucose but not of laminaribiose, so that the glucose residues on either side of the one linked through C_1 and C_3 must have been linked through C_1 and C_4.

From a study (54) of the tetrasaccharides produced by the partial acid hydrolysis of lichenin it was suggested that the glucose chain is a repeating sequence of β-cellotriose units joined through $1 \rightarrow 3$ linkages.

Although these structural data indicate that the molecule of lichenin is essentially linear, it has been argued that such a structure is not compatible with the physical properties of this polysaccharide, such as its solubility in hot water and the colloidal nature of its solutions. For these reasons, a branched structure has been proposed (31). It is perhaps unfortunate that the properties of linear molecules are so frequently compared with those of cellulose, the classical linear carbohydrate polymer, overlooking the fact that the presence of two or more different types of linkage in a linear polysaccharide will often result in the manifestation of properties which are found in branched molecules. Thus, nigeran, a bacterial polysaccharide from *Aspergillus niger*, is a linear molecule soluble in hot but insoluble in cold water and composed of glucose units with alternating $1 \rightarrow 3$ and $1 \rightarrow 4$ linkages (32). Similarly, the linear β-glucan from barley seeds (46), which has both $1 \rightarrow 3$ and $1 \rightarrow 4$ linkages (33–35), gives viscous solutions in water, and in fact may be analogous to oat lichenin (47,48) which also contains $1 \rightarrow 3$ and $1 \rightarrow 4$ (49,50) linkages, largely of the β-D-type. In both nigeran and barley β-D-glucan, there are approximately equal numbers of $1 \rightarrow 3$ and $1 \rightarrow 4$ linkages while lichenin has principally $1 \rightarrow 4$ linkages. This may explain why it is soluble in hot but not in cold water.

An enzyme which hydrolyzes lichenin (14–16) is found in the seeds of many plants enabling partial enzymic hydrolyses to be carried out, which will aid in determining, by the isolation of oligosaccharides, more concerning the relative frequencies of the two types of linkage. The wide distribution of lichenase in seeds has led to the suggestion that lichenin may be a common component in them (24,25,36), and barley β-D-glucan may be the latest reported example. An enzyme which hydrolyzes $1 \rightarrow 3$-β-D-glucosidic bonds has been reported in seeds and called laminarinase since its hydrolytic activity was checked on laminarin, a seaweed β-D-glucan having $1 \rightarrow 3$ linkages (37). It is very possible, however, that laminarinase and lichenase are the same enzymes, both having an optimum activity at $40°$ and pH 5. Such a possibility should be checked in order to avoid confusion in the literature.

Constitution of the Lichen-Glucan, Pustulin. Pustulin ($[\alpha]_D - 44°$ in water), which has been extracted from *Umbilicaria pustulata*, gives only D-glucose upon hydrolysis (1). Acetolysis furnished gentiobiose octaacetate (1) showing that this glucan contains $1 \rightarrow 6$-β-D-glucosidic bonds. Graded hydrolysis and characterization of gentiobiose, gentio-

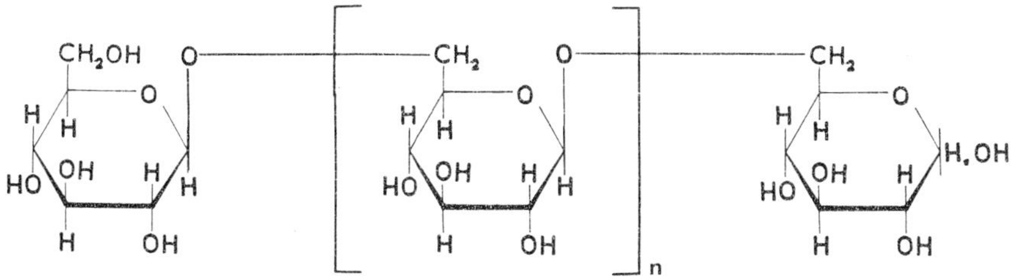

(CCCXXIII)

triose, and gentiotetraose, after separation on a charcoal column, coupled with the chromatographic evidence that still higher oligosaccharides of the gentiobiose type are present in the hydrolyzate of pustulin, lends strong support to the view that this lichen polysaccharide is linear and contains almost all 1 → 6-β-D-linkages as shown in CCCXXIII (4).

Constitution of Iso-Lichenins. Iso-lichenins have been reported in *Cetraria islandica*, *Parmelia abessinica* (Rathipuvva) (42), *Usnea longissima* (55), *Roccella montagnei* (43,55) and in some Japanese lichens (44). The presence of iso-lichenins in Iceland moss has been known for many years. In support of an earlier suggestion that iso-lichenin is not homogeneous (10), the polysaccharide mixture has been separated into five fractions (9), one of which was too small to be investigated further. The largest fraction, A, $[\alpha]_D^{15} + 203°$ (H$_2$O), was composed principally of glucose, as was another minor fraction, B, $[\alpha]_D^{15} + 35°$ (2N NaOH). The latter fraction was also differentiated from A by its reaction with iodine to give a blue color and by its precipitation with Fehling solution. A third fraction, C, $[\alpha]_D^{15} + 9.6°$ (2N NaOH), composed entirely of glucose was not soluble in cold water, did not precipitate with Fehling solution, but gave a blue color with iodine. The second largest fraction, D, $[\alpha]_D^{15} + 109°$ (water), was composed of glucose, mannose and galactose and was precipitated by Fehling solution. From the heterogeneity of iso-lichenins it is not surprising that the earlier work was at variance (38–41).

A glucan corresponding to fraction A above has been further purified through the fractional precipitation with acetone of the water-soluble copper complex (53). It showed $[\alpha]_D + 255°$ in water and unlike lichenin it gave a greenish-blue color with dilute iodine solution. The viscometric properties of the triacetate derivative ($[\alpha]_D + 160°$ in chloroform) indicated a DP of 40–50, a value supported by periodate oxidation studies in which the amount of formic acid produced was equivalent to an average chain length of 42 glucose residues. The polysaccharide contained 60 per cent of D-glucose residues which were unattacked by periodate. Taken in conjunction with methylation data this result indicates that the molecule contains 1 → 3 and 1 → 4 linkages in the ratio of 3:2.

The methylated glucan, $[\alpha]_D + 218°$ in chloroform, was obtained by methylation with methyl sulfate and sodium hydroxide, followed by Purdie reagents, and finally sodium and methyl iodide in liquid ammonia. Upon hydrolysis of the material (OMe, 44.4 per cent) with acid and separation of the methylated cleavage fragments on a cellulose column there was obtained 2,3,4,6-tetra-O-methyl-D-glucose (1 mole), tri-O-methyl-D-glucoses (42 moles), composed of 2,4,6- and 2,3,6-trimethyl ethers, and di-O-methyl-D-glucoses (1 mole). Since the latter amounted to about 2 per cent of the mixture and the original methylated glucan was not fully methylated (a tri-O-methyl glucan theoretically has OMe, 45.6 per cent) it was concluded that this polysaccharide is unbranched and composed of α-D-glucopyranose residues linked through C_1 and C_3 (about 60 per cent) and through C_1 and C_4 (about 40 per cent). The resistance of the glucan to hydrolysis by barley or soya-bean β-amylase shows that an α-D-(1 → 3) linkage must be situated near the nonreducing end of the polymer chain. The exact location of the 1 → 3 and 1 → 4 linkages still remains to be ascertained. Graded acid hydrolysis or acetolysis to give oligosaccharides in much the same way as those obtained from lichenin will throw light on this problem.

Other Lichen Polysaccharides. After extraction of *C. islandica* lichen with hot water, further estraction with cold 4 per cent sodium hydroxide gives another mixture of polysaccharides, the hydrolysis of which yields a mixture of sugars containing D-glucose (89 per cent), D-galactose (8 per cent), D-mannose (3 per cent), and a uronic acid (3 per cent), probably D-glucuronic acid (45). Preliminary methylation studies indicated that the mixture of polysaccharides is made up chiefly of β-D-glucose units linked through C_1 and C_2, C_1 and C_3, C_1 and C_4, and C_1 and C_6.

Constitution of the Alkali-Soluble Polysaccharides from Reindeer Moss (*Cladonia Alpestris*).

Extraction of the lichen with cold 5 per cent and with 24 per cent potassium hydroxide gave two polysaccharide preparations which differed in optical rotation, but gave the same sugars, namely, D-galactose, D-glucose, and D-mannose upon hydrolysis, although in different proportions (51). Fractionation of the polysaccharide extracted with 5 per cent alkali by means of Fehling solution effected only partial resolution of the mixture.

When methylated first with methyl sulfate and alkali, and then with silver oxide and methyl iodide, the corresponding methylated derivatives were produced. These methylated compounds were similar, differing little in their specific rotations and, since they gave rise upon hydrolysis to the same mixture of methylated sugars, they were combined for the subsequent detailed methylation study. Considerable difficulty was encountered, not only in effecting complete hydrolysis of the methylated carbohydrate polymers, but also in resolving the mixture of the derived methylated sugars. By a wide variety of the usual techniques of carbohydrate chemistry, the following methylated cleavage products were identified: 2,3,4,6-tetra-O-methyl-D-galactose (XXXIX), 2,3,4,6-tetra-O-methyl-D-mannose (CCLXXV), 3,4-di-O-methyl-D-mannose (CCLXXXVII) and 2,3,4,6-tetra-O-methyl-D-glucose (CCXXX). In addition, chromatographic evidence was obtained for the presence of various mono-, di-, and tri-O-methyl derivatives of glucose, galactose, and mannose. The isolation of two resistant fragments of the methylated polysaccharide was observed as well as the fact that each resistant fragment was built up of either glucose or mannose units, but not both; the structural significance of these findings is not clear. They may signify that the complex consists of at least two different polymers or that the polysaccharides consist of blocks of glucose and of mannose units that are individually stable, but which can be severed from each other as a result of the stable groups being joined together by some less stable linkages.

Periodate oxidation of the polysaccharides revealed that they contained units of glucose and mannose that were stable to oxidation. This observation clearly demonstrated the presence either of $1 \rightarrow 3$ linkages or of multiple branching. The highly branched structure was supported by the fact that the polysaccharides consumed 1.2 moles of periodate per residue, while one mole of formic acid was formed for every three to four hexose units. The findings from the methylation studies also appear to support the view that the polysaccharides possess a highly branched complex structure. It was pointed out in connection with this particular problem of the structure of lichen polysaccharides that better methods for resolving mixtures of polysaccharides must be developed before further progress can be made, a view generally agreed upon in connection with most problems in polysaccharide chemistry (52).

REFERENCES

1. Drake, B., *Biochem. Z.*, **313**, 388 (1943).
2. Hönig, M., and Schubert, St., *Monatsch.*, **8**, 452 (1887).
3. Hess, K., Lauridsen, L. W., *Ber.*, **73**, 115 (1940).
4. Lindberg, B., and McPherson, J., *Acta Chem. Scand.*, **8**, 985 (1954).
5. Berzelius, J., *Ann. Chim.*, **90**, 277 (1814).
6. Ulander, A., and Tollens, B., *Ber.*, **39**, 401 (1906).
7. Pigman, W. W., and Goepp, R. M., *Carbohydrate Chemistry*, Academic Press Inc., New York (1948), 602.
8. Whistler, R. L., and Smart, C. L., *Polysaccharide Chemistry*, Academic Press, Inc., New York (1953), 335.
9. Meyer, K., and Gürtler, P., *Helv. Chim. Acta*, **30**, 751 (1947).
10. Salkowski, E., *Z. physiol. Chem.*, **110**, 158 (1920).
11. Klason, P., *Ber.*, **19**, 2541 (1886).
12. Bauer, R. W., *J. pr. Chem.*, N.F. **34**, *46 (1886)*.
13. Müller, K., *Z. physiol. Chem.*, **45**, 265 (1905).
14. Karrer, P., and Staub, M., *Helv. Chim. Acta*, **7**, *518* (1924).
15. Karrer, P., Joos, B., and Staub, M., *Helv. Chim. Acta*, **6**, 800 (1923).
16. Pringsheim, H., and Seifert, K., *Z. physiol Chem.*, **128**, 284 (1923).
17. Karrer, P., and Joos, B., *Biochem. Z.*, **136**, 537 (1923).
18. Karrer, P., and Nishida, K., *Helv. Chim Acta*, **7**, 363 (1924).

19. Meyer, K. H., and Günther, P., *Arch. Sci. phys. nat.*, **27**, [v], *Suppl.*, 97 (1945).
20. Percival, E. G. V., and Granichstädten, H., *Nature*, **150**, 549 (1942).
21. Boissonnas, R. A., *Helv. Chim. Acta*, **30**, 1703 (1947).
22. Boissonnas, R. A., *Helv. Chim. Acta*, **30**, 1689 (1947).
23. Stüde, F., *Ann.*, **131**, 241 (1864).
24. Karrer, P., Staub, M., and Staub, J., *Helv. Chim. Acta*, **7**, 159 (1924).
25. Karrer, P., Staub, M., Weinhagen, A., and Joos, B., *Helv. Chim. Acta*, **7**, 144 (1924).
26. Bergmann, M., and Knehe, E., *Ann.*, **448**, 76 (1926), **452**, 151 (1927).
27. Pringsheim, H., and Routala, O., *Ann.*, **450**, 255 (1926).
28. Hess, K., and Friese, H., *Ann.*, **455**, 180 (1927).
29. Hess, K., *Z. Angew. Chem.*, **37**, 993 (1924).
30. Pringsheim, H., and Baur, K., *Z. physiol. Chem.*, **173**, 188 (1928).
31. Hess, K., Trogus, C., and Dziengel, K., *Ann.*, **501**, 49 (1933).
32. Barker, S. A., Bourne, E. J., and Stacey, M., *J. Chem. Soc.*, 3084 (1953).
33. Gilles, K. A., Meredith, W. O. S., and Smith, F., *Cereal Chem.*, **29**, 314 (1952).
34. Gilles, K. A., Huffman, G. W., Meredith, W. O. S., and Smith, F., unpublished.
35. Aspinall, G. O., and Telfer, R. G. J., *J. Chem. Soc.*, 3519 (1954).
36. Karrer, P., and Staub, M., *Helv. Chim. Acta*, **7**, 916 (1924).
37. Dillon, T., and O'Colla, P., *Nature*, **166**, 67 (1950); *Chemistry and Industry*, 111 (1951).
38. Pringsheim, H., *Ber.*, **57**, 1581 (1924).
39. Pringsheim, H., *Z. physiol. Chem.*, **144**, 241 (1925).
40. Karrer, P., *Z. physiol. Chem.*, **148**, 62 (1925).
41. Karrer, P., and Joos, B., *Z. physiol. Chem.*, **141**, 311 (1924).
42. Sastry, V. V. K., and Seshadri, T. R., *Proc. Indian Acad. Sci.*, **16A**, 137 (1942); *Chem. Abstracts.*, **37**, 1411 (1943).
43. Rao, V. S., and Seshadri, T. R., *Proc. Indian Acad. Sci.*, **12A**, 466 (1940); *Chem. Abstracts*, **36**, 757 (1942).
44. Minagawa, T., *J. Agr. Cnem. Soc. Japan*, **9**, 1198 (1933); *Chem. Abstracts*, **28**, 2375 (1934).
45. Granichstädten, H., and Percival, E. G. V., *J. Chem. Soc.*, 54 (1943).
46. Preece, I. A., and Mackenzie, K. G., *J. Inst. Brewing*, **58**, 353 (1952).
47. Morris, D. L., *J. Biol. Chem.*, **142**, 881 (1942).
48. Acker, L., Diemair, W., and Samhammer, E., *Z. Lebensm. Unters. u. Forsch*, **100**, 180 (1955).
49. Domenigg, H. S., Lewis, B. A., and Smith, F., unpublished.
50. Acker, L., Diemair, W., and Samhammer, E., *Z. Lebensm. u. Forsch*, **102**, 225 (1955).
51. Aspinall, G. O., Hirst, E. L., and Warburton, Margaret, *J. Chem. Soc.*, 651 (1955).
52. Montgomery, R., and Smith, F., *Ann. Rev. Biochem.*, **21**, 79 (1952).
53. Chanda, S. K., Hirst, E. L., and Manners, D. J., *J. Chem. Soc.*, 1951 (1957).
54. Peat, S., Whelan, W. J., and Roberts, J. G., *J. Chem. Soc.*, 3916 (1957).
55. Mittal, O. P., and Seshadri, T. R., *J. Sci. Ind. Res. India*, **13 B**, 244 (1954); **13A**, 174 (1954).
56. Abdel-Akher, M., Hamilton, J. K., Montgomery, R., and Smith, F., *J. Am. Chem. Soc.*, **74**, 4970 (1952).

CHAPTER 14

THE STRUCTURE OF POLYSACCHARIDES FROM SEAWEED

The large group of mucilaginous carbohydrates obtained from seaweeds (2) are in the main characterized by the presence of sulfate ester groups, the principal exceptions being alginic acid, laminarin, and the mannan from the red seaweed *Porphyra umbilicalis*. Of the large number which have been reported the structures of comparatively few have been investigated in detail (260). From the standpoint of the number of component monosaccharides, seldom more than two, in the seaweed polysaccharides, they might be considered as being simply constituted when compared with many of the plant gum exudates. The slow progress made in this field is principally due to the inadequate knowledge of the chemistry of the sugar sulfates. It is pertinent, therefore, to summarize the reactions of the sulfate ester group in carbohydrates in order that the structural investigations and deductions which follow may be understood.

The sulfate ester group, $ROSO_3'$, is hydrolyzed by acids. No sulfate ions can be detected in a solution of a sugar sulfate until the sulfate group has been cleaved. Such a simple test may lead one to suspect an unknown substance to be a sulfuric ester. This is verified when the amount of sulfate determined in the unknown by hydrolysis or fusion with sodium peroxide is double that found in the ash (1), since upon ignition the reaction may be represented: $2ROSO_3M \rightarrow M_2SO_4 + SO_3 +$ other gaseous combustion products.

The theoretical $2:1$ ratio is seldom found because M may be an ammonium radical which results in loss during ignition due to volatilization. In addition the sulfate is partially reduced to sulfide.

The effect of alkaline reagents upon sulfate ester groups is closely analogous to the reactions of the *p*-toluenesulfonic acid esters. In general it may be stated that unless the removal of the sulfate group with alkali can lead to the formation of an anhydro-ring, hydrolysis will proceed only slowly. With one exception, 1,2-*O*-isopropylidene-3,5-anhydro-α-D-xylofuranose, the only anhydro-rings known to be formed in a sugar

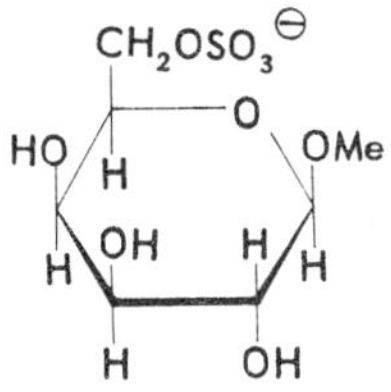

(CCCXXIV) 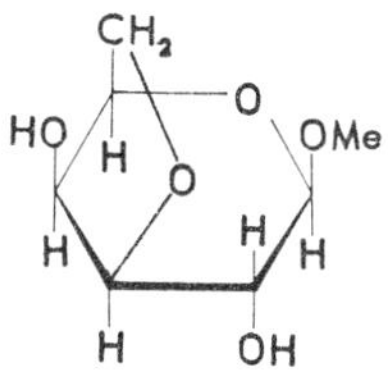   (CCCXXV)

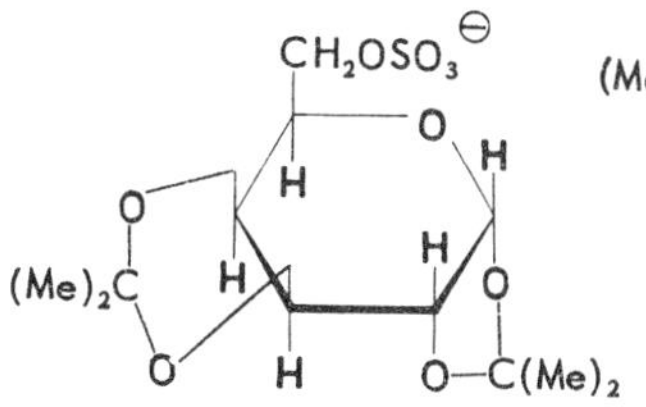

(CCCXXVI) 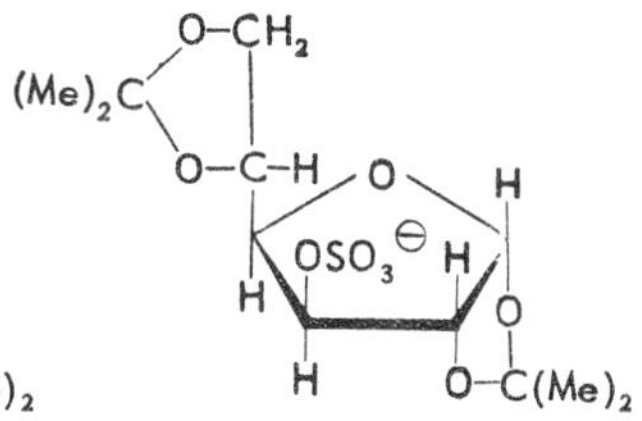   (CCCXXVII)

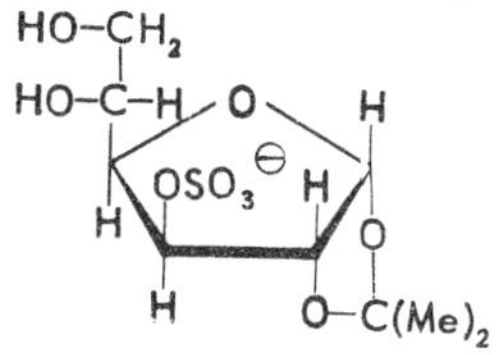

(CCCXXVIII)

glycoside are the ethylene oxide and 3,6-anhydro-types. In a study of the *p*-toluenesulfonic esters it was found that for the formation of an ethylene oxide ring the sulfonic ester group must be adjacent to a free hydroxyl group which bears a *trans*-configuration to it (3). The synthesis of a suitable carbohydrate sulfate to study ethylene oxide ring formation has not yet proved possible, but it is very likely that a similar structural requirement would be necessary for its alkaline hydrolysis.

A sulfate ester group in position six of a hexoside is labile to alkali if a hydroxyl group at C_3 is free; thus methyl β-D-galactoside 6-sulfate (CCCXXIV) is rapidly hydrolyzed to form methyl β-3,6-anhydro-D-galactoside (CCCXXV) and in the same way, the 6-sulfates of methyl α- and β-D-glucopyranosides, methyl α-D-mannopyranoside and D-galactopyranoside undergo rapid hydrolysis with the formation of the corresponding methyl 3,6-anhydro-hexosides (4). On the other hand, 1,2;3,4-di-O-isopropylidene-D-galactose 6-sulfate (CCCXXVI) is not attacked by 2N-sodium hydroxide during 6 hours at 100°. Similarly, 1,2;5,6-di-O-isopropylidene-α-D-glucose 3-sulfate (CCCXXVII) undergoes only 12 per cent hydrolysis in 47 hours at 100° with 2.8N-sodium hydroxide (5). It is somewhat surprising, however, to find that the hydrolysis of 1,2-O-isopropylidene-α-D-glucofuranose 3-sulfate (CCCXXVIII) is as slow as the hydrolysis of the di-O-isopropylidene compound even though the 3,6-anhydro derivative can and does form (5).

Since all the seaweed polysaccharide sulfates are composed principally of D-galactose or L-fucose (6-deoxy-L-galactose) it is interesting to consider in the light of the above observations the possible effect of alkali upon sulfate groups attached to D-galactose residues linked in various ways. This is summarized below:

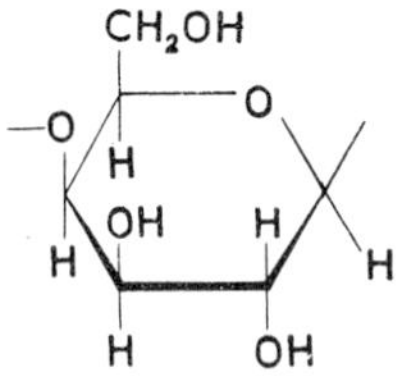

Sulfate group at any position should be alkali-labile.

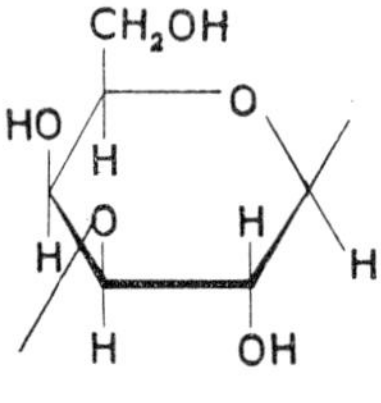

Sulfate group at any position should be stable to alkali.

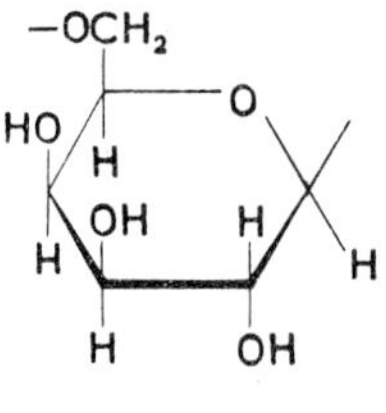

Sulfate group at position 4 should be stable to alkali; at positions 2 or 3, alkali labile.

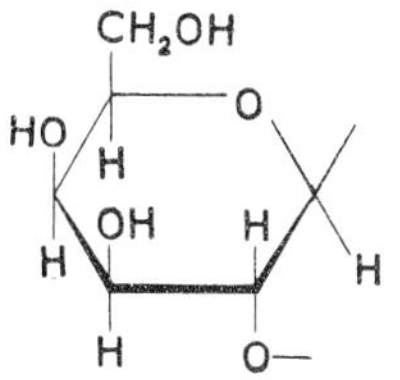

Sulfate group at positions 3 and 4 should be stable to alkali; at position 6, alkali labile.

If the chemical reactivity of sulfate groups in polysaccharides is the same as that in the known monosaccharide sulfates, and there is little reason to believe otherwise, it is seen that in the case of the frequently occurring 1 ⟶ 3 linked D-galactose residue, the position of a sulfate group cannot be ascertained by its behavior towards alkali. Its position can only be definitely assigned by a study of the cleavage fragments from the methylated polysaccharide sulfate and the methylated desulfated polysaccharide. However, the complete methylation of a polysaccharide sulfate is difficult and the removal of the sulfate groups from the polysaccharide without extensive cleavage of the glycosidic linkages has not yet been demonstrated in the seaweed polysaccharides. A detailed account of these salient points will be found below in discussions on several of the seaweed carbohydrate polymers.

Mucilages of the Rhodophyceae

Two of the most commercially important seaweed mucilages, agar and carrageenin, are obtained from species of marine algae belonging to the Rhodophyceae. As a group, the polysaccharide constituents of the red seaweeds have not been studied as thoroughly as the brown algae, the Phaeophyceae. The polysaccharides in the red algae have recently been reviewed (6) and 26 species of the Rhodophyceae have received detailed analytical investigation (7).

The principal component sugar in the red seaweeds appears from these analytical data to be galactose, present as a galactan or galactan sulfate. However, in Rhodymenia palmata and Rhodochorton floridulum the main component was found to be a xylan, while Dilsea edulis contained a comparatively large amount of glucose due probably to its constituent Floridean starch.

Carrageenin. Carrageenin, or Irish moss, is the material extracted with water from the red seaweeds, Chondrus crispus, Chondrus ocellatus, and Gigartina stellata. The ash-free polysaccharide is composed of D- and L-galactose, 3,6-anhydro-D-galactose, and sulfate ester groups. It was first studied by Schmidt (8) and its present name suggested by

Stanford. Extraction of *C. crispus* with cold and hot water appeared to give two polysaccharides (1,9,10, cf. 11), one showing $[\alpha]_D + 50°$ in water and the other $[\alpha]_D + 63°$ in water (12), although it was found that in the material from both extracts the galactose portions of the molecule are structurally similar (12). The products were first observed to differ chemically in the fact that the cold water extract contains mostly sodium and potassium with a little calcium in the ash while the hot water extract gives an ash high in calcium (12,13). The total sulfate to ash sulfate

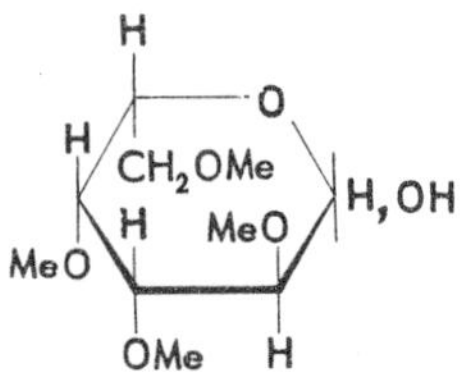

(CCCXX) 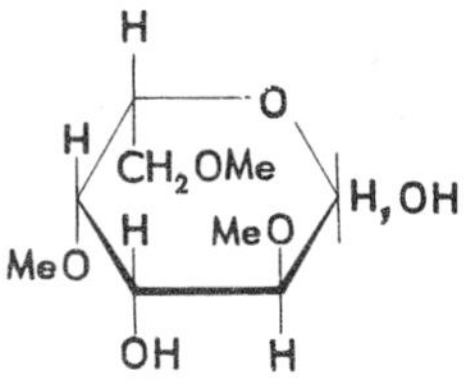   (CCCXXIX) 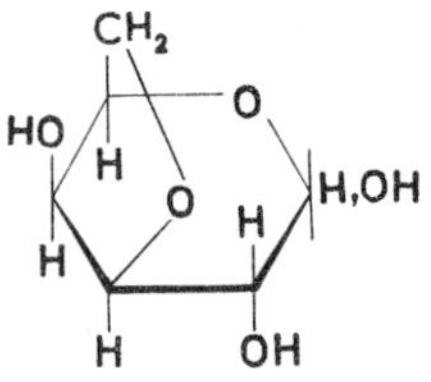   (CCCXXX)

ratio is approximately $2:1$ indicating that the polysaccharide contains sulfate ester groups (1). The high sulfate content of carrageenin, 35.1 per cent by cold water extraction of *C. crispus* (12), was long considered significant (14–16) and is equivalent to about one sulfate ester group per hexose residue.

The main component of carrageenin is D-galactose. It was first identified as mucic acid by the oxidation of the polysaccharide with nitric acid (17,18) and subsequently confirmed (19,20). By direct acid hydrolysis the polysaccharide from *C. crispus* gives 30–37 per cent (9,12) of galactose, that from *C. ocellatus* gives 40 to 44 per cent (21–23) and that from *Gigartina stellata* gives 40 per cent (24) galactose. A small amount of L-galactose is also present and this isomer has been isolated from *C. ocellatus* (25); it was also identified as the 2,3,4,6-tetra- (CCCXX) and 2,4,6-tri-*O*-methyl (CCCXXIX) derivatives from methylated carrageenin of *C. crispus* (26) and by mercaptolysis to give DL-galactose diethyl dithioacetal (27).

Also, by mercaptolysis of carrageenin from *C. crispus* the component which has long eluded identification has been proved to be 3,6-anhydro-D-galactose (CCCXXX) isolated as its diethyl dithioacetal (27–29). The reported presence of a component giving ketose reactions (12,18,20,21, 30,31) and at various times suspected to be D-fructose (17) is thus explained.

The presence of 2-keto-gluconic acid in carrageenin (30), which has not been confirmed (24), was also suggested to be derived from the "ketose" component (31), but the present knowledge shows that the positive ketose test was caused by the 3,6-anhydro-galactose.

The presence of D-glucose in carrageenin (9,12,20,32), subsequently found only in the hot water extracts of the seaweed (9,12), has been shown to be due to the presence of Floridean starch which is not extracted by cold water (31). Pentoses (9,20,30,33,34) and 6-deoxyhexoses (32) have also been reported, but it is doubtful whether they form an integral part of the carrageenin polysaccharide.

The chemical heterogeneity of carrageenin, suggested by earlier work (1,9–12) has received support from electrophoretic, sedimentation and diffusion studies from which it appeared that carrageenin is composed of a major component with a linear structure and a minor component which may be branched (41). The minor component has the higher rate of sedimentation. The two components indicated above were separated from aqueous solutions by fractionation with potassium chloride (42,43). At potassium chloride concentrations of about $0.15M$ a gel precipitates, designated K-carrageenin, which may be removed by centrifugation from the unaffected fraction, λ-carrageenin, in the supernatant. The λ-fraction is isolated by precipitation with ethanol. Cesium, rubidium and ammonium salts may replace potassium, but sodium and lithium salts are without effect, due to the fact that the diameters of the hydrated cations, $Na^{\oplus}$ and $Li^{\oplus}$, are too large to pack K-carrageenin molecules sufficiently close to maintain aggregation and cause precipitation (44).

From a commercial sample of *Chondrus* carrageenin with 29 per cent sulfate and showing $[\alpha]_D + 58°$, the K-fraction, 24 per cent sulfate and $[\alpha]_D + 63°$, amounted to 40 per cent of the original material while the λ-fraction, 33 per cent sulfate and $[\alpha]_D + 44°$, comprised 45 per cent. The proportion of the two fractions is dependent upon the temperature at which the seaweed is extracted. Extraction of *C. crispus* at 60° and then of the residue at 100° gives a product from the 60° extract with 64 per cent of the K-component and 26 per cent of the λ-component while the 100° extract is composed of 14 per cent K- and 78 per cent λ-fraction. Extracts of *Gigartina* species appear to contain less and those of *Hypnea musciformis* more of the K-component than does *C. crispus*.

In addition to differing in sulfate content and optical rotation, the K-carrageenin contains 24 per cent of 3,6-anhydro-D-galactose (28) while the λ-carrageenin has considerably less (29). Sedimentation and viscosity studies indicate that both the K- and λ-fractions are polydisperse, and that the higher molecular weight λ-carrageenin has a more elongated molecule in solution (43). No separation of the two fractions could be effected electrophoretically in free solution (41,45), but by glass paper electrophoresis (46) using N sodium hydroxide as the electrolyte, a resolution can be obtained (47).

These observations have been confirmed (48) and it is also found that an additional component of *C. crispus* may be obtained by successive extraction with 0.02M sodium acetate at 30°, 60° and 100° to 120°. The fraction obtained by extraction at 30° had no tendency to gel and that at 100° to 120° gave only a weak gel but a strong gelling tendency was found in the 60° extract. It was suggested that these differences may be due to different degrees of branching in the molecules, or, in view of the difference in 3,6-anhydro-D-galactose in the fractions obtained by potas - sium chloride fractionation (28,29), the gelling differences may be due to structural differences in the components. It would appear that the structural differences, if any, in the cold and hot extracts of *C. crispus* must be associated with the 3,6-anhydro-D-galactose, since the galactose portion of the molecule in each extract is essentially the same (12).

The degradation of aqueous solutions of the sodium salt of carrageenin at pH 7 involves two reactions, an initial rapid degradation representing about 0.3 per cent of the complete hydrolysis followed by a first-order random degradation which was interpreted to involve scission of the 3,6-anhydrogalactoside linkages (49). The latter reaction becomes important at temperatures above 60° and results in the formation of 5-hydroxy-methyl 2-furfural and formic acid (50).

The elucidation of the structure of carrageenin has been ascertained principally by application of methylation techniques. Methylation of the carrageenin from the cold and hot water extracts of *C. crispus* gave essentially the same methylated polysaccharide, which still contained the sulfate ester groups. The methyl derivative, upon hydrolysis with 0.5N-oxalic acid followed by acetylation and distillation of the cleavage fragments, gives the acetyl derivatives of 2,6-di-O-methyl-D-galactose (CCXVII) and 2-O-methyl-D-galactose (CCIII) (12). The positive rotations of the polysaccharide and its methyl derivative indicate a predominance of α-D-glycosidic linkages. The resistance of the sulfate group in carrageenin to alkaline hydrolysis (10,12) led to the suggestion that it is located at C_4 in the galactose residues and from the methylation data these residues are linked through C_1 and C_3 with some branching possibly occurring through C_6.

This postulation is confirmed by the study of a degraded carrageenin triacetate obtained by acetylation with concomitant desulfation of carrageenin using acetic anhydride and sulfuryl chloride catalyst (35). The

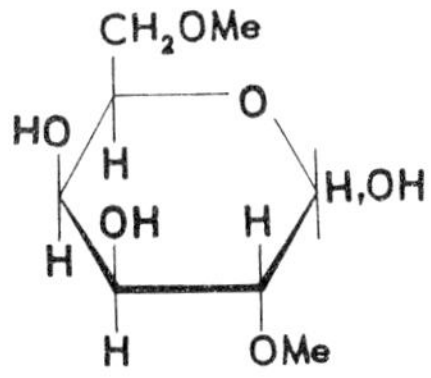

CH$_2$OMe ... (CCXVII)

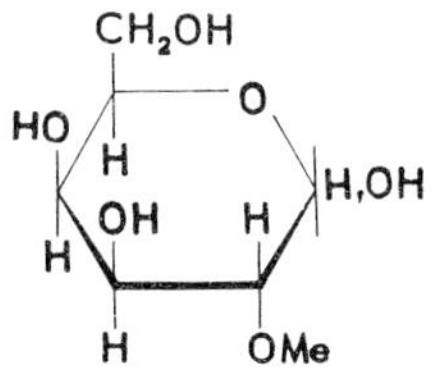

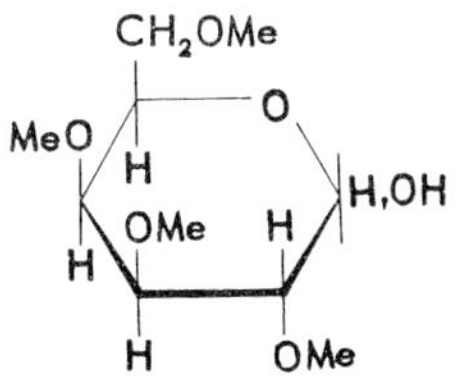

CH$_2$OH ... (CCIII)

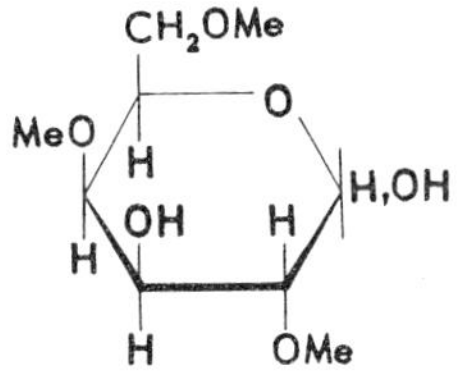

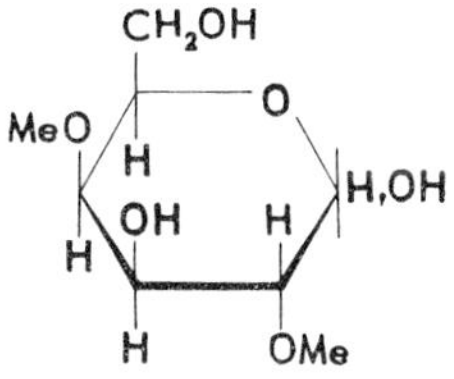

CH$_2$OMe ... (XXXIX)

CH$_2$OMe ... (XLVI)

CH$_2$OH ... (CLXXXII)

H ... (CCXII)

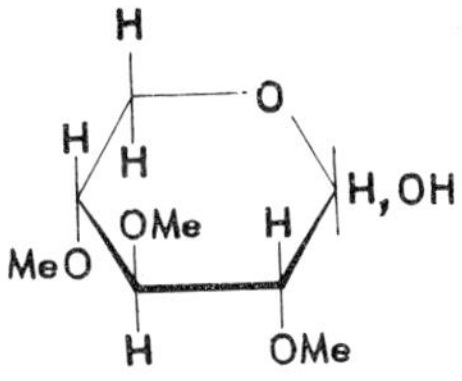

methyl derivative of the degraded desulfated carrageenin gives upon hydrolysis 2,3,4,6-tetra-O-methyl-D-galactose (XXXIX, 1 mole), 2,4,6-tri-O-methyl galactose composed of both D- (XLVI) and L- (CCCXXIX) isomers (4 moles), and 2,4-di-O-methyl-D-galactose (CLXXXII, 1 mole) (31). Since a degraded polysaccharide was used for methylation, the 2,3,4,6-tetra-O-methyl-D-galactose cleavage fragment bears little relationship to the original carrageenin, but a comparison of the tri- and di-O-methyl fragments with the di- and mono-O-methyl fragments from the methylated carrageenin shows that the sulfate groups are at C_4, and that the galactose residues are linked through C_1 and C_3. The presence of 1 → 3 linkages is further confirmed by the resistance of carrageenin to oxidation with sodium periodate (31).

A similar desulfated degraded polysaccharide is obtained from the mucilage of *Chondrus ocellatus* by acetylation with acetyl chloride in pyridine. The methyl derivative of the desulfated polysaccharide gives, upon methanolysis, a high yield of the methyl glycosides of 2,4,6-tri-O-methyl-D-galactose (XLVI) (36) thus again indicating the presence of 1 → 3 linkages.

The similarity between the polysaccharide extracted from *Gigartina stellata* and that from *Chondrus crispus* is shown by hydrolysis of the methyl derivative of the polysaccharide from the former which gives 2,6-di-O-methyl-D-galactose (CCXVII) (24). The retention of the ethereal sulfate during methylation with methyl sulfate and sodium hydroxide again emphasizes the stability of this grouping to alkali. It is interesting to note that, as in the case of the hydrolysis of the methyl derivative of agar, the hydrolyzate from methylated *Gigartina stellata* polysaccharide contained methyl levulinate. In both cases, this decomposition product undoubtedly arises from the 3,6-anhydrogalactose residues.

Since the completion of the methylation studies described above, carrageenin has been fractionated into two components, the *K*- and λ-fractions. From infra-red and X-ray data, it is proposed that stretched fibers of whole *Chondrus* carrageenin and the *K*- and λ-components all have fiber periods of 25.2Å (44). Furthermore, the fiber period of *K*-carrageenin appears to contain two trisaccharide units, each comprising two sulfated α-D-galactose residues linked 1 ⟶ 3 and one 3,6-anhydro-β-D-galactose residue joined by a 1 ⟶ 4 linkage within each 25.2Å period, a single side-chain residue of 3,6-anhydro-D-galactose appears to be linked through C_6 of a sulfated D-galactose unit in the main chain. The λ-carrageenin fiber period may represent three disaccharide units, the majority of which are composed of two 1 ⟶ 3-α-D-galactose sulfate residues. Such proposed structures, as far as the D-galactose residues are concerned, would be in keeping with the methylation data. Confirmatory evidence is, however, needed for the linkages of the 3,6-anhydro-D-galactose units.

That the above structural picture may be an oversimplification is supported by the results of partial hydrolysis of the *Gigartina stellata* polysaccharide with 1 per cent methanolic hydrogen chloride at room temperature (26). The greater part of the polysaccharide dissolves with the formation of methyl galactosides and an insoluble residue (15 per cent approx.) remains which is practically devoid of sulfate residues (1.5 per cent). This residue has a low negative rotation, $[\alpha]_D$ – 5° in water, as compared with carrageenin, $[\alpha]_D$ + 63° in water, and contains galactose (70 per cent) and xylose (7 per cent). It is methylated with difficulty (OMe, 40.9 per cent) and the methylated product upon hydrolysis affords a mixture of methylated sugars composed approximately as follows: 2,3,4-tri-*O*-methyl-D-xylose (CCXII, 1 part), 2,3,4,6-tetra-*O*-methyl-D-galactose (XXXIX, 1 part), 2,4,6-tri-*O*-methyl-D-galactose (XLVI, 2 parts), 2,4-di-*O*-methyl-D-galactose (CLXXXII, 4 parts), 2,3,4,6-tetra-*O*-methyl-L-galactose (CCCXX, 2 parts), 2,4,6-tri-*O*-methyl-L-galactose (CCCXXIX, 6 parts), and mono-*O*-methyl galactoses (3 parts) which are probably the result of incomplete methylation. No evidence for 2,4-di-*O*-methyl-L-galactose is found.

The 2,3,4-tri-*O*-methyl-D-xylose (CCXII) may have arisen from an associated xylan such as that found in *Rhodymenia palmata* (37-40), but if this is the case, it is surprising that no other methylated derivatives of D-xylose were detected, particularly since these are present in any xylan to a much greater extent (39,40) than 2,3,4-tri-O-methyl-D-xylose.

From these studies on the resistant nucleus of carrageenin it was proposed (26) that carrageenin may be based upon a resistant backbone, rich in L-galactose residues. This complex has 1 ⟶ 3 linkages and branch points at C_6 of some of the D-galactose residues. To this backbone, chains of 1 ⟶ 3 linked D-galactose units, having ethereal sulfate groups on C_4, would be attached to those units appearing as terminal groups in the resistant residue.

This picture, however, was proposed before the fractionation data and the identification of 3,6-anhydro-D-galactose in carrageenin had been reported. It seems more likely that the small insoluble fraction investigated above is another component of carrageenin—a possibility which was realized by the original authors (25) and supported somewhat by subsequent fractionation data (48).

The structure of carrageenin has been recently clarified by studies (29) on the K-fraction separated by potassium chloride. This K-fraction contains D-galactose (38.1 per cent), 3,6-anhydro-D-galactose (28.1 per cent) and sulfate (as SO_3Na) (28.0 per cent) in the molecular proportions of 6:5:7, respectively. Upon partial mercaptolysis followed by removal of the mercaptals (dithioacetals) of D-galactose and 3,6-anhydro-D-galactose there remained a residue from which a crystalline acetate (CCCXXXa) was prepared. Deacetylation afforded a crystalline compound (CCCXXXI) which was the diethyl mercaptal (dithioacetal) of a disaccharide composed of a unit of 3,6-anhydro-D-galactose and one of D-galactose. When CCCXXXI was hydrolyzed it yielded "ethylmercaptan (ethanthiol)," D-galactose and 3,6-anhydro-D-galactose, the last-named compound being recognized as its decomposition product 5-(hydroxymethyl)-2-furaldehyde. Reductive desulfurization of CCCXXXI afforded compound CCCXXXII the structure of which was established by the fact that upon periodate oxidation it consumed two molecular proportions of sodium periodate with the liberation of one molecular proportion of formic acid. Moreover CCCXXXII afforded by hydrolysis, D-galactose and 1-deoxy-3,6-anhydro-D-galactitol, an observation which also demonstrated that the 3,6-anhydro-D-galactose residue constituted the reducing portion of the molecule. Although these facts do not rule out the possibility of the presence of a 1 ⟶ 5 linkage this structural feature would require that the 3,6-anhydro-D-galactose unit in the K-carrageenin possesses a furanose ring, and this is stereochemically impossible (51). Inspection of the formulae will show that a disaccharide with a 1 ⟶ 2 linkage would consume three molecular propor-

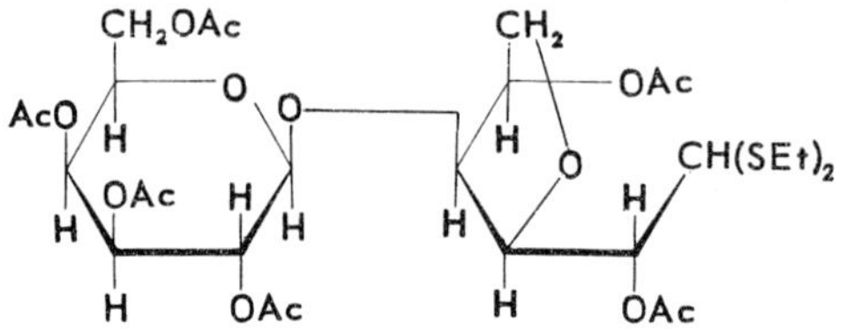

(CCCXXXa)

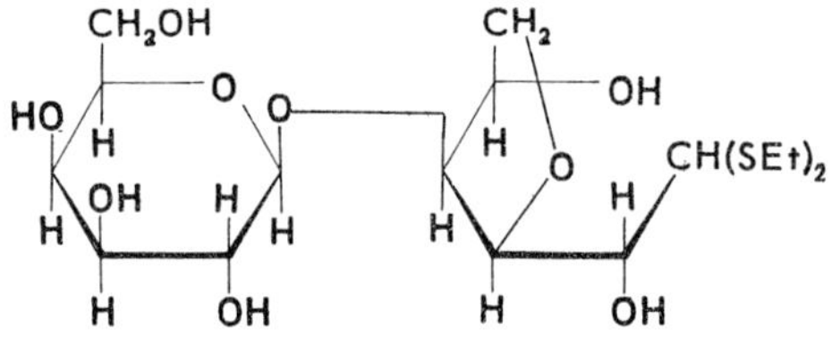

(CCCXXXI)

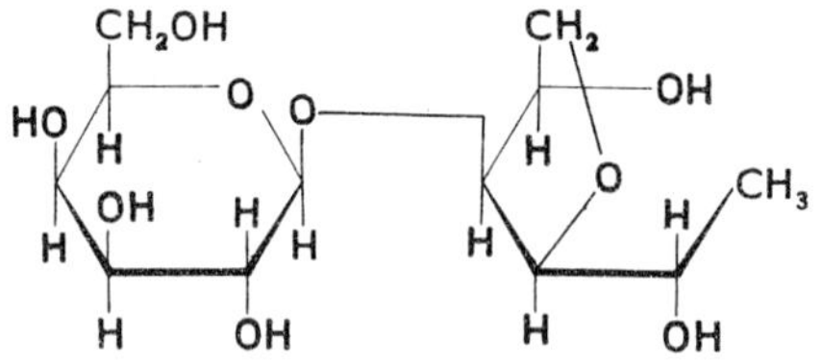

(CCCXXXII)

tions of periodate. Since the two compounds CCCXXXI and CCCXXXII show low specific rotations, the biose linkage is assumed to be of the β-D-type and consequently the disaccharide present in the polysaccharide is designated 4-O-β-D-galactopyranosyl-3,6-anhydro-D-galactose.

The ratio of the two building units, D-galactose and 3,6-anhydro-D galactose, as determined by mercaptolysis is 1.1:1 a value in good agreement with the value of 1.2:1 obtained directly by hydrolysis of the polysaccharide.

The sequential order of the two building units in the K-fraction of carrageenin is not yet known although it has been tentatively suggested that the high yield of the 4-O-β-D-galactopyranosyl-D-galactose diethyl dithioacetal favors the view that this disaccharide forms the repeating unit as in CCCXXXIII. The isolation and proof of the structure of oligosaccharides containing more than two sugar units would aid in the further elucidation of this constitutional problem.

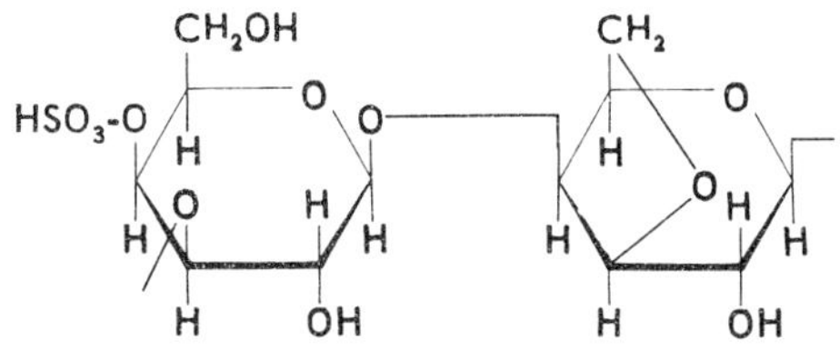

(CCCXXXIII)

Inasmuch as methylation studies (26) on carrageenin (unfractionated) indicate that the molecule is branched and since carrageenin does not react with periodate, it is deduced (29) that if the terminal units consist of D-galactose, they must contain two sulfate ester groups probably at C_3 and C_4. If this were the case, such terminal units of D-galactose 3,4-disulfate would react with alkali, losing the elements of sulfuric acid, and a partially desulfated polysaccharide would be formed with one less sulfate group on the terminal galactose unit. In addition, by Walden inversion other sugars might be expected upon hydrolysis of the alkali-treated carrageenin beside D-galactose and 3,6-anhydro-D-galactose. There is also the possibility that the stability of the carrageenin to periodate oxidation may be due to the fact that the terminal units consist of 3,6-anhydro-D-galactose with or without a sulfate substituent.

It is significant to note that the mercaptolysis experiments gave no evidence for the presence of L-galactose in *K*-carrageenin. Evidently more work remains to be done before the total structure of carrageenin is revealed.

Agar.   Agar appears to be a cell-wall constituent of the *Florideae* (sub-class of *Rhodophyceae*), several members of which form the source of this commercially important material. It was first studied by Payen (52) who assigned to the compound the name gelose and the formula $C_6H_{10}O_5$. Following the identification of galactaric and oxalic acids amongst the products of nitric acid oxidation (53), agar was first recognized as a galactan (54). From the fact that upon ignition it gave an ash which was high in calcium and sulfur, yet an aqueous solution contained no sulfate ions until it had been hydrolyzed with dilute hydrochloric acid, it was concluded (55) that the molecule contained ester sulfate groups. It was further shown that nearly all the sulfur in agar appeared as sulfuric acid upon hydrolysis with hydrochloric acid (56) and that electrodialysis yielded a free polysaccharide acid (57,58). A hot aqueous solution of this free acid does not gel upon cooling until a neutral salt is again formed by the addition of organic or inorganic bases (59).

Following the studies of these earlier workers, the composition and structure of agar has been extensively investigated. The constitutional picture, however, is still somewhat confusing, principally due to the fact that many studies have been carried out using commercial samples of agar, the preparative histories of which were largely unknown. Most of the agar of commerce originates in Japan where several species of seaweed are extracted together in order to obtain a product with desirable gelling properties (249). Apart from the obvious disadvantages which attend the study of such a mixed product, the effects of the extraction and purification procedures upon the structure of the polysaccharides as they occur in the plant are unknown.

Agar is composed of D-galactose, L-galactose, which is principally in the form of its 3,6-anhydro-derivative (CCCXXXIV), and a small amount of ester sulfate.

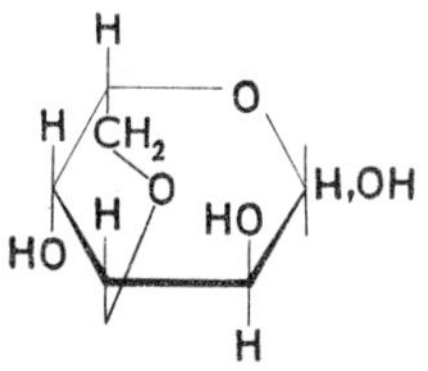

(CCCXXXIV) 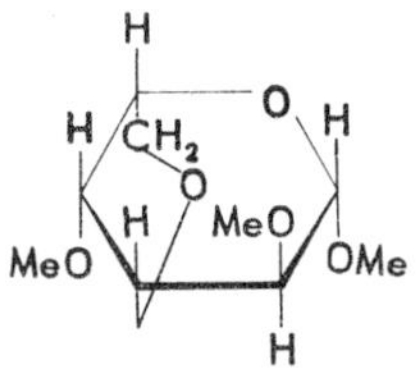   (CCCXXXV) 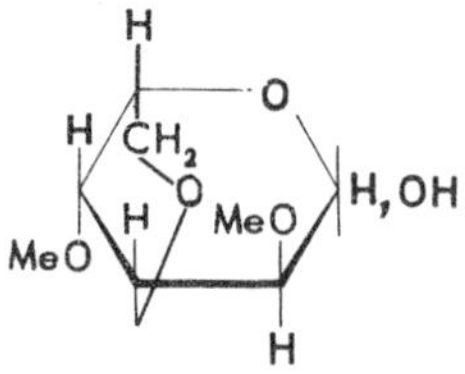   (CCCXXXVI)

Pentoses (1.8 to 5.7 per cent) (61–64) including xylose (60), 6-deoxy-hexose (1.0 to 3.6 per cent) (61,63,65,66), and uronic acid (3.6 to 7.4 per cent) (63,65,66) have also been reported, but it is not known whether they form an integral part of the molecule. The sulfur content of commercial agar may vary from about 0.3 (67) to 2 (68) per cent and specimens prepared from single species of seaweeds range from 0.36 per cent of sulfur in the agar from *Gelidium latifolium* (69), 0.43 and 0.47 per cent from *Gracilaria confervoides* (70) and *Gelidium crinale* (70), respectively, to 1.20 (71) to 2.22 (72) per cent from *Ceramium hypnaeoides*, though these last values may be high, since agar from *Gracilaria confervoides* was reported by the same worker (72) to contain 3.76 per cent of sulfur compared to 0.43 per cent given above (70). The low sulfur contents reported for some samples of agar cast doubt upon it being strictly a polysaccharide sulfate (68).

The hydrolysis of agar with mineral acid results in extensive decomposition with the formation of galactose and levulinic acid, the latter arising principally from the 3,6-anhydro-L-galactose residues. The hydrolyzate from commercial agar contained 65 per cent of hexose (72) and a crude product from *Gelidium amansii* yielded 67 per cent of hexose (65). Assays for galactose vary, agar from *Gelidium amansii* giving a value of 32 per cent (65), *Gelidium subcostatum* 37 per cent (72), *Gracilaria confervoides* 48 per cent (72), and commercial agar 40 (73) and 41 per cent (72). These figures are undoubtedly low and methylation studies indicate that D-galactose constitutes at least 55 per cent and more likely 65 per cent of agar (74).

L-Galactose was isolated from the products of enzymic hydrolyses of the agar from *Gelidium amansii*, *Gelidium subcostatum*, and *Acanthopeltis japonica* (75), and the diethyl dithioacetal of DL-galactose has been obtained in 1 per cent yield by the mercaptolysis of commercial agar (76). The isolation of hepta-*O*-acetyl-DL-galactose in 10 to 20 per cent yield by the acetolysis of agar was interpreted (77) as indicating the presence of *aldehydo*-DL-galactose in agar. It has been shown (78), however, that hepta-*O*-acetyl-DL-galactose is an acetolysis product of methyl 3,6-anhydro-β-D-galactoside, and, by inference, of the L-isomer. It is, therefore, most probable that the hepta-*O*-acetyl-DL-galactose arises from the 3,6-anhydro-L-galactose residues in agar.

The presence of 3,6-anhydro-L-galactose residues in agar was first demonstrated by the isolation in 10 to 13 per cent yield of methyl 3,6-anhydro-2,4-di-*O*-methyl-β-L-galactoside (CCCXXXV) from the further methylation of cleavage fragments of methylated commercial agar (79–81).

Because of the sensitivity of 3,6-anhydro-L-galactose and its derivatives to acid, the yield of the 2,4-dimethyl ether was not quantitative. For the same reason, the methanolysis of agar to give 3,6-anhydro-L-galactose dimethylacetal in yields of 18 per cent from *Gelidium amansii* and *Acanthopeltis japonica*, 10 per cent from *Gelidium subcostatum*, and 7 per cent from *Ceramium hypnaeoides*, indicates the minimum 3,6-anhydro-L-galactose content of the agar from these sources (82). This is borne out by the isolation of 3,6-anhydro-L-galactose diethyl dithioacetal in 24 per cent yield by the mercaptolysis of commercial agar, D-galactose diethyl dithioacetal also being obtained in 30.2 per cent yield (76).

Since 3,6-anhydro-L-galactose and its derivatives give a strong Seliwanoff ketose reaction and Bredereck test because of their facile conversion into 5-(hydroxymethyl)-2-furaldehyde, it is not surprising that earlier investigators (34,83) of agar suggested that fructose was a constituent sugar.

The structure of agar has been investigated by the partial hydrolysis of the polysaccharide with acid and with enzymes to give disaccharide residues, by periodate oxidation, and by methylation procedures.

Agar forms a chloroform soluble acetate when acetylated with acetic anhydride in pyridine (100). The acetylation apparently proceeded with concomitant desulfation since the acetate contained no sulfate group and upon deacetylation gave an almost ash-free agar which was identical with the original material in its ability to form a gel. It would appear, therefore, that little degradation occurred during acetylation. Deacetylation and methylation with methyl sulfate and alkali yielded the methylated derivative, $[\alpha]_D - 92°$ in chloroform, which appeared from fractional precipitation studies to be homogeneous (74). Upon hydrolysis with 6 per cent sulfuric acid, the methylated agar afforded 2,4,6-tri-O-methyl-D-galactose (XLVI) (65 per cent) and a sirup (14 per cent), which upon further methylation gave 10 to 13 per cent of the crystalline methyl glycoside (CCCXXXV) of 3,6-anhydro-2,4-di-O-methyl-L-galactose and methyl levulinate, the latter probably arising from the acid decomposition of the methylated 3,6-anhydro-L-galactose residues (81). The hydrolyzate of methylated agar also contained a very small amount of partially methylated L-galactose, which was isolated upon further methylation as N-phenyl 2,3,4,6-tetra-O-methyl-L-galactosylamine, and some unidentified di-O-methyl-D-galactose, probably arising from incomplete methylation (67,81). The cleavage of methylated commercial agar by methanolysis, which reduces decomposition to levulinic acid, gave the methyl glycoside of 2,4,6-tri-O-methyl-D-galactose, but no methyl di-O-methyl galactosides (101,102). Upon further methylation of the methanolyzate, 3,6-anhydro-2,4-di-O-methyl-L-galactose (CCCXXXVI) was also obtained. The hydrolysis of the methylated agar from Gelidium amansii also yielded 2,4,6-tri-O-methyl-D-galactose (103), so it is well established that in agar the D-galactose units are of the pyranose form and linked through C_1 and C_3. The high negative rotation of acetylated and of methylated agar are in agreement with the presence of 3,6-anhydro-α-L-galactopyranose and β-D-galactopyranose residues.

Methanolysis of the methylated agar from Gelidium amansii afforded 3,6-anhydro-2-O-methyl-L-galactose (CCCXXXVII), isolated as the dimethylacetal, which indicated that the 3,6-anhydro-L-galactose units are linked through C_1 and C_4 if these residues are present in the pyranose form (104). That this is the case was further proved by the ace-

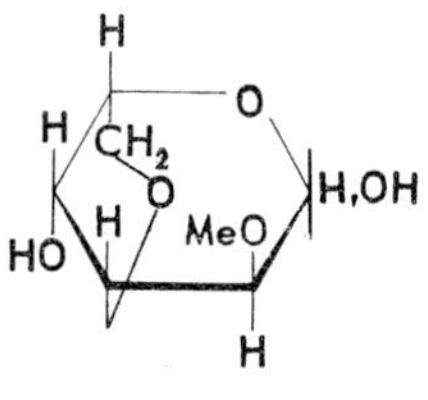

(CCCXXXVII) 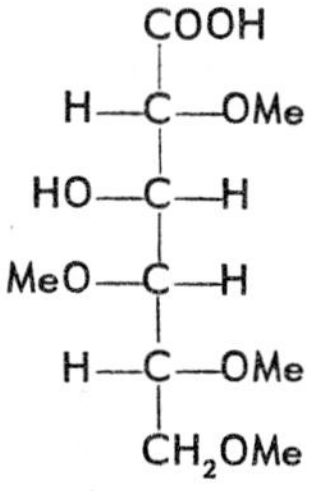   (CCCXXXVIII) 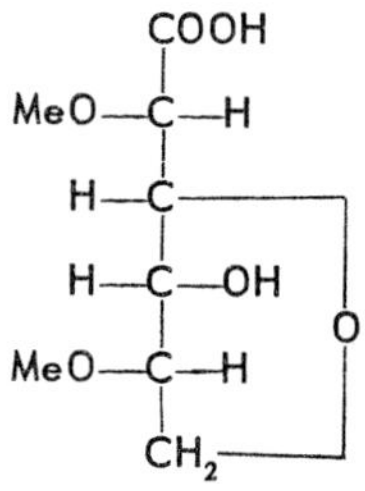   (CCCXXXIX)

tolysis of methylated agar (84) with acetyl bromide (67). The acetolysis products, when oxidized with bromine, remethylated, and then subjected to fractional distillation, gave mainly the methyl 2,4,5,6-tetra-O-methyl-D-galactonate together with a mixture of methylated disaccharide esters. Hydrolysis of this disaccharide mixture yielded 2,3,4,6-tetra-O-methyl-D-galactose, 2,4,5,6-tetra-O-methyl-D-galactonic acid (CCCXXXVIII), and smaller amounts of 3,6-anhydro-2,5-di-O-methyl-L-galactonic acid (CCCXXXIX). It follows, therefore, that the 3,6-anhydro-L-galactonic acid moiety of the disaccharides is linked through C_4.

From the above evidence, it would seem that agar is composed of about two thirds of D-galactopyranose residues linked through C_1 and C_3

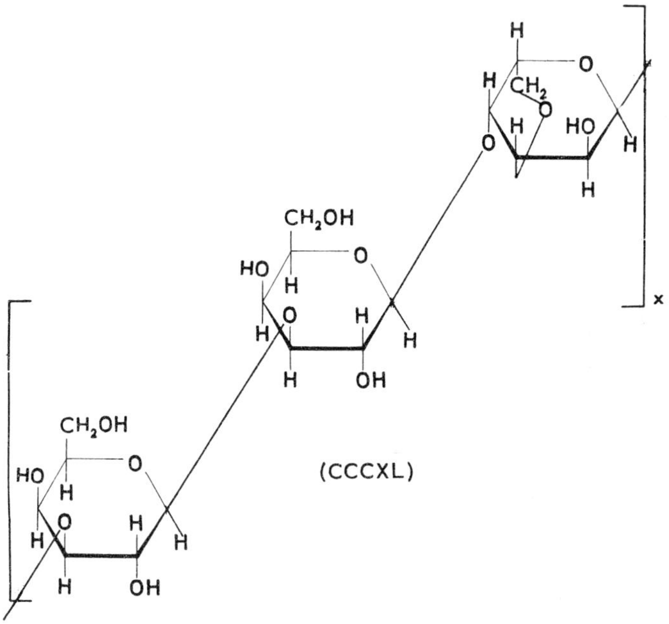

(CCCXL)

and that the 3,6-anhydro-L-galactopyranose units are linked through C_1 and C_4. It was suggested, therefore, that the principal structural feature of agar is represented by formula CCCXL. The fact that 2,3,4,6-tetra-O-methyl-D-galactose was not found in the cleavage fragments of the methylated agar indicated either that the unit of the molecule shown in CCCXL must be repeated many times or that 3,6-anhydro-L-galactose constitutes the terminal units of the polysaccharide. Also, since L-galactose has been detected in small amounts in both agar and as a methylated derivative from methylated agar then it must also occur in-

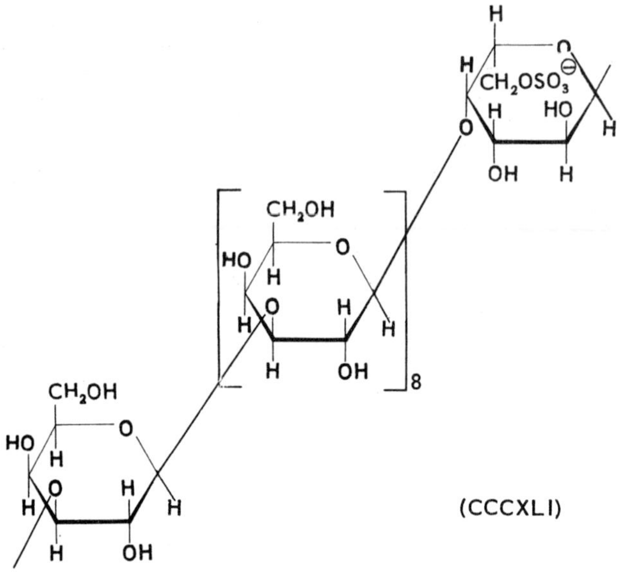

(CCCXLI)

frequently in this essentially linear molecule. It is probable also that the small amount of sulfuric acid ester groups in agar are attached to C_6 of some of the L-galactose residues that and these residues represent the precursors of the 3,6-anhydro-L-galactose units.

Since L-galactose 6-sulfate would afford the 3,6-anhydrogalactose upon treatment with alkali, it was originally suggested (105) that agar is probably composed of D-galactose and L-galactose 6-sulfate, as illustrated by formula CCCXLI. This view can no longer be sustained in view of the isolation from agar of derivatives of 3,6-anhydro-L-galactose. The study leading to this suggestion is worthy of further description in that it also illustrates some of the properties of agar. The agar was methylated with methyl sulfate and alkali and was obtained after eight treatments as a granular material, which was subjected to dialysis from acidic solution when some of the 3,6-anhydro-L-galactose glycosidic bonds hydrolyzed; it is known that 3,6-anhydrogalactosides are sensitive to weak acid. This, incidentally, explains why an agar gel is susceptible to hydrolysis with very dilute acid and the pH of acidic media for bacteriological purposes must be adjusted after sterilization. The aldehyde groups thus liberated undergo oxidation so that the resulting product is a methylated, acidic, degraded agar, with an equivalent weight of 1870, which corresponds to one carboxyl group in ten hexose units. The further methylation of the methylated degraded acid with Purdie reagents increases the methoxyl content from about 33 per cent to 38 per cent and hydrolysis of this material results in the formation of 2,3,4,6-tetra-O-methyl-D-galactopyranose (XXXIX), 2,4,6-tri-O-methyl-D-galactopyranose (XLVI), and 3,6-anhydro-2,5-di-O-methyl-L-galactonic acid (CCCXXXIX). Other methylated cleavage fragments were not identified. It was again confirmed, therefore, that the D-galactopyranose residues and those residues based upon L-galactose are linked through C_1 and C_3, and C_1 and C_4, respectively.

As stated before, it was believed that 3,6-anhydro-L-galactose residues did not pre-exist in agar, but that they were generated either during extraction and purification or when the agar was subjected to methylation. It was believed that alkaline conditions present at any of these manipulative stages would result in the hydrolysis of the sulfate group at C_6 of the L-galactose residues with the formation of a 3,6-anhydro ring. This concept (4,67) is not consistent with the facts as they are now known. The 3,6-anhydro ring could not be formed to any great extent during methylation of agar with methyl sulfate and sodium hydroxide by the action of the alkali upon L-galactose 6-sulfate residues since the proportion of sulfate in the agar is too small to account for the proportion of 3,6-anhydro-2,4-di-O-methyl-L-galactose which was identified in the cleavage fragments. Thus, from an agar containing 0.1 per cent of sulfur the crystalline 3,6-anhydro cleavage fragment is isolated from methylated agar in 10 to 13 per cent yield (74,81) and an agar with 0.9 per cent sulfur gives about 10 per cent of this product (101). Also, the isolation of agar from single species of seaweed under conditions which exclude the possibility of 3,6-anhydro ring formation with resulting loss of sulfate has given rise to products which are lower in sulfur than would be required by CCCXLI. Under such mild extraction conditions, agar containing 0.43 per cent and 0.47 per cent of sulfur, respectively (70), is obtained from Gracilaria confervoides and Gelidium crinale. In a similar way, agar is obtained from Gelidium latifolium with 0.36 per cent of sulfur corresponding to one sulfate group for every 53 galactose residues (69). The treatment of this sample of agar with periodic acid shows that no $\alpha\beta$-glycol groupings are present, such as would be required by L-galactose-6-sulfate residues linked through C_1 and C_4 (69), and by the same reasoning open-chain galactose residues cannot be present as formerly suggested (77). Commercial agar is also resistant to periodate oxidation (106).

It appeared, therefore, that the structure of agar based upon the forgoing evidence was best represented by CCCXL, a verification for which could have been obtained by a direct estimation of the 3,6-anhydro-L-galactose content. Such a determination is carried out by heating the

polysaccharide with 12 per cent hydrochloric acid and determining spec-
troscopically the amount of 5-(hydroxymethyl)2-furaldehyde produced in
a manner described for carrageenin (28). However, the later isolation
and identification of oligosaccharide fragments from agar has clarified
the constitutional picture considerably.

The partial hydrolysis of agar from *Gelidium amansii* has resulted in
the isolation of a disaccharide, called agarobiose (CCCXLII) (84). The
agar was treated with N sulfuric acid for one hour at $100°$, the solution
neutralized, concentrated, and the higher molecular weight fragments
precipitated with alcohol. After removing the D-galactose from the

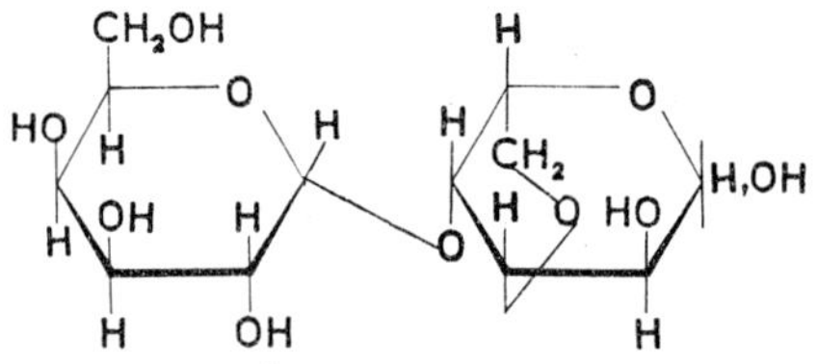

(CCCXLII)

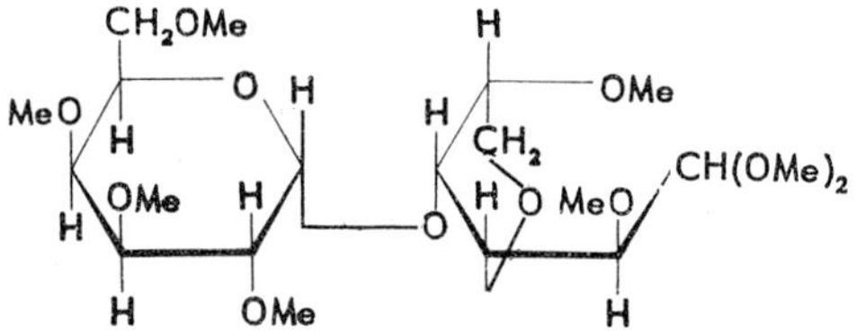

(CCCXLIII)

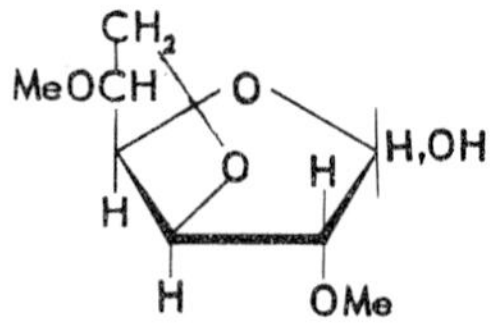

(CCCXLIV)

ethanol-soluble fraction by fermentation with *Saccharomyces sake*, the
crystalline disaccharide was isolated from the non-fermented residue.
Agarobiose showed $[\alpha]_D - 5.8°$ in water, it contained no sulfate group,
and was found to be 3,6-anhydro-4-O-(β-D-galactopyranosyl)-L-galactose

(CCCXLII) (84,85) since hexa-O-methyl-agarobiose dimethylacetyl (CCCXLIII), prepared by methylation of CCCXLII, gave upon hydrolysis 2,3,4,6-tetra-O-methyl-D-galactose (XXXIX) and 3,6-anhydro-2,5-di-O-methyl-L-galactose (CCCXLIV). The diethyl dithioacetal derivative of agarobiose has been obtained in 46 per cent yield from the partial mercaptolysis of commercial agar (86) and the dimethylacetal derivative from the partial methanolysis of agar was isolated in 59 per cent yield (87). As in the case of the methylation data it was proposed that 3,6-anhydro-L-galactose residues constitute about one third of the agar molecule, being joined to D-galactose residues through C_1 and C_4.

Enzymic hydrolysis of agar has provided some valuable information concerning the structure of the polysaccharide. In 1902, it was observed (253) and later confirmed (88, 254) that an enzyme termed "gelase," isolated from organisms of sea water, was capable of degrading agar. Later this agar-splitting enzyme was found to be present in the viscera of *Haliotus giganteus* Gm. (ear-shell) (89), of *Turbo cornutus* (top-shell) (90,91) and of other gastropods. Organisms growing on putrifying agar have been shown (92,93) to contain an enzyme called "agarase" which will degrade the polysaccharide. Among the degradation products was detected (94) a disaccharide that gave rise to a hitherto unknown osazone.

The same disaccharide has also been obtained from agar by the action of an enzyme extracted from the organism *Pseudomonas kyotoensis* (95). Treatment of agar in aqueous solution (pH 5.2) with the crude enzyme preparation at 40° was allowed to proceed for 72 hours, at which point the reducing power of the solution had reached a maximum. Inactivation of the enzyme by boiling, followed by filtration, concentration, and addition of methanol (to give 85 per cent methanol concentration), left in solution a mixture of reducing sugars amounting to 70 to 80 per cent of the weight of the original agar. Resolution of this mixture by column chromatography on carbon, using increasing concentrations of aqueous ethanol, gave a series of oligosaccharides. From the 5 to 7 per cent aqueous ethanolic eluate the crystalline disaccharide, neoagarobiose (CCCXLV), was isolated (96). The new disaccharide may be obtained as a crystalline acetate and phenylosazone; the latter appears to be identical with the unidentified disaccharide osazone isolated previously (94).

The glycosidic linkage of the disaccharide is readily hydrolyzed by dilute acid to give D-galactose and 3,6-anhydro-L-galactose. The ease of hydrolysis indicates that the disaccharide is the glycoside of 3,6-anhydro-L-galactose and not of D-galactose. Similarly, methanolysis furnishes methyl α-D-galactopyranoside and 3,6-anhydro-L-galactose dimethylacetal. This evidence confirmed that CCCXLV was composed of D-galactose and 3,6-anhydro-L-galactose. Reduction of CCCXLV to the corresponding alditol (CCCXLVI), followed by hydrolysis gave 3,6-anhydro-L-galactose and galactitol, thus establishing that D-galactose constitutes the reducing end. The disaccharide (CCCXLV) was thus recognized as an isomer of the previously characterized agarobiose (CCCXLII) and hence it was designated neoagarobiose.

Methylation of neoagarobiose (CCCXLV), first with methyl sulfate and alkali and then with silver oxide and methyl iodide, yielded the fully methylated crystalline derivative, methyl penta-O-methyl-β-neoagarobioside (CCCXLVII). Hydrolysis of CCCXLVII with 0.02 N sulfuric acid afforded methyl 2,4,6-tri-O-methyl-β-D-galactoside (CCCXLVIII) and 3,6-anhydro-2,4-di-O-methyl-L-galactose (CCCXLIX). Hydrolysis of

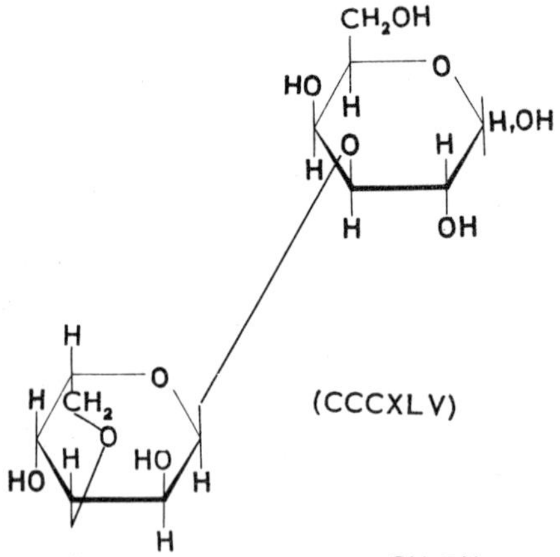

(CCCXLV)

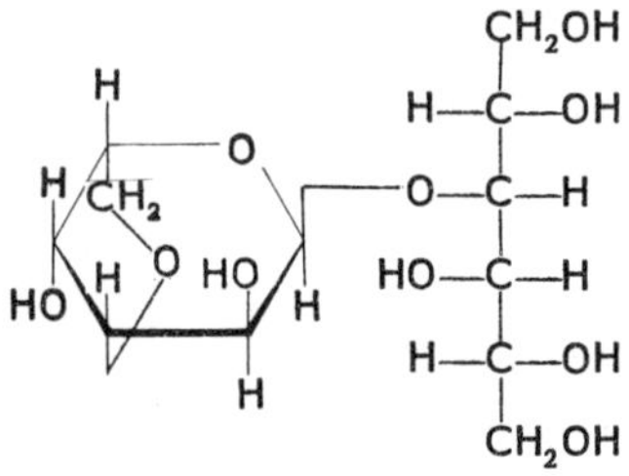

(CCCXLVI)

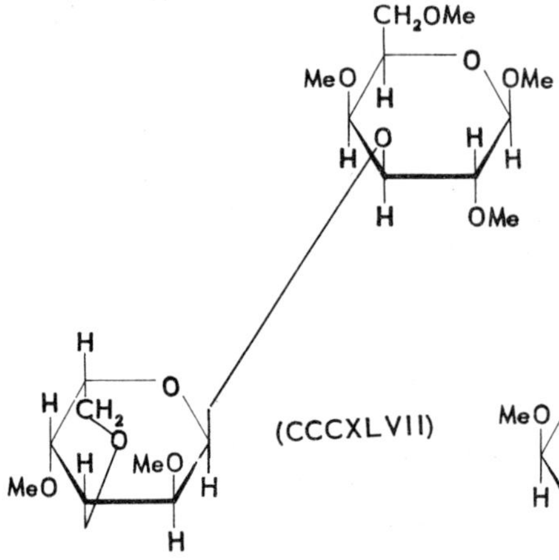

(CCCXLVII)

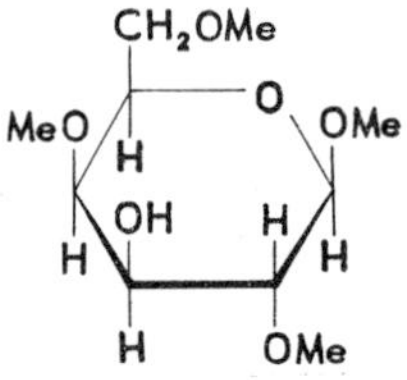

(CCCXLVIII)

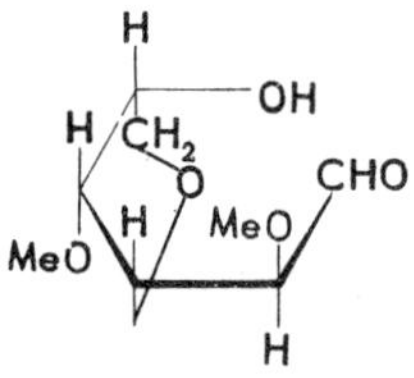

(CCCXLIX)

CCCXLVIII gave crystalline 2,4,6-tri-O-methyl-D-galactose (XLVI) and this in turn yielded a crystalline aniline derivative. The 3,6-anhydro-2,4-di-O-methyl-L-galactose was characterized, after bromine oxidation, as the crystalline aldonic acid and the corresponding amide. It is clear that the disaccharide from agar must have the structure shown in formula CCCXLV and it is, therefore, designated as 3-O-(3,6-anhydro-α-L-galac-topyranosyl)-D-galactose.

Inasmuch as the disaccharide alcohol (CCCXLVI), derived from the disaccharide by sodium borohydride reduction, may be regarded as a glycoside of 3,6-anhydro-L-galactopyranose (in which the aglycone group, galactitol, will contribute little to the rotation) which shows $[\alpha]_D - 20°$ (water), the biose linkage is most likely of the α-L-type. The same conclusion may be reached by comparing the equilibrium rotation of the disaccharide ($+20°$) with the two possible combinations of the α-L-($-80°$) and β-L-($+115°$) glycosides of 3,6-anhydro-L-galacto-pyranoside (97) with D-galactose ($+80°$) and hence neoagarobiose must be 3-O-(3,6-anhydro-α-L-galactopyranosyl)-D-galactose (96).

The isolation of the two disaccharides, agarobiose, 3,6-anhydro-4-O-(β-D-galactopyranosyl)-D-galactose, and neoagobiose, 3-O-(3,6-anhydro-α-L-galactopyranosyl)-D-galactose, the former obtained by acid and the latter by enzymic hydrolysis, has prompted the suggestion (98) that the main polysaccharide component of agar consists of a linear polymer "agarose" which is based on a combination of the above two disac-charides as the repeating unit (see formula CCCL).

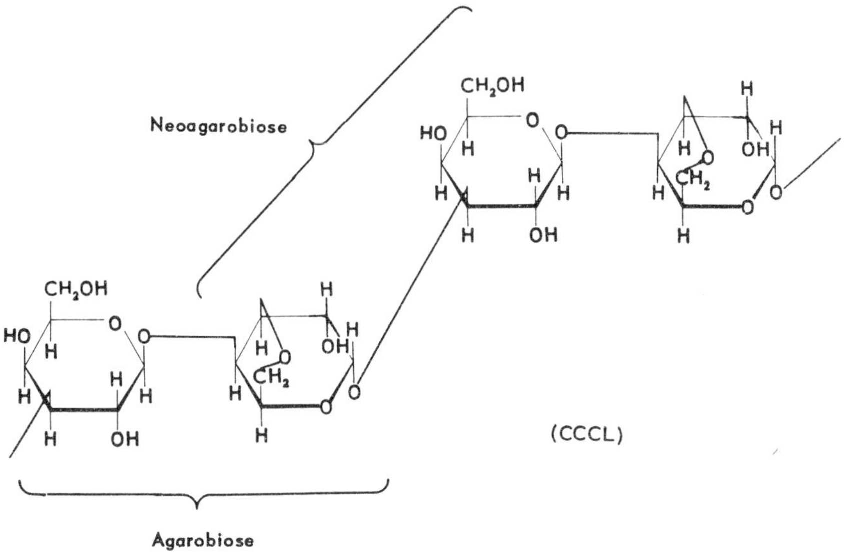

Neoagarobiose

(CCCL)

Agarobiose

A similar formula has been proposed (99) for the agar extracted from *Gelidium cartilagineum* as a result of analyses for D-galactose, 3,6-anhydro-L-galactose, and sulfate, and from an examination of the products of mercaptolysis. It is further suggested that there is one sulfate group for about every 10 galactose units (99).

The agar from *Gracilaria confervoides* has been shown (243) to be composed of 3,6-anhydro-L-galactose and D-galactose, the former being characterized as the methyl α-L-glycopyranoside and the latter as the methyl α- and the methyl β-D-galactopyranoside. Controlled hydrolysis of this agar with 1 per cent methanolic hydrogen chloride for one hour afforded 3,6-anhydro-L-galactose (12.7 per cent), D-galactose (22.6 per cent), and agarobiose, (62 per cent). Shorter periods of methanolysis gave increased yields (76 per cent) of agarobiose, which was characterized as its alditol derivative after reduction with sodium borohydride. As pointed out by the authors, there is good reason to believe that the polysaccharide may be considered to be a polymer of agarobiose units joined together by $1 \rightarrow 3$ glycosidic bonds. The presence of the $1 \rightarrow 3$ bonds was established by the observation that hydrolysis of the methylated *Gracilaria* agar (OMe, 33.8 per cent; theoretical, 34.2 per cent) yielded 2,4,6-tri-O-methyl-D-galactose (XLVI). Since the agar as its acetate showed a negative rotation ($[\alpha]_D - 34°$ in chloroform) the linkages are most likely of the β-D-type. As in earlier methylation studies no tetra-O-methyl derivative of D-galactose was isolated, suggesting again that the molecule is unbranched, but before a final decision is made on this point, perhaps the other components of the hydrolyzate of the methylated agar, besides the 2,4,6-tri-O-methyl-D-galactose, should be subjected to careful study.

The structure proposed (243) for the sample of *Gracilaria* agar agrees with CCCL, suggested above for a sample of agar that was probably extracted from *Gelidium amansii*, and with that from *G. cartilagineum.*

Interest in the structure of agar continues unabated and it has been found (244) that a small amount (1 per cent) of pyruvic acid is present in the agar molecule. The pyruvic acid was recognized by paper chromatography of the hydrolyzate of a commercial specimen of agar. Since the pyruvic acid was liberated with dilute acid (0.1N) it did not arise by decomposition of the sugar components of the agar polysaccharide, such as the 3,6-anhydro-L-galactose, and support for this view was provided by the observation that the mucilage of *Chondrus ocellatus* Holmes, which contains 3,6-anhydro-D-galactose (245), and that of *Gloiopeltis furcata*, which contains the L-isomer (246), do not give rise to pyruvic acid upon acid hydrolysis.

That the pyruvic acid does indeed form an integral part of the agar molecule follows from the fact that controlled degradation of the polysaccharide (a commercial specimen was used) by boiling for two hours with 0.5 per cent methanolic hydrogen chloride (247) gave an acidic substance, $(C_{14}H_{21}O_9(OCH_3)_2 \cdot COOH)$, characterized as a crystalline methyl ester and as the corresponding crystalline amide, which was shown by further hydrolysis to be composed of 3,6-anhydro-L-galactose, D-galactose, and pyruvic acid (247).

The complex acidic substance, $C_{14}H_{21}O_9(OCH_3)_2 \cdot COOH$, mentioned above was shown to be 3,6-anhydro-4-O-[4,6-O-(1-carboxyethylidene)-β-D-galactopyranosyl]-L-galactose dimethylacetal (CCCLI) in the same manner. Methanolysis of CCCLI afforded the known 3,6-anhydro-L-galactose dimethylacetal (CCCLIa) and the methyl ester methyl glycoside

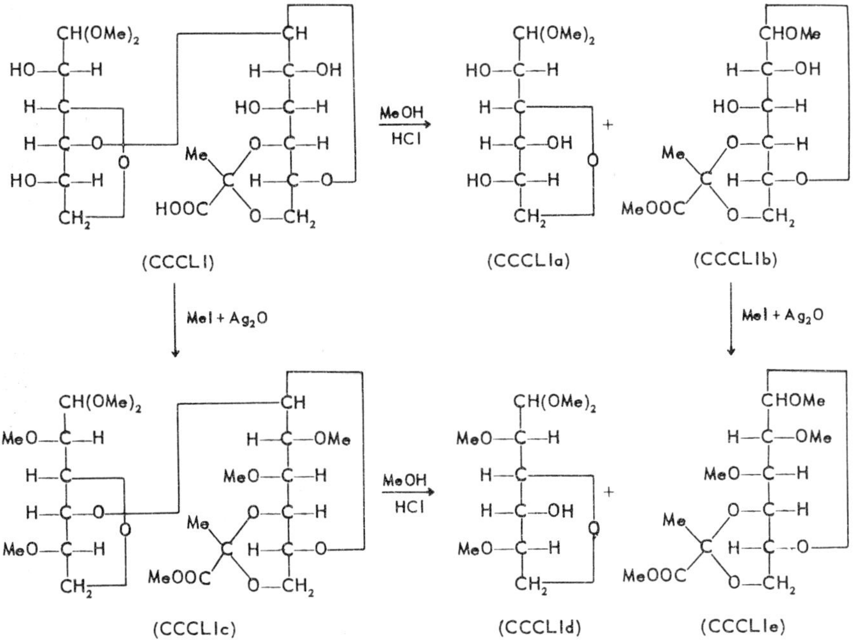

CH(OMe)₂ ... (CCCLI)   (CCCLIa)   (CCCLIb)

MeI + Ag₂O

(CCCLIc)   (CCCLId)   (CCCLIe)

(CCCLIb). Complete methylation of the latter with silver oxide and methyl iodide yielded CCCLIe which upon hydrolysis gave 2,3-di-O-methyl-D-galactose and pyruvic acid, the latter being recognized as its crystalline phenylhydrazone. Proof that the pyruvic acid molecule is combined through its carbonyl group was established by the fact that reduction of CCCLIe with lithium aluminum hydride followed by methylation and hydrolysis gave rise to 1-O-methyl-1-hydroxypropanone. It is believed that the carbonyl group of the pyruvic acid moiety engages C_4 and C_6 of the galactose residue because the glycoside (CCCLIb) shows a positive rotation expected for a methyl D-galactopyranoside. The position of the attachment of the biose linkage to the 3,6-anhydro-L-galactose residue was proved by the observation that methylation of CCCLI with silver oxide and methyl iodide afforded CCCLIc, which upon methanolysis furnished CCCLIe and 3,6-anhydro-2,5-di-O-methyl-L-galactose dimethyl acetal (CCCLId), recognized by hydrolysis and bromine oxidation as the corresponding glyconic acid. The isolation of CCCLIe, via CCCLIc, demonstrated that the direct methanolysis of CCLI does not result in any ring change in the galactoside moiety of the disaccharide (CCCLI). Further support for the structure CCCLI follows from the demonstration that careful hydrolysis of this hitherto unknown pyruvic acid-containing disaccharide affords pyruvic acid and agarobiose (CCCXLII). This derivative (CCCLI) of agarobiose therefore has been designated 3,6-anhydro-4-O-[4,6-O-(1-carboxyethylidene-)-β-D-galacto-pyranosyl]-L-galactose dimethylacetal (248). The distribution of the pyruvic acid residues in agar is not known but the author suggests (248) that the acid group is concerned with the gelling properties of the polysaccharide.

Further evidence in support of the structure (CCCL) suggested for agar has been provided (240) by the isolation of what appears to be a tetrasaccharide from the action, previously referred to, of the enzyme from *Pseudomonas kyotoensis* upon agar. The tetrasaccharide, for which no molecular weight value is recorded, is said to crystallize as a tetrahydrate and as a dihydrate though it is somewhat surprising to find the latter to have a lower melting point (104–107°) than that (214–218°) of the former. The tetrasaccharide, obtained as a crystalline acetate, gives upon methanolysis 3,6-anhydro-L-galactose dimethylacetal and methyl α-D-galactopyranoside in equimolecular amounts. Reduction of the tetrasaccharide with sodium borohydride followed by methanolysis yields galactitol, together with 3,6-anhydro-L-galactose dimethylacetal and methyl α-D-galactopyranoside. It was evident, therefore, that a D-galactose unit was at the reducing end of the molecule. Treatment of the tetrasaccharide with an extract of *P. kyotoensis* afforded only neoagarobiose, 3-O-(3,6-anhydro-L-galactopyranosyl)-D-galactose. Mild hydrolysis of the tetrasaccharide with 0.04N oxalic acid gave rise to equimolecular amounts of 3,6-anhydro-L-galactose, D-galactose, and agarobiose (4-O-(β-D-galactopyranosyl)-3,6-anhydro-L-galactose). The presence of 1 → 3 and 1 → 4 linkages in the oligosaccharide was thus established and it was deduced that the substance was probably neoagarobiosyl-neoagarobiose, or O-3,6-anhydro-α-ʟ-galactopyranosyl-(1 → 3)-O-β-ᴅ-galactopyranosyl-(1 → 4)-O-3,6-anhydro-α-ʟ-galactopyranosyl-(1 → 3)-ᴅ-galactose. Support for this structure was provided by the results of methylation studies in which it was established that the fully methylated oligosaccharide yielded upon methanolysis the methyl glycosides of 3,6-anhydro-2,4-di-O-methyl-ʟ-galactose, 3,6-anhydro-2-O-methyl-ʟ-galactose, and 2,4,6-tri-O-methyl-ᴅ-galactose.

It is apparent from the various studies described above that no one formula for agar satisfies all the experimental data. This conclusion reflects in part the different sources, sometimes ill-defined, from which the samples of agar originated. Perhaps more interesting, however, is the inference that the term agar represents a spectrum of polysaccharides with varying proportions of 3,6-anhydro-ʟ-galactose and ᴅ-galactopyranose residues linked through C_1 and C_4, and C_1 and C_3, respectively. Thus, the agar from *Gelidium amansii* would appear (from methylation studies and partial acid hydrolysis to agarobiose) to be composed of about one third of 3,6-anhydro-ʟ-galactose residues and probably conforms to formula CCCXL, whereas the agar from *Gracilaria confervoides* contains equimolecular amounts of the two types of residues and is best represented by formula CCCL. However, these molecular ratios are based on yields of various fragments after, in some cases, extensive manipulation. It would be valuable, therefore, as suggested earlier, to determine directly the 3,6-anhydro-ʟ-galactose residues in the many types of agar and in this way some correlation of the physical properties might possibly ensue.

The Mucilage of Gloiopeltis furcata

Extraction of *Gloiopeltis furcata* (family *Rhodophyceae*), Funori, with boiling water affords (246) a mucilaginous solution from which by alcoholic precipitation an amorphous powder is obtained. The product (yield 30 per cent), which is widely used in Japan as an adhesive, sizing agent for silk textiles, and as a thickener in mortar and plaster, shows $[\alpha]_D - 21°$ in water. It contains 18.5 per cent of sulfate, 13.1 per cent of ash, and 6.9 per cent of sulfated ash. Upon hydrolysis, the *Gloiopeltis* mucilage gives rise to ᴅ-galactose, together with smaller amounts of ʟ-arabinose and ʟ-fucose, and it has been reported that the substance shows a positive Seliwanoff test for ketoses. Since this has been traced to the presence of 3,6-anhydro-ʟ-galactose in agar and to the ᴅ-isomer in carrageenin it was suspected (246) that the *Gloiopeltis* mucilage also contained 3,6-anhydrogalactose.

Treatment of the mucilage with 3% methanolic hydrogen chloride under reflux for 24 hours afforded a mixture of 3,6-anhydro-ʟ-galactose dimethyl acetal (8 moles), D-galactose (12 moles), and L-galactose (1 mole), which components were separated by column chromatography. The 3,6-anhydro-L-galactose was characterized as its crystalline osazone, some of the D-galactose was separated as the monohydrate of the methyl α-D-glycopyranoside and the rest with the L-isomer as DL-galactose diethyl dithioacetal (246).

The Mucilage of Chondrus Ocellatus

Extraction of the seaweed *Chondrus ocellatus* Holmes with water affords (245) a mucilage which resembles the carrageenin obtained from *C. crispus.* Addition of ethanol to the aqueous extract gave the polysaccharide sulfate as a salt which showed $[\alpha]_D + 54°$ in water. The yield of polysaccharide based on the air-dried plant was about 53 per cent and the analysis showed that the moisture-free material contained sulfate (24.14 per cent), ash (17.34 per cent), and sulfated ash (7.25 per cent).

When subjected to the action of 0.5 per cent methanolic hydrogen chloride in the manner previously applied to agar (87) there were obtained (245), in addition to methyl hydrogen sulfate, methyl α-D-galactopyranoside (6 per cent), 3,6-anhydro-D-galactose dimethylacetal (5 per cent), 3,6-anhydro-4-O-(β-D-galactopyranosyl)-D-galactose dimethylacetal (68 per cent), and methyl 3,6-anhydro-4-O-(β-D-galactopyranosyl)-D-galactopyranoside (5 per cent).

The structure (CCCLII) assigned to this new disaccharide, obtained as the dimethylacetal (CCCLIIa) and as the crystalline methyl glycoside (CCCLIIb), is based on the following observations. Mild hydrolysis of CCCLIIa with dilute oxalic acid afforded the reducing disaccharide (CCCLII) which in turn furnished a crystalline phenylosazone. Methanolysis of CCCLIIa gave methyl α-D-galactopyranoside and 3,6-anhydro-D-galactose dimethylacetal, the latter being recognized by hydrolysis and the formation of the corresponding crystalline diphenylhydrazone. This observation showed that the *C. ocellatus* mucilage resembled carageenin rather than agar since the latter gives 3,6-anhydro-L-galactose (76,86) whereas carrageenin from *C. crispus* furnishes the D-isomer (27,28). Complete methylation of CCCLIIa, first with methyl sulfate and alkali and then with silver oxide and methyl iodide, yielded CCCLIIc which gave rise upon hydrolysis to 2,3,4,6-tetra-O-methyl-D-galactose, recognized as its aniline derivative, and 3,6-anhydro-2,5-di-O-methyl-D-galactose, identified after bromine oxidation as the corresponding crystalline 3,6-anhydro-2,5-di-O-methyl-D-galactonic acid, the enantiomorph (CCCXXXIX) of which had previously been obtained from methyl-

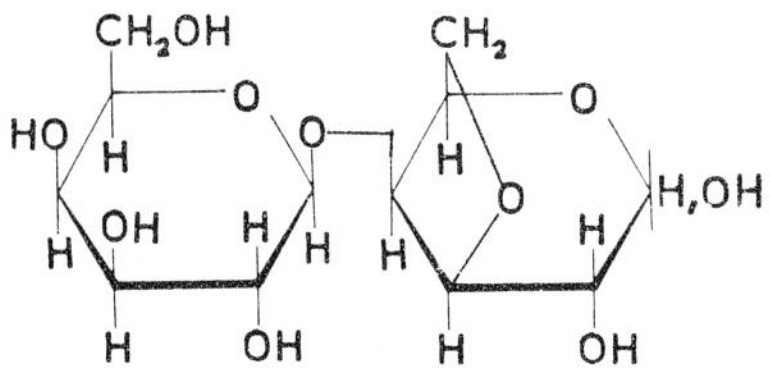

(CCCLII)

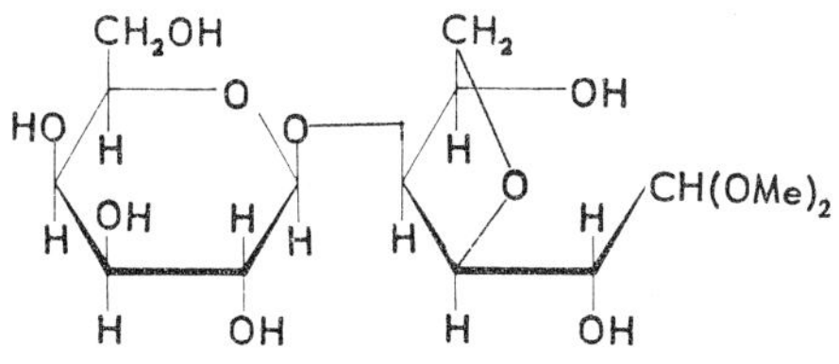

(CCCLIIa)

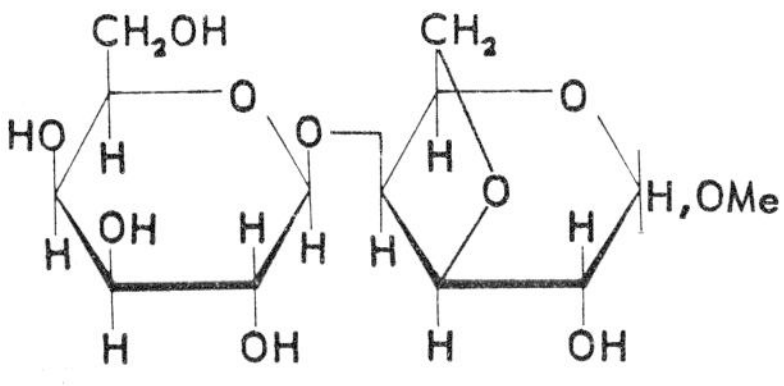

(CCCLIIb)

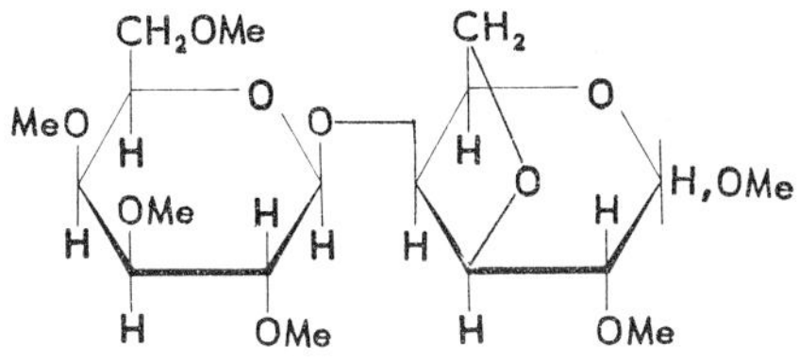

(CCCLIIc)

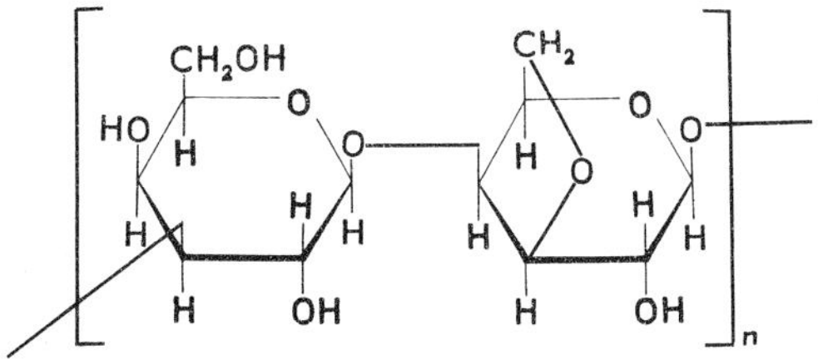

(CCCLIId)

ated agarobiose (84–86).   The 3,6-anhydro-2,5-di-O-methyl-D-galactonic acid was also identified as its crystalline amide.   This evidence showed that the disaccharide (CCCLIIa) contained a $(1 \rightarrow 4)$ linkage and from the low rotation, $[\alpha]_D + 16°$ (water), of the reducing disaccharide (CCCLII) it is suggested that it assumes a β-D-configuration.   This new disaccharide, called "carrobiose" must, therefore, have the structure CCCLII and is designated 3,6-anhydro-4-O-(β-D-galactopyranosyl)-D-galactose.   The methyl glycoside CCCLIIb of this disaccharide formed a crystalline monohydrate which upon treatment with methanolic hydrogen chloride readily gave the dimethylacetal (CCCLIIa).

On the assumption that the D-galactose units of the polysaccharide are joined through C_3, it is suggested that the repeating unit in the *Chondrus ocellatus* mucilage is to be represented by CCCLIId.   The positions of the sulfate groups still remain to be determined.

Iridophycin

The red alga, *Iridophycus faccidum* (syn. *Iridaea laminarioides*), contains a polysaccharide which resembles carrageenin and for which the name *iridophycin* has been suggested (107). It is extracted from the seaweed with either hot (108) or cold (109) water and precipitated from the resulting colloidal solution with ethanol or methanol as a colorless, amorphous substance. The polysaccharide comprises about 30 per cent of the dry weight of the plant. It does not reduce Fehling solution, shows $[\alpha]_D + 69.2°$ in water (108) and is composed of D-galactose units and sulfuric ester groups in the ratio of 1:1. Iridophycin occurs principally as the sodium salt together with smaller amounts of the calcium and magnesium salts (108). Removal of the cations by electrodialysis leaves the free acid, a 1 per cent aqueous solution of which has a pH of 2.86 (110). Acetylation of the iridophycin gives a di-O-acetyl derivative and methylation affords a di-O-methyl derivative, both of which still contain a sulfate residue. A sulfate-free galactan, $[\alpha]_D + 80°$ in water, is obtained when the polysaccharide is hydrolyzed at $70°$ with either 5 per cent sulfuric acid or 5 per cent barium hydroxide. The methylation of the galactan, prepared by desulfation with acid, gives a tri-O-methyl derivative which upon hydrolysis with 2*N* hydrochloric acid affords a tri-O-methyl-D-galactose as a sirup, $[\alpha]_D + 129°$ in water, and from which a phenylosazone could not be prepared. It was inferred therefore that the tri-O-methyl-D-galactose had one of the methoxyl groups on C_2. Its high positive rotation excludes a furanose sugar. Oxidation of the tri-O-methyl-D-galactose with bromine water followed by oxidative degradation of the product with nitric acid gives a dimethoxy-glutaric acid derivative, isolated as its dimethyl ester, $[\alpha]_D + 41°$ in water; this may have been a 2,3-di-O-methyl- (CCCLIII) or 2,4-di-O-methyl-L-arabaric acid (CCCLIV). In the first instance, the product could have arisen from the oxidation of 2,3,6-tri-O-methyl-D-galactose (CCXXXIII) whereas in the second case, the dimethyl ether would have been produced from 2,4,6-tri-O-methyl-D-galactose (XLVI). The dimethoxy-glutaric acid derivative was not identified so that no structure could be definitely assigned, but since no 1 → 3

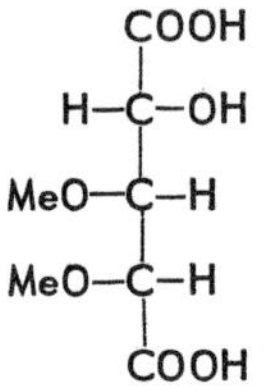

(CCCLIII) 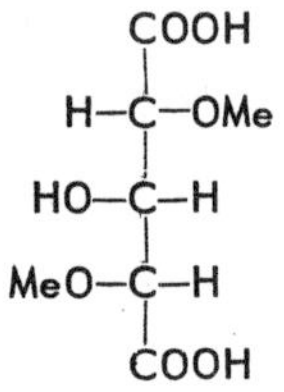   (CCCLIV) 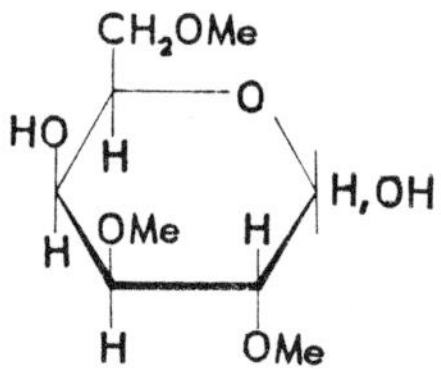   (CCXXXIII)

linked polysaccharides were known at that time, it was assumed that the tri-O-methyl-D-galactose was the 2,3,6-isomer, and that iridophycin therefore was composed of $1 \longrightarrow 4$ linked D-galactose units with the sulfate ester group at C_6. A re-examination of the evidence (111) indicated that the tri-O-methyl-D-galactose was more probably the 2,4,6-isomer, since this would give on oxidation 2,4-di-O-methyl-L-arabaric acid (CCCLIV), the dimethyl ester of which has the same rotation as that originally reported. That this is indeed the case was shown (23) by the fact that methanolysis of a methylated desulfated derivative of iridophycin gave the methyl glycoside of 2,4,6-tri-O-methyl-D-galactose (XLVI) as the main product.

The structure of iridophycin may, therefore, be described as a linear chain of D-galactopyranose residues linked through C_1 and C_3, the glycosidic bond being principally of the α-D-type in view of the high positive optical rotation of the polysaccharide. It was suggested that the sulfate group is at C_6 for stereochemical reasons and some support might be found in the fact that the polysaccharide isolated from the closely related red alga *Chondrus ocellatus* could not be tritylated (112). However, the situation here is very similar to that found in carrageenin, where the sulfate group is at C_4. It would seem, therefore, that a study of the di-O-methyl derivative of iridophycin sulfate is required before the position of the sulfate group can definitely be established.

The Galactan Sulfate of Dilsea Edulis

The red seaweed, *Dilsea edulis*, contains a polysaccharide which forms highly viscous solutions in water. This polysaccharide differs from carrageenin and agar in that solutions of it do not form gels.

The polysaccharide is prepared by extracting the seaweed with 1.7 per cent hydrochloric acid and precipitating with alcohol, followed by dialysis to reduce the ash content (113). In its purified form, the *Dilsea* polysaccharide is a colorless powder, showing $[\alpha]_D + 47.2°$ in water; it contains about 70 per cent of D-galactose on an ash-free basis. A search for the presence of L-galactose indicated that this sugar is absent. In addition to D-galactose the polysaccharide contains 9.6 to 11.0 per cent of an unidentified uronic acid which is believed to be an integral part of the molecule since the proportion of it remained approximately the same through the purification process and after acetylation. The ester sulfate content corresponds to one sulfate group in four or five D-galactose residues and the approximate ratio of D-galactose; sulfate; uronic acid was reported as $9:2:1$.

The sulfate residue is stable to treatment with alkali. It is removed, however, by acetylation of the polysaccharide at 75° with acetic anhydride in the presence of sulfur dioxide and chlorine (35,97), a method similar to that often employed for acetylating cellulose. This acetylation-desulfation reaction results in the degradation of the polysaccharide and a mixture of degraded triacetates is obtained in which, however, the ratio of D-galactose : uronic acid is still 9 : 1. It would be interesting to see if methanolic hydrogen chloride would effect desulfation as is the case with chondroitin sulfate (115). The absence of oligosaccharide acetates shows that the degradation is not too extensive. Methylation of the de-sulfated triacetate derivative with methyl sulfate and alkali gives a methylated product containing 41.5 per cent methoxyl (114). The methyl derivative affords upon methanolysis, a mixture of methyl glycosides composed principally of 2,4,6-tri-O-methyl-D-galactose (XLVI), 2,3,4,6-tetra-O-methyl-D-galactose (XXXIX), a di-O-methyl galactose, and a trace of 2,3,6-tri-O-methyl-D-galactose (CCXXXIII). Since the polysac-charide is degraded during the acetylation and desulfation, the amount of 2,3,4,6-tetra-O-methyl-D-galactose does not reflect the size of the aver-age repeating unit of the original material. The isolation in high yield of 2,4,6-tri-O-methyl-D-galactose shows a preponderance of $1 \rightarrow 3$ linked D-galactose residues in the molecule which, however, also contains some $1 \rightarrow 4$ linkages as evidenced by the identification of a trace of 2,3,6-tri-O-methyl-D-galactose. Again, due to the degradation mentioned above, the relative amounts of these two types of linkages cannot be estimated from the methylation data since their relative stability to acetolysis is not known. The presence of a di-O-methyl galactose cleavage fragment from the methylated degraded polysaccharide indicates that some branch-ing may occur in the molecule unless it arises from demethylation during hydrolysis. Only a trace of a methylated derivative of a uronic acid was identified in the cleavage fragments.

The oxidation of the *Dilsea* polysaccharide with periodic acid results after 6 hours in an optical rotation change from $+50°$ to $+15°$ (113). The oxidized product still contained the sulfate ester groups and upon hydrolysis followed by treatment with phenylhydrazine gave glyoxalosazone and galactosazone in amounts which have been taken to indicate that one in five galactose residues was cleaved by the periodate. However, the fate of the uronic acid, which might give some, though not all, of the glyoxalosazone in the series of reactions, was not known. Assuming that all the glyoxalosazone was derived from an oxidized D-galactose residue, then one in every five must contain free hydroxyl groups at C_2 and C_3, and, therefore, must be linked through C_1 and C_4, C_1 and C_6 or C_1, C_4 and C_6. The absence of 2,3,4-tri-O-methyl-D-galactose in the cleavage fragments of the methylated degraded polysaccharide suggested that D-galactose residues linked only through C_1 and C_6 are absent. Also, since only small amounts of $1 \rightarrow 4$ linked D-galactose residues were indicated by the methylation data, then either these linkages are preferentially cleaved by acetolysis or some of the glyoxalosazone is derived from the uronic acid residue.

The stability of the sulfate group to alkaline hydrolysis has prompted the suggestion that it is located at C_4 of a galactose residue (113). However, if the sulfate group is attached to a $1 \rightarrow 3$ linked galactose residue, its stability to alkali would be just as great at C_2 as at C_4. Its stability to alkaline hydrolysis suggests that it is not located anywhere on a $1 \rightarrow 4$ linked galactose residue because at any position it would probably be alkali labile.

Apart from the fact that the polysaccharide from *Dilsea edulis* is composed mainly of D-galactose units linked through C_1 and C_3, together with some linked through C_1 and C_4, little more could be said of its precise structure.

A reexamination (251) of the mucilage of *Dilsea edulis* has revealed that the polysaccharide contains in addition to D-galactose, some xylose (7 per cent) and traces of 3,6-anhydrogalactose (recognized chromatographically) as well as the glucuronic acid (10 per cent) formerly (114) recognized. These most recent findings show that the mucilage has a highly branched structure in which the galactose units are joined principally by $1 \rightarrow 3$-bonds. The xylose and glucuronic acid units appear to be present in the outer branches which are removed by degradation. The outer branches also contain galactose units joined by $1 \rightarrow 3$- and $1 \rightarrow 4$-glycosidic bonds.

The components of the *Dilsea edulis* mucilage were revealed by treating its hydrolyzate with phenylhydrazine whereby there were obtained the phenylosazones of D-galactose, D-xylose and 3,6-anhydro-D-galactose. Some of the 3,6-anhydro-D-galactose phenylosazone was found to arise from galactose-6-sulfate.

Oxidation of the mucilage with sodium periodate as previously described (113) gave a product which was still shown, by hydrolysis, to contain galactose, xylose and uronic acid.

When the periodate-oxidized mucilage was treated with *iso*nicotinhydrazide (222), the nitrogen content of the condensation product indicated that 31.5 per cent of the sugar residues had been cleaved by periodate. Elimination of these cleaved residues by treatment in boiling aqueous acetic acid with phenylhydrazine (252) afforded glyoxal bisphenylhydrazone, the phenylosazones of erythrose, galactose and xylose as well as a residual degraded polysaccharide material. This last substance had a higher sulfate content than the original mucilage and was composed largely of galactose. Two further periodate oxidations and phenylhydrazine degradations were conducted and after each treatment the recovered material was found to be a polysaccharide showing that the galactose polymer most likely contained $1 \longrightarrow 3$ linkages and was being degraded only at the ends. The reduction in the sulfate content by the periodate oxidation-phenylhydrazine treatment pointed to the presence of sulfate groups at C_6 of the galactose units which flank the periodate stable $1 \longrightarrow 3$-linked galactose framework as in Figure A.

$$—[3 \text{ Gal } p \text{ 1}]_3—3 \text{ Gal } p \text{ 1}—[3 \text{ Gal } p \text{ 1}]_3—$$

$$1$$

$$[SO_4\text{-6 Gal } p]_2$$

$$3$$

$$1$$

$$SO_4\text{-6 Gal } p \text{ } SO_4$$

Figure A

$$—[3 \text{ Gal } p \text{ 1}]_3—3 \text{ Gal } p \text{ 1}—[3 \text{ Gal } p \text{ 1}]_3—$$

$$1$$

$$SO_4\text{-6 Gal } p$$

$$3$$

$$1$$

$$SO_4\text{-6 Gal } p$$

Figure B

$$—[3 \text{ Gal } p \text{ 1}]_3—3 \text{ Gal } p \text{ 1}—[3 \text{ Gal } p \text{ 1}]_3—$$

$$1$$

$$SO_4\text{-6 Gal } p$$

Figure C

$$SO_4$$

$$6$$

$$G A 1—3 \text{ Gal } p \text{ 1}—4 \text{ Gal } p \text{ 1}—3 \text{ Xyl } p \text{ 1}—4 \text{ Gal } p \text{ 1}—3 \text{ Gal } p \text{ 1}—4 \text{ Gal } p\text{-}$$

Figure D

$$—[3 \text{ Gal } p \text{ 1}]_3—3 \text{ Gal } p \text{ 1}—[3 \text{ Gal } p \text{ 1}]_3—$$

$$1$$

$$[SO_4\text{-6 Gal } p]_3$$

$$1$$

$$SO_4\text{-6 Gal } p$$

Figure E

The 1,3-linked D-galactose 6-sulfate residues of the side chain are those eliminated by the stepwise degradation with periodate followed by phenylhydrazine, the second and third stages of the oxidation being represented by (B) and (C) respectively as shown.

Since the once periodate-oxidized mucilage still contains xylose and glucuronic acid these units are joined by $1 \longrightarrow 3$ glycosidic linkages. If the glucuronic acid is present as a $6 \longrightarrow 3$ lactone, the sugar ring must engage C_4 in which case the uronic acid must be involved in a linkage through C_2, C_3 or C_5. The second degradation step with periodate eliminates the glucuronic acid and virtually all the xylose and hence it may be concluded that these units are present in the side chains attached to the main framework of $1 \longrightarrow 3$-linked D-galactose units. The observation that erythrosephenylosazone is produced by the action of phenylhydrazine on the product after the first periodate oxidation step lends support to the view that the mucilage contains $1 \longrightarrow 4$-linked galactose residues since only these would give rise to erythrosephenylosazone.

The xylose units which are eliminated as xylosephenylosazone are believed to occupy a nonterminal position in the side chains and are attached to galactose units that are susceptible to periodate cleavage and are presumably joined by $1 \longrightarrow 4$ bonds as shown in Figure D. The side chains in D were also shown to contain $1 \longrightarrow 3$-linked galactose units since the action of phenylhydrazine on the periodate-oxidized mucilage yielded galactosephenylosazone.

The above considerations together with the composition of the original mucilage lead to the tentative conclusion that four of the side chains shown in Figure D are associated in the mucilage with a repeating unit of seven galactose and four galactose sulfate units as shown in Figure E. The location of the side chains in the mucilage is not yet known. As for the glucuronic acid, it is placed in a terminal position in the side chains for the reason that neither galactose nor xylose could be there. If galactose occupied the terminal nonreducing positions periodate oxidation followed by reaction with phenylhydrazine would furnish glycerosazone, whereas in practice no such product was noted. Similarly it was pointed out that since the first periodate oxidation products still contained xylose it is clear that they too do not occupy terminal positions in the polysaccharide. Certain terminal positions could be occupied by units of 3,6-anhydro-D-galactose but the small amount present shows that this building unit does not play a major structural role. If it is true that the glucuronic acid is present as a stable lactone then this building unit may well be present in the furanose form as in the case of glucurone itself (239). Methylation studies of this polysaccharide using the present day refined techniques of isolation would be of considerable help in limiting still further the number of structural possibilities for the *Dilsea edulis* mucilage.

A polysaccharide similar to that obtained from *Dilsea edulis* is obtained from another member of the family *Dumontaceae*, namely *Dumontia incrassata* (116). It is composed of galactose, ester sulfate and a uronic acid in the ratio 9:4:1, respectively. One explanation for the resistance of the polysaccharide to oxidation by periodate is that the majority of the galactose units are linked through C_1 and C_3.

Mannan of Porphyra Umbilicalis

The red marine alga, *Porphyra umbilicalis* (syn. *P. laciniata*), has been used as a food in South Wales (laver or laver bread), and Hawaii (limu). It contains a number of polysaccharides and when the whole plant is hydrolyzed with mineral acid, it gives principally fucose and galactose (117,118), together with mannose (117,118), xylose and glucose (118). Extraction of the seaweed with hot water removed polysaccharides containing approximately equal amounts of fucose and galactose. Further extraction with cold N sodium hydroxide and with hot $5N$ sodium hydroxide afforded a mannan in the latter extract from which it was isolated and purified as the insoluble copper complex. The copper complex was decomposed with alcoholic hydrogen chloride which also rendered the mannan insoluble in alkaline solution, even 30 per cent sodium hydroxide.

The mannan is hydrolyzed by anhydrous formic acid and upon oxidation with sodium periodate, it consumes one mole of periodate for every mannose residue, with the formation of formic acid in amounts corresponding to 6 per cent of end-group. Hydrolysis of the resulting mannan polyaldehyde indicated only a trace of D-mannose which had not been oxidized by the periodate. The polysaccharide is converted to its methyl derivative by the thallium procedure. Hydrolysis of the methylated product with anhydrous formic acid afforded 2,3,6-tri-O-methyl-D-mannose (CCLXXVI) and about 8 per cent of 2,3,4,6-tetra-O-methyl-D-mannose (CCLXXV).

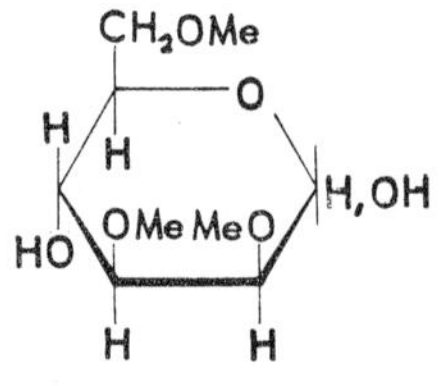

(CCLXXVI) 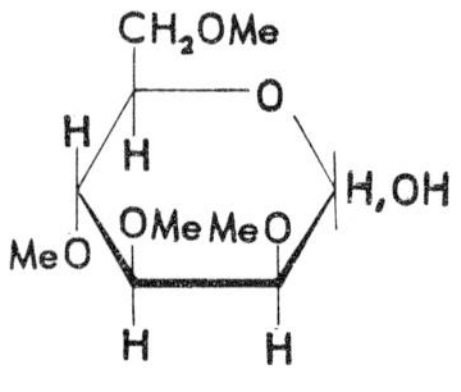   (CCLXXV)

The identification of 2,3,6-tri-O-methyl-D-mannose and the stability of the polysaccharide and its methylated derivative to hydrolysis indicate that the mannan is composed of D-mannopyranose units linked through C_1 and C_4. In view of the negative optical rotation of the mannan in formic acid ($[\alpha]_D - 41° \longrightarrow - 22°$) and of its acetyl derivative, $[\alpha]_D - 30°$ in acetone, it is probable that the majority of the glycosidic linkages are of the β-type.   The end-group assay from the periodate and methylation data indicates that the polysaccharide is of the branched-chain type with an average repeating unit of about 12 to 13 D-mannose residues.   The nature of the branch point is not known, but it is probably through C_6 since such a mannose residue linked through C_1, C_4 and C_6 has an $\alpha\beta$-glycol grouping and would be oxidized with periodate in accord with the experimental facts.

Several species of Porphyra form the basis of the delicacies of the Japanese gourmet, the most commonly eaten being P. tenera, Kjellman, known as asakusanori or amanori.   The latter term also may be applied to the preparation from P. suborficulata, Kjellman, more correctly called maruba-amanori.   Enteromorpha intestinalis Link is used in the preparation of aonori.   The outer membrane of P. tenera is said to contain a polysaccharide composed principally of D-mannose (119).   Other polysaccharides isolated from P. umbilicalis (118), P. crispata (120) and P. tenera (120) are reported to contain both D- and L-galactose.

Mucilages of the Phaeophyceae

From a chemical standpoint the Phaeophyceae are in general characterized by their laminarin and alginic acid contents which replace the galactan sulfates found in the Rhodophyceae.   The polysaccharide sulfate esters are not excluded from the brown seaweeds, being represented here by fucoidin and a similar mucilage recently isolated from Ascophyllum nodosum.

The chemical composition of the brown marine algae has received intensive examination, particularly during recent years in America, Canada, Japan and the United Kingdom.   The various factors which affect the carbohydrate constituents have been studied, since any industry based upon seaweed as a raw material must know when to harvest at the optimum concentration of the carbohydrate component.   Thus, the effects of seasonal variations (121–125), depth of immersion (126) and composition of sea water (127) have been shown to affect the alginic acid, laminarin and fucoidin contents of the seaweeds.   It has also been shown that these polysaccharides are not evenly distributed throughout the frond or stipe of the plant (128).   These factors will be discussed as they concern the individual polysaccharides described below.

Alginic Acid. Alginic acid was reported by Stanford (129) in 1883 who gave the name "algin" to the viscous solution obtained by treating *Laminariaceae* with dilute sodium carbonate. The alginic acid is obtained as a gelatinous precipitate upon acidification of the viscous extract.

Alginic acid constitutes, with cellulose and other polysaccharides (258), the cell wall of the brown algae, where it occurs as a salt (probably calcium or magnesium), usually associated with other polysaccharides such as fucoidin or laminarin. The alginic acid content of seaweeds may be estimated by a colorimetric procedure (130) which has many advantages over the gravimetric method previously employed (131). It was originally thought to be composed principally, if not entirely, of D-mannuronic acid residues, but recent studies (132) have shown that it also contains a considerable proportion of L-guluronic acid. Reliable analytical data on alginic acid are difficult to obtain since the polyuronide is difficult to hydrolyze with mineral acids, because of its insolubility. The severity of the hydrolytic conditions causing decomposition of the uronic acid residues. There is little doubt, however, that alginic acid is constituted entirely of uronic acid units, since the theoretical amount of carbon dioxide is obtained upon treatment with 19 per cent hydrochloric acid at 145° for two hours (133). Attempts to attain high yields of D-mannuronic acid have not been too successful, partly because of decomposition and partly because the mixture of D-mannuronic acid and L-guluronic acid is difficult to separate. Hydrolysis with concentrated sulfuric acid gives 20 to 30 per cent of D-mannuronolactone (134) whereas hydrolysis with formic acid yields 45 per cent of the lactone (135). The α- and β-anomers of D-mannuronic acid have also been obtained from the alginic acids of *Macrocystis pyrifera* and *Fucus serratus* (136,137).

One of the earliest studies of the hydrolysis of alginic acid (from *Macrocystis pyrifera*) resulted in the isolation of a pentose, believed to be xylose, in the form of its osazone (138). Subsequently, it was suggested that alginic acid is composed of residues of D-glucuronic or D-galacturonic acid residues without, however, any supporting evidence (139). Some indications of the presence of D-glucuronic acid residues followed from the isolation of its cinchonine salt, which was unfortunately identified only by melting point (140). The presence of D-glucuronic acid in alginic acid was still undecided until recently when it was proved (132) that whereas all the brown algae tested contain varying small amounts of glucuronic acid it is not a component of the alginic acid polymer. That alginic acid contains D-mannuronic acid residues was shown (141,142) by the fact that alginic acid from *Macrocystis pyrifera* and *Laminaria agardhii* evolves large amounts of carbon dioxide when an aqueous solution is boiled and that hydrolysis with 80 per cent sulfuric acid liberates D-mannuronic acid, which was identified, after oxidation with bromine, as the crystalline diamide and diphenylhydrazide derivatives of D-mannaric acid. Later, D-mannuronic acid was identified as its lactone (143) in hydrolyzates of alginic acid from *Fucus serratus* and *Laminaria saccharina* (144). Other workers (145,146) confirmed that D-mannuronic acid was a major constituent of alginic acid.

Certain soil bacteria cause the decomposition of alginic acid (147–149) and enzyme preparations from these bacteria produce D-mannuronic acid as well as a series of intermediate oligomannuronosides (150).

The puzzling fact that a polyglycuronoside supposedly composed only of D-mannuronic acid gave only at best a 45 per cent yield has now been recently explained by a re-examination (132) of the composition of alginic acid from a number of brown algae by means of chromatography. The hydrolyzates of the various samples of alginic acid have been found to contain considerable amounts of L-guluronic acid as well as D-mannuronic acid, the ratio of D-mannuronic acid to L-guluronic acid varying from 2:1 to 1:2 (see Table 58). The presence of L-guluronic acid was established by the isolation of the crystalline L-guluronolactone which proved to be identical with a synthetic specimen.

Early constitutional studies on alginic acid indicated that the D-mannuronic acid units (151,152) are joined by β-D-1 $\rightarrow$ 4 linkages. Again, the problem encountered in such investigations was that of extreme stability towards hydrolytic agents and, furthermore, in methylation studies it was difficult to achieve complete substitution of the free hydroxyl groups. However, partial degradation of sodium alginate by treatment with boiling 10 per cent methanolic hydrogen chloride for seventeen hours gave a product which was more amenable to chemical treatment (153). The degraded alginic acid gave viscous solutions in water, but with a viscosity considerably less than the original material, and in all other respects appeared to be similar to the undegraded acid. The fully methylated derivative (CCCLV) of the degraded product was prepared by the action of methyl iodide on its thallium salt. The methylated product was exceptionally stable to hydrolysis, but when boiled with 50 per cent nitric acid for eighteen hours it underwent hydrolysis, followed by degradative oxidation, with the formation of di-O-methyl erythraric acid (CCCLVI) which was identified as its crystalline methyl ester and amide. This indicated that, as far as the mannuronic acid residues are concerned, the methyl groups are attached either to C_2 and C_3 or C_4 and C_5 since optically active di-O-methyl-D-threaric acid would be produced if the methyl groups were attached to C_3 and C_4. Proof that the methyl groups were attached to C_2 and C_3 followed from the isolation of methyl (methyl 2,3-di-O-methyl-D-mannopyranosid)uronate (CCCLVII) from the partial hydrolysis of methylated degraded alginic acid with 4 per cent methanolic hydrogen chloride at 150° for twenty four hours. The methyl ester (CCCLVII) was identified by hydrolysis to 2,3-di-O-methyl-D-mannuronic acid (CCCLVIII) followed by oxidation with bromine to 2,3-di-O-methyl-D-mannaric acid (CCCLIX) which was in turn oxidized with periodic acid to glyoxylic acid (CCCLX) and 2,3-di-O-methyl-D-erythruronic acid (CCCLXI). The latter was oxidized with bromine to 2,3-di-O-methyl-erythraric acid (CCCLVI) which was recognized as its crystalline methyl ester and amide. This series of reactions is given below:

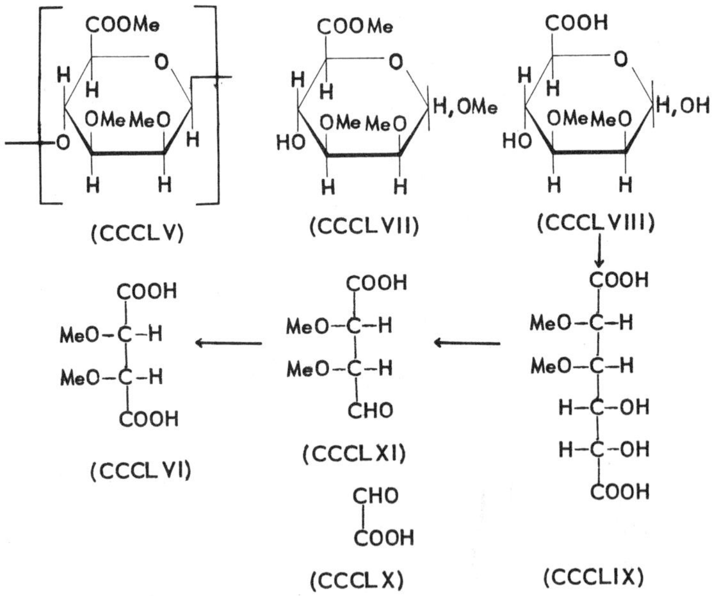

The identification of 2,3-di-O-methyl-D-mannuronic acid (CCCLVIII) indicated that the D-mannuronic acid residues in alginic acid are linked through C_1 and C_4 and, in view of the high negative rotations of sodium alginate ($[\alpha]_D - 130°$ to $-145°$ in water (154)) and methylated degraded alginic acid ($[\alpha]_D - 28°$ in methanol), the linkage is predominantly of the β-D-type.

The oxidation of the alginic acid from *Macrocystis pyrifera* with periodic acid consumed 1.1 moles of periodate per uronic acid residue in

TABLE 58. RATIO OF D-MANNURONIC ACID TO L-GULURONIC ACID IN
VARIOUS PHAEOPHYCEAE (132)

Source of Alginic Acid	Ratio $\dfrac{\text{D-Mannuronic Acid}}{\text{L-Guluronic Acid}}$
1. *Ectocarpus siliculosus* (Dillwyn) Lyngbyl	0.4
2. *Colpomenia sinuosa* (Roth) Derb. et Sol.	0.8
3. *Chorda filum* (L) Lamour	1.1
4. *Laminaria digitata* f. *flexicaulis*	3.1
5. *Laminaria hyperborea* (Gäu) To. R.	1.6
6. *Sphacelaria bipinnata* (Kütz) Sauv.	0.6
7. *Dictyota dichotoma* (Huds.) Lamour	0.6
8. *Taonia atomaria* (Good. et Wood.) Ag.	0.7
9. *Padina pavonia* (L.) Lamour	1.0
10. *Dictyota linearis* (Ag.) Grev.	0.9
11. *Dictyopteris polypodioides* (Desf.) Lamour	0.6
12. *Ascophyllum nodosum* Le Tol.	2.6
13. *Pelvetia canaliculata* (L.) Decs. et Thur.	1.5
14. *Fucus vesiculosus* L.	1.3
15. *Fucus serratus* L.	2.7
16. *Fucus spiralis* L. Var. *platycarpa*	2.6
17. *Himanthalia lorea* Lyngb. (*H. elongata* (L) S. T. Gray)	2.7
18. *Cysteseira barbata* J. Ag.	0.7
19. *Cystoseira abrotanifolia* C. Ag.	1.9
20. *Cystoseira mediterranea* Ag. Sauvageau	1.3
21. *Halidrys siliquosa* (L.) Lyngb.	1.1
22. *Sargassum linifolium* (Turn.) J. Ag.	0.8

twenty four hours and the polyaldehyde so formed was isolated by precipitation with 3 to 4 volumes of *tert*-butanol (155). Hydrolysis of the
polyaldehyde with mineral acid yielded glyoxal, isolated as the phenylosazone, and after oxidation of the hydrolyzate with bromine the brucine
salt of erythraric acid was obtained. The formation of these compounds
is in accord with the presence of $1 \rightarrow 4$ linked D-mannosyluronic acid
units in alginic acid. The fate of the L-guluronic acid units is not
known since the presence of this uronic acid was not then suspected. The
methylation of undegraded alginic acid from *Laminaria digitata* fronds has
recently been accomplished by repeated treatments (16 in all) with methyl
sulfate and alkali in an atmosphere of nitrogen (156). The fully methylated
material, obtained in 90 per cent yield, was hydrolyzed with 98 per cent
formic acid at 95 to 100° for eight hours. The mixed cleavage fragments
were converted to their methyl ester methyl glycoside derivatives with
methanolic hydrogen chloride which were then reduced with lithium
aluminum hydride. The resulting mixture of neutral methylated glycosides so formed was hydrolyzed to the free methylated sugars which

upon chromatographic analysis were found to be composed of 2,3,4-tri-
O-methyl-D-mannose (CCCLXII, 1 per cent), 2,3-di-O-methyl-D-mannose
(CCLXXXIII, 88 per cent), a mono-O-methyl-D-mannose (4.5 per cent),
and what was thought to be a di-O-methyl-D-glucose (6 per cent).

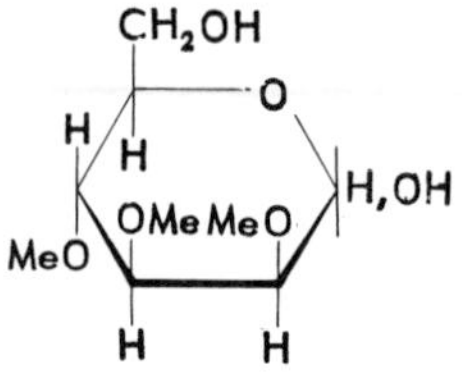

(CCCLXII) 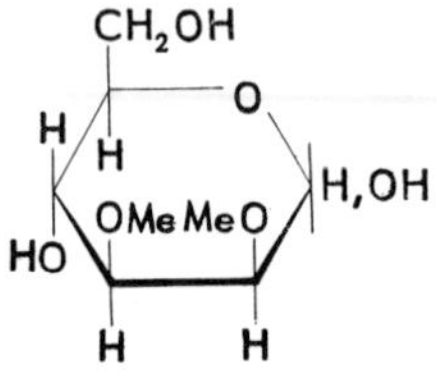   (CCLXXXIII)

The isolation of this supposed di-O-methyl-D-glucose cleavage fragment may arise from a D-glucuronic acid residue in the alginic acid
molecule, a possibility which would conform to previous suggestions
(139,140). It does not arise, apparently, by epimerization of 2,3-di-O-
methyl-D-mannose in the alkaline conditions of the reduction with
lithium aluminum hydride, since a control experiment indicated only that
a small degree of demethylation occurs. This demethylation reaction
might, however, account for the presence of a mono-O-methyl-D-mannose.

In view of the recent work demonstrating the presence of L-guluronic
acid in alginic acid (132), it is possible that the di-O-methyl sugar
is a derivative of L-gulose. The characterization of this di-O-methyl
sugar (?L-gulose) will reveal the mode of linkage of the L-guluronic acid
in the alginic acid. Graded hydrolysis before and after reduction of the
acid polysaccharide to the corresponding L-gulo-D-mannuran to suitable
oligosaccharides should enable the order of the two types of uronic acid
in the alginic acid to be ascertained.

It is now apparent that analogy between the structure of alginic acid
and cellulose as revealed by X-ray crystallographic analysis (157,158)
will require some modification.

Laminarin. Laminarin, first prepared by Schmiedeberg (159), appears
to be a reserve carbohydrate of the sub-littoral brown algae, especially
the family *Laminariaceae*, species which are abundant in the coastal
waters of Japan, Western Europe and North America. The amount of
laminarin in the seaweed undergoes definite seasonal fluctuation and is
present in the greatest amount during the late summer months after which
period it passes through a minimum concentration in the early spring. In
two species of *Laminaria* the laminarin amounted to 42 and 49 per cent of
the dry matter during August and October, respectively (160). A recent

study in the British Isles indicates that there are two periods of growth of plants in the sea (161). The period of slow growth coincides with a deficiency of nitrate and phosphate in the water (162) when laminarin constitutes 36 per cent of the dry frond of *L. cloustoni*. It is, however, absent from the stipe of the *Laminariaceae* throughout the year and from the actively growing section of the frond proximal to the stipe, but it forms 32 per cent of the dry matter of distal sections (128).

Laminarin exists in two forms which differ in their solubility in water. The form insoluble in cold water but readily soluble in hot water, generally referred to as "insoluble" laminarin, is present in the fronds of *L. cloustoni* and to a lesser extent in those of *L. saccharina*. The cold water soluble form is found in the fronds of *L. digitata*.

The "insoluble" laminarin is extracted from the seaweed by immersion in 1 per cent hydrochloric acid for about two days. The mixture containing the finely suspended polysaccharide is agitated and filtered through a coarse filter. Over a period of several days crude laminarin is deposited and is purified by successive depositions from aqueous solutions (163,164). The "soluble" laminarin is extracted with dilute hydrochloric acid (about 0.4 per cent) and the extract is neutralized to about pH 8 to 10 with lead acetate and barium hydroxide, and the insoluble inorganic salts are removed by filtration. The laminarin in the solution is precipitated with alcohol by adjusting the alcohol content to 85 per cent after which it is purified by dialysis of an aqueous solution followed by reprecipitation with alcohol.

The hydrolysis of both forms of laminarin affords D-glucose in high yield (163,165–173). From an autoclaved solution of the polysaccharide (18 per cent w/w) in 0.05N HCl at 135° for one hour, D-glucose monohydrate is obtained crystalline by a process similar to its production from starch (173).

Other components are reported to be present in laminarin. The occurrence of galactose in the laminarin of *L. flexicaulis* (174) was not encountered in later experiments (169). More recently D-mannose has been found in laminarin from *L. cloustoni* (259). Again, amongst the hydrolytic products of "soluble" laminarin from *L. digitata* 1.4 per cent of L-fucose was detected together with 1.2 per cent approximately of combined sulfate (172). The amount of sulfate was reduced to 0.83 per cent by regeneration of the polysaccharide from its acetate and to 0.38 per cent by electrodialysis. It would appear, therefore, that the fucose and sulfate are due to a proportion (3.2 per cent) of fucoidin which is difficult to remove from the laminarin chain.

Recently both forms of laminarin have been shown to contain mannitol, the mannitol to glucose ratio being 1:57 and 1:37 in the "insoluble" and "soluble" forms respectively (184).

Laminarin is hydrolyzed by an enzyme, laminarase, which is found in the dried powder of several kinds of seaweed (175), the digestive juice of the snail, *Helix pomatia* or *H. aspersa* (169,174,176), sea-hare (*Tethys puntata*) (170), and in the extracts of wheat, oats, barley, potato and hyacinth bulbs (177). A claim that malt diastase contains laminarase (167, 168) was later withdrawn (178).

In view of the hydrolysis of laminarin by soybean β-amylase which has been shown to contain an enzyme, the Z-enzyme (179), with a β-D-glucosidase activity, it is possible that laminarase and the Z-enzyme are very similar, if not identical. Also from the wide distribution of laminarase in seeds and other plant reserve organs, it is probable that its presence may be widespread in terrestrial plants. However, in view of the similarity of laminarin and lichenin from the standpoint of optical rotation and other physical properties, it is probable that some confusion will arise in the literature. It is also probable that the enzyme lichenase and laminarase are identical both having an optimum pH of 5.0 and acting upon β-D-(1 $\rightarrow$ 3) glucose linkages.

Partial hydrolysis of laminarin by the action of snail juices or N oxalic acid for 7 hours on a boiling water bath, gives a disaccharide, laminaribiose (CCCLXIII) (176). The structure of the disaccharide is shown to be 3-O-β-D-glucopyranosyl-D-glucopyranose by its synthesis through the reaction between tetra-O-acetyl-α-D-glucopyranosyl bromide and 1,2-O-isopropylidene-α-D-glucofuranose (180) or 1,2:5,6-di-O-isopropylidene-α-D-glucose (181). In the early stages of enzymic hydrolysis several other oligosaccharides of higher-molecular weight are also produced (177).

The isolation of laminaribose indicates the presence of 1 $\rightarrow$ 3 linkages in laminarin and this is confirmed by methylation studies. The

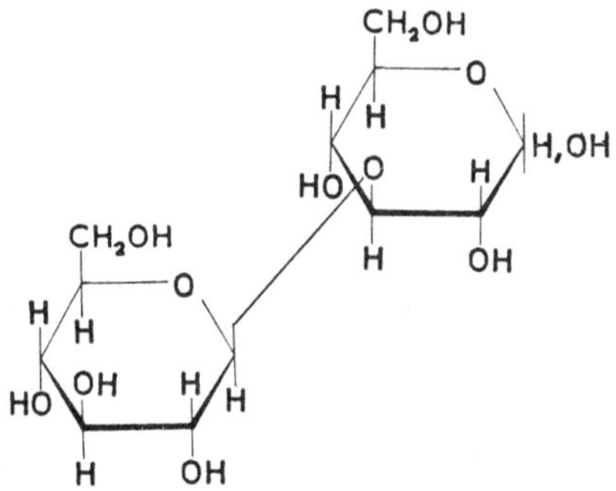

(CCCLXIII)

methyl derivative of laminarin, prepared from the acetylated polysaccharide by the action of methyl sulfate and alkali, was reported to produce only 2,4,6-tri-O-methyl-D-glucose (CCCVI) upon hydrolysis (163). Taken in conjunction with the negative rotation of laminarin, $[\alpha]_D - 13°$ in water, and the isolation of 3-O-β-D-glucopyranosyl-D-glucopyranose (CCCLXIII) it follows that the D-glucopyranose units in laminarin are joined by $1 \rightarrow 3$-β-D linkages. In the main, this general type of structure has been confirmed for both the soluble and insoluble forms of laminarin.

The methylation of laminarin from *L. cloustoni* with methyl sulfate and alkali gives a tri-O-methyl derivative which upon hydrolysis affords 2,3,4,6-tetra-O-methyl-D-glucose (CCXXX, 5 per cent) and the main product, 2,4,6-tri-O-methyl-D-glucose (CCCVI) which is accompanied by a mixture of 2,6- and 4,6-di-O-methyl-D-glucose (8 per cent) (171). The last two components probably have little structural significance since 2,4,6-tri-O-methyl-D-glucose was found to be susceptible to demethylation and, under the conditions employed for the hydrolysis of methylated laminarin, gives an 8 per cent yield of a mixture of di-O-methyl glucoses almost identical in composition with that mentioned above. The amount of tetra-O-methyl-D-glucopyranose corresponds to an average chain length of twenty D-glucose units. Nearly identical results are obtained with "soluble" laminarin from *L. digitata* (172).

The linear $1 \rightarrow 3$-β-D linked structure which is indicated by the methylation data is supported by the resistance of laminarin to oxidation by periodic acid (182) and by the fact that methylation of the trityl derivative of laminarin followed by hydrolysis gives 2,4-di-O-methyl-D-glucose (242). Little information regarding the molecular size of laminarin can be deduced from the periodate oxidation studies because a steady state is never reached (171,182). In the same way, laminaribiose undergoes continued oxidation with periodate and the reaction shows no sign of stopping.

The linear molecular structure for laminarin, which is deduced from the methylation data, has been questioned and there are now indications for the presence of branch linkages. Partial hydrolysis of "insoluble" laminarin by heating with 0.33N sulfuric acid for two hours gives a mixture of di- and tri-saccharides which are said not to be acid reversion products (183,184). The disaccharide fraction consists principally of laminaribiose (CCCLXIII) but also contains small amounts of gentiobiose (CCCLXIV) and 1-O-β-D-glucopyranosyl-D-mannitol (CCCLXV) previously (183) thought to be $\beta\beta$-trehalose. Five trisaccharides were obtained; one was crystalline and nonreducing, and yielded upon partial acid hydrolysis laminaribiose (CCCLXIII) and 1-O-β-D-glucopyranosyl-

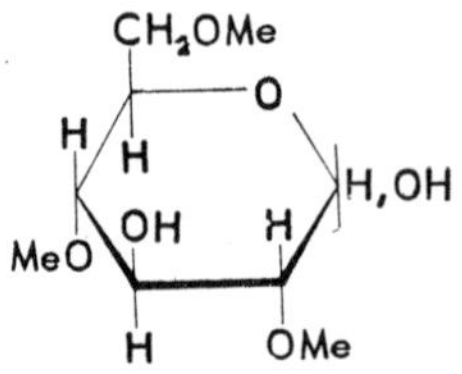

(CCCVI)

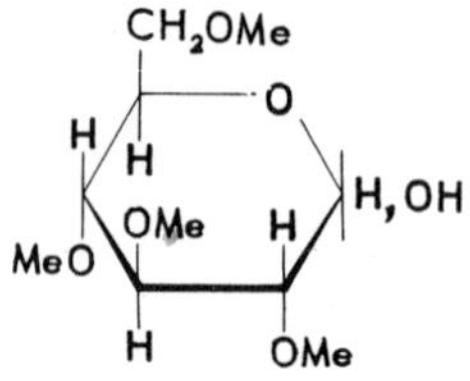

(CCXXX)

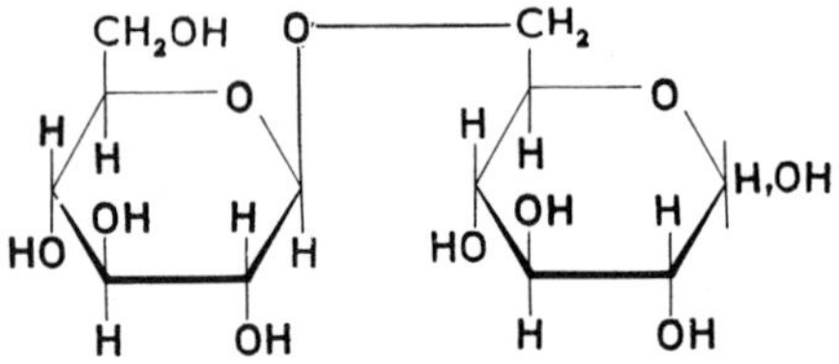

(CCCLXIV)

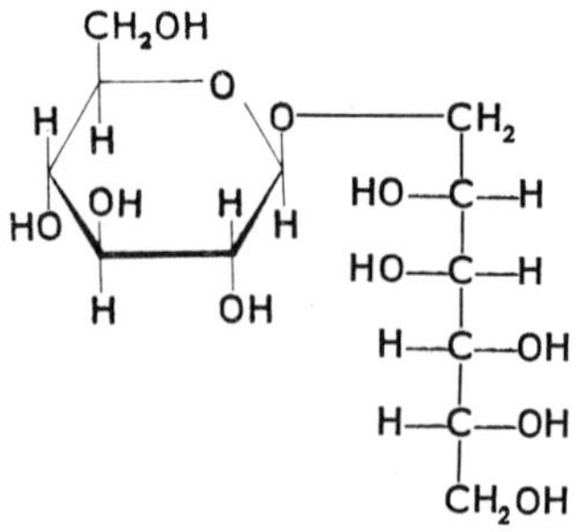

(CCCLXV)

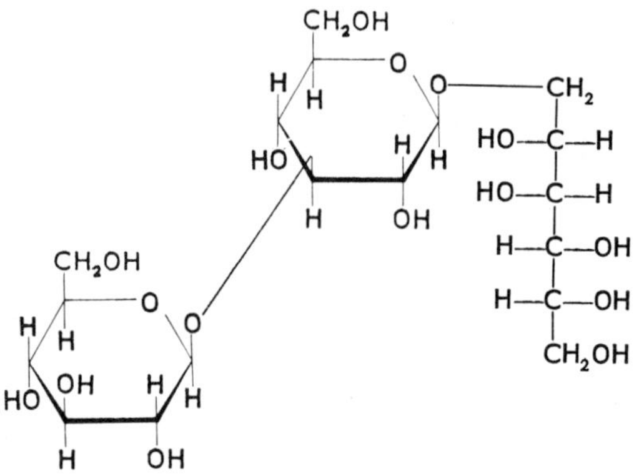

(CCCLXVI)

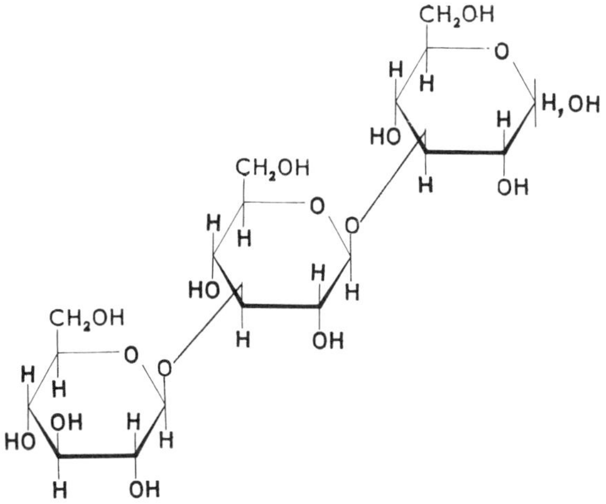

(CCCLXVII)

D-mannitol (CCCLXV). It was deduced, therefore, that this trisac-
charide is O-β-D-glucopyranosyl-$(1 \to 3)$-O-β-D-glucopyranosyl-$(1 \to 1)$-D-mannitol (CCCLXVI) and this has been confirmed (185) by synthesis as follows:

Laminaribiose $\to$ laminaribiose octaacetate $\to$ α-laminaribiosyl bromide

heptaacetate $\xrightarrow[\text{acetyl-D-mannose}]{\text{1,2,3,4-tetra-O-}}$ 6-O-β-laminaribiosyl-

β-D-mannose undecaacetate $\to$ 1-O-β-laminaribiosyl-D-mannitol.

Three of the trisaccharides upon partial hydrolysis yield gentiobiose
and laminaribiose while the principal trisaccharide yields laminaribiose
and is presumably laminaritriose (CCCLXVII). The formation of gentiobiose suggests the presence of $1 \to 6$ linkages in laminarin.

By analogy with the action of lime-water on glucose substituted in
C_3, it would be expected that a linear glucose polysaccharide composed
exclusively of $1 \to 3$ linkages terminated by a reducing group would be
completely broken down from end to end, whereas lime-water treatment
resulted in only 50 per cent cleavage (188). It is suggested, therefore,
that laminarin has a branched structure (presumably a $1 \to 6$ link in a
linear chain would also explain this result) and accordingly any proposed
structures must be looked on with reserve until further work is done.
Another explanation for this phenomenon is that 50 per cent of the molecules of laminarin terminate in a nonreducing mannitol residue as suggested by the isolation of 1-O-β-laminaribiosyl-D-mannitol by graded
hydrolysis (185,186). Although the characterization of 1-O-β-laminari-

biosyl-D-mannitol establishes the presence of a D-mannitol residue in laminarin, it does not *prove* that the D-mannitol residue occupies a terminal position. Indeed the observation that periodate oxidation of laminarin followed by reduction and hydrolysis fail to yield any ethylene glycol points to the view that the D-mannitol unit is located in a nonterminal position (256).

Examination of the products formed by periodate oxidation of the soluble form of laminarin from *L. cloustoni* has revealed (186,255) that formaldehyde is present. When laminarin is reduced with sodium borohydride it yields laminaritol (187) which likewise affords formaldehyde upon periodate oxidation. The amount of formaldehyde produced indicates that the laminaritol has an average DP of 17. Since three times as much formaldehyde is produced after reduction as before, it may be concluded (186) that about 30 per cent of the laminarin consists of nonreducing molecules that are probably terminated by mannitol residues; the remaining 70 per cent of the laminarin consists of molecules terminated by a reducing group that is presumably D-glucose. If this is the case, then hydrolysis of the reduced laminarin should furnish upon hydrolysis mannitol and sorbitol in the approximate ratio of 3 : 7.

When the number of hexose residues in laminarin is determined by the cyanohydrin reaction a value of 25 is obtained (190). On the assumption that only 70 per cent of the laminarin molecules have a reducing group, and react with hydrocyanic acid, it follows that the average repeating unit is 17 to 18, which agrees with the value determined by periodate oxidation of the laminaritol and measurement of the formaldehyde produced.

The explanation for the existence of a "soluble" and an "insoluble" form of laminarin is not yet clear. One suggestion was that laminarin is a mixture of polymers of different molecular sizes (167,168), but fractionation studies showed later that laminarin is a single polysaccharide (163,189, cf 259). It should be realized that fractionation studies would probably not separate laminarin molecules of the same D. P. differing only in the nature of the end groups, one having a reducing and the other a nonreducing residue. When deposited from aqueous solution, laminarin is obtained in the form of grains which are very sparingly soluble in cold water. On the other hand, the addition of alcohol to an aqueous solution of the polysaccharide gives a precipitate which when isolated is a white powder, soluble in 65 to 70 per cent alcohol and readily soluble in cold water. Laminarin appears, therefore, to be an unstable colloid which slowly undergoes an increase in colloid particle size by an aggregation process until the aggregates become large enough to precipitate. This process is similar to the retrogradation of the linear fraction of starch (amylose). In the case of "insoluble" laminarin this spontaneous precipitation can be prevented indefinitely by the addition of glycerol (182). It is suggested that the only difference between the "insoluble" and "soluble" lies in the size of the colloidal particles and that the soluble form contains a substance which interferes with the aggregation of the colloidal molecules (182). It is interesting to recall that the fucoidin which occurred in one sample of soluble laminarin was thought to be associated with it through the reducing group (172).

A study of the physical properties, reducing power, and molecular weight of the two forms shows little marked differences (see Table 59). Both types show the same X-ray powder diagram (172) and for their acetylated and methylated derivatives, no obvious differences were detectable in such properties as specific rotation or specific viscosity. The determinations of the apparent chain length by reducing action on hypoiodite and 3,5-dinitrosalicylic acid must be taken with reserve since alkaline conditions exist in both determinations and it is known that laminarin is sensitive to alkali. This is well-demonstrated by the fall in apparent chain length, when estimated by the hypoiodite method, to seventeen after contact with $2N$ sodium hydroxide at $40°$ for 5 minutes and to eight after 30 minutes at $65°$. It is interesting to note, however, that the soluble form has the lowest reducing powder, i.e. highest

TABLE 59. PHYSICAL PROPERTIES OF SOLUBLE AND INSOLUBLE
FORMS OF LAMINARIN

Laminarin	Insoluble form		Soluble form	
$[\alpha]_D$ in water	$-14.4°$	(171)	$-12.0°$	(172)
Mol. Wt. by sedimentation diffusion & viscosity	3500	(191)	5300	(191)
Apparent chain length				
(i) by hypoiodite	45	(172)	112	(172)
(ii) by 3,5-dinitrosalicylic acid	13	(172)	27	(172)
Acetyl derivative				
$[\alpha]_D$ in chloroform	$-62°$	(172)	$-65°$	(172)
$\eta sp/c$ in chloroform	5.41	(172)	6.61	(172)
in m-cresol	3.66	(172)	3.73	(172)
Methyl derivative				
Mol. wt.				
(i) by Barger's method	2600–3500	(171)	2800–3800	(172)
(ii) by osmometry	3500–5000	(171)	...	
Chain length by methylation	20	(171)	20	(172)

apparent chain length, which may be due to the presence of associated
fucoidin.   This possibility' is supported by the increase in reducing
power after electrodialysis during which treatment it is known that the
fucoidin content decreases (172).   Somewhat more significant differences
exist in the molecular weights as determined by ultracentrifuge techniques (191).   However, it is the soluble form which has the highest
molecular weight so that the solubility differences are not accounted for
by polymer size.   It was noted in this study that mild methylation decreases molecular weight and increases the polydispersity of laminarin
so that molecular weight determinations on the methylated laminarin
are probably not too reliable.

A more recent study of fractionated methyl laminarin appears to indicate that laminarin has a very wide range of molecular weight with some
molecules having a D. P. of 65 (192).   It is evident that the structure of
laminarin is by no means as simple as it once appeared.

The insolubility of the laminarin from L. cloustoni is not associated
with the reducing groups since their oxidation or reduction did not confer
solubility on the molecule (193).   Solubilization is achieved by the
introduction of methyl-, 2-hydroxyethyl-, 3-hydroxypropyl- or carboxymethyl ether groups or sulfate ester groups.

Fucoidin.   Fucoidin is a mucilaginous polysaccharide composed
principally if not entirely of L-fucose and sulfate ester residues.   It is
present, together with laminarin and alginic acid, in the intercellular
tissues of all the common brown seaweeds but to a much greater extent
in the Fucaceae than in the Laminariaceae.   The fucoidin content undergoes marked seasonal variation and in general for the British seaweeds
is at a minimum in May with increasing accumulation through the summer
months to a maximum at around the end of the year (124).   Variations
also occur with the depth of immersion of the weed, the tidally exposed
plants like Pelvetia canaliculata containing 13 per cent of the dry
matter as fucoidin while in the permanently submerged Laminariaceae
there is less than 4 per cent on a dry weight basis (124).   The function
of fucoidin particularly in the Fucaceae, may be that of a food reserve,
although in view of its hygroscopic nature it may also serve to prevent
dehydration of the plant upon long exposure.

A polysaccharide containing L-fucose was first indicated by Gunther
and Tollens (194) in a Fucus species from which the crystalline sugar
was obtained by hydrolysis of the whole seaweed.   Fucoidin was first
described and named by Kylin (167,168) who isolated it from Laminaria
digitata, Fucus vesiculosus, and Ascophyllum nodosum, and showed that
it afforded L-fucose, by isolating the phenylosazone derivative, and a

small amount of pentose after hydrolysis. A fucoidin obtained by soaking the fresh fronds of L. digitata in water contained 30.9 per cent ash
(chiefly calcium sulfate) and 30.3 per cent sulfate and since the total
sulfate content was approximately double that found in the ash it was
suggested that sulfate was combined by an ester linkage to the L-fucose
units (145). Similar sulfate ester groups were detected in the mucilage
from the giant kelp Macrocystis pyrifera (195) from which a polysaccharide, probably fucoidin, had been isolated earlier (138). Fucoidin
may also be obtained (196) by allowing the droplets exuded from fresh
L. digitata fronds to fall into ethanol. However, on a larger scale,
fucoidin is extracted and isolated by stirring the dried milled seaweed
with 10 parts (W/V) of hydrochloric acid at pH 2 to 4.5 for 3 to 7.5
hours at 100° (197). A single extraction removes 50 to 60 per cent of
the fucoidin and three extractions increases this to over 80 per cent.
The disadvantage, however, of extraction with water is the difficulty of
separating the insoluble residue from the solution. The crude fucoidin
is isolated from the acid extracts by neutralization and evaporation of
the solution to dryness in vacuo. The dark-brown residue is dissolved
in water and fractionally precipitated with alcohol at 30 per cent and
60 per cent concentration. The 60 per cent fraction is crude fucoidin
which has been isolated in 76 per cent yield from P. canaliculata, 62
per cent from F. vesiculosus, 53 per cent from A. nodosum and 20 per
cent from L. cloustoni frond. It is purified by treating an aqueous solution of the crude material with formaldehyde and evaporating the mixture
to dryness in vacuo. The residue is extracted with water and alcohol
added to the extract to give a 70 per cent alcohol concentration. The
precipitate is collected and dried by solvent exchange with alcohol and
ether. The formaldehyde treatment results in the insolubilization of
most of the impurities, but the formation of the water-insoluble material
leads to a 20 to 30 per cent loss of fucoidin.

The composition of fucoidin has been variously reported, the difficulties of the analysis being due to complete removal of associated polysaccharides and the avid retention of solvents by fucoidin. A calcium
salt of pure fucan monosulfate would give upon analysis ash, 37.1 per
cent; sulfate, 39.2 per cent; calcium, 8.2 per cent; and fucose, 66.9 per
cent. This analysis will vary with the inorganic ion and samples of
fucoidin have been reported with calcium (138,198) or sodium (196) as
the main cation together with small amounts of sodium or calcium, respectively, and potassium and magnesium. The fucose content has been
determined by distillation of the fucoidin with hydrochloric acid to give
(5-methyl)-2-furaldehyde (weighed as the phloroglucide) or by hydrolysis

and oxidation of the liberated fucose with periodic acid to acetaldehyde which is determined either as the bisulfite addition compound (131,199) or colorimetrically (200,201). Until the introduction of chromatographic methods of analysis, only about 80 per cent of the fucoidin could be accounted for which led to the postulation that carbohydrate building units other than L-fucose were present (196). In one case, uronic acid 2.6 per cent was detected, but was thought to be due to contaminating alginic acid (195). Recent analyses, however, have accounted for 99 per cent of fucoidin which was prepared by the extraction of *F. spiralis*, *F. vesiculosus*, *L. cloustoni*, and *Himanthalia lorea* with hot water for twenty four hours (198). The extract was treated with lead acetate solution until precipitation of alginates and proteins was complete. The addition of barium hydroxide resulted in the precipitation of a lead hydroxide-fucoidin complex which was decomposed with sulfuric acid and the polysaccharide isolated after prolonged dialysis. Following several treatments with a celite filter aid, the fucoidin was precipitated with alcohol. It was noted that despite drying at 40° *in vacuo* at 0.1 mm pressure for 18 hours, the polysaccharide still retained 9.4 per cent water and 6 per cent ethanol. The fucoidin preparations from the four varieties of seaweed gave similar analysis, but the purest (from *H. lorea*) contained, after correction for absorbed solvents: sulfate, 38.3 per cent; metals (principally calcium), 8.2 per cent; uronic acid, 3.3 per cent; L-fucose, 56.7 per cent; D-galactose, 4.1 per cent; and D-xylose, 1.5 per cent. A comparison of these analytical data with those calculated for a calcium fucan monosulfate has led to the suggestion that the principal constitutent of fucoidin is a fucan monosulfate and that the carbohydrate constituents, other than fucose, resulted from other closely associated polysaccharides.

The action of alkali on fucoidin results in a fairly rapid initial removal of about 10 per cent of the total sulfate ester groups, but the remaining sulfate is stable (202). Since only a sulfate ester which has an adjacent free hydroxyl group in a *trans* position to it is labile to alkali (68), an inspection of the fucose molecule (CCCLXVIII) will show that an alkali-stable sulfate group must be at C_4. It follows, therefore, that about 90 per cent of the ester sulfate is so situated in fucoidin.

The methylation of fucoidin with methyl sulfate and alkali gave a product having $[\alpha]_D - 107°$ in water and containing essentially the same cations as the original polysaccharide (202). It is seen, therefore, that the metals combined with the sulfate group are not displaced by sodium during the methylation process. The sulfate content is reduced from 32/8 per cent to 25.9 per cent. The hydrolysis of the methylated fucoidin gives 2,3-di-O-methyl-L-fucose (CCCLXIX, 1 part), 3-O-methyl-L-fucose (CCCLXX, 3 parts) and L-fucose (CCCLXVIII, 1 part).

Since the sulfate groups are principally attached to C_4, the identification of 3-O-methyl-L-fucose in the cleavage fragments of the methylated

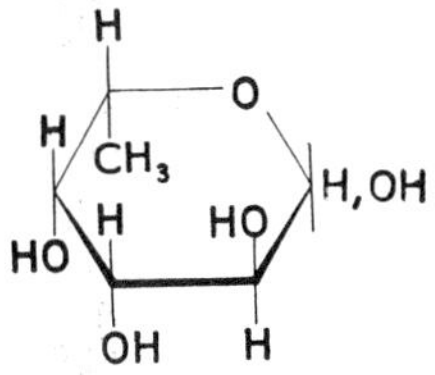

(CCCLXVIII) 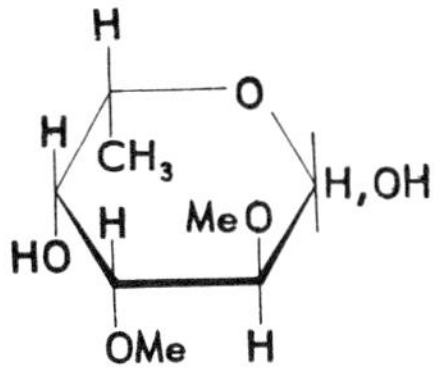   (CCCLXIX) 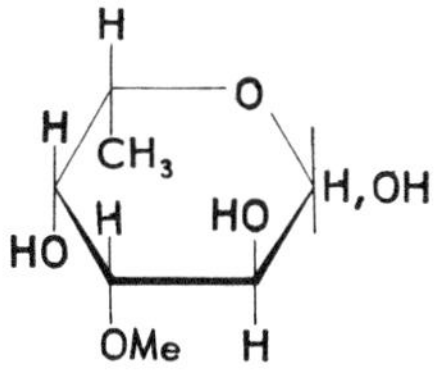   (CCCLXX)

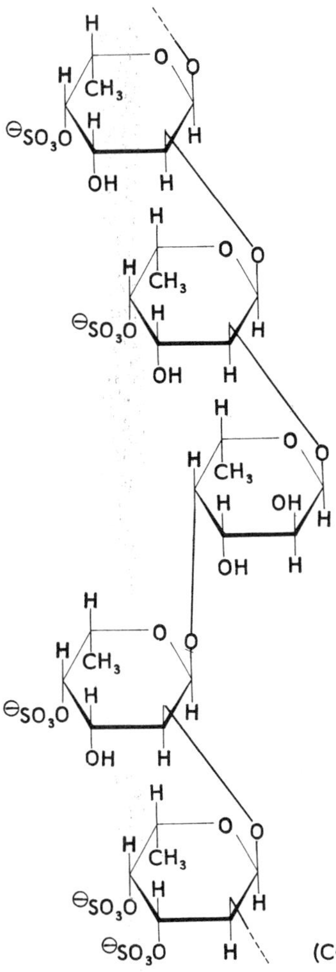

(CCCLXXI) 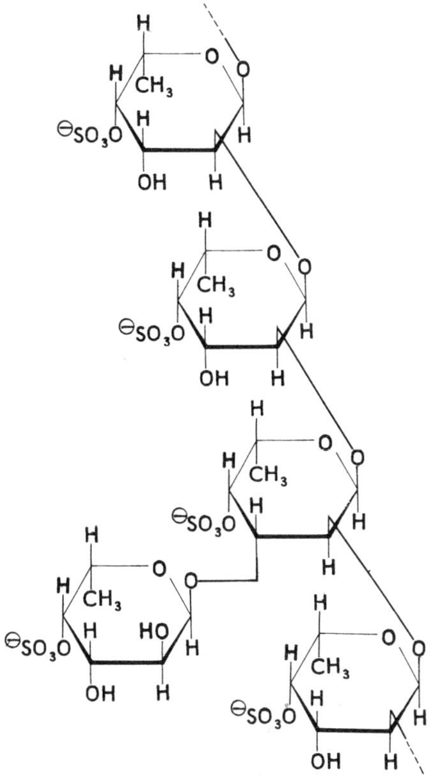   (CCCLXXII)

polysaccharide indicates that they arise from residues which are linked through C_1 and C_2. The presence of free L-fucose in the cleavage fragments may be explained either by the presence of a branching point with linkages at C_1, C_2 and C_3, or by a residue which is linked through C_1 and C_2 and carries two sulfate groups at C_3 and C_4. Again, two possible explanations have been proposed for the isolation of 2,3-di-O-methyl-L-fucose (202). It may arise from an end-group with a sulfate on C_4 or from a residue which is linked through C_1 and C_4 and which has no sulfate group. With these several possibilities in mind, two formulae, CCCLXXI and CCCLXXII, are proposed for the general structural features of fucoidin (202). The glycosidic linkages are considered to be of the α-type from the negative rotation of fucoidin, $[\alpha]_D - 140°$, and of its methyl derivative, $[\alpha]_D - 107°$ (198).

It is also possible that the 2,3-di-O-methyl-L-fucose arises from a fucose residue which is linked through C_1 and C_4 and esterified with a sulfate group on C_2 or C_3. Such a sulfate ester would be labile to alkali under the conditions of methylation, and it is known that some of the sulfate groups are hydrolyzed by alkali (202). The presence of this residue in formula CCCLXXI would also render unnecessary the inclusion of a residue bearing two sulfate groups although no known facts exclude this possibility.

The presence of $1 \rightarrow 2$ linkages in fucoidin is demonstrated by subjecting the polysaccharide to mild acetolysis (203). The mixture of sugars so obtained was reduced catalytically, then reactylated and separated chromatographically. In this way, 2-O-α-L-fucopyranosyl-L-fucitol (CCCLXXIII) was obtained as its crystalline acetate, m.p. 119–120° (an isomorphous form had m.p. 99 to 102°), $[\alpha]_D - 81.5°$ in chloroform, and from which the free alcohol, m.p. 190 to 192°, $[\alpha]_D - 118°$ in water, was obtained by deacetylation. The structure of the fucobiitol (CCCLXXIII) was proved by oxidation with sodium periodate in which four moles of periodate were consumed with the formation of one mole of acetaldehyde and 1.9 moles of formic acid. These results, together with the signifi-

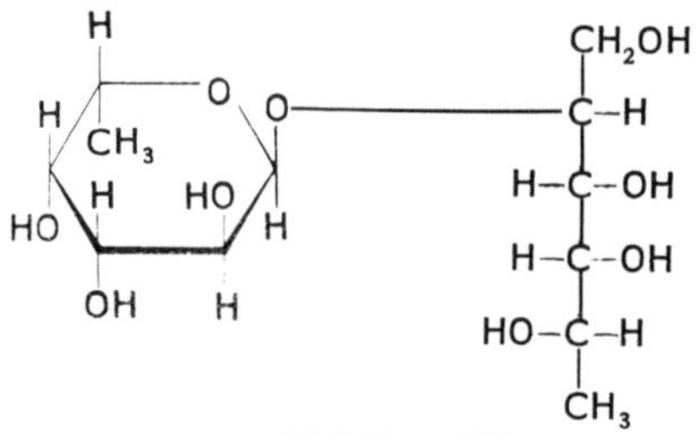

(CCCLXXIII)

cant absence of formaldehyde, show that the L-fucopyranose moiety is joined to C_2 of the L-fucitol unit.

Although the principal structural features of fucoidin have been demonstrated the several possibilities cannot be appreciably narrowed down until the structure of a desulfated fucoidin can be studied. From such a study one of the two formulae, CCCLXXI and CCCLXXII, could be eliminated or an alternative one proposed.

A mucilage, similar to fucoidin, is isolated from the fruit bodies of *Ascophyllum nodosum* and *Fucus spiralis* by immersing them for some time in distilled water and then in 0.02–0.03 per cent hydrochloric acid (204). Immersion in acid without previous water treatment extracts little or no mucilage, nor is any extracted when the fruit bodies are immersed in stronger acid after previous water treatment. The mucilage is also found in the thallus of the seaweed. It is the neutral salt of a polysaccharide sulfuric ester composed of L-fucose and D-galactose in the molar ratio of 8 : 1, with one sulfate group per monosaccharide residue.

Mucilages of the Green Marine Algae (*Chlorophyceae*)

The carbohydrate components of the green seaweeds have received little attention. Mucilages containing L-rhamnose and a uronic acid have been reported from *Ulva lactuca* (205–207), *Ulva pertusa* (208), and *Enteromorpha compressa* (209,210), and a galactan sulfate from *Cladophora rupestris* (211).

A preliminary constitutional study has been carried out on the mucilage from *Ulva lactuca* (207). It was extracted from the seaweed with 0.2 to 0.5 per cent sodium carbonate and the ash-free polysaccharide obtained from the extracts by dialysis. The free-acid had $[\alpha]_D - 84°$ in water and an equivalent weight of 386, the latter being due to sulfate ester groups (15.9 per cent), which were resistant to alkaline hydrolysis, and glucuronic acid (19.2 per cent). From a hydrolysis with $0.3N$ sulfuric acid at 100° for twelve hours, the neutral component sugars were shown to be D-xylose (9.4 per cent), L-rhamnose (31 per cent) and D-glucose (7.7 per cent).

The mucilage was difficult to methylate with methyl sulfate and sodium hydroxide and after seven treatments a product with 24 per cent methoxyl was obtained, a portion (25 per cent) of which was soluble in chloroform. By further methylation with Purdie reagents the chloroform-soluble fraction, containing 3 per cent sulfate, gave a product (OMe 43 per cent) which upon hydrolysis afforded 2,3,4-tri-*O*-methyl-L-rhamnose (CLXXXIX), 2,3-di-*O*-methyl-D-glucose (CCXCV), and 2,3,6-tri-*O*-methyl-D-glucose (CCLXXXVIII). The chloroform-insoluble fraction, containing 13 per cent sulfate, yielded upon hydrolysis 2,3,4-tri-O-methyl-D-xylose (CCXII), 2,3-di-O-methyl-D-xylose (CCCI), 2,3,4-tri-O-methyl-L-rhamnose (CLXXXIX), 2,3-di-O-methyl-L-rhamnose (CCCLXXIV), monomethylethers of L-rhamnose and of D-xylose, L-rhamnose and D-xylose.

Little can be deduced from these methylation data and further work will be required to establish the homogeneity of the mucilage, the linkages of the D-glucuronic acid and sulfate residues and the relative proportions of the methylated cleavage fragments. However, it would appear that the mucilage bears no relationship to those from the red and brown algae except for the presence of sulfate groups.

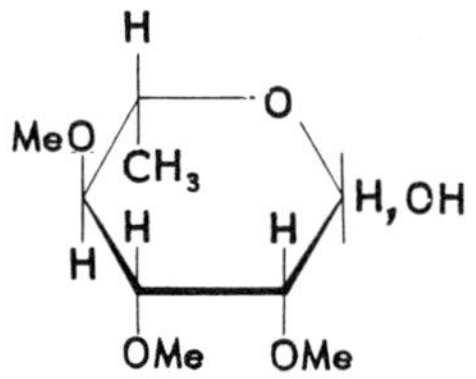

(CLXXXIX) 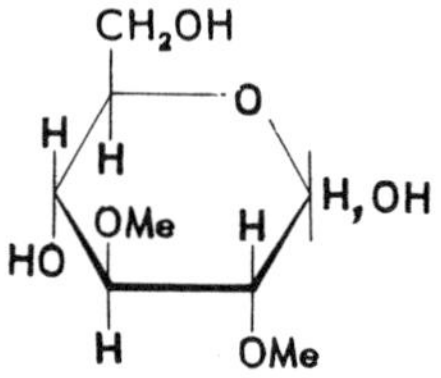   (CCXCV)

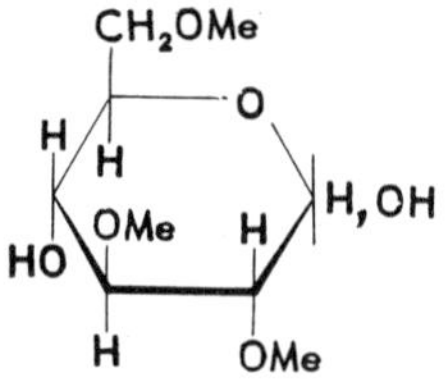

(CCLXXXVIII) 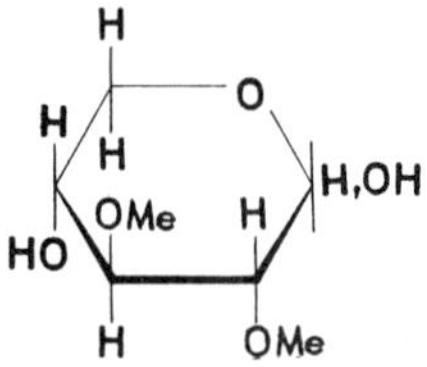   (CCCI)

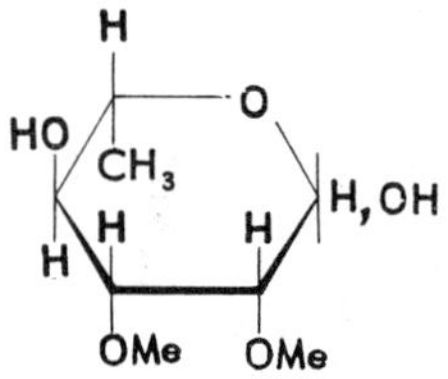

(CCCLXXIV)

The Water-soluble Polysaccharides of *Cladophora rupestris.*

Extraction of the green seaweed, *Cladophora rupestris* with boiling water or dilute hydrochloric acid affords (250) a mixture of polysaccharides together with a considerable amount (20 to 25 per cent) of protein. Removal of the protein by the usual trichloroacetic acid technique furnished a polysaccharide material which contained about 2 per cent protein. The polysaccharide ($[\alpha]_D + 69°$ in water) was shown by hydrolysis and chromatographic analysis to contain L-arabinose (3.7 moles), D-galactose (2.8), D-xylose (1.0), L-rhamnose (0.4), D-glucose (0.2) and 19.6 per cent sulfate. The glucose arose from a contaminating glucan, possibly laminarin, since fractionation of the acetylated polysaccharide or precipitation with cetyl trimethylammonium bromide gave a main fraction which contained no glucose.

In order to determine the general structural features of the polysaccharide it was methylated with methyl sulfate and alkali. The methylated compound (OMe 25.1 per cent) gave upon methanolysis followed by hydrolysis the following mixture of sugars:

2,3,4,6-tetra-, 2,3,5-tri-, 2,4-di-, and 2-O-methyl-D-galactose, D-galactose, 2,4-di-, 2-O-, and 3-O-methyl-L-arabinose, L-arabinose, 2,3,4-tri- and 2,3-di-O-methyl-D-xylose, 2,4-di-, 3,4-di-, and 4-O-methyl-L-rhamnose.

As it was pointed out (250), this highly complex mixture does not enable any one formula to be proposed for the polysaccharide and the problem was made still more complicated by the fact that the polysaccharide may not have been fully methylated. It may be deduced nevertheless that the polysaccharide has a highly complex structure. It possesses the unusual feature of containing furanose units of galactose and pyranose units of L-arabinose as proved by the isolation of 2,3,5-tri-O-methyl-D-galactose and 2,4-di-O-methyl-L-arabinose, respectively.

Proof that arabinose, xylose and galactose are mutually joined in the polysaccharide followed from the observation that partial hydrolysis of the polysaccharide afforded di- and trisaccharides containing these three sugars. Graded hydrolysis also provided oligosaccharides composed only of arabinose thus showing that a number of the arabinose residues are joined to each other in the polymer. Periodate oxidation cleaved almost all the xylose and about two thirds of the galactose residues. This is in agreement with the methylation studies which revealed the presence of terminal units of D-galactose and 1 → 4 linked D-xylose residues.

The periodate-oxidized polysaccharide gave upon hydrolysis arabinose and galactose and it also contained 19.95 per cent sulfate. Evidently the inner portion of the molecule consists of units of galactose and arabinose and some of the latter must be sulfated.

All of the results indicate (250) that the polysaccharide of C. *rupestris* is highly branched and that the terminal non-reducing ends of the molecule consist of galactose and xylose. The exact location of the sulfate group remains to be ascertained as does the homogeneity of the polysaccharide itself (47).

Other Seaweed Polysaccharides

Although all the carbohydrate polymers present in seaweeds do not by themselves exhibit gum- or mucilagenous-like properties, they undoubtedly contribute to the character of other polysaccharides which do behave as gums and mucilages. For this reason, a brief outline will be given of some of these polysaccharides.

Floridean Starch. This is a reserve polysaccharide, found in such red algae (212) as *Dilsea edulis* (241), *Furcellaria fastigiata* (213), *Lemania nodosa* (214,215) (a fresh water red algae), which has been designated as a starch since it gives a brown or violet color with iodine. Some (217, 218) have held the view that Floridean starch is identical with ordinary starch while others (167,168,219) have reported it to be different. The polysaccharide is a glucan, since it gives D-glucose upon acid hydrolysis (241), while it gives maltose upon treatment (213) with a dialyzed malt extract. Contrary to an earlier communication (241) that the *Dilsea* "starch" was not affected by crystalline sweet potato β-amylase, a more recent study indicates (216) that a 45 per cent conversion to maltose occurs either with the crystalline β-amylase or a crude preparation from soybean flour. Wheat β-amylase also causes a 50 per cent conversion to maltose (221). Salivary α-amylase effects a 65 per cent conversion of the *Dilsea* material to maltose (216). The same *Dilsea* starch underwent a further 9 per cent β-amylolysis if subjected also to the action of yeast iso-amylase which contains an α-D-$(1 \rightarrow 6)$ glucosidase (220) from which observation it is deduced that α-D-$(1 \rightarrow 6)$ linkages are probably present in the *Dilsea* starch. Such investigations have indicated that the polysaccharide from this particular red alga is a branched α-D-$(1 \rightarrow 4)$-glucan and that it resembles the amylopectin and glycogen classes of polysaccharides. This is also supported by the fact that the polysaccharide is degraded to the extent of 35 per cent by potato phosphorylase in the presence of inorganic phosphate.

Periodate oxidation shows (216,222) that the uptake was about 1 mole per glucose unit and that liberation of formic acid corresponded to an average repeating unit of 9 to 13 D-glucose residues (216). The periodate-oxidized polymer contained an insignificant amount of glucose. The above findings indicate a relationship between the *Dilsea* starch and glycogen. Previous low results for periodate uptake of 0.6 (221,241) and 0.8 mole per D-glucose residue have been traced (216) to the fact that oxidation had not proceeded to completion although it seems quite likely that this might be due to impurity in the polysaccharide such as protein which markedly affects periodate oxidation (223). The precipitin reaction (224) with concanavalin-A which readily distinguishes amylopectin from glycogen, shows that *Dilsea* Floridean starch gives little or no precipitate (225), indicating that it is not related to glycogen. There seems no reason, at present, to assign it to either the glycogen or the starch group of polysaccharides and it is more than likely that it will prove to be different from both and should therefore be classed as algal glucan or *Dilsea* glucan.

A similar algal glucan (227–230), sometimes called *Cyanophycean* Starch, has been isolated from the green alga (*Calothrix scopulorum*) but little is known about this material except that it gives maltose when treated (226) with dialyzed malt extract.

Algal Cellulose. The presence of a cellulose-like substance in marine algae (231) and in green algae (232) has long been known (cf 258). The information available has led to the assumption that the algae material is indistinguishable from the cellulose of plants. Thus, it gave the characteristic color reaction with iodine and sulfuric acid (168) and it was found to be soluble in cuprammonium hydroxide (233,234). Somewhat later, it was shown that the cellulose from *L. digitata* gave a viscose (235), acetyl (233,235), and methyl (235) derivative. Cellulose is said (236) to be present in brown algae, but absent (139,237) in many others. The cellulose of *Iridaea laminarioides* was reported to consist of 91 per cent α-cellulose. Acetolysis of cellulose material from *Gelidium amansii* (238) and from *L. cloustoni* (234), *L. digitata* (234), and *Fucus vesiculosus* (234) has afforded cellobiose octaacetate thus establishing the presence of β-D-(1 → 4)-linkages in these polysaccharides. Examination of the hydrolyzates of the algal cellulose (234) gave only the one sugar, D-glucose. The cellulose reacted with 1 mole of periodate per D-glucose unit with the liberation of formic acid indicating an average chain length of about 160. These observations show that only 1 → 4 linkages are present in the specimens of algal cellulose (234). The presence of 1 → 3- or 1 → 6- linkages is unlikely for the former would not react with periodate whereas the latter would require 2 moles of periodate per D-glucose unit and at the same time formic acid would be liberated. X-ray crystallographic studies showed (234) that the algal cellulose gave the characteristic patterns of normal cellulose.

Algal Xylan. Extraction of the red algae *Rhodymenia palmata* with dilute hydrochloric acid followed by addition of alcohol gives a pentosan (38). This was recognized as a xylan since it furnished upon hydrolysis only the one sugar D-xylose (39). Methylation of the polysaccharide followed by hydrolysis gave: 2,3,4-tri-O-methyl-D-xylose (CCXII), 2,4-di-O-methyl-D-xylose (CCXVI), 2,3-di-O-methyl-D-xylose (CCCI), and 2-O-methyl xylose (CCCII). This result indicated the abnormal character of the seaweed xylan as compared with the other plant xylans inasmuch as the characterization of 2,4-di-O-methyl-D-xylose established the presence of 1 → 3 linkages (39,40), an unknown structural feature of the linear portions of plant xylans. The possibility of two polysaccharides being present in the natural material was ruled out on the grounds that attempted resolution of the acetylated and methylated derivative of the algal xylan failed to reveal any heterogeneity.

The green seaweed, *Caulerpa filiformis* has provided a xylan-like polysaccharide (A) $[\alpha]_D - 31°$ (NaOH) which contained 95 per cent D-xylose and 5 per cent D-glucose. Extensive purification yielded a pure xylan $[\alpha]_D - 35°$ (NaOH). Hydrolysis of the methylated derivative of A gave rise to a considerable proportion of 2,4-di-O-methyl-D-xylose together with 2,3,4-tri-O-methyl-D-xylose, 2- and 4-O-methyl-D-xylose and small proportions of methylated glucose derivatives (from a contaminating D-glucan). As far as the xylan molecule is concerned this evidence indicates that the polysaccharide is composed of chains of β-D-xylopyranose units joined by 1 → 3 bonds (257).

REFERENCES

1. Haas, P., *Biochem. J.*, **15,** 469 (1921).
2. Chapman, V. J., *"Seaweeds and their Uses,"* Methuen and Co. Ltd., London (1950).
3. Peat, S., *Advances in Carbohydrate Chem.*, **2,** 37 (1946), Tipson, R. S., *ibid.*, **8,** 108 (1953).
4. Duff, R. B., and Percival, E. G. V., *J. Chem. Soc.*, 830 (1941).
5. Percival, E. G. V., *J. Chem. Soc.*, 119 (1945).
6. Dillon, T., *Congr. intern. botan. Paris, Rapps. et communs.*, **8,** sect. 17, 29 (1954); *Chem. Abstracts*, **48,** 11568 (1954).
7. Ross, A. G., *J. Sci. Food Agric.*, **4,** 333 (1953).
8. Schmidt, C., *Ann.*, **51,** 29 (1844).
9. Russell-Wells, Barbara, *Biochem. J.*, **16,** 578 (1922).
10. Haas, P., and Russell-Wells, Barbara, *Biochem. J.*, **23,** 425 (1929).
11. Rose, R. C., *Can. J. Research*, **F28,** 202 (1950).
12. Buchanan, J., Percival, E. E., and Percival, E. G. V., *J. Chem. Soc.*, 51 (1943).
13. Haas, P., and Hill, T. G., *Ann. Appl. Biol.*, **7,** 352 (1921); *Chem. Abstracts*, **16,** 2710 (1922).
14. Harwood, F. C., *J. Chem. Soc.*, **123,** 2254 (1923).
15. Butler, Margaret R., *Biochem. J.*, **28,** 759 (1934).
16. Butler, Margaret R., *Biochem. J.*, **30,** 1338 (1936).
17. Fluckiger, F. A., and Obermaier, L., *Neues Repertorium Pharm.*, 380 (1868).
18. Bente, F., *Ber.*, **8,** 416 (1875); **9,** 1157 (1876).

19. Haedicke, J., Bauer, R. W., and Tollens, B., Ann., **238,** 302 (1887).
20. Sebor, J., Oesterr, Chem. Z., **3,** 441 (1920).
21. Mori, T., and Tsuchiya, Y., J. Agr. Chem. Soc. Japan, **14,** 616 (1938); Chem. Abstracts, **32,** 9176 (1938).
22. Mori, T., and Tsuchiya, Y., J. Agr. Chem. Soc. Japan, **15,** 1065 (1939); Chem. Abstracts, **34,** 3313 (1940).
23. Mori, T., J. Agr. Chem. Soc. Japan, **19,** 297 (1943); Chem. Abstracts, **44,** 7783 (1950).
24. Dewar, E. T., and Percival, E. G. V., J. Chem. Soc., 1622 (1947).
25. Araki, C., and Arai, K., Collected Papers for the Celebration of the Forty-fifth Anniversary of the Founding of Kyoto Technical College, 80 (1948); see Mori, T., Adv. Carb. Chem., **8,** 315 (1953).
26. Johnston, R., and Percival, E. G. V., J. Chem. Soc., 1994 (1950).
27. Percival, Elizabeth E., Chemistry and Industry, 1487 (1954).
28. O'Neill, A. N., J. Am. Chem. Soc., **77,** 2837 (1955).
29. O'Neill, A. N., J. Am. Chem. Soc., **77,** 6324 (1955).
30. Young, E. G., and Rice, F. A. H., J. Biol. Chem., **164,** 35 (1946).
31. Dillon, T., and O'Colla, P., Proc. Roy. Irish Acad., **54B,** 51 (1951).
32. Müther, A., and Tollens, B., Ber., **37,** 298 (1904).
33. Ohle, H., and Berend, Gertrud, Ber., **60,** 1159 (1927).
34. Takao, Y., Repts. Central Inst., Government of Formosa, **6,** 13 (1918).
35. Dillon, T., and O'Colla, P., Nature, **145,** 749 (1940).
36. Mori, T., and Tsuchiya, Y., J. Agr. Chem. Soc., Japan, **14,** 585 (1941).
37. Sauvageau, C., and Denigès, G., Compt. rend., **174,** 791 (1922).
38. Barry, V. C., and Dillon, T., Nature, **146,** 620 (1940).
39. Percival, E. G. V., and Chanda, S. K., Nature, **166,** 787 (1950).
40. Barry, V. C., Dillon, T., Hawkins, B., and O'Colla, P., Nature, **166,** 788 (1950).
41. Cook, W. H., Rose, R. C., and Colvin, J. R., Biochim. et Biophys. Acta, **8,** 595 (1952).
42. Smith, D. B., and Cook, W. H., Arch. Biochem. Biophys., **45,** 232 (1953).
43. Smith, D. B., Cook, W. H., and Neal, J. L., Arch Biochem. Biophys., **53,** 192 (1954).
44. Bayley, S. T., Biochim. et Biophys. Acta, **17,** 194 (1955).
45. Goring, D. A. I., J. Colloid Sci., **9,** 141 (1954).
46. Briggs, D. R., Garner, E. F., and Smith, F., Nature, **178,** 154 (1956).
47. Lewis, Bertha A., and Smith, F., J. Am. Chem. Soc., **79,** 3929 (1957).
48. Goring, D. A. I., and Young, E. G., Can. J. Chem., **33,** 480 (1955).
49. Masson, C. R., Can. J. Chem., **33,** 597 (1955).
50. Masson, C. R., Santry, D., and Caines, G. W., Can. J. Chem., **33,** 1088 (1955).
51. Haworth, W. N., Owen, L. N., and Smith, F., J. Chem. Soc., 88 (1941).
52. Payen, A., Compt. rend., **49,** 521 (1859).
53. Morin, H., Compt. rend., **90,** 924 (1880).
54. Bauer, R. N., J. prakt. Chem., [2], **30,** 367 (1884).
55. Neuberg, C., and Ohle, H., Biochem. Z., **125,** 311 (1921).
56. Fairbrother, F., and Mastin, H., J. Chem. Soc., **123,** 1412 (1923).
57. Harvey, E. H., Am. J. Pharm., **97,** 66, 447 (1925).
58. Hoffman, W. F., and Gortner, R. A., J. Biol. Chem., **65,** 371 (1925).
59. de Waele, H., Ann. physiol. et physicochim. biol., **5,** 869 (1929); Chem. Abstracts, **24,** 3152 (1930).

60. Hirase, S., and Araki, C., Memoirs of the Faculty of Industrial Arts, Kyoto Technical University, 1, 19 (1952).
61. Matsui, H., J. Coll. Agr. Imp. Univ. Tokyo, 5, 413 (1916); Chem. Abstracts, 11, 2920 (1917).
62. Fellers, C. R., Ind. Eng. Chem., 8, 1128 (1916).
63. Yanagawa, T., and Nishida, Y., Repts. Imp. Ind. Research Inst., Osaka, Japan, 11, No. 14 (1930); Chem. Abstracts, 25, 1642 (1931).
64. Furuichi, M., Repts. Tottori Higher Agr. School, Japan, 1, 31 (1927).
65. Araki, C., J. Chem. Soc., Japan, 58, 1214 (1937); Chem. Abstracts, 32, 4172 (1938).
66. Hayashi, K., J. Soc. Trop. Agr. Taihoku Imp. Univ., 14, 5 (1942); Chem. Abstracts, 42, 5425 (1948).
67. Percival, E. G. V., and Thomson, T. G. H., J. Chem. Soc., 750 (1942).
68. Percival, E. G. V., Quart. Rev., (London), 3, 369 (1949).
69. Barry, V. C., and Dillon, T., Chemistry and Industry, 167 (1944).
70. Percival, E. G. V., Nature, 154, 673 (1944).
71. Araki, C., Collected papers for the celebration of the forty-fifth anniversary of the founding of Kyoto Technical College, 69 (1948); see Mori, T., Advances in Carb. Chem., 8, 322 (1953).
72. Yanagigawa, T., Repts. Imp. Ind. Research Inst. Osaka, Japan, 14, No. 5, 1 (1933); Chem. Abstracts, 30, 3541 (1936).
73. Ludtke, M., Biochem. Z., 212, 419 (1929).
74. Percival, E. G. V., and Somerville, J. C., J. Chem. Soc., 1615 (1937).
75. Araki, T., J. Chem. Soc. Japan, 59, 424 (1938); Chem. Abstracts, 35, 7946 (1941).
76. Araki, C., and Hirase, S., Bull. Chem. Soc., Japan, 26, 463 (1953); Chem. Abstracts, 49, 9516 (1955).
77. Pirie, N. N., Biochem. J., 30, 369 (1936).
78. Cottrell, T. L., and Percival, E. G. V., J. Chem. Soc., 749 (1942).
79. Percival, E. G. V., Somerville, J. C., and Forbes, I. A., Nature, 142, 797 (1938).
80. Percival, E. G. V., and Forbes, I. A., Nature, 142, 1076 (1938).
81. Forbes, I. A., and Percival, E. G. V., J. Chem. Soc., 1844 (1939).
82. Araki, C., J. Chem. Soc. Japan, 65, 725 (1944); Chem. Abstracts, 41, 3496 (1947).
83. Takahashi, E., and Shirahawa, K., J. Fac. Agr. Hokkaido Imp. Univ. Japan, 35, 101 (1934); Chem. Abstracts, 28, 5412 (1934).
84. Araki, C., J. Chem. Soc. Japan, 65, 533 (1944); Chem. Abstracts, 42, 1210 (1948).
85. Araki, C., J. Chem. Soc., Japan, 65, 627 (1944); Chem. Abstracts, 42, 1210 (1948).
86. Hirase, S., and Araki, C., Bull. Chem. Soc. Japan, 27, 105 (1954); Chem. Abstracts, 49, 9517 (1955).
87. Araki, C., and Hirase, S., Bull. Chem. Soc. Japan, 27, 109 (1954); Chem. Abstracts, 49, 9518 (1955).
88. Kadota, H., Mem. Coll. Agr. Kyoto Univ., 59, 54 (1951).
89. Oshima, K., J. Agr. Chem. Soc., Japan, 17, 328 (1941).
90. Mori, T., J. Agr. Chem. Soc. Japan, 15, 1070 (1939); Chem. Abstracts, 34, 3285 (1940).
91. Mori, T., and Okafuji, T., J. Agr. Chem. Soc. Japan, 16, 886 (1940); Chem. Abstracts, 35, 4399 (1941).

92. Fukumoto, J., and Ishimatsu, K., *Bull. Osaka Municipal Tech. Research Inst.*, **13**, 1 (1951).
93. Ishimatsu, K., *Bull Osaka Municipal Tech. Research Inst.*, **14**, 1 (1953).
94. Ishimatsu, K., Kibesaki, Y., and Maitani, S., *Science and Industry (Japanese)*, **28**, 100 (1954); *Chem. Abstracts*, **49**, 14070 (1955).
95. Araki, C., and Arai, K., *Memoirs of the Faculty of Industrial Arts, Kyoto, Tech. Univ.*, **3B**, 7 (1954).
96. Araki, C., and Arai, K., *Bull Chem. Soc. Japan*, **29**, 339 (1956); *Chem. Abstracts*, **51**, 3465 (1957).
97. Haworth, W. N., Jackson, J., and Smith, F., *J. Chem. Soc.*, 620 (1940).
98. Araki, C., *Bull Chem. Soc. Japan*, **29**, 543 (1956); *Chem. Abstracts*, **51**, 3462 (1957).
99. O'Neill, A. N., and Stewart, D. K. R., *Can. J. Chem.*, **34**, 1700 (1956).
100. Percival, E. G. V., and Sim, W. S., *Nature*, **137**, 997 (1936).
101. Hands, S., and Peat, S., *Nature*, **142**, 797 (1938).
102. Hands, S., and Peat, S., *Chemistry and Industry*, 57, 937 (1938).
103. Araki, C., *J. Chem. Soc. Japan*, **58**, 1362 (1937); *Chem. Abstracts*, **32**, 4172 (1938).
104. Araki, T., *J. Chem. Soc. Japan*, **61**, 775 (1940); *Chem. Abstracts*, **37**, 90 (1943).
105. Jones, W. G. M., and Peat, S., *J. Chem. Soc.*, 225 (1942).
106. Barry, V. C., Dillon, T., and McGettrick, Winifred, *J. Chem. Soc.*, 183 (1942).
107. Tseng, C. K., in "Colloid Chemistry," **6**, Reinhold Publ. Corp., New York (1946) 629.
108. Hassid, W. Z., *J. Am. Chem. Soc.*, **55**, 4163 (1933).
109. Mori, T., and Tsuchiya, Y., *J. Agr. Chem. Soc.*, Japan, **14**, 609 (1938); *Chem. Abstracts*, **32**, 9175 (1938).
110. Hassid, W. Z., *J. Am. Chem. Soc.*, **57**, 2046 (1935).
111. Jones, J. K. N., and Smith, F., *Adv. Carbohydrate Chem.*, **4**, 243 (1949).
112. Mori, T., *J. Agr. Chem. Soc.*, Japan, **23**, 81 (1949); *Chem. Abstracts*, **44**, 7783 (1950).
113. Barry, V. C., and Dillon, T., *Proc. Roy. Irish. Acad.*, **50B**, 349 (1945).
114. Dillon, T., and McKenna, J., *Proc. Roy. Irish Acad.*, **53B**, 45 (1950).
115. Kantor, T. G., and Schubert, M., *J. Am. Chem. Soc.*, **79**, 152 (1957).
116. Dillon, T., and McKenna, J., *Nature*, **165**, 318 (1950).
117. Oshima, K., and Tollens, B., *Ber.*, **34**, 1422 (1901).
118. Jones, J. K. N., *J. Chem. Soc.*, 3292 (1950).
119. Muva, T., *Japan J. Botany*, **11**, 41 (1940); *Chem. Abstracts*, **35**, 7466 (1941).
120. Hayashi, K., *Nogaku*, **2**, 226 (1948); *Chem. Abstracts*, **44**, 2086 (1950).
121. Black, W. A. P., *J. Soc. Chem. Ind.*, **67**, 165 (1948).
122. Black, W. A. P., *J. Soc. Chem. Ind.*, **68**, 183 (1949).
123. Black, W. A. P., *J. Marine Biol. Assoc.*, (United Kingdom) **29**, 45 (1950).
124. Black, W. A. P., *J. Sci. Food Agric.*, **5**, 445 (1954).
125. Holdt, M. M., Von Ligthelin, S. P., and Nunn, J. R., *J. Sci. Food Agr.*, **6**, 193 (1955).
126. Black, W. A. P., *J. Soc. Chem. Ind.*, **69**, 161 (1950).
127. Black, W. A. P., and Dewar, E. T., *J. Marine Biol. Assoc.* (United Kingdom), **28**, 673 (1949).
128. Black, W. A. P., *J. Marine Biol. Assoc.* (United Kingdom), **33**, 49 (1954).

129. Stanford, E. C. C., *Chem. News.*, **47**, 254, 267 (1883).
130. Percival, E. G. V., and Ross, A. G., *J. Soc. Chem. Ind.*, **67**, 420 (1948).
131. Cameron, M. C., Ross, A. G., and Percival, E. G. V., *J. Soc. Chem. Ind.*, **67**, 161 (1948).
132. Fischer, F. G., and Dörfel, H., *Z. physiol. Chem.*, **302**, 186 (1955).
133. McCready, R. M., Swenson, H. A., and Maclay, W. D., *Ind. Eng. Chem., Anal. Ed.* **18**, 290 (1946).
134. Frush, Harriet, L., and Isbell, H. S., *J. Research. Natl. Bur. Standards.*, **37**, 321 (1946).
135. Spoehr, H. A., *Arch. Biochem.*, **14**, 153 (1947).
136. Link, K. P., *Science*, **76**, 386 (1932).
137. Schoeffel, E., and Link, K. P., *J. Biol. Chem.*, **100**, 397 (1933).
138. Hoagland, D. R., and Lieb, L. L., *J. Biol. Chem.*, **23**, 287 (1915).
139. Atsuki, K., and Tomoda, Y., *J. Soc. Chem. Ind. Japan*, **29**, 509 (1926); *Chem. Abstracts*, **21**, 115 (1927).
140. Schmidt, E., and Vocke, F., *Ber.*, **59**, 1585 (1926).
141. Cretcher, L. H., and Nelson, W. L., *Science*, **67**, 537 (1928).
142. Nelson, W. L., and Cretcher, L. H., *J. Am. Chem. Soc.*, **51**, 1914 (1929).
143. Nelson, W. L., and Cretcher, L. H., *J. Am. Chem. Soc.*, **52**, 2130 (1930).
144. Nelson, W. L., and Cretcher, L. H., *J. Am. Chem. Soc.*, **54**, 3409 (1932).
145. Bird, Gladys M., and Haas, P., *Biochem. J.*, **25**, 403 (1931).
146. Miwa, T., *J. Chem. Soc. Japan*, **51**, 738 (1930).
147. Hansen, J. E., and Káss, E., *Acta Path. Microbiol. Scand.*, **23**, 140 (1946); *Chem. Abstracts*, **40**, 6119 (1946).
148. Thjøtta, Th., and Kass, E., *Avhandl. Norske Videnkaps—Akad.*, *Oslo.*, *Mat.—Naturv. Klasse*, No. 5, 1 (1945); *Chem. Abstracts*, **41**, 791 (1947).
149. Tseng, C. K., *Colloid. Chem.*, **6**, 629 (1946).
150. Kooiman, P., *Biochim. et Biophys. Acta*, **13**, 338 (1954).
151. Lunde, G., Heen, E., and Öy, E., *Kolloid-Z.*, **83**, 196 (1938).
152. Heen, E., *Tidskr. Kjemi og Bergvesen*, **17**, 127 (1937); *Chem. Abstracts*, **32**, 5792 (1938).
153. Hirst, E. L., Jones, J. K. N., and Jones, Winifred O., *J. Chem. Soc.*, 1880 (1939).
154. Black, W. A. P., Cornhill, W. J., and Dewar, E. T., *J. Sci. Food Agric.*, **3**, 542 (1952).
155. Lucas, H. J., and Stewart, W. T., *J. Am. Chem. Soc.*, **62**, 1792 (1940).
156. Chanda, S. K., Hirst, E. L., Percival, E. G. V., and Ross, A. G., *J. Chem. Soc.*, 1833 (1952).
157. Astbury, W. T., *Nature*, **155**, 667 (1945).
158. Palmer, K. J., and Hartzog, M. B., *J. Am. Chem. Soc.*, **67**, 1865 (1945).
159. Schmiedeberg, J. E. O., *Tagebl. d. Naturforscherversamenlung*, **231** (1885).
160. Colin, H., and Ricard, P., *Bull. soc. chim. biol.*, **12**, 1392 (1930).
161. Parke, Mary, *J. Marine Biol. Assoc.* (United Kingdom), **27**, 651 (1948).
162. Black, W. A. P., and Dewar, E. T., *J. Marine Biol. Assoc.* (United Kingdom), **27**, 673 (1948).
163. Barry, V. C., *Sci. Proc. Roy. Dublin Soc.*, **21**, 615 (1938).
164. Black, W. A. P., Cornhill, W. J., Dewar, E. T., and Woodward, F. N., *J. Applied Chem.*, **1**, 505 (1951).
165. Krefting, A., *Tidsskr. Kemi, Farm. Terapi*, 151 (1909); *Pharmacia*, **6**, 151 (1910); *Chem. Abstracts*, **4**, 460 (1910).

166. Torup, S., *Tidsskr. Kemi, Farm. Terapi*, 153 (1909); *Pharmacia*, **6**, 153 (1910); *Chem. Abstracts*, **4**, 460 (1910).
167. Kylin, H., *Z. physiol. Chem.*, **83**, 171 (1913).
168. Kylin, H., *Z. physiol. Chem.*, **94**, 337 (1915).
169. Colin, H., and Ricard, P., *Compt. rend.*, **188**, 1449 (1929).
170. Nisizawa, K., *J. Chem. Soc. Japan*, **60**, 1020 (1939).
171. Connell, J. J., Hirst, E. L., and Percival, E. G. V., *J. Chem. Soc.*, 3494 (1950).
172. Percival, E. G. V., and Ross, A. G., *J. Chem. Soc.*, 720 (1951).
173. Black, W. A. P., Dewar, E. T., and Woodward, F. N., *J. Sci. Food Agr.*, **4**, 58 (1953).
174. Gruzewska, Z., *Compt. rend.*, **170**, 521 (1920); **173**, 52 (1921).
175. Davis, A. R., *Ann. Missouri Botan. Garden*, **2**, 771 (1915).
176. Barry, V. C., *Sci. Proc. Roy. Dublin Soc.*, **22**, 423 (1941).
177. Dillon, T., and O'Colla, P., *Nature*, **166**, 67 (1950); *Chemistry* and *Industry*, 111 (1951).
178. Kylin, H., *Kgl. Fysiograf Sällskap. Lund Förh.*, **14**, 226 (1944); *Chem. Abstracts*, **42**, 8891 (1948).
179. Peat, S., Thomas, Gwen J., and Whelan, W. J., *J. Chem. Soc.*, 722 (1952).
180. Freudenberg, K., and Oertzen, K. v., *Ann.*, **574**, 37 (1951).
181. Bächli, P., and Percival, E. G. V., *J. Chem. Soc.*, 1243 (1952).
182. Barry, V. C., *J. Chem. Soc.*, 578 (1942).
183. Peat, S., Whelan, W. J., and Lawley, H. G., *Biochem. J.*, **54**, *Proc.*, xxxiii (1953).
184. Peat, S., Whelan, W. J., and Lawley, H. G., *Chemistry* and *Industry*, **35**, (1955).
185. Peat, S., Whelan, W. J., Lawley, H. G., and Evans, J. M., *Biochem. J.*, **61**, *Proc.*, x (1955).
186. Unrau, A., and Smith, F., *Chemistry* and *Industry*, 330 (1957).
187. Abdel-Akher, M., Hamilton, J. K., and Smith, F., *J. Am. Chem. Soc.*, **73**, 4691 (1951).
188. Corbett, W. M., Kenner, J., and Richards, G. N., *Chemistry* and *Industry*, 462 (1953).
189. Gruzewska, Z., *Bull. soc. chim. biol.*, **5**, 216 (1923).
190. Scheurer, P. G., and Smith, F., *Anal. Chem.*, **27**, 1616 (1955).
191. Friedlaender, M. H. G., Cook, W. H., and Martin, W. G., *Biochim. et Biophys. Acta*, **14**, 136 (1954).
192. Broatch, W. N., and Greenwood, C. T., *Chemistry* and *Industry*, 1015 (1956).
193. Black, W. A. P., and Dewar, E. T., *J. Sci. Food Agric.*, **5**, 176 (1954).
194. Günther, A., and Tollens, B., *Ber.*, **23**, 2585 (1890).
195. Nelson, W. L., and Cretcher, L. H., *J. Biol. Chem.*, **94**, 147 (1931).
196. Lunde, G., Heen, E., and Oy, E., *Z. physiol Chem.*, **247**, 189 (1937).
197. Black, W. A. P., Dewar, E. T., and Woodward, F. N., *J. Sci. Food Agr.*, **3**, 122 (1952).
198. Percival, E. G. V., and Ross, A. G., *J. Chem. Soc.*, 717 (1950).
199. Nicolet, B. H., and Shinn, L. A., *J. Am. Chem. Soc.*, **63**, 1456 (1941).
200. Fromageot, C., and Heitz, P., *Mikrochim. Acta*, **3**, 52 (1938).
201. Black, W. A. P., Cornhill, W. J., Dewar, E. T., Percival, E. G. V., and Ross, A. G., *J. Soc. Chem. Ind.*, **69**, 317 (1950).
202. Conchie, J., and Percival, E. G. V., *J. Chem. Soc.*, 827 (1950).

203. O'Neill, A. N., J. Am. Chem. Soc., 76, 5074 (1954).
204. Dillon, T., Kristensen, K., and Oh'Eochdha, C., Proc. Roy. Irish Acad., 55B, 189 (1953).
205. Plant, M. M. T., and Johnson, E. D., Nature, 147, 390 (1941).
206. Norris, F. W., Ann. Repts. Chem. Soc. (London), 39, 235 (1942).
207. Brading, Joyce, W. E. Georg-Plant, M. M. T., (Mrs.), and Hardy, Doreen M., J. Chem. Soc., 319 (1954).
208. Miyake, S., Hayashi, K., and Takimo, Y., J. Soc., Trop. Agr., Taihoku Imp. Univ., 10, 232 (1938); Chem. Abstracts, 33, 8239 (1939).
209. Miyake, S., and Hayaski, K., J. Soc., Trop. Agr. Taihoku Imp. Univ., 11, 269 (1939); Chem. Abstracts, 34, 6933 (1940).
210. Kylin, H., Kgl. Fysiograf. Sällskap. Lund, Förh., 16, 102 (1946); Chem. Abstracts, 41, 6605 (1947).
211. Black, W. A. P., Ann. Repts. Chem. Soc. (London), 50, 322 (1953).
212. Mori, T., Advances in Carbohydrate Chem., 8, 315 (1953).
213. Kylin, H., Kgl. Fysiograf. Sällskap. Lund, Förh., 13, 51 (1943); Chem. Abstracts, 42, 4245 (1948).
214. Colin, H., and Augier, J., Compt. rend., 197, 423 (1933).
215. Colin, H., Compt. rend., 199, 968 (1934).
216. Fleming, I. D., Hirst, E. L., and Manners, D. J., J. Chem. Soc., 2831 (1956).
217. Schumper, F.-W., Ann. sci., nat. Botan., [7], 6, 77 (1887).
218. Kolkwitz, R., Wissenschaftliche Meersuntersuchungen N. F., 4 Abt. Helgoland, 31 (1900).
219. Bruns, E., Flora (Ger.), 79, 159 (1894).
220. Manners, D. J., and Maung, Khin, Chemistry and Industry, 950 (1955).
221. O'Colla, P., Proc. Roy. Irish Acad., 55B, 321 (1953).
222. Barry, V. C., McCormick, Joan E., and Mitchell, P. W. D., J. Chem. Soc., 3692 (1954).
223. Abdel-Akher, M., and Smith, F., J. Am. Chem. Soc., 73, 994 (1951).
224. Cifonelli, J. A., Montgomery, R., and Smith, F., J. Am. Chem. Soc., 78, 2485 (1956).
225. Cifonelli, J. A., Lewis, Bertha A., and Smith, F., unpublished.
226. Kylin, H., Kgl. Fysiograf. Sällskap. Lund. Förh., 13, 64 (1943).
227. Errera, L., Rec. Inst. botan., T. 1 Bruxelles (1906). (see Mori, T., Advances in Carb. Chem., 8, 350 (1953).
228. Büschli, O., Arch., Protistenk, 1, 41 (1902); Mori, T., Advances in Carb. Chem., 8, 315 (1953).
229. Hegler, R., Jahr. Wiss. Botan., 36, 229 (1901).
230. Fischer, A., Botan. Ztg., 63, 51 (1905).
231. Stanford, E. C. C., J. Soc. Chem. Ind., 4, 518 (1885).
232. Mirande, R., Compt. rend., 156, 475 (1913).
233. Russell-Wells, Barbara, Nature, 133, 651 (1934).
234. Percival, E. G. V., and Ross, A. G., J. Chem. Soc., 3041 (1949).
235. Dillon, T., and O'Tuama, T., Sci. Proc. Roy. Dublin Soc., 21, 147 (1935).
236. Naylor, Gladys, L., and Russell-Wells, Barbara, Ann. Botany (London), 48, 635 (1934).
237. Ricard, P., Bull. soc. chim. biol., 13, 417 (1931).
238. Araki, C., and Hashi, Y., Collected Papers for the Celebration of the Forty-fifth Anniversary of the Founding of Kyoto Technical College 64 (1948).

239. Smith, F., *J. Chem. Soc.*, 584 (1944).
240. Araki, C., and Arai, K., *Bull. Chem. Soc., Japan*, **30**, 287 (1957).
241. Barry, V. C., Halsall, T. G., Hirst, E. L., and Jones, J. K. N., *J. Chem. Soc.*, 1468 (1949).
242. Bell, D. J., and Manners, D. J., *J. Chem. Soc.*, 1145 (1954).
243. Clingman, A. L., Nunn, J. R., and Stephen, A. M., *J. Chem. Soc.*, 197 (1957).
244. Hirase, S., *Bull. Chem. Soc. Japan*, **30**, 68 (1957); *Chem. Abstracts*, **52**, 9479 (1958).
245. Araki, C., and Hirase, S., *Bull. Chem. Soc. Japan*, **29**, 770 (1956).
246. Hirase, S., Araki, C., and Ito, T., *Bull. Chem. Soc. Japan*, **29**, 985 (1956).
247. Hirase, S., *Bull. Chem. Soc. Japan*, **30**, 70 (1957).
248. Hirase, S., *Bull. Soc. Chem. Japan*, **30**, 75 (1957); *Chem. Abstracts*, **52**, 9481 (1958).
249. Nunn, J. R., *S. African Ind. Chemist*, **10**, 236 (1956).
250. Fisher, I. S., and Percival, Elizabeth, *J. Chem. Soc.*, 2666 (1957).
251. Barry, V. C., and McCormick, Joan E., *J. Chem. Soc.*, 2777 (1957).
252. Barry, V. C., and Mitchell, P. W. D., *J. Chem. Soc.*, 4020 (1954).
253. Gran, H. H., *Bergens Museums Aarbog*, **2**, 1 (1902).
254. *Duke University Marine Station Bulletin No. 3*, Duke University Press (1946). (Utilization of Seaweeds from the South Atlantic and Gulf Coasts for Agar and its Decomposition by Bacteria).
255. Anderson, F. B., Hirst, E. L., and Manners, D. J., *Chemistry and Industry*, 1178 (1957).
256. Unrau, A., Goldstein, I. J., and Smith, F., *Chemistry and Industry*, 124 (1959).
257. Mackie, I. M., and Percival, Elizabeth, *J. Chem. Soc.*, 1151 (1959).
258. Cronshaw, J., Myers, A., and Preston, R. D., *Biochim. et Biophys. Acta*, **27**, 89 (1958).
259. Smith, F., and Unrau, A. M., *Chemistry and Industry*, 636 (1959).
260. Hirst, E. L., *Third International Seaweed Symposium*, Galway (1958) p. 52.

CHAPTER 15

STRUCTURE OF GUMS BY SPECIFIC
IMMUNOLOGICAL REACTIONS

Injection of pneumococcus organisms into an animal produces antibodies which are proteinaceous in character. The pneumococcus organisms contain a polysaccharide which is characteristic of the particular organism injected into the animal and when minute amounts of this polysaccharide are mixed with the serum prepared from the blood of the injected animal a precipitate is formed. The polysaccharide is said to give a precipitin reaction with the antipneumococcus serum.

Investigations into the reaction between the specific pneumococcus polysaccharide and the protein in the anti-pneumococcus serum by means of cross reactions using structurally related polysaccharides, has revealed that the polysaccharide has certain specific structural features concerning the nature, number, and arrangement of the sugar building units and the glycosidic bonds by which these units are mutually joined; terminal nonreducing groups play an important role in the antigen-antibody reaction (36,56). Other polysaccharides of totally different origin having some, but not necessarily all, structural features in common with the pneumococcus polysaccharide will also react to some extent with the anti-pneumococcus serum (43–51,53–55). Inhibition studies with oligosaccharides have recently been shown to aid in the determination of the structure of certain polysaccharides and mucopolysaccharides (60).

The behavior of gum arabic, agar, and cherry gum as antigens has been examined (1). It has also been shown that gum arabic is ineffective in neutralizing anti H agglutinins in serum (2) and that it inhibits agglutination of chicken red blood corpuscles by influenza A virus (3). Gum arabic also lessens the severity of infection of mice with pneumonia virus (4). In addition, the binding capacity of normal and immune human and animal serum globulins with gum arabic has been examined (6). It has also been found that gum arabic does not produce antibodies *in vitro* (5). These and other classical studies in immuno-chemistry have reached a stage at the present time when they can be of immense value in structural studies of polysaccharides of all kinds (35,62).

The amount of reaction taking place between a polysaccharide and a serum, measured by the quantity of protein in the precipitate is roughly proportional to the structural similarity (7-10,35) between the polysaccharide under examination and the specific polysaccharide. It is this aspect of the precipitin reaction that is extremely valuable in the elucidation of the structure of gums and mucilages and indeed of a number of other polysaccharides (57,58).

Type XIV pneumococcus polysaccharide contains three molecular proportions of D-galactose and one molecular proportion of N-acetyl-D-glucosamine. Certain other galactose-containing polysaccharides will also react with the Type XIV immune serum, the amount of precipitate formed being proportional to the structural similarity between the galactose portions of the polysaccharides and of the Type XIV polysaccharide. Among the galactose-containing polysaccharides that give a positive reaction with Type XIV antipneumococcus serum are the following (11): gum arabic, degraded gum arabic, the gum of *Acacia pycnantha*, the arabogalactans of Jeffrey pine and larch, the galactan of the seeds of *Strychnos nux vomica*, karaya gum, the galactomannans of the seeds of the carob bean (*Ceratonia siliqua* L.), guar (*Cyamopsis* sp.), Kentucky coffee bean (*Gymnocladus dioica*), the galactose containing polysaccharide, "jellose", extracted from the seeds of the Tamarind tree (*Tamarindus indica*) and the galactan extracted from ox-lung tissue. From the present knowledge of the structural requirements for a positive precipitin reaction, it is possible to deduce that all the polysaccharides just mentioned have some structural feature in common with the Type XIV polysaccharide.

The observation that ox lung galactan reacts about three times more than the Tamarind seed gum with Type XIV antipneumococcus serum indicates that the former polysaccharide is more like the Type XIV pneumococcus polysaccharide than the latter (12). The ox lung galactan was also found to give a precipitate with Type II immune serum. Since Type II was known to contain D-glucuronic acid, but no D-galactose, it was concluded that the beef lung galactan probably contained D-glucuronic acid. Early structural studies on this polysaccharide had not revealed any glucuronic acid, but re-examination of the hydrolyzate of beef lung galactan using the sensitive paper chromatographic techniques showed that the polysaccharide did indeed contain a small amount of D-glucuronic acid. Further confirmation of the presence of D-glucuronic acid in the ox lung galactan was provided by the fact that reduction of the uronic acid residues, after esterification, with sodium borohydride followed by hydrolysis gave glucose (12). Still further investigation revealed that the ratio of uronic acid to galactose in the lung galactan of 1 : 50 did not hold for the ratio of uronic acid to galactose in the polysaccharide fraction precipitated with Type II and Type XIV pneumococcus sera. From this it has been concluded that the lung galactan is a mixture of two polysaccharides, a view in agreement with the results of previous electrophoretic studies (13). The quantitative immunological data are recorded (12) in Table 60.

TABLE 60. GALACTOSE AND GLUCURONIC ACID IN SPECIFIC
PRECIPITATES FROM LUNG GALACTAN AND TYPE XIV AND
TYPE II ANTIPNEUMOCOCCAL SERA

(1 mg. lung galactan + 1 ml. Type XIV antiserum; 1 mg. lung galactan + 1 ml.
Type II antiserum)

Substance	Galactan ppted./ml. antiserum (ug.)	Ratio of glucuronic acid to galactose in the ppt.
Type XIV ppt.	205	1.2 : 150
Type II ppt.	57	6.0 : 150
Original galactan	...	2.8 : 150

Little is known of the structure of the Type XIV pneumococcus polysaccharide itself except, as stated above, that it is composed of D-galactose and N-acetyl-D-glucosamine in the ratio of 3 : 1, but since "jellose" or tamarind gum, which also reacts with Type XIV antiserum, possesses only terminal nonreducing D-galactopyranose units (14), it is possible to deduce that at least some of the galactose units in the type XIV polysaccharide will likewise be found in terminal nonreducing positions (12).

This type of approach to the problem of the structure of polysaccharides including gums, has been extended to a number of D-galactose-containing polysaccharides (11).

Since Type XIV antipneumococcus serum cross reacts with ox-lung galactan, which has been shown by the chemical methods using periodate oxidation and methylation (13) to contain 1 $\longrightarrow$ 3 and 1 $\longrightarrow$ 6 glycosidic bonds, it was predicted and verified that this same Type XIV serum would react with gum arabic which is also known to contain the same type of glycosidically linked galactose residues (15,16). It was also possible to conclude that most of the labile arabofuranose units in gum arabic are not attached to the internal galactose units joined by the 1 $\longrightarrow$ 3 and 1 $\longrightarrow$ 6 bonds for the reason that the degraded gum which contains all of the galactose units of the original gum except those which are removed in the form of the labile disaccharide, 3-O-D-galactopyranosyl-L-arabinose, proved to be about as effective as the parent gum in reacting with Type XIV antiserum (11).

Type II serum reacts much more with degraded arabic acid than with the parent gum (52) and it has been possible to trace this to the fact that, in the degraded gum (40), as in the Type II polysaccharide (37), glucuronic acid residues occupy nonreducing terminal positions, whereas in the parent gum they are substituted with arabinose and/or rhamnose units and hence not available for reaction with Type II serum (38). Another interesting observation is that the Acacia pycnantha gum, which contains about one third of the glucuronic acid content of gum arabic, precipitates less than a third of the antibody from Type II serum; this shows that the terminal glucuronic acid residues play a major role in the precipitin reaction and also that the reaction can be used to determine the presence of terminal uronic acid residues in gums and mucilages.

The precipitate formed when gum arabic reacts with Type II pneumococcus serum has been found to contain only a third as much rhamnose as the parent gum (38,39). This evidence of the heterogeneity of gum arabic is based on the results given in Table 61 wherein it may be seen that the ratio of galactose to rhamnose is quite different for the original gum and the gum recovered (35,38) from the precipitate with Type II serum.

TABLE 61. PERCENTAGE COMPOSITION OF GUM ARABIC AND ITS PRECIPITATE WITH TYPE II ANTIPNEUMOCOCCUS HORSE SERUM 1054 (38)

Polysaccharide	Arabinose	Galactose	Rhamnose	Glucuronic acid	Galactose / Rhamnose
Gum arabic	30	52	12	15	4.3
Gum recovered from the specific precipitate	39	48	3	11	16

These results illustrating the inhomogeneity of gum arabic are supported by electrophoretic studies in solution (41) and on glass-fiber paper (42).

Extension of these studies has also shown how it is possible to use the immunological reaction to prove the presence of rhamnose residues in other gums and mucilages (35).

The presence of galactose units linked through C_1 and C_6, and through C_1, C_3 and C_6 in the arabogalactans of Jeffrey pine and larch, previously established by methylation studies (17,18), is also supported by the immunological studies which showed that both these polysaccharides gave a positive test with Type XIV antiserum.

The galactan of *Strychnos nux vomica*, shown (19) to contain one non-reducing end group for every 28 D-galactose units and few branching points, was found, as expected, to give a weak positive reaction with Type XIV antiserum.

The precipitin reaction also reveals the close relationship between the galactomannan polysaccharide gums obtained from the seeds of the carob, guar, and Kentucky coffee bean plants. Methylation and periodate studies (20–24,61) have already demonstrated that in all three of these polysaccharides all of the galactose residues occupy terminal nonreducing positions.

The main difference between the three carbohydrate polymers is in the ratio of the nonreducing terminal D-galactose units to the nonterminal $1 \longrightarrow 4$ linked D-mannose units, a deduction that is supported by the observation that all react with Type XIV antiserum (11).

Karaya gum from *Cochlospermum gossypium* behaved in an interesting manner when tested with antipneumococcal sera. Since the gum contains equal proportions of L-rhamnose, D-galactose and D-galacturonic acid, of which two thirds of the galactose is present as terminal nonreducing units and the rest linked by $1 \longrightarrow 4$ bonds, it was expected that this gum would give a strong positive reaction with Type XIV antiserum. The reaction, however, though positive, was weaker than expected, as was the case with gum arabic. This apparent anomaly is believed to be due to the interference from the uronic acid residues. That the specificity of the galacturonic acid residues was not related to that of the uronic residues in the capsular polysaccharide of Type I pneumococcus, which also contains galacturonic acid residues, was shown by the fact that karaya gum gave no precipitate when added to Type I antipneumococcus serum.

Some idea of the potential usefulness of the immunological approach to the problem of the structure of polysaccharides is shown by the recent work on dextrans (25). The structures of these gum-like polyglucosans, have been correlated by the precipitin reaction they display with human anti-dextran serum. Although details remain to be worked out, it appears that the high proportion of $1 \longrightarrow 6$ linked terminal nonreducing glucose units is responsible for the precipitin reaction. It is of interest to note that, as in the case of the concanavalin-A - polyglucosan reaction (see below), certain differences in the precipitin reaction were noticed for these glucans, which were otherwise structurally identical from the point of view of chemical tests; these differences have been traced to the possibility that other linkages beside those of the $1 \longrightarrow 6$ type are responsible. In a similar manner $2 \longrightarrow 6$ and $2 \longrightarrow 1$ linked fructans have been distinguished (59).

The phenomenon discussed above is not confined to reactions between pneumococcus polysaccharides and blood group substances (26,27) with the proteins of pneumococcus anti-sera, for it has been found to occur when certain polysaccharides, such as glycogen (28–30), yeast mannan (28,29) and certain dextran polymers (31) are treated with concanavalin-A, a protein from Jack Bean meal (28,29). A similar precipitin reaction is also shown by papain and glycogen (32).

An analogous type of reaction involving glycogen has been observed by other workers (33,34).

The phenomenon discussed above not only serves as an excellent diagnostic method for ascertaining with reasonable certainty the types of linkages and sugar residues present in many polysaccharides including gums, but it will most likely throw new light on the relationship between the molecular architecture of proteins and carbohydrates and also on the manner in which a protein comes into contact with a polysaccharide, as for example in enzymic reactions. It is also notable that many of the reactions can be carried out with minute amounts of material. It is conceivable that the reactions may lead to the separation and identification of closely related polysaccharides which is something that is not readily achieved with other methods. The availability of pure material would be of incalculable value in studies on the fine structure of polysaccharides of all types. Purification of certain proteins may also be effected by these techniques. The carbohydrate chemist would do well to make full use of the new techniques developed by the immunologists.

REFERENCES

1. Partridge, S. M., and Morgan, W. T. J., *Brit. J. Exptl. Path.*, **23**, 84 (1942).
2. Watkins, W. M., and Morgan, W. T. J., *Nature*, **169**, 825 (1952).
3. Green, R. H., and Woolley, D. W., *J. Exptl. Med.*, **86**, 55 (1947).
4. Horsfall, F. L., and McCarthy, M., *J. Exptl. Med.*, **85**, 623 (1947).
5. Kuzin, A. M., and Nevraeva, N. A., *Biokhimiya*, **12**, 49 (1947).
6. Przylecki, St. J. V., *Kolloid-Z.*, **85**, 251 (1938).
7. Kabat, E. A., and Mayer, M. M., *Experimental Immunochemistry*, C. C. Thomas, Springfield, Ill., 1948.
8. Burger, M., *Bacterial Polysaccharides*, C. C. Thomas, Springfield, Ill., 1950.
9. Boyd, W. C., *Fundamentals of Immunology*, Interscience Publishers, New York, 1956.
10. Landsteiner, K., *The Specificity of Serological Reactions*, C. C. Thomas, Springfield, Ill., 1936.
11. Heidelberger, M., *J. Am. Chem. Soc.*, **77**, 4308 (1958).

12. Heidelberger, M., Dische, Z., Neely, W. Brock, and Wolfrom, M. L., *J. Am. Chem. Soc.*, **77**, 3511 (1955).
13. Wolfrom, M. L., Sutherland, G., and Schlamowitz, M., *J. Am. Chem. Soc.*, **74**, 4883 (1952).
14. White, E. V., and Rao, P. S., *J. Am. Chem. Soc.*, **75**, 2617 (1953).
15. Smith, F., *J. Chem. Soc.*, 1035 (1940).
16. Smith, F., and Spriestersbach, D., *Abstracts 128th A.C.S. Meeting, Minneapolis, Minn.* (1955).
17. Wadman, W. H., Anderson, A. B., and Hassid, W. Z., *J. Am. Chem. Soc.*, **76**, 4097 (1954).
18. Campbell, W. G., Hirst, E. L., and Jones, J. K. N., *J. Chem. Soc.*, 774 (1948).
19. Andrews, P., Hough, L., and Jones, J. K. N., *J. Chem. Soc.*, 806 (1954).
20. Hirst, E. L., and Jones, J. K. N., *J. Chem. Soc.*, 1278 (1948).
21. Smith, F., *J. Am. Chem. Soc.*, **70**, 3249 (1948).
22. Ahmed, Z. F., and Whistler, R. L., *J. Am. Chem. Soc.*, **72**, 2524 (1950).
23. Swanson, J. W., *J. Am. Chem. Soc.*, **71**, 1510 (1949).
24. Larson, E. B., and Smith, F., *J. Am. Chem. Soc.*, **77**, 429 (1955).
25. Allen, P. Z., and Kabat, E. A., *J. Am. Chem. Soc.*, **78**, 1890 (1956).
26. Goebel, W. F., Beeson, P. B., and Hoagland, C. L., *J. Biol. Chem.*, **129**, 455 (1939).
27. Beeson, P. B., and Goebel, W. F., *J. Exptl. Med.*, **70**, 239 (1939).
28. Sumner, J. B., and O'Kane, D. J., *Enzymologia*, **12**, 251 (1948).
29. Cifonelli, J. A., and Smith, F., *Anal. Chem.*, **27**, 1639 (1955).
30. Cifonelli, J. A., Montgomery, R., and Smith, F., *J. Am. Chem. Soc.*, **78**, 2485 (1956).
31. Cifonelli, J. A., and Smith, F., *J. Am. Chem. Soc.*, **79**, 5055 (1957).
32. Ewe, G. E., *J. Am. Pharm. Assoc.*, **30**, 18 (1941).
33. Plyshevskaya, E. G., and Rozenfel'd, E. L., *Doklady akad. Nauk U.S.S.R.*, **94**, 1141 (1954); *Chem. Abstracts*, **48**, 8835 (1954); *Biokhimya*, **19**, 161 (1954).
34. Pillemer, L., Schoenberg, M. D., Blum, Livia, and Wurz, Leona, *Science*, **122**, 545 (1955).
35. Heidelberger, M., *Ann. Rev. Biochem.*, **25**, 641 (1956).
36. Kabat, E. A., *J. Am. Chem. Soc.*, **76**, 3709 (1954).
37. Butler, K., and Stacey, M., *J. Chem. Soc.*, 1537 (1955).
38. Heidelberger, M., and Adams, J., *J. Exptl. Med.*, **103**, 189 (1956).
39. Heidelberger, M., Adams, J., and Dische, Z., *J. Am. Chem. Soc.*, **78**, 2853 (1956).
40. Smith, F., *J. Chem. Soc.*, 1724 (1939).
41. Joubert, F. J., *J. South African Chem. Institute*, **7** [2], 107 (1954).
42. Lewis, Bertha A., and Smith, F., unpublished.
43. Heidelberger, M., and Goebel, W. F., *J. Biol. Chem.*, **74**, 613 (1927).
44. Goebel, W. F., *J. Biol. Chem.*, **74**, 619 (1927).
45. Marrack, J., and Carpenter, B. R., *Brit. J. Exptl. Path.*, **19**, 53 (1938).
46. Heidelberger, M., Kendall, F. E., *J. Exptl. Med.*, **50**, 809 (1929).
47. Heidelberger, M., Kendall, F. E., and Soo Hoo, C. M., *J. Exptl. Med.*, **58**, 137 (1933).
48. Heidelberger, M., and Kendall, F. E., *J. Exptl. Med.*, **61**, 559 (1935).
49. Heidelberger, M., Kabat, E. A., and Shrivastava, D. L., *J. Exptl. Med.*, **65**, 487 (1937).

50. Heidelberger, M., Kabat, E. A., and Mayer, M., *J. Exptl. Med.*, **75**, 35 (1942).
51. Heidelberger, M., and Kendall, F. E., *J. Exptl. Med.*, **61**, 563 (1935).
52. Heidelberger, M., Avery, O. T., and Goebel, W. F., *J. Exptl. Med.*, **49**, 847 (1929).
53. Goebel, W. F., *J. Exptl. Med.*, **64**, 29 (1936).
54. Goebel, W. F., and Hotchkiss, R. D., *J. Exptl. Med.*, **66**, 191 (1937).
55. Woolf, B., *Proc. Roy. Soc.*, London, Series B, **130**, *60 (1941)*.
56. Kabat, E. A., *Blood Group Substance: Their Chemistry* and *Immunochemistry*, Academic Press, New York, 1956.
57. McCarty, M., *J. Exptl. Med.*, **104**, 629 (1956).
58. McCarty, M., and Lancefield, R. C., *J. Exptl. Med.*, **102**, 11 (1955).
59. Allen, P. Z., and Kabat, E. A., *J. Exptl. Med.*, **105**, 383 (1957).
60. Kabat, E. A., *Chemistry* and *Biology of Mucopolysaccharides*, Ciba Foundation Symposium, 42 (1958).
61. Rafigue, R. M., and Smith, F., *J. Am. Chem. Soc.*, **72**, 4634 (1950).
62. Heidelberger, M., and Rebers, P. A., *J. Am. Chem. Soc.*, **80**, 116 (1958); Heidelberger, M., Jahrmärker, H., Björklund, B., and Adams, J., *J. Immunol.*, **78**, 419 (1957).

CHAPTER 16

SYNTHETIC GUMS AND GUM DERIVATIVES

In order to gain some understanding of the properties of natural gums, it is of interest to note the structure and behavior of certain synthetic polymers which display gum-like properties.

Among the industrially important polymers is poly(vinyl) acetate, prepared by polymerization of vinyl acetate. Saponification of polyvinyl acetate gives poly(vinyl) alcohol, a material which forms viscous gum-like solutions in water. The constitution of this polyhydroxy compound is characterized by structural regularity, the hydroxyl groups being attached to alternate carbon atoms. The linear molecules of poly(vinyl) alcohol are oriented so that pairs of chains are linked through hydroxyl groups by hydrogen bonds (2). It is this rather close molecular association which gives rise to the gum-like properties.

Certain structurally related poly(acryl)amides (3), the corresponding poly-(N-methylolacryl)amide and poly(vinyl)pyrrolidone, behave in a similar manner and give viscous mucilaginous solutions which find use as soil conditioners, dye additives and sizes in the natural and synthetic textile industry.

The parent polymer, poly(acryl)amide (CCCLXXV), is made by the vinyl polymerization of acrylamide. The material is a white powder which dissolves in water to give solutions containing up to 17 percent poly(acryl)-amide. The solubility of polyacrylamide does not decrease as the temperature is raised, as is the case with Methocel and, unlike those of a number of the natural gums, solutions of it are stable. Moreover, solutions containing poly(acryl)amide are not sensitive to ionic systems including acids and alkalis.

$$CH_2 = CH \rightarrow \left[CH_2 - CH \right]_n \rightarrow \left[CH_2 - CH \right]_n \quad \left[CH_2 - CH \right]_n$$
$$\quad\; CONH_2 \qquad\quad CONH_2 \qquad\qquad NH_2 \qquad\qquad COOH$$

$$\text{(CCCLXXV)} \qquad\qquad \text{(CCCLXXVI)} \qquad\qquad \text{(CCCLXXVII)}$$

Treatment of (CCCLXXV) with sodium hypochlorite (120), according to the usual Hofmann reaction, transforms some of the amide groups to amino

476

groups. This affords a cationic polymer (CCCLXXVI), a water-soluble product which improves sizing of paper and increases its wet strength. Complexes with inorganic ions such as copper, cobalt and chromium have a similar beneficial effect on paper.

Partial hydrolysis of poly(acryl)amide with alkali transforms some of the amide groups to carboxyl groups thus producing an anionic polymer containing the group (CCCLXXVII) (122). These anionic polymers form good flocculating agents for suspensions of clays (123) and they have been recommended as soil stabilizers and as a suspending agent in making concrete (121).

These synthetic gum-like polymers appear to be worthy of examination as substitutes for the natural gums in many industrial applications.

Partially Alkylated Derivatives of Cellulose

When cellulose is treated with alkali and an alkyl halide or sulfate under controlled conditions one to three alkyl groups may be introduced per glucose residue. Usually the cellulose is pretreated with sodium hydroxide to give alkali-cellulose which is then alkylated with such reagents as methyl sulfate (1,4,5) or methyl chloride to give O-methylcellulose (Methocel); treatment with ethyl sulfate or ethyl chloride (6,7) yields O-ethylcellulose. In other processes the cellulose is swelled with such reagents as alkaline copper hydroxide (8–10), the quarternary ammonium hydroxides (11,12), or liquid ammonia (13). Another procedure that has been extensively used on a small scale is to alkylate the cellulose in the form of a suitable derivative such as the acetate in an organic solvent (15). Multiple stage alkylation (14) makes the most efficient use of the alkylating agent.

The solubility of these alkyl derivatives of cellulose depends largely upon the degree of substitution (DS). O-Methylcelluloses with a DS of 0.1 to 0.38 are soluble in dilute (4 to 8 per cent) sodium hydroxide at freezing temperatures (15). With a DS between 0.4 to 0.6 the products are soluble in 4 to 8 per cent sodium hydroxide at room temperature (4,16). O-Methylcellulose becomes soluble in cold water when the DS is between 1.3 and 2.6 (17). As the degree of substitution approaches 2.6 and is increased above this figure the methylated cellulose becomes soluble in organic solvents. The O-methylcelluloses which are soluble in water are precipitated when the solutions are heated (18) and the typical three dimensional gel structure is formed as the hydrated O-methylcellulose molecules become dehydrated and move close enough to each other to form hydrogen bonds. These remarks refer to O-methylcelluloses prepared in a certain way such as methylation of alkali cellulose. Products prepared by the methylation of cellulose in other ways, for example, from sodium cupricellulose, display somewhat different properties. These differences have been correlated with differences in the uniformity of methyl substitution along the cellulose chains. One explanation given for this phenomenon is that a comparatively small number of water molecules attached to a uniformly substituted linear molecule will effect complete separation of it from an adjacent molecule, whereas a relatively large number of water molecules will be needed to separate non-uniformly substituted linear molecules of cellulose (19,20).

This negative solubility coefficient referred to above has been noted for many methylated polysaccharides including the gums and mucilages and in certain unmethylated carbohydrate polymers, for example Iles glucomannan (from *Amorphophallus oncophyllus*) (21). The water-soluble types of O-methylcellulose have been subjected to a great deal of investigation from a practical standpoint and as a result they are replacing the natural gums for certain purposes in industry, in pharmaceuticals and in textile printing (19). O-Methylcellulose preparations can be made to simulate almost all the natural gums from the standpoint of viscosity.

O-Ethyl derivatives of cellulose are usually made from alkali cellulose by the action of excess ethyl chloride under pressure at 90 to 140° with or without an inert diluent such as benzene, toluene, xylene, alcohols and methyl ethers of various glycols (6,7).

O-Ethylcelluloses like the related O-methylcelluloses usually exhibit uniformity of molecular weight distribution which fact makes these products useful as plastic materials.

As in the case of the methylated derivatives the degree of substitution of the ethyl ethers of cellulose controls their solubility. Between a DS of 0.8 and 1.3 the products are soluble in water. Below this figure the derivatives are soluble only in sodium hydroxide solutions and above it the products become soluble in organic solvents. Commercial O-ethylcelluloses contain 2.1 to 2.6 ethoxy groups per glucose unit and they are best dissolved in mixtures of polar and non-polar solvents; their properties depend not only on the DS but also upon the uniformity of substitution (22–25). As stated previously for the methyl ethers, uniform substitution depends to a large extent on the preliminary treatment of the cellulose with alkali so as to swell the crystalline regions of cellulose as well as the amorphous regions (32,33).

By treatment of alkali cellulose with ethylene oxide and ethyl chloride the corresponding mixed ether, O-ethyl-O-(hydroxyethyl)-cellulose, is formed. Often referred to as Modocoll, these cellulose derivatives appear to offer industrial possibilities (108–111) in place of certain gums.

Of increasing industrial importance are the O-(carboxymethyl) (26, 28-31,118,127,128) and O-2 (hydroxyethyl) - (27) derivatives of cellulose made by the action of chloracetic acid and ethylene oxide (or 2-chloroethanol), respectively, upon alkalicellulose. The low substituted derivatives of these two types of cellulose ethers can be dispersed in dilute alkali, especially in the cold. Neither derivative is quite as readily accessible in the pure form as the O-methyl derivative, although by suitable mixtures of water and certain organic solvents, such as ethanol (118), the impurities can be eliminated (126). The water-soluble derivatives of O-(hydroxyethyl) cellulose, for example, give solutions which, unlike those of Methocel, do not gel on heating and hence are more difficult to purify on a large scale (25).

O-(Carboxymethyl) celluloses of varying DS display different solubilities and viscosities and by suitably mixing these compounds in the correct proportions viscosities of almost any desired value can be obtained between the two extremes. The viscosity decreases with increase in temperature but the effect is reversible. At high concentrations O-(carboxymethyl) cellulose forms gels which, however, are sensitive to pH and electrolytes. While sterile solutions of O-(carboxymethyl) cellulose are stable they decompose when exposed to air from the action of molds and bacteria although it is to be noted that starch and certain other natural gums, especially those from seeds, are less stable. O-(Carboxymethyl) cellulose can be mixed with other water soluble synthetic and natural polymers, such as starch, gum arabic, gum karaya, guar gum, locust bean gum, gum tragacanth, alginates, gelatine, casein, pectin, poly(vinyl) alcohol, O-methylcellulose, O-(2 hydroxyethyl) cellulose, and sodium polyacrylate. Unlike the natural gums, O-(carboxymethyl) cellulose as its sodium salt is soluble in 50 per cent aqueous ethanol and in 40 per cent aqueous acetone, and with acid the free O-(carboxymethyl)-cellulose precipitates. O-(Carboxymethyl) cellulose which behaves as a weak organic acid is not affected by alkali although being a polyelectrolyte the viscosity of its solution changes. The salts of the heavy metals with the exception of calcium and magnesium chloride precipitate O-(carboxymethyl) cellulose. Solutions of the sodium salt and of the free cellulose glycolic acid form fairly stable films upon evaporation.

Since O-(carboxymethyl) cellulose is a good suspending agent its major uses are found in oil-drilling muds, where it appears to give more stable muds than the natural gums, as a soil suspending agent in synthetic and natural laundry preparations, in the manufacture of ceramics, and also in the food industry. It forms a good adhesive, being particularly useful as a wall-paper paste where poor, wet-tack properties are desirable, as ε size in conjunction with starches and gums, and in a variety of textile finishing operations, enabling cotton weaving to be carried out at lower humidities since it holds moisture better for example than starch preparations. This synthetic "cellulose gum" derivative may also be used in the paper industry as a beater additive, surface sizing, and as a deflocculating agent for cellulose fibers.

In conformity with the observation (129) that polyhydroxy compounds react with acrylamide under the influence of a basic catalyst such as benzyltrimethylammonium iodide to give poly-β-carbamylethyl ethers, cellulose has been found to undergo a similar reaction thus:-

$$\text{Cellulose—OH} + CH_2 = CH \cdot CO \cdot NH_2 \xrightarrow{\text{NaOH}}$$

$$\text{Cellulose—O} \cdot CH_2CH_2 \cdot CONH_2 \rightarrow \text{Cellulose—O—}CH_2CH_2COONa.$$

The resulting 2-carboxyethyl ethers of cellulose dissolve in alkali and in water (130,131) to give viscous colloidal solutions.

Acid-soluble cellulose derivatives are obtained when cellulose is treated with diethylaminoethyl chloride in the presence of 20 per cent sodium hydroxide. The resulting O-(N,N-diethyl-2-aminoethyl)cellulose is soluble in water, 5 per cent sodium hydroxide, 10 per cent hydrochloric acid and 20 per cent acetic acid (135). These derivatives have been found to be useful for the chromatographic separation of proteins including enzymes.

Dextrins

The term "dextrin" usually signifies a product made from various granular starches by the action of heat, with or without the addition of acidic substances. Dextrinization in an inert solvent has also been advocated (132). In the commercial production of starch dextrins, hydrochloric acid is the usual acid catalyst (147). In spite of the accumulated knowledge in the art of their manufacture and the fact that large quantities of dextrins are used as adhesives and as sizes in the textile industry, little is known of the structure of these substances or of the structural changes that take place during the dextrinization reaction. Although produced from starch, their properties are much more like those displayed by such natural gums as gum arabic and mesquite in which there are found a diversity of building sugar units and a variety of glycosidic bonds (see Chapter 11).

During the process of dextrinization of starch the conditions are favorable for hydrolytic degradation and modification of the types of linkages present in the intact parts of the molecule. As dextrinization proceeds the products become increasingly soluble in cold water; the practical limit of dextrinization is reached with those products termed high conversion dextrins (the yellow dextrins) which are completely soluble in water. There are indications that the amylopectin component of starch undergoes dextrinization more readily than the amylose (34,35).

Recent methylation and periodate oxidation studies (37) have shown that the high conversion dextrins are indeed related to the natural gums used for adhesives, insofar as the glycosidic bonds are concerned, for a wide variety of methyl derivatives of glucose have been recognized amongst the cleavage products of the methylated dextrin (see Table 62) (37).

TABLE 62. CLEAVAGE FRAGMENTS OF A METHYLATED CORN STARCH DEXTRIN[a] (37)

O-Methyl-D-Glucose Derivative	Amounts (%)
2,3,4,6-tetra-(CCXXX)	16.5
2,3,6-tri-(CCLXXXVIII)	57.3
2,3,4-tri-(CCLXI)	2.6
2,4,6-tri-(CCCVI)	1.2
2,3-di-(CCXCV)	6.3
2,6-di-(CCXCII)	10.0
3,6-di-(CCCLXXVIII)	3.2
2-mono-(CCCLXXIX)	1.5
3-mono-(CCCLXXX)	0.8
6-mono-(CCCLXXXI)	0.5

(a)These components were separated by column and paper chromatography.

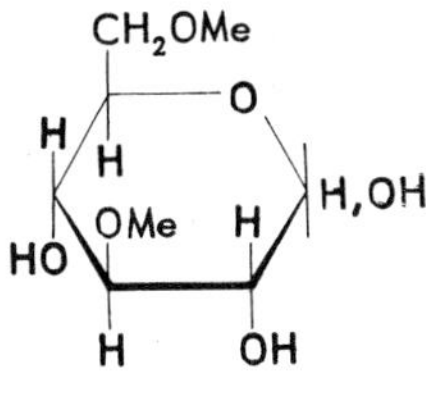

(CCCLXXVIII)

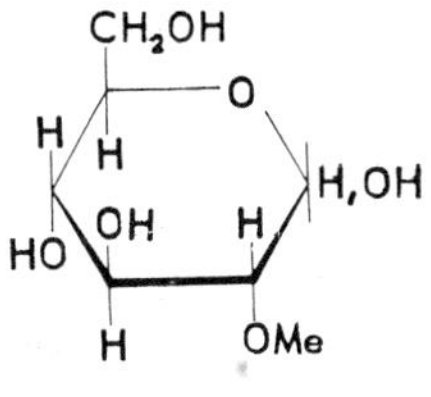

(CCCLXXIX)

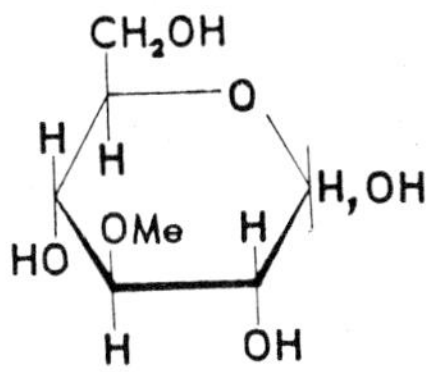

(CCCLXXX)

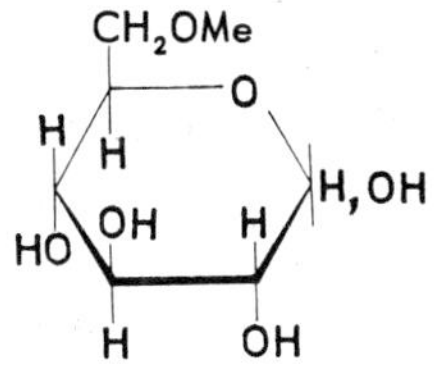

(CCCLXXXI)

A comparison of the products shown in Table 62 with those obtained from methylated starch, namely, 2,3,4,6-tetra- (5 per cent), 2,3,6,-tri- (90 per cent) and 2,3-di-O-methyl-D-glucose (5 per cent) approximately, shows that a profound change takes place in the glycosidic bonds as the starch is converted to the dextrin (35). New bonds are formed, and the dextrin polymer is much more highly branched than the original starch. Periodate oxidation studies involving determination of the formic acid produced and the amount of glucose immune to periodate, determined after reduction and hydrolysis of the polyaldehyde (38), also supported this conclusion (37).

When crystalline D-glucose is heated (140°) in the presence of 5 per cent metaboric acid (55,56) polymerization occurs to give glucans showing $[\alpha]_D$ + 60° approx. in water and a DP of 6 to 20 (134). A methylation study of one of these polymeric products which is stable to salivary α-amylase has revealed that the substance possesses a branched structure with 1 → 6 and 1 → 4 linkages as indicated by the fact that hydrolysis of the methylated polymer was shown by paper chromatography to give: 2,3,4,6-tetra-, 2,3,4-tri-, 2,3,6-tri-, 2,3-di-, 2,6-di- and 2-mono-O-methyl-D-glucose. It was suggested that the nonreducing character of these D-glucose polymers is due to the presence of terminal residues of β-1,6-anhydro-D-glucose (134).

In view of the profound changes that occur in the structure of the starch molecule during dextrinization, it will be of considerable interest to ascertain by chemical and physical methods, such as differential thermal analysis (99), whether the same changes occur under other conditions of dextrinization (cf. 36) and also whether the same changes can be produced in other carbohydrate polymers with a resultant development of gum-like properties. Co-polymerization during dextrinization between two or more gums also seems to be within the bounds of possibility, since dextrinizing amylopectin in the presence of such sugars as D-xylose or D-galactose has been shown to give heterodextrins, namely, xyloglucodextrin and galacto-glucodextrin, respectively (114). Similarly D-glucose has been induced to react with guar galactomannan and with yeast mannan (114). A somewhat similar type of transglycossylation reaction can be brought about by the action of phenyl β-D-glucoside on amylose and on cellulose in the presence of alkali (125). It would appear that the application of these reactions could provide an insight into the effect of substituting side chain sugar units on the properties of carbohydrate polymers.

Little work has been done on the dextrinization of natural gums, but there is some evidence that guar and locust bean gums can be converted into dextrins by the usual roasting process (40). It is also reported that the viscosity of gum arabic falls off when the gum is heated (39). This is not surprising in view of the labile character of the arabofuranose residues which constitute about half the gum molecule (see Chapter 11) and, for the same reason, it is very likely that considerable degradation occurs in this reaction.

Gum-Like Derivatives of Starch

The gum-like properties of the natural gums can be introduced into natural starches by suitable substitution reactions.

Partial methylation has not been extensively utilized, but the introduction of hydroxyethyl groups can be accomplished readily to give products of commercial value (41,109). Hydroxyethylation can be effected by the action of ethylene oxide or 2-chloroethanol on alkali starch (41) or, better still, on granular starch in the presence of controlled amounts of alkali (41) as follows:

$$\text{Starch (ONa)}_n \xrightarrow[\text{or}]{\overset{\displaystyle \overset{O}{\diagup \diagdown}}{CH_2\!-\!CH_2}} \text{Starch (OCH}_2\text{CH}_2\text{OH)}_n$$
$$CH_2OH\!-\!CH_2Cl$$

The introduction of the hydroxyethyl groups makes the starch much more readily dispersible in water and the tendency to gel and to retrograde is also eliminated; such starch derivatives behave like the waxy starches and amylopectin. The properties will, of course, depend on the degree of substitution by hydroxyethyl groups just as the properties of O-methylcellulose depend on the degree of methylation. To impart gum-like properties to starch, it is necessary to introduce a sufficient number of substituent groups to prevent aggregation of the chains of $1 \rightarrow 4\text{-}\alpha\text{-}D\text{-glucose}$ residues. With the chains wedged open, the molecules of water can enter the starch molecule and as a result the chains are able to move about freely thus enabling the molecule to be dispersed. The chains of each starch molecule may become entangled, but they do not associate with each other through hydrogen bonding and aggregation and retrogradation do not take place.

O-(2-Aminoethyl) starches have been prepared by the action of ethylene imine (42). The action of 2-aminoethyl sulfate would presumably bring about the same reaction and might be less dangerous to execute. Such substances are interesting since the starch molecules become cationic in nature, a property which may make them very useful in combining more effectively with other substances of anionic character. The related quarternary alkyl aminoethyl ethers of starch should prove to be of some interest.

The wedging open of the starch chains to prevent association, to induce greater dispersibility in water, and, hence to transform the starches into gum-like polymers, can be effected by small molecular weight fatty acid anhydrides (143). The use of long chain fatty acid anhydrides leads to loss of hydrophilic character so that the derivatives become water repellent (see Appendix I). A similar reaction can be effected with formaldehyde (139,140,142) and with ethylene carbonate (141). Control of the solubility of the starch formaldehyde compound can be effected by varying the degree of substitution; starch adhesives (140) and sizes (142) may be produced in this manner.

Dextran

This substance, obtained by the synthetic action of certain organisms such as *Leuconostoc mesenteroides* on sucrose or *Acetobacter xylinum* on starch dextrins (43) displays the properties of a typical gum. Although it has been investigated chiefly because of its use as a blood extender there is an excellent chance that the manufacturing facilities will also be utilized for producing dextrans and other polymers to be used as a substitute for natural gums when suitable organisms can be isolated.

The synthetic dextran polysaccharide which forms highly viscous solutions even at low concentrations would on the basis of the old definitions be called a mucilage. Some dextran preparations swell and dissolve

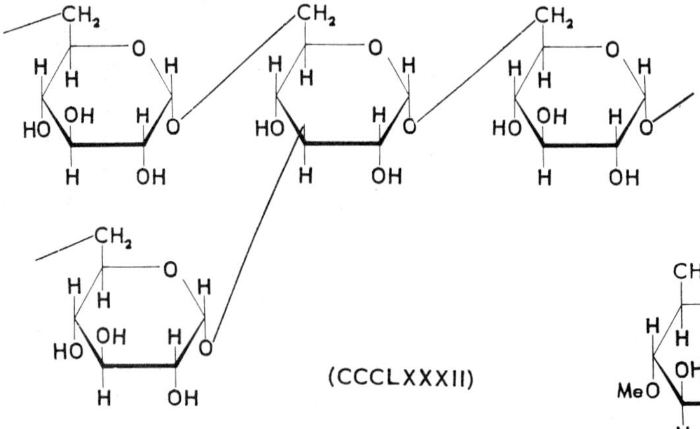

(CCCLXXXII)

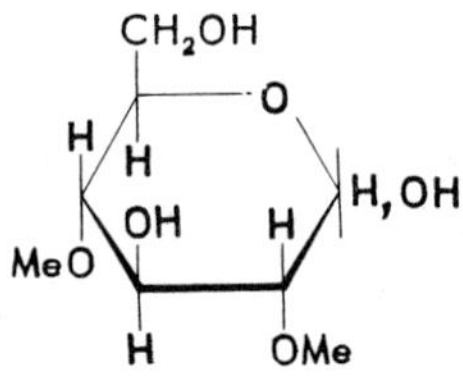

(CCCLXXXIII)

only slowly in water while others dissolve relatively easily. The dextran polysaccharide is a glucan having a highly branched structure. Most of the D-glucopyranose residues are joined by $1 \rightarrow 6$-glycosidic bonds, principally of the α-D-type. The branches are attached to C_3 of certain of these D-glucose residues as in CCCLXXXII.

Evidence in support of this formula has come from methylation studies, which have shown that hydrolysis of the methylated dextran gives rise to 2,3,4-tri-O-methyl-D-glucose (CCLXI) and 2,4-di-O-methyl-D-glucose (CCCLXXXIII) (44–46). The formula has also been supported by periodate oxidation studies in which periodate consumption and the production of formic acid have been determined (47,48). Further supporting evidence has been obtained by subjecting the dextran polysaccharide to oxidation with periodate and then reducing it to the corresponding polyalcohol. Hydrolysis of this latter provides principally glycerol from the $1 \rightarrow 6$ linked residues, and a small amount of D-glucose from the $1 \rightarrow 3$ linked glucose residues located at the branch points in the molecule (38,49). Traces of erythritol were also detected by chromatographic analysis indicating the presence of a small percentage of $1 \rightarrow 4$ linked glucose residues in the dextran molecule (38).

Other Bacterial Gums

The utilization of microorganisms has received too little study as a possible route to synthesis of gums and mucilages (144). The successful manufacture of dextrans of various types for use as blood plasma expanders has already shown that this kind of industrial synthesis can be accomplished. The time is long overdue for some attention to be paid to an extension of some interesting preliminary experiments made by Sanborn (115) who showed that gums could be obtained from the following organisms: *Escherichia leporis, Aerobacter aerogenes, Bacillus vulgatus, Oidium lactis, O. pullulans, Monilia candida, Aspergillus fumigatus, Mucor racemosus,* and *Penicillium guttulosum*. One species of organism resembling *O. lactis* was reported to produce high yields of gum from D-glucose, glycerol, and D-mannose. Cultures in potato decoction and glycerol form in four weeks, from 200 ml. of this medium, growth masses weighing 80 to 100 g. of which 90 per cent was water (115). The pulps made from fleshy bracket fungi can be used to make films and membranes and with suitable solvents rubber-like masses were formed (115,116,119). Certain gum-like growths from fungi have been suggested as leather substitutes (117). More recently fungi with or without a small proportion (10%) of cellulose fibers have been shown to form paper sheets (133).

The extracellular polysaccharide of *Aerobacter aerogenes* (Klebsiellar Type 54) forms highly viscous secretions (145,146) which appear to contain proteinaceous material. The polysaccharide is of the heteroglycan type and contains D-glucose (50 per cent), D-glucuronic acid (29 per cent) and L-fucose (10 per cent). Upon graded hydrolysis it gives cellobiose. The main feature of the polysaccharide is that it possesses a highly branched structure. This is revealed by the fact that hydrolysis of the methylated polysaccharide gave rise to a complicated mixture of methyl sugars. Four methylated sugars, namely, 2,3,4,6-tetra-O-methyl-D-glucose (CCXXX), 2,3-di-O-methyl-D-glucose (CCXCV), 3,5-di-O-methyl-L-fucose (CCCLXXXIV), and 2-O-methyl-L-fucose (CCCLXXXV) were identified by the isolation of crystalline compounds and there was chromatographic evidence for the presence in the mixture of 2,3,4-tri-O-methyl-D-glucose (CCLXI), 2,3,6-tri-O-methyl-D-glucose (CCLXXXVIII), and other tri-O-methyl glucoses, 2,6-di-(CCXCII) and 3,6-di-O-methyl-D-glucose (CCCLXXVIII) and also mono-O-methyl-glucose including the 2-O-(CCCLXXIX) and 3-O-methyl derivative (CCCLXXX). In addition there were indications of tri-O-, di-O- and mono-O-methyl derivatives of D-glucuronic acid.

While fractionation studies were not carried out on the polysaccharide thus making it possible that more than one polysaccharide was present in the original material, there is little doubt, as the authors claim, that the structure of this particular bacterial polysaccharide is by no means simple.

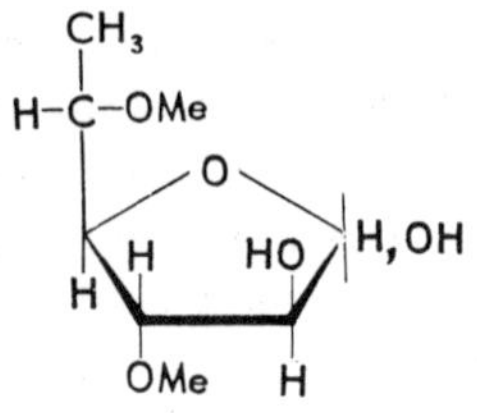

(CCCLXXXIV) 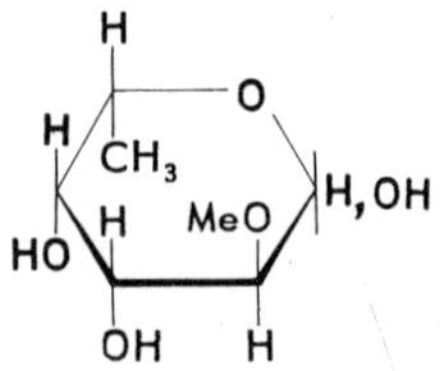   (CCCLXXXV)

In an attempt to solve the problem of the origin of plant gums Smith (124) showed that the various exudates contained a common organism and he came to the conclusion that this organism *Bacterium acaciae*, so named because he isolated it from gum exudates from *Acacia binervata* and *A. penninervis*, was responsible for the gummosis or gum flux of the various trees. This author examined the nutritional requirements of the bacterium and discovered that with a suitable culture medium, such as a potato-agar-sucrose broth, the *B. acaciae* could synthesize a gum in good yield which he claimed belonged to the arabin group (old classification) since upon hydrolysis the gum yielded arabinose and galactose as did gum arabic.   There is little knowledge on the physical properties of this bacterial gum except that the material forms viscous solutions, but it would appear that these investigations are worthy of further study.

Synthetic Polysaccharides

The knowledge that reducing sugars form hemi-acetals with alcohols has been utilized for bringing about condensation of sugars with each other to give polymers.   Based upon the reversion reaction (50) that takes place when sugars are treated with acids, it has been shown that concentration of aqueous solutions of sugars *in vacuo* in the presence of dilute hydrochloric acid or cation exchange resins gives rise to glucans (51,52); a similar reaction takes place when glucose is exposed to an acidic atmosphere (53,54).   This type of polymerization, which can be applied to any reducing sugar and probably to mixtures of sugars and sugar alcohols, may be the forerunner of a number of reactions for synthesizing new gum-like carbohydrate polymers.

Infrared studies (53) of these polymers indicate that many of the glycosidic linkages are of the $1 \rightarrow 6$ type and methylation studies have shown the complex nature of these glucans (51).

Gum-Like Products from Oxidized Polysaccharides

Some gums, such as gum karaya and gum tragacanth disperse slowly in water to give highly viscous mucilaginous solutions.   For some purposes this is a disadvantage and in order to increase solubility and to decrease the viscosity it has been recommended that the gums should be oxidized under controlled conditions with hydrogen peroxide in the presence of sodium hydroxide.   This modification with peroxide has been applied not only to karaya, tragacanth (100), and arabic (100), but also to agar (101), carrageenin (101), Iceland moss (101), and the galactomannans, such as guar and locust bean gum (102).   Gum-like products for use as mucilages and adhesives may be prepared from starch or starch dextrin by suitable oxidizing agents, for example hydrogen peroxide (103) or persulfate (104,105), the reaction being carried out in solution (103–105), in air-suspension (106), or suspended in a liquid such as glycerol.

Modification of starch by oxidation with periodate to give intermediate polyaldehydes (oxo-polysaccharides) is likely to provide new derivatives and uses for starch as a gum-like substance; heating the starch polyaldehyde under compression produces a resin (113) and treatment with acidified methanol gives a polymer containing methoxyl groups (112).   Since the oxidation can be effected electrolytically (107) using only small amounts of periodate, the reaction appears to be economically feasible.

Natural Gum Derivatives

In spite of the great usefulness of gums of all types, little seems to have been accomplished hitherto in preparing and examining the properties of derivatives of gums. Such derivatives might prove to be even more useful than the gums themselves.

Some idea of what may be accomplished in the way of derivatizing the gums can be illustrated by reference to the few studies that have been reported in the literature (148).

Locust bean gum and guar gum react smoothly with 1-chloro-2-cyanoethane in alkaline solution to give the corresponding 2-cyanoethyl ethers (57,58). These gums will also react similarly with 2-chloroethanol and with ethylene oxide to give the O-(2-hydroxyethyl) gums (59–61), substances which are readily soluble in water. Locust bean gum reacts with 2-chloro-propan-1-ol in alkaline solution (63) to give elastic irreversible gels (59–62).

Acetates of guar (66,67) and locust bean gum (68) which are insoluble in water might be useful for making films (63,66). O-Carboxymethyl derivatives of guar and locust bean gum, made (58,64,65) with chloracetic acid, form viscous solutions in water that are stable to alkaline reagents (62). 2-Hydroxypropyl ethers have been made (59–61) from guar and locust bean gums by reaction in alkaline solution with propylene oxide.

By a similar series of reactions laminarin has been transformed into the corresponding 2-hydroxyethyl, 2-hydroxypropyl and carboxymethyl ethers which are much more water soluble than the parent laminarin. There is a possibility that some of these might be suitable as blood extenders (69). Sulfation also increases the solubility of laminarin.

An alginic acid derivative which has become industrially important is the 2-hydroxypropyl ester, made by the action of propylene oxide upon swollen alginic acid under mild conditions which produces little or no degradation. Unlike the parent gum, alginic acid, this derivative is much less sensitive to the addition of acids and remains in solution. Analogous esters have been made by using ethylene oxide, butylene oxide, trimethylene-1,3-epoxide and long chain epoxides such as 1,2-epoxydecane, and the 9,10-epoxides of stearic acid and stearyl alcohol (70–72). All these esters are hydrolyzed by alkalis.

Alginic acid will react with glycerol when heated at 145°, but degradation occurs in this reaction (73). No doubt much decarboxylation takes place.

Acetates of alginic acid (74–78) and laminarin (69) have been prepared successfully but as yet they have been little used in industrial applications. Alginic acid has also been reacted with mustard gas to form a thiodiethylene derivative (79) and it is also reported to give derivatives with diisocyanates (80,81).

Polysaccharide Sulfates

Attention has been directed in recent years to the preparation of synthetic blood anti-coagulants as substitutes for heparin. The sulfated derivatives of guar and locust bean gums (63), agar (98), laminarin (69, 82), cellulose (91-95), starch (89,90-95), glycogen (91-95), dextran (83-85), polyvinyl alcohol (91,136), chondroitin sulfuric acid (137), xylan (137), and synthetic glucans (138) have been investigated. Some of these derivatives show activity *in vivo* and though none approached the activity of heparin, certain sulfamic acid derivatives such as the sulfated 2-aminoethyl ether of laminarin shows about half the activity of heparin (82). Alginic acid sulfate (Paritol) (96) is no more toxic than heparin and its effect lasts twice as long. Extracts of *Chondrus crispus* have about 40 per cent of the activity of heparin while fucoidin, a fucan sulfate, is inactive (97).

Phosphorylated derivatives of polysaccharides can be made in the usual way (86-88) but little information is available concerning their properties and possible applications. Perhaps such substances could be used as both soil conditioners and fertilizers.

REFERENCES

1. Suida, W., *Monatsh.*, **26**, 413 (1905).
2. Mooney, Rose C. L., *J. Am. Chem. Soc.*, **63**, 2828 (1941).
3. Anonymous, *Chem. and Eng. News*, 4869 (1956).
4. Denham, W. S., and Woodhouse, Hilda, *J. Chem. Soc.*, **103**, 1735 (1913).
5. Denham, W. S., and Woodhouse, Hilda, *J. Chem. Soc.*, **105**, 2357 (1914).
6. Donohue, J. M., U. S. Pat., 1,489,315 (1924).
7. Young, G., U. S. Pat., 1,504,178 (1924).
8. Traube, W., and Funk, A., *Ber.*, **69**, 1476 (1936).
9. Traube, W., Piwonka, R., and Funk, A., *Ber.*, **69**, 1483 (1936).
10. Piwonka, R., *Ber.*, **69**, 1965 (1936).
11. Lieser, T., *Ann.*, **528**, 276 (1937).
12. Bock, L. H., *Ind. Eng. Chem.*, **29**, 985 (1937).
13. Peterson, F. C., and Barry, A. J., U. S. Pat., 2,145,273 (1939).
14. Swinehart, R., and Maasberg, A. T., U. S. Pat., 2,254,249 (1941).
15. Ellsworth, D. C., and Hahn, F. C., U. S. Pat., 2,249,754 (1941).
16. Lorand, E. J., *Ind. Eng. Chem.*, **30**, 527 (1938).
17. Berl, E., and Schupp, H., *Cellulose Chem.*, **10**, 41 (1929).
18. Upright, R. M., and Peterson, F. C., *Paper Trade J.*, **110**, [18], 31 (1940).
19. Young, A. E., and Kin, M., *Colloid Chemistry*, **6**, Ed. Alexander, Reinhold Publishing Corp., New York, (1946) 928.

20. Ott, E., *The Chemistry of Large Molecules*, Ed. Burk, R. E., and Grummitt, O., Interscience Pub. Inc., New York (1943) 243.
21. Rebers, P. A., and Smith, F., *J. Am. Chem. Soc.*, **76**, 6097 (1954).
22. Hahn, F. C., U. S. Pat., 2,161,815 (1939).
23. Spurlin, H. M., *J. Am. Chem. Soc.*, **61**, 2222 (1939).
24. Ott, E., *Ind. Eng. Chem.*, **32**, 1641 (1940).
25. Haskins, J. F., *Advances in Carbohydrate Chem.*, **2**, 279 (1946).
26. Jansen, E., Ger. Pat., 332,203 (1918).
27. Schorger, A. W., and Shoemaker, M. J., *Ind. Eng. Chem.*, **29**, 114 (1937).
28. Hader, R. N., Waldeck, W. F., and Smith, F. W., *Ind. Eng. Chem.*, **44**, 2803 (1952).
29. Waldeck, W. F., U. S. Pat., 2,510,355 (1950).
30. Chowdhury, J. K., *Biochem. Z.*, **148**, 76 (1924).
31. Höppler, F., *Chem. Ztg.*, **66**, 132 (1942).
32. Harris, C. A., and Purves, C. B., *Paper Trade J.*, **110**, No. 6, 29 (1940).
33. Reeves, R. E., Thompson, H. Jeanne, *Contrib. Boyce Thompson Inst.*, **11**, 55 (1939).
34. Ulmann, M., *Kolloid. Z.*, **130**, 31 (1953).
35. Brimhall, Bernadine, *Ind. Eng. Chem.*, **36**, 72 (1944).
36. Stacey, M., and Pautard, F. G., *Chemistry and Industry*, 1058 (1952).
37. Geerdes, J. D., Lewis, B. A., and Smith, F., *J. Am. Chem. Soc.*, **79**, 4209 (1957).
38. Abdel-Akher, M., Hamilton, J. K., Montgomery, R., and Smith, F., *J. Am. Chem. Soc.*, **74**, 4970 (1952).
39. Mantell, C. L., *The Water-Soluble Gums*, Reinhold Pub. Corp. New York (1947).
40. Swanson, J. W., U. S. Pat., 2,553,485 (1951).
41. Kesler, C. C., and Hjermstad, E. T., U. S. Pat., 2,516,632, 2,516,633, 2,516,634 (1950).
42. Kerr, R. W., and Neukom, H., *Die Stärke*, **4**, 255 (1952).
43. Hehre, E. J., *Advances in Enzymology*, **11**, 297 (1951).
44. Levi, I., Hawkins, W. L., and Hibbert, H., *J. Am. Chem. Soc.*, **64**, 1959 (1942).
45. Stacey, M., and Swift, G., *J. Chem. Soc.*, 1555 (1948).
46. Van Cleve, J. W., Schaefer, W. C., and Rist, C. E., *J. Am. Chem. Soc.*, **78**, 4435 (1956).
47. Rankin, J. C., and Jeanes, Allene, *J. Am. Chem. Soc.*, **76**, 4435 (1954).
48. Jeanes, Allene, Haynes, W. C., Wilham, C. A., Rankin, J. C., Melvin, E. H., Austin, Marjorie, J., Cluskey, J. E., Fisher, B. E., Tsuchiya, H. M., and Rist, C. E., *J. Am. Chem. Soc.*, **76**, 5041 (1954).
49. Sloan, J. W., Alexander, B. H., Lohmar, R. L., Wolff, I. A., and Rist, C. E., *J. Am. Chem. Soc.*, **76**, 4429 (1954).
50. Fischer, E., *Ber.*, **23**, 3687 (1890).
51. Pacsu, E., and Mora, P. T., *J. Am. Chem. Soc.*, **72**, 1045 (1950).
52. O'Colla, P. S., and Lee, Miss E., *Chemistry and Industry*, 522 (1956).
53. Ricketts, C. R., *J. Chem. Soc.*, 4031 (1954).
54. Bishop, C. T., *Can. J. Chem.*, 34, 1255 (1956).
55. Leuck, G. J., U. S. Pat., 2,375,564 (1945).
56. Durand, H. W., U. S. Pat., 2,563,014 (1951).
57. Moe, O. A., Miller, S. E., and Buckley, M. I., *J. Am. Chem. Soc.*, **74**, 1325 (1952).

58. Moe, O. A., U. S. Pat., 2,461,502 (1949); 2,520,161 (1950).
59. I. G. Farbenindustrie A.G., Brit. Pat., 498,149 (1939); Fr. Pat., 838,184 (1939).
60. Ziese, W., Ebel, F., and Schneevoight, A., U. S. Pat., 2,190,179 (1940).
61. Gaver, K. M., Lasure, E. P., and Tieszen, D. V., U. S. Pat., 2,572,923 (1951).
62. Deuel, H., and Neukom, H., Advances in Chem. Series, 11, 51 (1954).
63. Deuel, H., Solms, J., and Neukom, H., Chimia, 8, 64 (1954).
64. Filbert, W. F., U. S. Pat., 2,599,620 (1952).
65. Moe, O. A., U. S. Pat., 2,599,771 (1952); 2,477,544 (1949).
66. Smart, C. L., and Whistler, R. L., J. Polymer Sci., 4, 87 (1949).
67. Rafique, C. M., and Smith, F., J. Am. Chem Soc., 72, 4634 (1950).
68. Smith, F., J. Am. Chem. Soc., 70, 3249 (1948).
69. Black, W. A. P., and Dewar, E. T., J. Sci. Food Agr., 5, 176 (1954).
70. Steiner, A. B., and McNeely, W. H., Ind. Eng. Chem., 43, 2073 (1951).
71. Steiner, A. B., and McNeeley, W. H., U. S. Pat., 2,463,824 (1949).
72. Steiner, A. B., and McNeeley, W. H., U. S. Pat., 2,494,911, 2,494,912 (1950).
73. Malvezin, P., Bull. assoc. chim., 60, 213 (1943).
74. Wasserman, M. A., J. Chem. Soc., 197 (1948).
75. Wassermann, A., Nature, 158, 271 (1946).
76. Chamberlain, N. H., Cunningham, G. E., and Speakman, J. B., Nature, 158, 553 (1946).
77. Cunningham, G. E., Chamberlain, N. H., and Speakman, J. B., U. S. Pat., 2,403,707 (1946).
78. Carson, J. F., and Maclay, W. D., J. Am. Chem. Soc., 68, 1015 (1946).
79. Deuel, H., and Neukom, H., J. Polymer. Sci., 4, 755 (1949).
80. Speakman, J. B., Chamberlain, N. H., and Darkin, C. M. C., U. S. Pat., 2,584,508 (1952).
81. Peill, P. L. D., Chamberlain, N. H., and Cefoil Ltd., Brit. Pat., 575,611 (1946); 621,362 (1949).
82. Hawkins, W. W., and O'Neill, A. N., Can. J. Biochem. and Physiol., 33, 545 (1955).
83. Ricketts, C. R., and Walton, K. W., Chemistry and Industry, 869 (1952).
84. Ricketts, C. R., Biochem. J., 51, 120 (1952).
85. Ricketts, C. R., J. Chem. Soc., 3752 (1956).
86. Lohmar, R., Sloan, J. W., and Rist, C. E., J. Am. Chem. Soc., 72, 5717 (1950).
87. Reid, J. D., and Mazzeno, L. W., Ind. Eng. Chem., 41, 2828 (1949).
88. Reid, J. A., Mazzeno, L. W., and Buras, E. M., Ind. Eng. Chem., 41, 2831 (1949).
89. Astrup, T., Galsmar, I., and Volkert, M., Acta Physiol. Scand., 8, 215 (1944).
90. Piper, J., Acta Pharmacol. et Toxicol., 2, 138 (1946).
91. Chargaff, E., Bancroft, F. N., and Stanley-Brown, M., J. Biol. Chem., 115, 156 (1936).
92. Bergström, S., Z. physiol. Chem., 238, 163 (1936).
93. Karrer, P., Koenig, H., and Usteri, E., Helv. Chim. Acta, 26, 1296 (1943).
94. Gebauer-Fuelnegg, E., and Dingler, O., J. Am. Chem. Soc., 52, 2849 (1930).
95. Traube, W., Blaser, B., and Lindemann, E., Ber., 65, 603 (1932).

96. *Chem. and Eng. News*, **27**, 2162 (1949).
97. Percival, E. G. V., *Quart. Rev., (London)*, **3**, 369 (1949).
98. Neuberg, C., and Schwietzer, C. H., *Monatsh.*, **71**, 46 (1938).
99. Morita, H., and Rice, H. M., *Anal. Chem.*, **27**, 336 (1955).
100. Heermann, P., *Farberei und Textil chemische Untersuchungen*, 7th Ed., J. Springer, Berlin (1940), 196.
101. Fritzsche, F., U. S. Pat., 900,274 (1908).
102. Roberts, P. L., U. S. Pat., 2,483,936 (1948).
103. Perkins, F. G., U. S. Pat., 1,020,656 (1912).
104. Kühl, H., and Soltau, G., Ger. Pat., 522,555 (1928).
105. Müller, J., U. S. Pat., 2,173,040; 2,173,041 (1940).
106. Nivling, W. A., U. S. Pat., 2,204,615 (1940).
107. Dvonch, W., and Mehltretter, C. L., *J. Am. Chem. Soc.*, **74**, 5522 (1952); U. S. Pat., 2,648,629 (1953).
108. Jullander, I., *Svensk Kem. Tids.*, **65**, 223 (1953); *Chimie et Industrie*, **71**, 288 (1954).
109. Sönnerskog, S., *Some Ethers of Cellulose and Starch*, Dissertation, Stockholm Högskola, Stockholm (1952).
110. Jullander, I., *Svensk Papperstidning*, **55**, 197 (1952).
111. Manley, R. St. John, *Arkiv för Kemi*, **9**, 519 (1956).
112. Goldstein, I. J., and Smith, F., *Chemistry and Industry*, 40 (1958).
113. Mellies, R. L., Sloan, J. W., Hofreiter, B. T., and Wolff, I. A., *Abstracts 128th A.C.S. Meeting, Minneapolis* (1955).
114. Christensen, G. C., and Smith, F., unpublished.
115. Sanborn, J. R., *Ind. Eng. Chem.*, **28**, 1189 (1936).
116. Sanborn, J. R., *Ind. Eng. Chem.*, **26**, 532 (1934); U. S. Pat., 2,026,253 (1935).
117. Herzog, R. O., and Meier, A., U. S. Pat., 1,141,545 (1915).
118. Klug, E. D., and Tinsley, J. S., U. S. Pat., 2,517,577 (1946).
119. Russian Pat., 11,305 (1926); *Chem. Abstracts*, **25**, 1120 (1931).
120. Schiller, A. M., and Suen, T. J., *Abstracts 129th A.C.S. Meeting, Dallas, Texas* (1956).
121. Lea, P. J., U. S. Pat., 2,614,998 (1952).
122. Swift, A. M., *Polyacrylamide, A New, Synthetic, Water-soluble gum.* Presented before Plastics Section, *Tappi*, Appleton, Wisc. Oct. 4, 1956.
123. Michaels, A. S., *Ind. Eng. Chem.*, **46**, 1485 (1954).
124. Grieg-Smith, R., *Proc. Linn. Soc., N. S. Wales*, **27**, 383 (1902); **28**, 114,541 (1903); **29**, 217 (1904).
125. Häggroth, S., and Lindberg, B., *Svensk Papperstidning*, **59**, 870 (1956).
126. Dieckman, S. F., Jarrell, J. G., and Voris, R. S., *Ind. Eng. Chem.*, **45**, 2287 (1953).
127. Klug, E. D., and Tinsley, J. S., Brit. Pat., 623,276 (1949).
128. Karabinos, J. V., and Hindert, Marjorie, *Advances in Carbohydrate Chem.*, **9**, 285 (1954).
129. Bruson, H. A., U. S. Pat., 2,372,808 (1945).
130. Vaughan, C. L. P., U. S. Pat., 2,618,633 (1952).
131. Vaughan, C. L. P., U. S. Pat., 2,618,635 (1952).
132. Bode, H. E., U. S. Pat., 2,156,488 (1939).
133. Van Horn, W. M., Conkey, J. H., Shema, B. F., and Shockley, W. H., U. S. Pat., 2,811,442 (1957).

134. Durand, H. W., Dull, M. F., and Tipson, R. S., *J. Am. Chem. Soc.*, **80**, 3691 (1958).
135. Vaughn, C. L. P., U. S. Pat., 2,623,042 (1952).
136. Karrer, P., Usteri, E., and Camerino, B., *Helv. Chim. Acta*, **27**, 1422 (1944).
137. Meyer, K. H., Piroué, R. P., and Odier, M. E., *Helv. Chim. Acta*, **35**, 574 (1952).
138. Wood, J. W., and Mora, P. T., *J. Am. Chem. Soc.*, **80**, 3700 (1958).
139. Classen, A., *Therap. Monatsh.*, **33** (1897); U. S. Pat., 602,697 (1898).
140. Leuck, G. J., U. S. Pat., 2,222,872, 2,222,873 (1940).
141. Opie, J. W., U. S. Pat., 2,767,171 (1956).
142. Weiss, E., U. S. Pat., 2,411,818 (1946).
143. Brit. Pat., 691,364 (1953).
144. Burger, M., *Bacterial Polysaccharides Their Chemical and Immunological Aspects*, Charles C. Thomas, Publisher, Springfield, Ill. (1950).
145. Wilkinson, J. F., Dudman, W. F., and Aspinall, G. O., *Biochem. J.*, **59**, 446 (1955).
146. Aspinall, G. O., Jamieson, R. S. P., and Wilkinson, J. F., *J. Chem. Soc.*, 3483 (1956).
147. Kerr, R. W. E., *Chemistry and Industry of Starch*, 2nd ed., Academic Press, New York (1950).
148. Goheen, G. E., *Tappi*, **41**, 737 (1958).

CHAPTER 17

PHYSICAL PROPERTIES OF GUMS AND MUCILAGES

General

Considering the use that is made of the physical properties of gums and mucilages in industry, it is surprising how few of them have been studied from a physico-chemical point of view. This may be due in part to the fact that gums and mucilages are neither pure nor homogeneous. The natural gums and mucilages usually contain proteinaceous matter of an unknown nature and those gums of an acidic nature occur as the Ca, Mg, K, Na etc. salts. Moreover, at the present time, it is extremely difficult to purify any of the simple polysaccharides, let alone the more complex gums, and it is equally difficult to ascertain their homogeneity, although ultrafiltration and electrophoretic studies (55,57) are said to show that gum arabic, for example, is heterogeneous (10). Most of the physical studies have been carried out with gum arabic and gum tragacanth. This might be expected, since these were two of the most important industrial gums until relatively recently.

The tears of gum arabic crumble and become opaque when kept warm, but this does not destroy the gum-like properties. When heated, the gum undergoes changes of an unknown nature that are recognized by a decrease in the viscosity of its aqueous solution (1). This may be due to depolymerization (2), and if the heating is sufficient rearrangement of the glycosidic bonds may also take place, a transformation that has been shown to occur during the dextrinization of starches by the roasting process (3).

When aqueous solutions of gums such as gum arabic, gum tragacanth and guar gum are heated, degradation occurs as indicated by the liberation of free sugars and a loss in viscosity (4). This instability in hot aqueous solution is very noticeable with those gums containing sugars such as arabinose, L-rhamnose, and L-fucose.

The viscosity of gum solutions also decreases in the presence of inorganic salts; a two-thirds reduction in the viscosity of gum arabic occurs when normal saline is added (5). The same phenomenon has been

494

noted in the case of starch. Care should therefore be taken to check the effect of salts on solutions of gums and other polysaccharides to be used as plasma extenders.

Gum arabic is reported to show fluorescence and phosphorescence (6,7) and to depolarize light (8,9).

Molecular Weight and Shape

Sedimentation studies show that, like its sodium salt, gum arabic has a molecular weight of about 250,000 to 300,000 (11) and a length of 100 Å. (13). Hydration studies indicate that gum arabic with a molecular weight of 240,000 (12) has a diameter of $11m\mu$ and that its calcium and sodium salts bind 0.9 and 1.1g. water per gram of salt respectively (14).

Osmotic pressure measurements on the salts (Li, Na, K, Mg and Pb) of gum arabic indicate a particle weight of 220,000 (58). Gum tragacanth has a higher molecular weight (840,000) than gum arabic and the molecules appear to have an elongated shape, 4500 Å. by 19 Å. (4). (This elongated structure of gum tragacanth explains its high viscosity).

Of considerable interest from a structural point of view is the report (11) that treatment with acid (pH 2 to 4) hydrolyzes gum arabic into fragments with a molecular weight less than 10,000. Ultra-centrifugation studies (15), showing degraded arabic acid to have a molecular weight less than 20,000, agree with this. These observations show that the concept (16) of the structure of the molecule of gum arabic, consisting of a central nucleus to which the labile residues of L-arabinose, L-rhamnose, and 3-O-D-galactopyranosyl-L-arabinose are attached, needs modification. It now seems more likely that the gum consists of a series of groups of residues of D-galactose and D-glucuronic acid corresponding to a molecular weight of 10,000 to 20,000. These groups of stable residues constitute the degraded gum arabic produced by mild acid hydrolysis of the gum. In the native gum these stable groups are mutually joined by a relatively labile residue (probably L-arabopyranose) and the whole assembly of units of degraded arabic acid is clothed with the labile sugar residues of L-arabofuranose, L-rhamnopyranose and 3-O-D-galactopyranosyl-L-arabofuranose (see Chapter 11).

Gum arabic (17–21), like gum tragacanth (22), apricot gum (23) and peach gum (23), serves as an excellent protective colloid (24). Use is made of this same property displayed by the galactomannan gums, such as guar and locust bean gum, in mineral ore dressing and in inorganic analysis when it is necessary to avoid precipitation, as in the case of fluoride analysis using thorium nitrate.

The effect of trivalent metal salts on gum arabic has been investigated viscometrically (25). The observation that gum arabic is irreversibly adsorbed by aluminum hydroxide (26) indicates that such a method, already put to good use for separating amylose and amylopectin (27), and others employing weaker adsorptive materials, might be valuable for the fractionation and purification of gums. This type of reaction should be compared with the precipitin reaction that occurs between polysaccharide gums and certain proteins (28-32) which is also concerned with immunological specificity; a closer study of this phenomenon may be useful, not only in ascertaining the building units of gums, but also in determining the molecular architecture of polysaccharides in general, and of the proteins that enter into these reactions (see Chapter 15). This precipitin reaction is to be distinguished from the acid-base coacervation reaction between the free acid of gum arabic, arabic acid, and gelatin (33). Coacervation is not displayed by either gum arabic or its salts.

Viscosity Studies on Gums

Many of the useful industrial applications of gums are based on the viscous character of their solutions concerning which much empirical work has been carried out. Dilute solutions of gum arabic obey the Einstein equation governing viscosity, thus indicating that the disperse phase is a liquid (34). At higher concentrations flow elasticity enters in (35,36). The effect of added ethanol (37), formaldehyde (38), acetone (39), and various electrolytes (39) on the viscosity, has been investigated. The viscosity of solutions of gum arabic is sensitive to pH change, a maximum being observed at neutral pH (40).

Salts and other gums decrease the viscosity of solutions of gum arabic. Thus, addition of gum tragacanth first causes a decrease in viscosity and finally the gum tragacanth is precipitated. This observation might be worth investigating as a means of preparing gum tragacanth free from such contaminants as araban (41). Other carbohydrates, for example, sucrose and starch, do not precipitate gum tragacanth from aqueous solution (42).

Electroviscous studies on gum arabic solutions have shown that the per cent volume occupied by the disperse phase is inversely proportional to the concentration of the gum solution (43), the molecules of gum readily undergoing change both in shape and size (44), thus indicating that the forces of attraction between neighboring sugar units are quite weak. This behavior is typical of gums possessing a highly branched chain structure and it should be compared with that of gums and mucilages like guar gum and locust bean gum, whose molecules, though branched, are essentially linear in character (see Chapter 12). The difference is illustrated in part at least by the fact that a 20 per cent solution of gum arabic has the same viscosity as a 0.5 per cent solution of locust bean gum (45). The high viscosity of solutions of salts of alginic acid (alginates) has also been traced to the same phenomenon (46,47). Gum tragacanth, whose molecules are elongated and have a certain amount of linear character, shows maximum viscosity in aqueous solution at pH 8(48).

Gums which give solutions that are sensitive to pH are usually characterized by the presence of carboxyl or sulfate groups. Neutral gums, such as guar, form solutions which are not dependent on pH. The viscosity does fall, however, in the presence of strong alkali, but this may be due to destruction of the protein which forms a complex with the carbohydrate polymer. Solutions of konjak glucomannan show first an increase and then a decrease in viscosity in high concentrations of alkali. The decrease is probably due to precipitation of the glucomannan (47).

Gum tragacanth solutions, at a concentration of 0.5 per cent and above, exhibit structure viscosity, a phenomenon displayed by elongated molecules and recognized by the fact that the rate of flow of the solution in a capillary tube is not proportional to the pressure (50). Locust bean gum and flax seed mucilages behave similarly, whereas solutions of gum arabic and cashew gum do not show structure viscosity even at concentrations as high as 30 per cent, presumably because the molecules of these gums have a spherical shape.

Mechanical grinding of gums, a process usually practiced in commerce, leads to molecular breakdown. This is revealed by the fact that solutions made from unground pieces of gum tragacanth are more viscous than those of the same concentration made from the powdered gum (51). That the structural interpretation of viscosity data is not simple, however, is shown by the observations that solutions of gum tragacanth show a maximum viscosity after keeping for 48 hours at 40° and that the viscosity is proportional to the methoxyl content of the gum (52).

Aqueous solutions of some gums show a decrease in viscosity with time. This is true of guar and locust bean gums and is probably due to enzymic degradation. Solutions of the alginates also lose their viscosity on standing; it is said that this is due to "spontaneous depolymerization" and that it could be controlled by adding 0.1 to 0.2 per cent phenol (53). Solutions of gum arabic and flax seed mucilage become less viscous upon irradiation with UV light (54).

Many of the physical properties of gums discussed above will have to be reconsidered in the light of recent results on the electrophoretic behavior of gums in free solution (56,57) and on glass fiber paper (55), which indicates rather strongly that many gums and mucilages, to say nothing of a number of other polysaccharides, are probably not homogeneous.

REFERENCES

1. Boutaric, A., and Roy, Madeleine, *Compt. rend.*, **199**, 1219 (1934).
2. Ende, C., Lange, F. E. M., and Nord, F. F., *Ber.*, **68**, 2004 (1935).
3. Geerdes, J. D., Lewis, B. A., and Smith, F., *J. Am. Chem. Soc.*, **79**, 4209 (1957).
4. Graten, Nils, and Kärrholm, Marianne, *J. Colloid Sci.*, **5**, 21 (1950).
5. Davies, D. R., *Biochem. J.*, **28**, 529 (1934).
6. Frohlich, P., *Z. Physik.*, **35**, 193 (1925).
7. Millson, H. E., *Textile Colorist*, **65**, 495, 503 (1943); *Chem. Abstracts*, **38**, 1883 (1944).
8. Boutaric, A., and Breton, J., *J. phys. radium*, **10**, 176 (1939); *Chem. Abstracts*, **33**, 5263 (1939).
9. Tourneur, C., *Compt. rend.*, **200**, 1756 (1935).
10. Amat Bargues, M., *Farmac nueva*, **7**, 82 (1942); *Chem. Abstracts*, **37**, 5635 (1943).
11. Saverborn, S., *The Svedburg (Mem. Vol.)*, 508 (1944).
12. Oakley, H. B., *Trans. Faraday Soc.*, **31**, 136 (1935).
13. Snellman, O., *Acta Chem. Scand.*, **1**, 291 (1947).
14. Oakley, H. B., *Biochem. J.*, **31**, 28 (1937).
15. Briggs, D. R., Spriestersbach, D. R., and Smith, F., unpublished.
16. Smith, F., *J. Chem. Soc.*, 1035 (1940).
17. Sauer, E., and Aldinger, W., *Kolloid Z.*, **85**, 295 (1938).
18. Pauli, W., Szper, J., and Szper, St., *Trans. Faraday Soc.*, **35**, 1316 (1939).
19. Lloyd, R. V., and Evans, D. P., *Trans. Faraday Soc.*, **38**, 179 (1942).
20. Kranz, J. C., Jr., and Gordon, N. E., *J. Am. Pharm. Assoc.*, **15**, 83 (1926).
21. Clark, G. L., and Mann, W. A., *J. Biol. Chem.*, **52**, 157 (1922).
22. Gutbier, A., Huber, J., and Krivoss, Z., *Kolloid Z.*, **18**, 141 (1916).
23. Zaprometov, B. G., and Nurmukhamedov, F. M., *Kolloid J.* (USSR), **6**, 705 (1940).
24. Gutbier, A., Huber, J., and Eckert, P., *Kolloid Z.*, **32**, 255, 329 (1923).
25. Haller, R., and Frankfort, B., *Kolloid Z.*, **80**, 68 (1937).
26. Rakuzur, M. A., *J. Russ. Phys. Chem. Soc.*, **53**, I, 357 (1921).
27. Bourne, E. J., Donnison, G. H., Peat, S., and Whelan, W. J., *J. Chem. Soc.*, 1 (1949).
28. Sumner, J. B., and Howell, S. F., *J. Biol. Chem.*, **115**, 583 (1936).
29. Cifonelli, J. A., and Smith, F., *Anal. Chem.*, **27**, 1639 (1955).
30. Cifonelli, J. A., Montgomery, R., and Smith, F., *J. Am. Chem. Soc.*, **78**, 2485 (1956).
31. Cifonelli, J. A., and Smith, F., *J. Am. Chem. Soc.*, **79**, 5055 (1957).
32. Heidelberger, M., Dische, Z., Neely, W. B., and Wolfrom, M. L., *J. Am. Chem. Soc.*, **77**, 3511 (1955).
33. Graham, T., *J. Chem. Soc.*, **15**, 216 (1862).
34. Walter, H., *Sitzb. Akad. Wiss. Wien*, IIA, **129**, 709 (1920); *Chem. Abstracts*, **16**, 2435 (1922).
35. Ostwold, W., and Auerbach, R., *Kolloid Z.*, **38**, 261 (1926).
36. Ostwald, W., Auerbach, R., Feldmann, I., Trakas, V., and Malss, H., *Kolloid Z.*, **67**, 211 (1934).
37. Boutaric, A., and Roy, Madeleine, *Bull. soc. chim.*, **6**, 316 (1939).

38. Watanabe, R., *Mitt. med. Akad. Kioto*, **30**, 785 (1940); *Chem. Abstracts*, **35**, 3506 (1941).
39. Boutaric, A., *Rev. Gen. sci.*, **51**, 231 (1940-1941); *Chem. Abstracts*, **37**, 2978 (1943).
40. Tendeloo, H. J. C., *Rec. trav. chim.*, **48**, 23 (1929).
41. James, Sybil P., and Smith, F., *J. Chem. Soc.*, 749 (1945).
42. Ronson, J. M., *Quart. J. Pharm.*, **10**, 404 (1937).
43. Briggs, D. R., *J. Phys. Chem.*, **45**, 866 (1941).
44. Briggs, D. R., and Hanig, M., *J. Phys. Chem.*, **48**, 1 (1944).
45. Coumou, J., *Chem. Weekblad.* **32**, 426 (1935).
46. Cook, W. H., and Smith, D. B., *Can. J. Biochem. and Physiol.*, **32**, 227 (1954).
47. Black, W. A. P., Cornhill, W. J., and Dewar, E. T., *J. Sci. Food Agric.*, **3**, 542 (1952).
48. Schou, S. A., and Fürst, W. J., *Dansk Tids Farm*, **15**, 34 (1941); *Chem. Abstracts*, **35**, 5253 (1941).
49. Torigata, H., *J. Chem. Soc.* (Japan), **72**, 373 (1951); *Chem. Abstracts*, **46**, 3009 (1952).
50. Frith, E. M., and Tuckett, R. F., *Linear Polymers*, Longmans Green and Co. London (1951).
51. Chambers, W. P., *J. Pharm. Pharmacol.*, **1**, 103 (1949).
52. Rowson, J. M., *Quart. J. Pharm. and Pharmacol.*, **10**, 161 (1937).
53. Gayezo Diaz, E., and Otero Aenlle, E., *Anales real soc. espan. fis. y quim.*, **46B**, 441 (1950); *Chem. Abstracts*, **45**, 5000 (1951).
54. Zucca Carla, *Ist. botan. univ.*, *Lab. crittogram.*, *Pavia, Atti*, [5], **10**, 85 (1953); *Chem. Abstracts*, **48**, 2399 (1954).
55. Lewis, B. A., and Smith, F., *J. Am. Chem. Soc.*, **79**, 3929 (1957).
56. Briggs, D. R., *J. Phys. Chem.*, **52**, 76 (1948).
57. Joubert, F. J., *J. S. African Chem. Instit.*, **7**, [2], 107 (1954).
58. Oakley, H. B., *Trans. Faraday Soc.*, **32**, 1360 (1936); **33**, 372 (1937).

APPENDIX I

APPLICATIONS OF GUMS AND MUCILAGES

An account has been given (1,2,3) of some of the details of industrial applications including formulations for making certain preparations and concoctions in the fields of cosmetics, pharmacy, paints, coating compositions, textiles, adhesives, beater additives, etc. Reviews on various applications as adhesives (4), in cosmetics (5–7) and on general uses of gum arabic (8,9), tragacanth and carob gum (10,11) and seaweed gums (12), should also be consulted. Examination of these uses demonstrates the tremendous scope and possibilities of the gums and mucilages and it also shows the rather empirical knowledge that underlies almost all these applications.

Listed below are some uses of gums and mucilages arranged according to application; they are included only to indicate the widespread use of these polysaccharides and possibly to stimulate the further application of other gums and the transformation of readily accessible polysaccharides into new synthetic gums and mucilages.

I. *Adhesives*
1. Plant exudates (13–15).
2. Seed mucilages (16,17).
3. Cactus mucilages (18).
4. Seaweed mucilages (19–22).
5. Gums for increasing strength of starch pastes (23).
6. Review on gums as adhesives in industry (4).
7. Mucilages given in U. S. Pharmacopia and National Formulary (24).

II. *Cosmetics and Soap*
1. Gum tragacanth as coating for soap to prevent dusting and lumping (25).
2. Gum arabic to prevent sweating of soap (26).
3. Gum tragacanth in tooth pastes (27,28).
4. Review on use of gums in cosmetics industries (5–7).
5. *O*-(Carboxymethyl) cellulose in detergent soaps (192).

6. Gums in hair waving preparations and the allergic reactions by some of them (29,30).

III. *Drilling Fluids*

1. Gums for water retention in saline strata and removal of calcareous deposits (31–35, 186).
2. Fermentation of gums in drilling fluids prevented by 0.1 per cent cresolic acid (36).
3. O-(Carboxymethyl) cellulose improves suspending and emulsifying action of drilling muds (192).

IV. *Emulsions*

1. Formation of emulsions with gum arabic (37–39), tragacanth (40) and karaya (41).
2. Emulsification of medicinals (42,43).
3. Superiority of apricot gum over gum arabic for emulsions (44).
4. Gum tragacanth to emulsify insect repellents (46) and paraffin oil (47).
5. Gums in cosmetic emulsions (45).
6. Gum arabic for stabilizing kerosene emulsions (48).
7. Locust bean gum for creaming of latex (49).
8. Emulsion stability and effect of pH (50).
9. Gel forming properties of carboxy-alkyl ethers of gum guar, carob and tragacanth (51–53).
10. Hydroxy-alkyl and carboxy-alkyl derivatives of laminarin (54).

V. *Food Products*

1. Dairy Products
   (a) Gum tragacanth as a preservative for milk (55).
   (b) Gum (or starch) mixed with cream and gelatin as substitute for milk (56).
   (c) Irish moss as stabilizer for ice cream and cheese (57).
   (d) Gum tragacanth unsuitable in cheese making (58).
   (e) Gums as ice cream stabilizers (59–63) and their function (62,63).
   (f) Water absorption and binding capacity of gum arabic and its application in dairy products (64).
2. Baking and Beverages
   (a) Gum arabic as a fixative for 2,3-butanedione in bakery products (65).
   (b) Mixture of gum arabic and karaya said to be better than one of gum arabic and tragacanth for making citrus oil emulsions (66).
   (c) Galactomannans for cloud stabilization in citrus juice (67).

(d) Use of gums in alcoholic beverages (68).

3. Miscellaneous

   (a) Use of gums in confectionery (69–71), jams and jellies (72) and diabetic sirups containing saccharin (73).

   (b) Various gums in catsup and mayonnaise (74,75), but rated as poor carriers in foodstuffs (76).

   (c) Oat gum as thickener in foods (187).

VI. *Lithography*

   1. Gum arabic for treatment of lithographic plates (77,78).

   2. Carboxy-alkyl ethers of cellulose, starch and of water soluble gums are superior to gum arabic in treatment of lithographic plates (79).

VII. *Metallurgy*

   1. Effect of gum tragacanth and gum arabic on the deposition of copper (80,81).

   2. Effect of gum arabic on zinc corrosion and electrolysis of zinc sulfate (82,83).

   3. Gum arabic—metal complexes formed electrolytically (84).

   4. Effect of gum arabic on electrode reactions (85).

   5. Gum tragacanth inhibits solution of aluminum in sodium hydroxide (86).

VIII. *Medical and Pharmaceutical*

   1. Apricot, plum and cherry gums are not good substitutes for gum arabic (87).

   2. Tragacanth as a component of medicinal jellies (88,89).

   3. Tragacanth, locust bean and karaya gum as laxatives (90–92).

   4. "Glycerate" of tragacanth as a lubricant for surgical instruments (93).

   5. Tragacanth in formulations of the British Pharmaceutical Codex (94).

   6. Effect of gum ghatti on uterus (95).

   7. Karaya in medicinal and pharmaceutical preparations (96,97).

   8. Mucilages in the prophylaxis of lead poisoning (98).

   9. Gums and mucilages used in the treatment of paper for trapping or destroying bacilli in sputum (99).

   10. Effect of gums and mucilages on drug preparation (100).

   11. Physical changes in blood caused by gum arabic (101).

   12. Anticoagulant action in blood of sulfated derivatives of laminarin (54,102,104) and of dextran (103).

   13. Oat gum (187,188) and flax mucilage (189) in medical preparations.

IX. *Paper*

  1. Guar, oxidized guar gum, locust bean (carob bean) meal and mucilage of *Abelmoschus manihot* as additives to paper to improve sizing, bursting strength and opacity (105-110).

  2. Gums for deflocculation of paper pulp suspensions (111).

  3. Penetration of gummed paper by gum solutions (112,113).

  4. Effect of mucilages on hygroscopic properties of paper (114).

  5. Algin in making corrugated paper (115).

  6. Poly(acryl)amide and related compounds and their use in the paper industry (193).

X. *Photography*

  1. Various gums (116,117) and the dicarboxylic acid esters of gum arabic (118) recommended.

XI. *Soils*

  1. Gum arabic as a soil deflocculant and its value in road building (119).

  2. Gum arabic does not increase soil stability (120).

  3. Effect of quince seed mucilages and other polysaccharides on soil aggregation (121).

  4. Effect of gum ghatti on filtration of salt-water muds (122).

  5. Algin (123) and other gums (124) found to be good soil conditioners.

XII. *Textiles*

  1. Various gums as thickeners for sizing (125-148,172).

  2. Films and threads from gums (146).

  3. Preparation and properties of some inorganic alginate fibers (147).

  4. Leather substitute from fungus gums (172).

  5. Reduction of viscosity of gums by oxidation with peroxides (149).

XIII. *Miscellaneous Uses*

  1. Gum arabic as a deflocculant for carbon black (148).

  2. Gum arabic and tragacanth with terpineol as plasticizers (150).

  3. Mesquite gum as a substitute for gum arabic (151).

  4. Karaya gum used in nicotine sprays but has no activating effect (152-154).

  5. Production of furfural from peach gum (155).

  6. Gums for suspending insoluble powders (156-159).

  7. As additives to surface active materials in laundry practice (160).

  8. As binding materials (161) in welding rods (162), in thermite mixtures (163), brazing compounds, coal briquettes (164), as a

plasticizer in clay used for ceramics industry (165), and as a thickener in battery electrolyte (186).

9. Stabilizers in low-penetration coatings (166).

10. Mucilage in linseed oil as an antioxidant and as a promoter of yellowing (167).

11. Membranes prepared from mixtures of gums and cellulose esters (168).

12. Gums as raw materials (169).

13. Gums from fungi (170–172).

14. Gums as slime precipitants in ore refining by flotation (173).

15. Review on uses of gum arabic (8,9), and carob gums (10,11).

16. Utilization of seaweed polysaccharides by rumen microflora *in vitro* (176).

17. Membranes and sheets from fungus gums (177,178).

18. Seaweed gums (algin) for control of scale formation in boilers and evaporators (180,181).

19. Rubber-like material produced from fungus gums (179).

20. Review of miscellaneous applications of seaweed gums (algin) (12,182–185).

21. Oat gum as a substitute for other plant gums (190,191).

22. O-(Carboxymethyl)cellulose for detergents for forming films, laundry finishes, warp sizing, adhesives, and as a beater additive in paper manufacture (192).

23. Guar gum for use in under-water explosives (186).

24. O-(Aminoethyl) starch as a precipitant for negative colloids (174) and as a flotation agent (175) for mineral separation.

Table 63 which follows is included not only to show the industrial application of seaweed gums but also to indicate how other natural and synthetic gums may be employed.

TABLE 63. SOME APPLICATIONS OF SEAWEED POLYSACCHARIDES (12)

Composition	Applications (12)
Sodium alginate, sugar, and dextrin.	Stabilizer for ice cream, cheese, fountain sirups and toppings.
Sodium alginate, emulsifier, sugar and dextrin.	Combination ice-cream stabilizer and emulsifier.
Propylene glycol alginate, vegetable gum and sugar.	Stabilizer for ice cream and ice milk.
Propylene glycol alginate, sugar, vegetable gum and emulsifier.	Combination ice-cream and ice-milk stabilizer and emulsifier.
Propylene glycol alginate, sugar, and vegetable gum.	Stabilizer for sherbets, ices, sirups, and frozen fruits.

TABLE 63 (CONTINUED)

Composition	Applications (12)
Sodium alginate, carrageenin, sugar, and dextrin.	Suspending agent in chocolate milk.
Sodium alginate.	Stabilizer for bakery icings, toppings, and meringues.
Sodium alginate, sodium phosphate, and calcium tartrate.	Gelling agent for dessert gels, and stabilizer in icing bases.
Alginic acid.	Tablet disintegrant, and hemostatic.
Sodium alginate, medium viscosity, 40 or 80 mesh.	Cosmetics, pharmaceuticals, foods, ceramics, adhesives, paper and textile sizing.
Sodium alginate, low viscosity.	Films, coatings and emulsions.
Sodium alginate, extra low viscosity.	Films, coatings, and suspensions.
Sodium alginate, high viscosity.	Cosmetics, pharmaceuticals, foods, dry compositions, and misc. industrial uses.
Potassium alginate, medium viscosity.	Dental impression compositions.
Propylene glycol alginate, high viscosity, 20 or 80 mesh.	Foods, drugs, cosmetics, miscellaneous acidic uses.
Sodium alginate, high viscosity.	Textile print pastes, water paints, adhesives, polishes, textile sizing, boiler compounds, wallboard coatings and slime flocculation.
Sodium alginate, medium viscosity.	Corrugated paperboard adhesives, paper and paperboard surface sizing compositions and coatings, rubber latex thickening.
Ammonium alginate, high viscosity.	Bodying and creaming rubber products, water paints, and other miscellaneous uses.
Amine alginate derivative.	Thickener for hydroxylated solvents.
Sodium alginate, low, medium, and standard viscosities.	Textile printing pastes, stabilizer for ice cream and sirups.
substantially free of calcium, low, medium and high viscosities.	Same as regular grade.
highly dispersible.	Same as regular grade.
highly dispersible, nonedible.	Polyvinyl emulsion paints, and latex thickening.
Potassium alginate, low, medium and standard viscosities.	Dental impression compounds.
Ammonium alginate, low and standard viscosities.	Latex creaming, ashless binder for ceramics.
Calcium alginate.	Film manufacture.
Calcium alginate, full swelling.	Tablet disintegrant.
Alginic acid.	Tablet disintegrant.

TABLE 63. (CONTINUED)

Composition	Applications (12)
Alginic acid, full swelling.	Hemostatic products.
Carrageenin (Irish moss extract), varying gel strengths from 18 to 350. varying degrees of milk reactivity from 20 to 100.	Products prepared with or in water. Milk or milk products.
Carrageenin with all metallic ions replaced by sodium. Sodium carrageenate, non-gelling.	Bodying, stabilizing, and suspending agent that is soluble in cold water. Toilet goods, cosmetics, foods.
Carrageenin (Irish moss extract), varying viscosities and gel strengths.	Stabilizing, thickening, and gelling agents for various food products.
Carrageenin plus added potassium chloride, varying proportions, viscosities and gel strengths.	General purpose gelling agents.
Carrageenin plus added potassium chloride and locust bean gum, varying proportions and gel strength.	General gelling and thickening agents.
Extract from *Gigartina* family and related forms.	Stabilizer, bodying agent and thickener for tooth powder, whipped cream, frostings and syrups.
Carrageenin (Irish moss extract), varying viscosities and gel strengths.	General stabilizing, thickening, and gelling agents for food, drug, cosmetic and industrial products.
Milk soluble mixture of carrageenin and other vegetable gums.	Stabilizer for ice cream and other frozen desserts. Imitation jellies for bakery products. Combination emulsifier and stabilizer for ice cream.
Agar, extremely clear, free from organisms and impurities, good gel and surface hardness.	Microbiology and orchid culture, research in physical and colloid chemistry, photography, pharmacy and medicine.
excellent color, tasteless, odorless, and free from irritants.	Laxative, and ingredient of health. foods.
high gel strength and resilience, high solubility and excellent stability.	Impression materials, wire-drawing lubricants, wine and juice fining, and luxury fabric sizing.
same as Bacteriological Grade but less clear.	Canning jellied fowl, fish and meat, stabilizing sherberts, ices, cheeses and bakery products, confectionery, and conserves.
Calcium salt of carrageenin.	Various foods, cosmetic, pharmaceutical and industrial uses.
Highly refined calcium salt of carrageenin.	

TABLE 63 (CONTINUED)

Composition	Applications (12)
Irish moss extracts.	For stabilizing ice cream, chocolate milk, toothpaste, etc.; for beer clarification; for other industrial uses.
Irish moss extract and sugar.	Various food, cosmetic, pharmaceutical and industrial uses.

REFERENCES FOR APPENDIX I

1. Mantell, C. L., *The Water Soluble Gums*, Reinhold Pub. Co., New York (1947).
2. Chapman, V. J., *"Seaweeds and Their Uses,"* Methuen and Co., Ltd., London (1950).
3. Newton, Lily, *"Seaweed Utilization,"* Sampson Low, London (1951).
4. Gutman, A. E., *Colloid Chem.*, **6**, 248 (1946).
5. Hilfer, H., *Drug and Cosmetic Ind.*, **67**, 774, (1950).
6. Redgrove, H. S., *Ind. Chemist*, **16**, 145 (1940).
7. Anderson, E., *J. Chem. Ed.*, **9**, 853 (1932).
8. Obst, W., *Gelatine, Leim, Klebstoffe*, **3**, 13 (1935); *Chem. Abstracts*, **29**, 4202 (1935).
9. Mason, C. F., *Chem. Industries*, **53**, 680 (1943).
10. Janistyn, H., *Riechstoff-Ind. Kosmetik*, **11**, 120 (1936), *Chem. Abstracts*, **31**, 4846 (1937).
11. Mason, C. F., *Chemical Industries*, **54**, 66 (1944).
12. Idson, B., *"Chemical Week!"* **79**, No. 3, 57 (1956).
13. Schneider, H. S., *Rev. quím. ind., (Rio de Janeiro)*, **6**, 286 (1937); *Chem. Abstracts*, **31**, 8980 (1937).
14. McBain, J. W., and Hopkins, D. C., *J. Phys. Chem.*, **29**, 188 (1925).
15. Delaunay, A., and Sarciron, R., *Compt. rend. soc. biol.*, **135**, 794 (1941); *Chem. Abstracts*, **37**, 4137 (1943).
16. Windgassen, W., Brit. Pat., 315,173 (1928).
17. Müller, A., U. S. Pat., 1,749,833 (1930).
18. Stewart, E. G., *Bull. Torrey Botan. Club*, **46**, No. 5, 157 (1919); *Expt. Sta. Record*, **43**, 226; *Chem. Abstracts*, **15**, 2898 (1921).
19. Warr, W., Brit. Pat., 4227 (1911).
20. Gruzewska, M., *Compt. rend.*, **173**, 52 (1921).
21. Takahashi, E., *J. Coll. Agr. Hokkaido, Imp. Univ.*, **8**, 183 (1920); *Chem. Abstracts*, **15**, 249 (1921).
22. Komatsu, S., and Ueda, H., *Mem. Coll. Sci. Kyoto Imp. Univ.*, **8**, 51 (1925); *Chem. Abstracts*, **19**, 3481 (1925).
23. Chaplet, A., *Rev. chim. ind.*, **25**, 12, 37 (1914); *Chem. Abstracts*, **8**, 2037 (1914).
24. Hommell, P. E., *Merck's Rep.*, **22**, 12 (1913); *Chem. Abstracts*, **7**, 864 (1913).
25. De Wayne Miles, G., U. S. Pat., 2,456,437 (1948).

26. Mukherjee, J. N., Chobe, M. T., and Nambiar, P. S. R., *Indian Soap J.*, **8**, 182 (1942); *Chem. Abstracts*, **42**, 3596 (1948).

27. Sedgwick, F. H., Soap, *Perfumery, and Cosmetics*, **14**, 42 (1941); *Chem. Abstracts*, **35**, 3389 (1941).

28. Schlaeger, J. R., U. S. Pat., 2,588,324 (1952).

29. Schwarz, H., *Seifensieder Ztg.*, **61**, 45 (1936); *Chem. Abstracts*, **30**, 2323 (1936).

30. Feinberg, S. M., and Schoenkerman, B. B., *Wisconsin Med. J.*, **39**, 734 (1940); *Chem. Abstracts*, **35**, 511 (1941).

31. Gray, G. R., *Bull. Agr. Mech. Coll. Texas; Texas Eng. Expt. Sta. Bull.* No. 96, 63 (1946); *Chem. Abstracts*, **42**, 1725 (1948).

32. Owen, W. L., *Sugar*, **45**, No. 11, 35 (1950).

33. Fast, C. R., U. S. Pat., 2,596,137 (1952).

34. Marcusson, J., *J. Soc. Chem. Ind.*, **37**, 725A, (1918).

35. Tchillingarian, G., and Beeson, C. M., *Petroleum Engr.*, **24**, B45 (1952); *Chem. Abstracts*, **46**, 5299 (1952).

36. Badar-Ud-Din, *Pakistan J. Sci, Research*, **2**, 28 (1950); *Chem. Abstracts*, **46**, 4771 (1952).

37. Westerhof, I., and van der Wielen, P., *Pharm., Weekblad*, **76**, 811 (1939); *Chem. Abstracts*, **33**, 7042 (1939).

38. Schwarz, H., *Seifensieder Ztg.*, **65**, 634 (1938); *Chem. Abstracts*, **32**, 9542 (1938).

39. Kremner, L. Ya., and Kuprik, V. S., *Kolloid Zhur.*, **14**, 98 (1952).

40. King, A., and Mukherjee, L. N., *J. Soc. Chem. Ind.*, **59**, 185 (1940).

41. Kranz, J. C., and Gordon, N. E., *Colloid Symposium Monograph*, **6**, 173 (1928).

42. Will, H., *Apoth. Ztg.*, **49**, 1443 (1934); *Chem. Abstracts*, **29**, 885 (1935).

43. Swiss Pat., 225,886 (1943).

44. Umanskii, Z. M., *Farmatsiya*, **6**, 28 (1943); *Chem. Abstracts*, **38**, 4100 (1944).

45. Jannaway, S. P., *Perfumery Essent. Oil Record*, **35**, 185 (1944).

46. Pijoan, M., U. S. Pat., 2,528,544 (1950).

47. Schulek, E., and Vastagh, G., *Pharm. Zentralhalle*, **69**, 275 (1928).

48. Mori, C., and Izume, S., *J. Agr. Chem. Soc. Japan*, **18**, 439 (1942); *Chem. Abstracts*, **45**, 2618 (1951).

49. Livingston, H. K., *Ind. Eng. Chem.*, **39**, 550 (1947).

50. Lotzkar, H., and Maclay, W. D., *Ind. Eng. Chem.*, **35**, 1294 (1943).

51. Moe, O. A., U. S. Pat., 2,520,161 (1950).

52. Moe, O. A., U. S.,Pat., 2,599,771 (1952).

53. Filbert, W. F., U. S. Pat., 2,599,620 (1952).

54. Black, W. A. P., and Dewar, E. T., *J. Sci. Food. Agr.*, **5**, 176 (1954).

55. Perrin, P. H., Fr. Pat., 860,210 (1941).

56. Scholz, L. A., U. S. Pat., 2,568,369 (1951).

57. Naugle, J. J., Brit. Pat., 533,258 (1941).

58. Scheimpflug, W., *Molkerei-Ztg.*, **53**, 1964 (1939); *Chem. Abstracts*, **34**, 2943 (1940).

59. Blihovde, N., U. S. Pat., 2,604,406 (1952).

60. Werbin, S. J., U. S. Pat., 2,502,397 (1950).

61. Peyer, W., Liebisch, W., and Rosenthal, K., *Apoth. Ztg.*, **44**, 978 (1929); *Chem. Abstracts*, **23**, 4978 (1929).

62. Potter, F. E., and Williams, D. H., *Milk Plant Monthly*, **39**, 76 (1950).

63. Josephson, D. V., and Dahle, C. D., *Ice Cream Reviews,* **28,** (11), 32, 76, 78, 80 (1945).
64. Pyenson, H., and Dahle, C. D., *J. Dairy Sci.,* **21,** 169 (1938).
65. Stall, Anne C., *Food Research,* **17,** 278 (1952).
66. Ferri, C., *Food Inds.,* **19,** 784 (1947); *Chem. Abstracts,* **41,** 7653 (1947).
67. Stevens, J. W., and Pritchett, D. E., U. S. Pat., 2,599,519 (1952).
68. Lilienfeld, L., Ger. Pat., 638,935 (1936).
69. Carles, P., *Ann. Fals.,* **6,** 384 (1914); *Chem. Abstracts,* **8,** 985 (1914).
70. Jacobs, M. B., *Am. Perfumer Essent. Oil Rev,* **54,** 54 (1949); *Chem. Abstracts,* **43,** 8573 (1949).
71. Langwill, K. E., *Mfg. Confectioner,* **19,** 37 (1939); *Chem. Abstracts,* **33,** 5083 (1939).
72. Leo, A., Can. Pat., 284,906 (1928).
73. Woo, M., and Huyck, C. L., *Bull. Natl. Formulary Comm.,* **16,** 140 (1948).
74. Strange, T. E., *J. Assoc. Offic. Agr. Chemists,* **35,** 354 (1952).
75. Coulter, E. W., *J. Assoc. Offic. Agr. Chemists,* **32,** 524 (1949).
76. Brenner, Sadie, Wodicka, V. O., and Dunlop, S. G., *Food Research,* **12,** 253 (1947).
77. Smethurst, P. C., *Process Engravers Monthly,* **54,** 5, 7, 31 (1947); *Chem. Abstracts,* **41,** 5028 (1947).
78. Reed, R. F., *Modern Lithography,* **47,** 62 (1951); *Chem. Abstracts,* **46,** 5225 (1952).
79. Taft, R., and Bingham, O. R., *J. Phys. Chem.,* **36,** 2338 (1932).
80. Hood, W. H., U. S. Pat., 2,589,313 (1952).
81. Jacquet, P. A., *Compt. rend.,* **201,** 953 (1935).
82. Krochmal, F., *Roczniki Chem.,* **20,** 14 (1946); *Chem. Abstracts,* **42,** 1865 (1948).
83. Izgaruishev, N. A., and Titov, P. S., *J. Rus. Phys. Chem. Soc.,* **49,** 573 (1917); *Chem. Abstracts,* **18,** 1410 (1924).
84. Izgaruishev, N. A., *J. Russ. Phys. Chem. Soc.,* **50,** 225 (1918); *Chem. Abstracts,* **18,** 1411 (1924).
85. Izgaruishev, N. A., *Kolloidchem. Beihefte,* **14,** 25 (1921).
86. Muller, J. C., *Rev. facultad guím. ind., y. agr.,* **19,** No. 32, 92 (1950); *Chem. Abstracts,* **45,** 6144 (1951).
87. Greco, A., *Boll. chim. farm.,* **81,** 97 (1942); *Chem. Abstracts,* **38,** 3417 (1944).
88. Nichols, A. B., *J. Am. Pharm. Assoc.,* **28,** 98 (1939).
89. Nichols, A. B., *J. Am. Pharm. Assoc.,* **26,** 823 (1937).
90. Gray, H., and Tainter, M. L., *Am. J. Digestive Diseases,* **8,** 130 (1941).
91. Serrallach, J. A., U. S. Pat., 2,522,306 (1950).
92. Blythe, R. H., Gulesich, J. J., and Tuthill, H. L., *J. Am. Pharm. Assoc.,* **38,** 59 (1949).
93. Pégurier, G., *Rép. de Pharm.,* 246 (1912).
94. Brown, H. T., *Quart. J. Pharm. Pharmacol.,* **6,** 506 (1933).
95. Guidetti, E., *Arch. Farmacol. sper.,* **55,** 69 (1933); *Chem. Abstracts,* **27,** 1937 (1933).
96. Welin, B. P., U. S. Pat., 2,146,867 (1939).
97. Brit. Pat., 496,689 (1938).
98. Weyrauch, F., and Necke, A., *Z. Hyg. Infectionskrankh.,* **114,** 629 (1933); *Chem. Abstracts,* **27,** 5814 (1933).

99. Koester, F., and Rhode, J., Brit. Pat., 275,935 (1926).
100. Schenck, G., *Med. Monatsschr.*, **3**, 700 (1949); *Chem. Abstracts*, **44**, 1223 (1950).
101. Hanzlik, P. J., De Eds, F., Empey, L. W., and Farr, W. H., *J. Pharmacol.*, **32**, 273 (1927).
102. Hawkins, W. W., and O'Neill, A. N., *Can. J. Biochem. Physiol.*, **33**, 545 (1955).
103. Ricketts, C. R., and Walton, K. W., *Chemistry and Industry*, 869 (1952).
104. O'Neill, A. N., *Can. J. Chem.*, **33**, 1097 (1955).
105. Swanson, J. W., *Tappi*, **33**, 451 (1950).
106. Swanson, J. W., *Pulp Paper Mag. Can.*, **51**, No. 10, 99 (1950).
107. Swanson, J. W., *Tappi*, **33**, 77 (1950).
108. Swanson, J. W., U. S. Pat., 2,553,485 (1951).
109. Valliet-Durand, G. R. H., Fr. Pat., 943,887 (1949).
110. Ozawa, T., *J. Chem. Ind.*, *(Japan)*, **25**, 389 (1922); *Chem. Abstracts*, **16**, 4086 (1922).
111. Broadbent, F. D., and Harrison, H. A., *Worlds' Paper Trade Rev.*, **115**, TS49 (1941); *Chem. Abstracts*, **35**, 6451 (1941).
112. Herzberg, W., *Wochenblatt für Papierfabr.*, **25**, 2040 (1908); *Chem. Abstracts*, **2**, 2728 (1908).
113. Herzberg, W., *Mitt. kgl. Materialsprufungsamt, Gross Lichterfelde West*, **27**, 133 (1909); *Chem. Abstracts*, **3**, 2870 (1909).
114. Schwalbe, C. G., and Becker, E., *Angew. Chem.*, **33**, 58 (1920).
115. Vollandigham, V. V., Magnuson, A. L., and Miller, A., *Paper. Ind.*, **33**, 788 (1951); **33**, 1176 (1952).
116. Crabtree, J. I., U. S. Pat., 1,279,276 (1918).
117. Slade, R. E., *3rd Report on Colloid Chem.*, Brit. Assoc., (1920); *Chem. Abstracts*, **15**, 1259 (1921).
118. Fordyce, C. R., and Emerson, J., Brit. Pat., 554,758 (1943).
119. Ariano, R., *Ricerche e studi ist. sper. stradale C. T. I. e R. A. C. I.*, **4**, 45 (1940); *Chem. Abstracts*, **42**, 704 (1948).
120. Burr, W. W., *Nebraska Agr. Expt. Sta. Ann. Rept.*, 58 (1945).
121. Geoghegan, M. J., and Brian, R. C., *Biochem. J.*, **43**, 5 (1948).
122. Perkins, F., and Craft, B. C., *Am. Inst. Mining Met. Engrs.*, Tech. Pub., No. 1551 (1943); *Chem. Abstracts*, **37**, 1586 (1943).
123. Quastel, J. H., and Webley, D. M., *J. Agr. Sci.*, **37**, 257 (1947); *Chem. Abstracts*, **43**, 6771 (1949).
124. Geoghegan, M. J., *Trans. 4th Intern. Congr. Soil Sci.*, Amsterdam, **1**, 198 (1950); **4**, 103 (1950).
125. Chambers, I. F., *Trans. Am. Soc. Mech Engrs.*, **59**, TEX, 741 (1937); *Chem. Abstracts*, **32**, 785 (1938).
126. Brit. Pat., 200,523 (1923).
127. Beer, L., and Klein, J., Ger. Pat., 287,215 (1914).
128. Clark, J. A., *Cotton*, **97**, No. 9, 36 and No. 11, 31 (1933); *Chem. Abstracts*, **28**, 4241 (1934).
129. Harris, T. R., *Proc. Am. Assoc. Textile Chem. Colorists*, 59 (1928); *Chem. Abstracts*, **22**, 1043 (1928).
130. Williams, A. L., *Analyst.*, **53**, 411 (1928).
131. Stolle and Kopke, Ger. Pat., 199,753 (1906), 204,361 (1907); *Chem. Abstracts*, **3**, 849 (1909).

132. Greenwood, C. V., U. S. Pat., 1,105,195 (1914).
133. Walter, K., *Melliand Textilber.*, **31**, 351 (1950).
134. Fitzgerald, J. F., *Textile Age*, **15**, No. 10, 21 (1951); *Chem. Abstracts*, **45**, 10595 (1951).
135. Haller, R., *Teintex.*, **15**, 257 (1950); *Chem. Abstracts*, **44**, 8664 (1950).
136. Shikher, M. G., *J. App. Chem.* (U.S.S.R.), **18**, 329 (1945) (English Summary); *Chem. Abstracts*, **40**, 3267 (1946).
137. Kaplan, P., U. S. Pat. 1,990,330 (1935).
138. Apsey, G. W., Jr., U. S. Pat., 2,093,405 (1937).
139. Carlson, F. P., U. S. Pat., 2,094,348 (1937).
140. Ger. Pat. 707,847 (1941).
141. Glarum, S. N., *Am. Dyestuff Reptr.*, **26**, P 124 (1937); *Chem. Abstracts*, **31**, 3283 (1937).
142. Patwardhan, V. C., and Ramachandran, S. R., *J. Indian Chem. Soc., Ind. and News Ed.*, **8**, 14 (1945); *Chem. Abstracts*, **40**, 3608 (1946).
143. Mukoseev, N. A., *Tekstil. Prom.* No. 1/2 23 (1943); *Chem. Abstracts*, **38**, 647 (1944).
144. Fuller, A. R., U. S. Pat., 2,403,575 (1946).
145. Burton, A., *Can. Chem. J.*, 4, 102 (1920).
146. Pinel, A., Brit. Pat., 522,815 (1940).
147. Dudgeon, (Mrs.) M. J., Thomas, R. S., and Woodward, F. N., *J. Soc. Dyers and Colorists*, **70**, 230 (1954).
148. Chapin, R. M., *Ind. Eng. Chem.*, **19**, 1275 (1929).
149. Opie, J. W., Nordgren, R., and Hamilton, R. M., U. S. Pat., 2,767,167 (1956).
150. Beyer, C., Ger. Pat., 243,248 (1911).
151. Diaz, H., *Rev. quim.* 6, No. 11, 8 (1931); *Chem. Abstracts*, **25**, 5588 (1931).
152. Eddy, C. O., and Meadows, C. M., *J. Econ. Entomol.*, **30**, 430 (1937).
153. Sharp, S. S., *J. Econ. Entomol.*, **32**, 394 (1939).
154. Garman, P., *Conn. Agr. Expt. Station (New Haven) Bull.*, **428**, 76 (1939).
155. Penn, A. B. K., and Wen, T. S., *Bull. Chungking Inst. Ind. Research*, No. 10 (1948); *Chem. Abstracts*, **44**, 8564 (1950).
156. Bateson, F. R. C., *Pharm. J.*, **126**, 52 (1931).
157. Brindle, H., and Rowson, J. M., *Quart. J. Pharm. Pharmacol.*, **9**, 161 (1936).
158. DeNavarre, M. G., and Kolhler, M., *Am. Perfumer Essent. Oil Rev.*, **51**, 160 (1948); *Chem. Abstracts*, **42**, 5613 (1948).
159. Stratta, R., *Ann. chim. applicata*, **29**, 115 (1939); *Chem. Abstracts*, **33**, 9087 (1939).
160. Lindner, K., *Seifensieder Ztg.*, **72**, 174 (1946); *Chem. Abstracts*, **43**, 6436 (1949).
161. Violini, T., Ital. Pat., 428,148 (1947).
162. Georg, W., U. S. Pat., 2,456,121 (1948).
163. Fonda, V., Ital. Pat., 460,630 (1950).
164. Besnard, Fr. Pat., 364,341 (1906).
165. Geller, H. H., U. S. Pat., 2,559,612 (1951).
166. Colomb, P., *Ind. vernice (Milan)*, **4**, 64 (1950); *Chem. Abstracts*, **44**, 10346 (1950).
167. Schlick, W., *Farben, Lacke, Anstrichstoffe*, **3**, 303 (1949); *Chem. Abstracts*, **44**, 849 (1950).
168. Loiseleur, J., and Velluz, L., *Compt. rend.*, **192**, 159 (1931).

169. Mantell, C. L., *Chem. Industries*, **38**, 577 (1936); *Chem. Abstracts*, **30**, 5323 (1936).
170. Sanborn, J. R., *J. Bact.*, **31**, 90 (1936).
171. Sanborn, J. R., *Ind. Eng. Chem.*, **28**, 1189 (1936).
172. Herzog, R. O., and Meier, A., U. S. Pat., 1,141,545 (1915).
173. Atwood, G. E., and Bourne, D. J., *Mining Engineering*, **5**, No. 11, 1099 (1953).
174. Kerr, R. W., and Neukom, H., *Die Stärke*, **4**, 255 (1952).
175. Cook, S. R. B., Schulz, N. F., and Lindroos, E. W., *Mining Engineering*, **4**, 697 (1952).
176. McNaught, M. L., Smith, J. A. B., and Black, W. A. P., *J. Sci. Food. Agric.*, **5**, 350 (1954).
177. Sanborn, J. R., *Ind. Eng. Chem.*, **26**, 532 (1934).
178. Sanborn, J. R., U. S. Pat., 2,026,253 (1936).
179. Russian Pat., 11,305 (1926).
180. Rawlings, F. N., *Proc. Am. Soc. Sugar Beet Technol.*, **6**, 528 (1950).
181. Gaddie, R. S., *Proc. Am. Soc. Sugar Beet Technol.*, **6**, 532 (1950).
182. Steiner, A. B., and McNeely, W. H., *Advances in Chem. Series*, No. 11, 68 (1954).
183. Tseng, C. K., *Colloid Chemistry*, Ed. J. Alexander, *Vol.* **6**, Reinhold Pub. Corp., New York (1946) 629.
184. McDowell, R. H., *Trans. Plastics Inst. (London)*, **17**, 62 (1949); *Chem. Abstracts*, **44**, 2674 (1950).
185. Tressler, D. K., and Lemon, J. M. *Marine Products of Commerce*, 2nd ed., Reinhold Pub. Corp., New York (1951) 94.
186. Anonymous, *Chem. and Eng. News*, **34**, 5184 (1956).
187. Musher, S., U. S. Pat., 2,355,029 (1944).
188. Musher, S., U. S. Pat., 2,436,818 (1948).
189. Bolley, D. S., and McCormac, R. H., U. S. Pat., 2,593,528 (1952).
190. Clark, G. M., Brit. Pat., 578,802 (1946).
191. Musher, S., U. S. Pat., 2,355,028 (1944).
192. Anonymous, *Chem. and Eng. News*, **35**, No. 4, 78 (1957).
193. Swift, A. M., *"Polyacrylamide—A New Synthetic, Water-Soluble Gum"* Presented before Plastics Section, *Tappi*, Appleton, Wisc. Oct. 4 (1956).

APPENDIX II

PHYSICAL CONSTANTS OF METHYL SUGARS AND THEIR DERIVATIVES ISOLATED IN THE STUDY OF GUMS AND MUCILAGES

DERIVATIVES OF PENTOSES, HEXOSES, DEOXYHEXOSES, URONIC ACIDS AND ALDOBIOURONIC ACIDS ISOLATED FROM GUMS AND MUCILAGES

Compound	M.p.	$[\alpha]_D$ (solvent)	Reference
L-Arabinose			
2-O-Methyl-			
3,4-O-isopropylidene	116–118	+100 (W)	1–4
		+91.5 (C)	1
		+125 (M)	1
		+117.5 (A)	1
N-phenylglycosylamine	143		4
methyl β-pyranoside	63–65	+208 (M)	1
hydrate	46–47		1
phenylhydrazone	115,116		2–4
3-O-Methyl-		+110 (W)	5
N-phenylglycosylamine	117		5
phenylosazone	163		6
2,3-Di-O-methyl-		+107 (W)	2,3,6
di-p-nitrobenzoate	150–153		316
N-phenylglycosylamine	139		2,3,6

514

	m.p.	Rotation	References
2,4-Di-O-methyl-			268,269
N-phenylglycosylamine	145, 126	+118, +129 (W)	268,269
(2,5-Di-O-methyl-D-arabinose)		−21, −23 (W)	12,13,272,273)
3,4-Di-O-methyl-		+104, +116, +125 (W)	268,270,271
phenylosazone	142		268
3,5-Di-O-methyl-			
phenylosazone	170		7
2,3,4-Tri-O-methyl-		+120, +127 (W)	8,9,268,269
methyl α-pyranoside	44–46	+250 (W), +223 (M)	8,9
methyl β-pyranoside	46–48	+46.2 (W), +24 (M)	8
2,3,5-Tri-O-methyl-		−39.5 (W)	234
L-Arabonic acid			
2-O-Methyl-			
amide	130	+51 (W)	2,3
3-O-Methyl-			
γ-lactone	78	−74 (W)	5
amide	132		5
2,3-Di-O-methyl-			
γ-lactone	35	−38 ⟶ −25 (W)	2,3,6,53
amide	162	+17 (W)	2,3,6,10,53
2,4-Di-O-methyl-			
amide	158		11
2,5-Di-O-methyl-			
lactone	60	−58 (W) (initial value)	11,12
amide	132	+38 (W)	11,12
phenylhydrazide	163		11,12,13

NOTE:

Unless stated otherwise rotations quoted for reducing methyl sugars are equilibrium values.

The following abbreviations are used: A(acetone), B(benzene), C(chloroform), D(1,4-dioxane), E(ethanol), EA(ethyl acetate), ET(diethyl ether), M(methanol), P(pyridine), W(water).

APPENDIX II (Continued)

Compound	M.p.	$[\alpha]_D$ (solvent)	Reference
L-Arabonic acid (Cont.)			
3,4-Di-O-methyl-			
amide	133	+28.2 (W)	271
3,5-Di-O-methyl-			
lactone	78	−43 (C), −84 (W)	5,7,14,15
amide	145	+10 (W)	5,14,15
phenylhydrazide	144		5
2,3,4-Tri-O-methyl-			
amide	107	+24.4 (W), +45 (M)	11,192
phenylhydrazide	156		11
2,3,5-Tri-O-methyl-			
lactone	33	−45 ⟶ −24 (W)	11,16,235
amide	138	+16 (W), +21 (E)	7,11−15,17,192
D-Xylose			
2-O-Methyl-	132−133	−24 ⟶ +36 (W)	18
	135−137	−23 ⟶ +35 (W)	19
N-phenylglycosylamine	125−126, 128	+214, +237[a] (EA)	19,274
3,4-diacetate	78−79	−38 (C)	18
1,3,4-triacetate	95	−2.2 (C)	18
3,4-di-O-tosyl	123	−16 (C)	18
methyl β-pyranoside	111−112	−67.7 (C)	18
3-O-Methyl-	103−104	+55 ⟶ +17 (W)	20,21
N-phenylglycosylamine	137	+80 (EA)	20,35,249
phenylosazone	172		19
p-bromophenylosazone	153−155	+6 ⟶ −14 (P-E)	21

(a)Recorded incorrectly as 23.7 in reference (274).

Compound	M.p.	[α]	References
4-O-Methyl-			
methyl β-pyranoside	95	+9 (W)	275
phenylosazone	158–158.5	−69 (W)	275
	160–161	+25 → ±0 (P-E)	22
5-O-Methyl-		+36 (W)	275
p-bromophenylosazone	170–171	−50 → −30 (P-E)	21
1,2-O-isopropylidene-3-O-tosyl	81–82	−31.8 (C)	21, 23
2,3-Di-O-methyl-			
α-	79–80	+70 → +23 (W)	24–26
β-	79–80	−7.3 → +26.7 (W)	236
N-phenylglycosylamine	146, 126	+185 (EA)	25,276,277
methyl β-pyranoside	63	−47.3 (W)	276
di-p-nitrobenzoate	193	−96 (C)	281
2,4-Di-O-methyl-	108	−30 → +22 (W)	27
	111		20
N-phenylglycosylamine	116–118	−26 (C)	22
	170	−82 (D)	27
methyl β-pyranoside	155–157	−40 (EA)	22
	77.5–78.5	−70 (C)	22
	60–61	−82.4 (C)	18
3,4-Di-O-methyl-		+20.5 (W)	18,28
methyl β-pyranoside	89–90	−82 (C)	18
2-O-tosyl	105	−34.8 (C)	18
3,5-Di-O-methyl-		+25 (W)	278
p-bromophenylosazone	107–108	−46 (P-E)	21
2,3,4-Tri-O-methyl-	91–92	+64 → +18 (W), +54 (C)	20,24,28–34
N-phenylglycosylamine	102	−84 → +47 (E)	20,35
methyl β-pyranoside	49–50	−73 (C)	22
p-nitrobenzoate	136	−76 (C)	281

APPENDIX II (*Continued*)

Compound	M.p.	$[\alpha]_D$ (solvent)	Reference
D-Xylonic acid			
2-O-Methyl-			
γ-lactone	66–68	+101 (W)	19
amide	96–98	+52.5 (W)	19
3-O-Methyl-			
γ-lactone	94	+76 (W)	20
2,3-Di-O-methyl-			
amide	133.5	+46 (W)	33,36
p-bromophenylhydrazide	150–151		25
phenylhydrazide	107–108	+30 (E)	25
2,4-Di-O-methyl-			
amide	98–100	+51 (W)	22
phenylhydrazide	143.5–144.5	+47 (E)	22
3,4-Di-O-methyl-			
lactone	68	$-56 \longrightarrow -27$ (W) (65 hr.)	28,37
phenylhydrazide	132		275
3,5-Di-O-methyl-			
phenylhydrazide	95–96	+6 (E)	21
2,3,4-Tri-O-methyl-			
lactone	56	$-4 \longrightarrow +21$ (W)(120 hr.)	28,38
phenylhydrazide	138		28,38
2,3,5-Tri-O-methyl-			
amide	84–85		279
phenylhydrazide	89		25
L-Fucose			
2-O-Methyl-			
methyl 3,4-O-isopropylidene-	147–149	$-71 \longrightarrow -81$ (W)	256
β-pyranoside	88–89	−10.9 (M)	39

Compound	M.p.	[α]	References
3-O-Methyl-			
methyl α-pyranoside	110	−94 (W), −97 (W), −61 (E)	40,330
phenylosazone	130–132	−173 (W)	40
5-O-Methyl-	172–176		40
phenylosazone	190	+28.3 (W)	330
2,3-Di-O-methyl-			330
methyl α-pyranoside	49–51	+4.6 (W), −97 (W)	40,330
3,4-Di-O-methyl-	82	−190 (W)	40
methyl α-pyranoside	100	−118 (W)	41
2,4-Di-O-methyl-	118–121	−213 (W)	41
	131–132	−100 ⟶ −69 (W)	256
		−85 (W)	330
2,3,4-Tri-O-methyl-			
hydrate	36–37	−184 ⟶ −128 (W)	39
	65	−169 ⟶ −118 (W)	39
N-phenylglycosylamine	133–134	−77 (E)	28,39
methyl α-pyranoside	97–98	−209 (W)	39
	85–92	−196 (W)	28
methyl β-pyranoside	101.5–102.5	−21 (W)	39
2,3,5-Tri-O-methyl		+70 (W), +55 (E)	330
L-Fuconic acid			
3-O-Methyl-			
amide	176–180	+16.4 (W)	40
2,3-Di-O-methyl-			
amide	78–79	+30.2 (W)	40
3,5-Di-O-methyl-			
lactone	102–103	+66 ⟶ +51 (W)	256
2,3,4-Tri-O-methyl-			
amide		−35 (W)	28
L-Rhamnose			
2-O-Methyl	113–114	+31, +24 (W)	42,43,261
methyl pyranoside	139–140		43
N-phenylglycosylamine	152	+43 (P)	261

APPENDIX II (Continued)

Compound	M.p.	$[\alpha]_D$ (solvent)	Reference
L-Rhamnose (Cont.)			
3-O-Methyl-	113, 115	+35 (W)	262,263
phenylosazone	128–130	+57 (P-E) (after 17 hr.)	44
hydrate	118		44
4-O-Methyl-	125–126	+13 (M)	45
	122	+12.9 (M)	46,47
		−12.9 (M-NH₃)	47
methyl α-pyranoside	60–61	−87.3 (M)	238
phenylosazone	162–163	+26.0 ⟶ +14 (P-E)	45
5-O-Methyl-	102–103	−4.3 (W)	45
phenylhydrazone	162–163	−18.4 ⟶ +8.1 (P) (1 week)	45
phenylosazone	123–124	+65.3 ⟶ +44.4 (P-E) (3 days)	45
α-triacetate	115–116	−76.3 (M)	45
methyl α-furanoside	59–60	−89.2 (W)	45
2,3-Di-O-methyl-	138–139	+47.6, +42.5	44,264
N-phenylglycosylamine	93	+147.8 ⟶ +42.8 (E)(70 hr.)	41,238
methyl 5-O-benzyl-glycoside		−72 (A)	44
2,4-dinitrophenyl-hydrazone	168 (dec.)	+45.4 (D)	238
3,4-Di-O-methyl-	102–103	±0 ⟶ +18.6 (W)	48,49
1,2-(methyl orthoacetate)	91–92	−10 ⟶ +18.6 (W)	50
2,4-dinitrophenylhydrazone	67	+36 (W)	50
2,4-Di-O-methyl-	170 (dec.)	+75.6 (D)	238
N-phenylglycosylamine	80, 91–93	+3 (E), +10.6 (W)	238
2,4-dinitrophenylhydrazone	141–142.5	+136 ⟶ +4 (E)(24 hr.)	238
	164–165 (dec.)	+39 (D)	238

	m.p.	[α]	References
2,3,4-Tri-O-methyl-			
N-phenylglycosylamine	111	+27, +25 (W)	50,265,266
methyl β-pyranoside	53–54	+130 (A)	12,267
		+106 (W)	50
L-Rhamnonic acid			
2-O-Methyl-			
lactone	116–117	−62 ⟶ −64 (W)	261
amide	117–118		261
4-O-Methyl-			
lactone	82	−141 ⟶ −115 (W)	46,261
5-O-Methyl			
lactone	164–166	−36 (W)	261
3,4-Di-O-methyl-			
lactone	76–78	−150 ⟶ −116 (W)	48,51
amide	152–155		50,51
2,3,4-Tri-O-methyl-			
lactone	40–41	−130 ⟶ −78 (W)	52
phenylhydrazide	177		12,52,53
2,3,5-Tri-O-methyl-			
phenylhydrazide	160		12
D-Galactose			
2-O-Methyl-			
N-phenylglycosylamine	145–148	+52 ⟶ +83 (W)	17,54,55
methyl β-pyranoside	165		17,55
3-O-Methyl-	131–132	+1.7 (W)	54,56
phenylosazone	144–147	+150.6 ⟶ +108.6 (W)	57
	178–184	+17.2 (E)	57
	200		57
	176–179	+63.5 (P)	54,58,59
4-O-Methyl-	207	+62 ⟶ +92 (W)	17
	218–221	+61 ⟶ +83 (W)	254

APPENDIX II (*Continued*)

Compound	M.p.	$[\alpha]_D$ (solvent)	Reference
D-Galactose (Cont.)			
N-phenylglycosylamine	168,182–183	$-84 \longrightarrow -39$ (M)	17,254
phenylosazone	150		17,60
	147–150		61
	148–150		62
6-O-Methyl-	128	$+114$ (W)	63,255
	113–114	$+137 \longrightarrow +77$ (W)	59
methyl α-pyranoside	138	$+165$ (W)	319
methyl β-pyranoside	114–115	± 0 (W)	54
phenylosazone	204–205	$+141$ (P)	56,59,63,255
2,3-Di-O-methyl-		$+81, +116$ (W)	59,64
N-phenylglycosylamine	130–131	$+119.4$ (E)	58
	128–129		59
	154–155	-57 (20 min.) $\longrightarrow +12.1$ (E)	64
2,4-Di-O-methyl-			
hydrate	103, 105–108	$+122 \longrightarrow +86$ (W)	17,60,62,254
methyl α-pyranoside	105	$+142$ (W)	60,62
methyl β-pyranoside	166, 162	± 0 (W), $+5$ (M)	7,17,60
N-phenylglycosylamine	216	-180 (P)	17,60,62,67
	219–220	$+30$ (M)	254
2,6-Di-O-methyl-	128–130, 134	$+47 \longrightarrow +87.5$ (W)	54,257
	120	$+48 \longrightarrow +87$	65,252
monohydrate	90,98–100		253,257
methyl β-pyranoside	46.5	-23 (C)	54
	73–75	-24 (C)	66
	72	-22 (C)	252
		$+2$ (W)	66
N-phenylglycosylamine	121–122	$+15$ (E)	65,252

Compound	M.p.	Rotation	References
3,4-Di-O-methyl-	164–166	+95 → +117 (W)	68
methyl β-pyranoside	102–103	−9.1 (C)	68
4,6-Di-O-methyl-	131–133	+133 → +76.9 (W)	69
hydrate	105	+123 → +82 (W)	29
methyl β-pyranoside	140	−41.5 (C)	69
N-phenylglycosylamine	207	−174 (P)	29
phenylosazone	158	−25 (E)	70
	153	+60 → −24 (E)	29
	159–160		71
2,3,4-Tri-O-methyl-	160–162	+51 → −21 (E)	69
	86, 82–83	+156 → +119 (W)	55,97,98
monohydrate	80	+152 → +114 (W)	55,60
N-phenylglycosylamine	167, 170	−65 → +43 (M)	60,29,55,72
methyl α-pyranoside	30	+198.4 (W)	97
		+161 (M)	97
2,3,6-Tri-O-methyl-	105	+80, +87	86,258
2,4,6-Tri-O-methyl-	102–105	+124 → +89 (W)	70,71,318
	113–114	+124 → +90.4 (W)	71
		+112.6 → +90.9 (W)	260
hydrate	83–85		17
methyl α-pyranoside	73–74	+164 (W)	70,71
methyl β-pyranoside	102	+18 (M)	17
N-phenylglycosylamine	111–112	−40.9 (C)	71
	179	−92 → +38 (A)	17,29,67
	170		318
3,4,6-Tri-O-methyl-	88–89	+154 → +110 (W)	237
2,3,4,6-Tetra-O-methyl-	75	+149 → +117 (W)	60,73–75
	72	+142 → +118 (W)	11,76,77
	192	−83 → +41 (A)	78,79
N-phenylglycosylamine	197		29
	195–196		62
	192	−77 → +37.7 (A)	74,79

APPENDIX II (*Continued*)

Compound	M.p.	$[\alpha]_D$ (solvent)	Reference
D-Galactose (Cont.)			
methyl β-pyranoside	48.5	+19.6 (W), −24 (E)	80
	48–49	+18.7 (W)	81
L-Galactose			
2,3,4,6-Tetra-O-methyl-N-phenylglycosylamine	197	+70(A)	82
D-Galactonic acid			
2,4-Di-O-methyl-			
lactone	113	+162 ⟶ +52.6 (W)	60,62
amide	167	+59 (W)	17,60,62
phenylhydrazide	183		60
2,6-Di-O-methyl-			
amide	154–155	+46 (W)	65,252
phenylhydrazide	140	−45 (E)	65,66,252
3,4-Di-O-methyl-			
amide	172–174		68
4,6-Di-O-methyl-			
amide (hydrate)	164	+54 (W)	29
2,3,4-Tri-O-methyl-			
amide	165	+32 (W)	60
phenylhydrazide	176	+36 (E)	14,15,55,60
	165–167		80
2,3,5-Tri-O-methyl-			
lactone	90	−5, −8	83,84
		−37 ⟶ −32 (W)	83,84
amide	152	+3 (W)	83
	162–163	+5 (W)	84

phenylhydrazide	144	+18 (E)	83
2,3,6-Tri-O-methyl-			
γ-lactone	98	−44 ⟶ −37	95,253,258
amide	99	−40 ⟶ −28 (W)	46,85,86
phenylhydrazide	101	−44 ⟶ −29 (W)	14,15,85
2,4,6-Tri-O-methyl-	135		46,86,259
amide	175		259
3,4,6-Tri-O-methyl-	166, 167	+73 (W)	17,70
2,3,4,6-Tetra-O-methyl-	127–128		237
amide	84	+22.6 (W)	87
phenylhydrazide	121–122	+36 (A)	6,88
2,3,4,5,6-Penta-O-methyl-	135–137		6,73
methyl ester	46	+20 (W)	82
D-Galacturonic acid			
methyl α-pyranoside	148		89
methyl ester	110–112	+131 (W)	90
hydrate	225–226	+127 (W)	89
amide			
2-O-Methyl-			
methyl α-pyranoside	174	+55 (E)	91
amide	174–175	+60 (W)	92
2,3-Di-O-methyl-		+62 (W)	46
methyl β-pyranoside	111	−11 (W)	93
methyl ester			
methyl β-furanoside			
amide	124	−151 (W)	83
2,4-Di-O-methyl-		+93 (W)	95
3,4-Di-O-methyl-		+37 (E), +93 (W)	92
methyl α-pyranoside	154–155	+158 (C), +156 (M)	92
		+163 (W)	92

APPENDIX II (*Continued*)

Compound	M.p.	$[\alpha]_D$ (solvent)	Reference
D-Galacturonic acid (Cont.)			
methyl ester	113–114	+165 (C)	92
amide	130–131	+108 (E)	92
methylamide	205	+116 (W)	92
2,3,4-Tri-*O*-methyl-monohydrate	96–98	+126 $\longrightarrow$ +104.2 (W)	94
	98–99	+120 $\longrightarrow$ +104 (W)	95
methyl α-pyranoside			
methyl ester	73	+169 (W)	48,96
		+149 (A)	83,97
		+142 (C)	89
amide	153–153.5	+121.5 (C)	98
	154	+139 (W)	93
methyl β-pyranoside	70–72	+11 (W)	93
methyl ester	102	−21 (M), −7 (W)	93
2,3,5-Tri-*O*-methyl-methyl β-furanoside			
methyl ester	42, 43	−123, −129 (M)	83
amide	106	−151 (W)	83
Galactaric acid			
D-2-*O*-Methyl-diamide	200, 205		91,92
D-2,3-Di-*O*-methyl-6-methyl ester-1,4-lactone	92	−56 $\longrightarrow$ −4 (W)	83
	96	−40 (W)	99
diamide	228		83
bis(methylamide)	184	−7.5 (W)	83

D-2,4-Di-O-methyl-			
1-methyl ester-6,3-lactone	111	+120 (W)	60
diamide	229	+30 (W)	60
bis (methylamide)	214	+27 (W)	60
3,4-Di-O-methyl-			
diethyl ester	148–149		92
dimethyl ester	172–173		92
diamide	230		92
D-2,3,4-Tri-O-methyl			
dimethyl ester	101	+42 (A)	89
	103	+36 (W)	60,80
	101.5	+29 (W)	35,89
diamide	273 (dec.)		60
bis(methylamide)	205	+7.5 (W)	60
	207	+12.6 (M)	89
6-methyl ester-1-amide	156	+34 (W)	60
D-2,3,5-Tri-O-methyl			
6-methyl ester-1,4-lactone	62	−83 (W)	83
diamide	255		83
bis(methylamide)	232	−22 (W)	83
D-2,4,5-Tri-O-methyl-			
1-methyl ester-6,3-lactone	64	+85 (W)	60
diamide	225 (dec.)		60
bis(methylamide)	232 (dec.)	+23 (W)	60
2,3,4,5-Tetra-O-methyl-			
dimethyl ester	109		60
diamide	276		100
Galactitol			
D-2,3,5,6-Tetra-O-methyl-	41–41.5	−24 (W)	283
	83–84	−27 (W)	284
1,4-diazobenzoate	99–100		283

APPENDIX II (Continued)

Compound	M.p.	$[\alpha]_D$ (solvent)	Reference
3,6-Anhydro-D-galactose		+27.5 (W)	285
		+24 (W)	286
diethyldithioacetal	113	−10 (W), +27 (P)	289,290
phenylosazone	216	±0 (P)	286
	215	+71 (M)	289,291
dimethylacetal			286
2,4,5-tri-p-nitrobenzoate	112	+36.5 (W)	286,289
2,4-di-O-methyl-		+24 (W)	286
N-phenylglycosylamine	122		286,287,288
dimethylacetal	36 n_D^{18} 1.4450	+36 (W)	286
2,4,5-tri-O-methyl-	n_D^{17} 1.4510	+41 (W)	286
dimethylacetal		+41 (W)	286
methyl α-pyranoside	140	+84 (W)	285,286,293
2,4-diacetate	87	+71 (E)	281
2-O-methyl	102	+88 (W)	294
4-O-methyl	55	+75 (W)	294
2-O-tosyl	126	+88 (C)	294
2,4-di-O-methyl	n_D^{17} 1.4640	+73 (W), +99 (ET)	286
2-O-tosyl	138	+56 (C)	294
methyl β-pyranoside	119	−115 (W)	286–288,295
2,4-diacetate	93	−95 (E)	281
2,4-di-O-methyl	83	−77 (W)	286
3,6-Anhydro-D-galactonic acid			
methyl ester	n_D^{18} 1.4840	+33 (W)	286
2,4-di-O-methyl-	152	+38 (W)	286
methyl ester	51	+66 (W)	286
	151	+67 (W)	286
		+81 (W)	286

	m.p. / n_D^{18}	$[\alpha]_D$	References
2,4,5-tri-O-methyl-			
methyl ester	n_D^{18} 1.4480	+64 (W)	286
brucine salt	114	+67 (W)	286
		−3 (W)	286
3,6-Anhydro-L-galactose		−39.4 ⟶ −25.2 (W)	298
diphenylhydrazone	153	−34.6 (M)	297
phenylosazone	218	−75.4 ⟶ −53.5 (P:M,2:3)	296–298,318
diethyldithioacetal	111	+14.1 (W), −21.1 (E),	298
		−26.3 (P)	298
1,2,4-tri-p-nitrobenzoate	140–142	+18.5 (C)	298
dimethylacetal			
2,4-di-O-methyl-		−24.6 (W)	297
N-phenylglycosylamine	117	−23 (W)	287,288,297,299
methyl α-pyranoside	139		299
methyl β-pyranoside		−85 (W)	318
2,4-di-O-methyl-	83	+85 (C), +75 (W)	287,288,299
3,6-Anhydro-L-galactonic acid			
2,4-di-O-methyl-	150	−60.8 (W)	297
methyl ester	49	−72.5 (C), −64 (W)	287,288
amide	150	−74 (W)	288,297
2,5-di-O-methyl-	160	−65 (W)	82
amide	173		82,301

DERIVATIVES OF DISACCHARIDES CONTAINING 3,6-ANHYDRO-D- AND L-GALACTOSE

	m.p.	$[\alpha]_D$	References
3-O-(3,6-Anhydro-L-galacto-pyranosyl)-D-galactose (Neoagarobiose)	208	+34.4 ⟶ +20.3 (W)	297
hexaacetate	112	+2 (C), +0.8 (M)	297
phenylosazone	200	+59.8 ⟶ +56.1 (M:P,3:2)	297

APPENDIX II (Continued)

Compound	M.p.	$[\alpha]_D$ (solvent)	Reference
3-O-(3,6-Anhydro-L-galacto-pyranosyl)-D-galactitol (Neoagarobiitol)		−20 (W)	297
Methyl 3-O-(2,4-di-O-methyl-3,6-anhydro-β-L-galactopyranosyl)-2,4,6-tri-O-methyl-D-galacto-pyranoside	128	−19.6 (M), −22 (C)	297
4-O-β-D-Galactopyranosyl-3,6-anhydro-L-galactose (agarobiose)		−17.4 ⟶ −14.2 (W)	302
		−17 (0.01 N oxalic acid)	318
dimethylacetal	163–166	−36 (M)	318
hexaacetate	137.5–138.5	−13.5 (B)	318
	87–88	−5.8 (C), −12.5 (B)	303
phenylosazone	220–221	−115 (P : E, 2 : 3)	303,318
diethyldithioacetal	171–172	−20.9 (M), −8.5 (W), −51.7 (P)	303
hexaacetate	101–103.5	−11.8 (C), −22.1 (B), −16.7 (E)	303
4-O-(2,3,4,6-Tetra-O-methyl-β-D-galactopyranosyl)-2,5-di-O-methyl-3,6-anhydro-L-galactose	92–93	−4 ⟶ −9.3 (W), −9.8 ⟶ −53.7 (C)	303
4-O-β-D-Galactopyranosyl-3,6-anhydro-L-galactitol (Agarobiitol)	174	−15 (W)	318
hepta-O-methyl		−36 (M)	318
4-O-β-D-Galactopyranosyl-3,6-anhydro-D-galactose (Carrabiose)		+15.6 (W)	325
diethyldithioacetal	117.5	+4 (W)	325
hexaacetate	119	−4 (C)	325
phenylosazone	216	+46 (P : E, 2 : 3)	325

D-Glucose

	M.p.	Rotation	References
2-O-Methyl-	157–159	+12.0 ⟶ +66.0 (W)	101–104
phenylhydrazone	175–178	−12.3, −13.3 (P)	102,105–107
1,3,4,6-tetrabenzoate	169–170	−6.2 (C)	108
methyl α-pyranoside	147–148	+155 (W)	101
methyl β-pyranoside	97–98	−37.5 (W), −41.9 (M)	108
3-O-Methyl-			
α-	161, 168	+104.5 ⟶ +55.5 (W)	109–112
β-	133.5–135	+31.9 ⟶ +55.5 (W)	109–113
N-phenylglycosylamine	154–155	−105.5 ⟶ −41.6 (E)	109
phenylosazone	178, 185	−5.2 (C)	110,112,114,115
β-tetraacetate	95–96	+3.6 (C)	116
β-tetrabenzoate	198–199	+163 (C)	108
tetraazobenzoate	220–224	+163 (C)	117,118
4-O-Methyl-	98	+191 (E)	331
methyl α-pyranoside	94–95	167 (W)	334
methyl β-pyranoside	102–103	−17.6 (W)	326–328
2,3,6-triacetate	106	−34 (C)	327,329
phenylosazone	158–160	−32.6 ⟶ −15.5 (E)	119,120
5-O-Methyl-			
phenylosazone	117, 128	−72 ⟶ −12 (E)	121,122
6-O-Methyl-	143–145	+110 ⟶ +59, +55 (W)	123–126
1,2-O-isopropylidene	71–72	−6.2 (C)	123,124
methyl β-pyranoside	133–135	−27.0 (W)	127
phenylosazone	184–187	−75 ⟶ −44 (E)	123,125,126,128,129
α-1,2,3,4-tetraacetate	120	+111.8 (C)	129
β-1,2,3,4-tetraacetate	93, 96	+21 (C)	123,129
1,2,3,4-tetraazobenzoate	141–143	+180 (λ, 6252) (C)	126
2,3-Di-O-methyl-			
α-	85–87	+81.9 ⟶ +48.3 (A)	130
β-	110, 121	+6.5 ⟶ +50.9 (A)	130,131

APPENDIX II (Continued)

Compound	M.p.	$[\alpha]_D$ (solvent)	Reference
D-Glucose (Cont.)			
N-phenylglycosylamine	134	+97.8 (λ, 6252) (C)	132
1,4,6-triazobenzoate	185, 209	+142.6, +150.2 (W)	117,133
methyl α-pyranoside	83–85	–47.8 (C)	130,134
methyl β-pyranoside	62–64		108,135
p-nitrophenylhydrazone	164–165		317
N-p-tolyglycosylamine	156–157	–88 $\longrightarrow$ +38 (E)	317
2,4-Di-O-methyl-	128–130	+37.3 $\longrightarrow$ +76.5 (W)	136,137
methyl α-pyranoside	79–81	+159, +186 (A)	138,139
methyl β-pyranoside	124	–16.3, –18.6 (A)	138–141
N-(p-nitrophenyl)glycosylamine	250–251	–252 $\longrightarrow$ –268 (P)	137
N-(p-bromophenyl)glycosylamine	243–244	–147 (P)	137
N-phenylglycosylamine	196		136
2,6-Di-O-methyl-		+58.3, +63.3 (W)	126,145
methyl α-pyranoside	50–52	+152, +156 (W)	144
methyl β-pyranoside	131	–43.5 (C)	145
1,3,4-triazobenzoate	207	–172 (λ, 6252) (C)	126
	206–208	–275 (λ, 6252) (C)	126
		–341 (C)	320
3,4-Di-O-methyl-	113	+65 $\longrightarrow$ +94.8 (W)	146
β-	79–81	–11.9 (C)	146,147
methyl β-pyranoside	126		148
phenylosazone		–21 (W)	273,321
3,5-Di-O-methyl-	64–65	–83 (E)	321
phenylosazone			
3,6-Di-O-methyl-	113–116	+102.5 $\longrightarrow$ +61.5 (W)	149–151
α-		–45.8 (C)	150
1,2-O-isopropylidene			

Compound	m.p.	$[\alpha]$	References
methyl β-pyranoside		+55.4 (E)	149
4,6-Di-O-methyl-			
α-	156–158	+110 ⟶ +64 (W)	117,152–154
methyl α-pyranoside		+157 (C)	117,154
methyl β-pyranoside	50–52	−28 (C)	153,155
1,2,3-triazobenzoate	145	+551 (λ,6252) (C)	117
5,6-Di-O-methyl-		+3.7 (A)	117
		+4.0 (W)	156
p-bromophenylosazone	156		156
1,2-O-isopropylidene	56	−12.8 (W)	156
1,2,3-triazobenzoate	192	+13.3 (λ,6252) (A)	117
1,2,3-tri-p-nitrobenzoate	90–120	+90.0 (A)	117
2,3,4-Tri-O-methyl-		+70.5 (A)	159
N-phenylglycosylamine	145–146, 150	−103 (E)	157,320
1,6-diazobenzoate	165	−25 (λ,6438) (C)	117,126,158
methyl β-pyranoside	92–95	−22.9, −25.1 (M)	159–161
N-(p-nitrophenyl)glycosylamine	224–225	−251 (P)	233
N-(p-bromophenyl)glycosylamine	198	−146 (P)	233
2,3,5-Tri-O-methyl-		+17, −4.5 (W)	164,165
1,6-anhydro	51–52	+18.9 (A)	165
2,3,6-Tri-O-methyl-			
α-	121–123	+70 (W)	167–169
β-1,4-diacetate	67–68	−8.7 (C)	170
1,4-diazobenzoate	172	+12.6 (λ,6252) (A)	117,118,158
diethyldithioacetal	71–72	−15 (C)	171
1,4-di-p-nitrobenzoate	189–190	−33 (C)	239
methyl α-pyranoside	58–60	+149 (M)	117
methyl β-pyranoside		−48 (C)	108,172–174
2,4,6-Tri-O-methyl-			
α-	123–126	+111 ⟶ +70 (M)	152,175–178
3-O-benzyl	127–128	+54.6 (C)	177
1,3-diazobenzoate	115–120	+190 (λ,6252) (A)	117,158
methyl β-pyranoside	70–71	−27.4 (C)	108,141,180

APPENDIX II (Continued)

Compound	M.p.	$[\alpha]_D$ (solvent)	Reference
D-Glucose (Cont.)			
N-phenylglycosylamine	162–166	−113 (M)	179
2,5,6-Tri-O-methyl-		+11 (W)	181
3,4,6-Tri-O-methyl-			
α-	76–77	+91.9 ⟶ +77.4 (W)	182
β-	97–98	+41.1 ⟶ +77.5 (W)	182
α-1,2-di-azobenzoate	162–164	+342 (λ,6438)(C)	158
methyl β-pyranoside	51–52	−20, −16 (C)	155,182,183
phenylosazone	163–164		184
3,5,6-Tri-O-methyl-			
phenylosazone	70–72		110
1,2-O-(2,2,2-trichloro)ethylidene	113–114	−28 (C)	185,186
1,2-O-(2,2-dichloro)ethylidene	68		185
2,3,4,6-Tetra-O-methyl-			
α-	96	+92 ⟶ +84 (W)	159
β-azobenzoate	125–126	−36 (λ,6438)(C)	117,158
methyl α-pyranoside		+144 (A)	189,190
methyl β-pyranoside	40–42	−17.4 (E)	76,189,191
p-nitrobenzoate	102		281
N-phenylglycosylamine	137–138	+230 (A)	159
N-p-tolylglycosylamine	144	+157 ⟶ +53 (M)	188
2,3,5,6-Tetra-O-methyl-		−7.2, −11.1 (W)	196–199
methyl α-furanoside	11	+106.5 (M)	199
D-Gluconic acid			
2,6-Di-O-methyl- phenylhydrazide	127–128	+48.6 (E)	145

3,5-Di-O-methyl-			
amide	150–152	+29 (M)	273
lactone	148–150	+23 (M)	321
2,3,4-Tri-O-methyl-		+14 (? solvent) (initial)	321
lactone	157	+80 ⟶ +32 (W)	157
2,3,5-Tri-O-methyl-			
lactone	156–157	+62 (W) (initial)	164
phenylhydrazide	98–100	+32, +38 (M)	164,165
2,4,6-Tri-O-methyl-			
amide	116–117	+37 (C)	176,180
2,5,6-Tri-O-methyl-			
amide		+40 (W)	181
3,4,6-Tri-O-methyl-			
lactone		+87 ⟶ +15 (W)	183
3,5,6-Tri-O-methyl-			
lactone	44–45	+51.8 ⟶ +14.1 (W)	187
amide	144	+34.0 (W)	187
2,3,4,6-Tetra-O-methyl-			
amide	68–70	+60.4 (A)	192,193
phenylhydrazide	115	+42.1 (E)	194,195
2,3,5,6-Tetra-O-methyl-			
lactone	26–27	+63 ⟶ +41 (W)	110,192,195,200
amide	91	+39.2 (W)	192
phenylhydrazide	136		110,169,194

D-Glucuronic acid

3-O-Methyl-		+6 (W)	242
p-bromophenylosazone-p-bromo-phenylhydrazine salt	157	−104 ⟶ −14 (P)	243
4-O-Methyl-		+45, +83 (W)	244,245

APPENDIX II (Continued)

Compound	M.p.	$[\alpha]_D$ (solvent)	Reference
D-Glucuronic acid (Cont.)			
methyl α-pyranoside			
methyl ester		+128 (W)	246
amide	236	+150 (W)	246
methyl β-pyranoside			
amide	232	−50 (W)	246
2,3-Di-O-methyl-		+36, +42 (W)	17,29
methyl pyranoside			
phenylhydrazide	225–227, 195–197	+85 (C)	12,280
methyl pyranoside			
methyl ester			
4-p-nitrobenzoate	157	+69 (C)	12,280
2,5-Di-O-methyl-			
methyl α-pyranoside			
6,3-lactone	131–132	+197.5 (W)	247
		+151 (C)	142
	132–133	+179 ⟶ +134 (W) (139 days)	248
	121	+149.5 (W)	248
amide			
methyl β-pyranoside			
6,3-lactone	90–91	+2.0 (W)	142
		−2.3 (C)	142
amide	95		166
	184	+60 (W)	249
3,4-Di-O-methyl-			
methyl pyranoside			
amide	191–193	+100 (W)	250
		+58, +45 (W)	80,60
2,3,4-Tri-O-methyl-			
methyl α-pyranoside			
amide	183	+137.5 (W)	60
	188–189	+149 (W)	246

	M.p.	[α]	References
methyl ester	133, 137	+156 (M)	246
methyl β-pyranoside amide	193	−38 (W)	80,96
2,3,5-Tri-O-methyl-methyl α-furanoside		−47 (W)	60
methyl ester		+122 (W)	248
D-Glucaric acid			
2,3-Di-O-methyl-diamide	156	+28 (W)	12
6-methyl ester	101	+14 ⟶ +27.7 (W) (10 days)	12
1,4-lactone	175	+17 (W)	248
2,5-Di-O-methyl-diamide	169–170		142
1-methyl ester 6,3-lactone	164–165	+56 ⟶ +34 (W) (22 hr.)	248
3,5-Di-O-methyl-1,4-lactone		+5 ⟶ −3 (W) (4 days)	321
diamide		+19 (M)	321
2,3,4-Tri-O-methyl-6-methyl ester	107	+103 ⟶ +32 (W) (equil.)	60
		+102 ⟶ +52 (M) (equil.)	60
1,5-lactone	110	+102 (E)	227
	106, 112	+176 (B)	29,251
2,3,5-Tri-O-methyl-diamide	106–107	+146 (B)	162,163
6-methyl ester	213	+18 (W)	164
1,4-lactone	78	−9.5 ⟶ +6 (W) (102 days)	164,166,248

APPENDIX II (*Continued*)

Compound	M.p.	$[\alpha]_D$ (solvent)	Reference
D-Glucitol			
2,3-Di-O-methyl-	(n_D^{20} 1.4852)	+13 (W)	282
1,4,5,6-tetraazobenzoate	181	+104 (B)	282
2,3,4-Tri-O-methyl-	64	+8 (W)	282
1,5,6-triazobenzoate	85	+50 (B)	282
2,3,6-Tri-O-methyl-	(n_D^{20} 1.4725)	+3 (W)	282
1,4,5-Triazobenzoate	170	+30 (B)	282
2,4,6-Tri-O-methyl-	(n_D^{20} 1.4728)	+15 (W)	282
1,3,5-triazobenzoate	61	−36 (B)	282
3,4,6-Tri-O-methyl-	(n_D^{20} 1.4728)	+15 (W)	282
1,2,5-triazobenzoate	201	−86 (B)	282
2,3,4,6-Tetra-O-methyl-	(n_D^{20} 1.4593)	+11 (W)	282
1,5-diazobenzoate	159	−55 (B)	282
1,2,3,5,6-Penta-O-Methyl-	(n_D^{20} 1.4428)	−7.8 (E)	304,305
D-Mannose			
2-O-Methyl-			
α-	136–137	+7.0 ⟶ +5 (W)	201
	137	+15 ⟶ +5 (W)	324
dimethylacetal	111–112	−11.3 (W)	201
phenylhydrazone	163	−49.1 ⟶ −60.7 (P)	201
methyl α-furanoside	82	+129.5 (W)	201
3-O-Methyl-			
α-	133–134	+14 ⟶ +3(W)	324
4-O-Methyl-			
α-	127–128	+34.0 ⟶ +22.6 (W)	202
	129–130	+32.4 ⟶ +22.3 (W)	203

benzylphenylhydrazone	128–130	$+49.2 \longrightarrow +46.9$ (M)	203
phenylosazone	158	$-32.3 \longrightarrow \pm 0$ (E)	203
α-1,2,3,6-tetraacetate	157–158	$-36 \longrightarrow -14.4$ (P)	202
methyl α-pyranoside	75–76	$+59.2$ (C)	202
	101–103	$+84.9$ (W)	203
	101–102	$+83.9$ (W)	202
6-O-Methyl-		$+15.3$ (C)	204
phenylosazone	172	$-68.6 \longrightarrow -48.0$ (E)	204
2,3-Di-O-methyl-		$+6.0$ (M)	205
		$+10.6$ (E)	205
		-15.8 (W)	205
oxime	112–114		205
methyl α-pyranoside		$+43.5$ (C)	205
1,4,6-tri-p-nitrobenzoate	194	$+65$ (C)	281
3,4-Di-O-methyl-	107–109	$+3$ (W)	206
monohydrate	114	$+22 \longrightarrow +4$ (W)	207
		$+30.0$ (M)	207
	78–80	$+18 \longrightarrow +6$ (?)	324
1,2-O-isopropylidene	94	-17 (W)	207
methyl α-pyranoside	87	$+67$ (W)	207
		$+107$ (C)	207
4,6-Di-O-methyl-		$+25$ (W)	208
2,3-O-isopropylidene	76–77	$+11$ (M)	208
		$0 \longrightarrow -9.5$ (W)	208
methyl α-pyranoside		$+80.5$ (W)	208
		$+99$ (M)	208
2,3,4-Tri-O-methyl-		$+2, -5$ (W)	209,210
methyl α-pyranoside		$+47$ (W)	96
1,6-anhydro	52	-70.7 (A)	210
		-65.5 (W)	210
2,3,6-Tri-O-methyl-		$+6, -10$ (W)	211,212
N-phenylglycosylamine	127–128, 133	$-155 \longrightarrow -39$ (M)	211,212,213
1,4-di-p-nitrobenzoate	187–188	$+33$(C)	239

APPENDIX II (*Continued*)

Compound	M.p.	$[\alpha]_D$ (solvent)	Reference
D-Mannose (Cont.)			
2,4,6-Tri-O-methyl-			
α-(monohydrate)	90	$+21 \longrightarrow +14$ (W)	207
β-	104–107	$-5.7 \longrightarrow +19.0$ (W)	207
N-phenylglycosylamine	134	$-150 \longrightarrow +8$ (M)	207
3,4,6-Tri-O-methyl-			
α-	101–102, 104	$+36$ (M)	207
		$+21 \longrightarrow +8.2$ (W)	207
N-phenylglycosylamine	140–143	$+154.5 \longrightarrow -55.5$ (M)	207
2,3,4,6-Tetra-O-methyl-			
α-	49–50	$+11.5 \longrightarrow +2.5$ (W)	214
N-phenylglycosylamine	142–143	$-87.9 \longrightarrow -8.3$ (M)	79
	144–145	$-84.0 \longrightarrow -7.5$ (M)	207
methyl α-pyranoside	37–38, 38–40	$+43$ (W)	115
		$+70.5$ (M)	216
methyl β-pyranoside	36–37	-80 (W)	216
		-79 (M)	216
2,3,5,6-Tetra-O-methyl-		$+43$ (W)	217
methyl α-furanoside	24	$+99$ (W)	217
D-Mannitol			
2,3,4,6-Tetra-O-methyl-	n_D 1.4560	$+22.1$ (W)	222
		$+39.8$ (E)	222
D-Mannonic acid			
4-O-Methyl-		$+24$ (W)	218
lactone	165–166	$+163.8 \longrightarrow +94.2$ (W)	202,218

Compound	M.p.	Rotation	References
amide	171–172, 176	+11.7 (W)	202,218
phenylhydrazide	147–148	+10 (W)	202,218
6-O-Methyl-			
phenylhydrazide	178	+3.5 (W)	219
2,3-Di-O-methyl-		−31.0 (W)	78
γ-lactone	109–110	+61, +64 (W) (initial)	78,220,221
phenylhydrazide	170, 156, 158	−25 (W)	78,212,220
3,4-Di-O-methyl-		+32 (W)	206
lactone	159–160	+178 ⟶ +131 (W)	206,207
amide	141	+25.7 (W)	206,207
4,6-Di-O-methyl-		+20 ⟶ +68 (W)	208
lactone	55	+165 ⟶ +70 (W)	208
amide	119	+15 (W)	208
phenylhydrazide	151	+14 (W)	208
5,6-Di-O-methyl-			
lactone	112–114	+22.4 ⟶ +16.2 (M)	222
2,3,4-Tri-O-methyl-			
lactone monohydrate	73	+138 ⟶ +81 (W)	96,209,210
amide	143	+5 (W)	96,209
phenylhydrazide	166	−31 (W)	223
2,3,5-Tri-O-methyl-			
sodium salt		−27 (W)	224
lactone	118	+67 (W) (initial)	224
amide	162	−28 (W)	224
2,3,6-Tri-O-methyl-		−19.5 (W)	224
γ-lactone	89, 84–85	+73 (W) (initial)	78
amide		+65.5 (W) (initial)	78,213
phenylhydrazide	125, 130	−21 (W)	78,212,225
phenylhydrazide hydrate	144	−16.5 (W)	220
2,4,6-Tri-O-methyl-	133	−21 (W)	78,220
lactone	97–98	+141 ⟶ +30 (W)	207
amide	145	+7.0 (W)	207

APPENDIX II (*Continued*)

Compound	M.p.	$[\alpha]_D$ (solvent)	Reference
D-Mannonic acid (Cont.)			
3,4,6-Tri-O-methyl-			
lactone	96–97, 99–100	$+31 \longrightarrow +111$ (W)	226
amide	143	$+167.4 \longrightarrow +110$ (W)	226,227
phenylhydrazide	137–139	$+28$ (W)	207,227
2,3,4,6-Tetra-O-methyl-			
sodium salt		$+14.8, +17.5$ (W)	200,228
		$+41.6$ (W)	228
lactone	24–25	$+150 \longrightarrow +67$ (W)	200,206,229,230
phenylhydrazide	185, 186–187	-22 (C)	200,208,231
2,3,5,6-Tetra-O-methyl-			
sodium salt		$-25.3 \longrightarrow +48.2$ (W)	228
		-22.5 (W)	228
lactone	107–108	$+65.2$ (W) (initial)	213,228,232
phenylhydrazide	167		221
D-Mannuronic acid			
4-O-Methyl-			
methyl α-pyranoside methylamide	151–153	$+23$ (W)	280
2,3-O-isopropylidene		$+30$ (M)	240
2,3-Di-O-methyl-		$+36.4$ (W)	240
2,3,4-Tri-O-methyl-			
methyl α-pyranoside			
methyl ester		$+74$ (M)	241
methylamide	103–105	$+42$ (W)	280
D-Mannaric acid			
2,5-Di-O-methyl-			
diamide hemihydrate	183–185	-55.4 (W)	323

diphenylhydrazide	183–186	−57.5 (M)	323
1,4;6,3-dilactone	143	+249 ⟶ −4.4 (W)	323
2,3,4-Tri-O-methyl-diamide	228, 211	−17 (M)	209,240,280

METHYL DERIVATIVES OF ALDOBIOURONIC ACIDS

2-O-D-Glucopyranosyluronic acid-D-xylose			
methyl ester methyl α-pyranoside pentaacetate	178–180	+163 (C)	306,307
methyl ester methyl β-pyranoside pentaacetate	255–257	+103 (C)	306,307
Methyl 2-O-(2,3,4-tri-O-methyl-D-glucosyluronic acid)-3-O-methyl-D-xylopyranoside			
Methyl 2-O-(2,3,4-tri-O-methyl-D-glucosyl)-3-O-methyl-D-xylopyranoside	165–167	+79 (W)	308
2-O-(4-O-methyl-D-glucosyluronic acid)-D-xylose methyl ester methyl α-pyranoside tetraacetate	201, 202	+100, +98 (C)	332,333
Methyl 2-O-[methyl-(2,3,4-tri-O-methyl-D-galactosyl)-uronate]-3,4-di-O-methyl-L-rhamnoside	93–94	+129.8 (W)	48
Methyl 3-O-(2,3,4-tri-O-methyl-D-glucosyluronamide)-2,4-di-O-methyl-D-galactoside	194		309

APPENDIX II (Continued)

Compound	M.p.	$[\alpha]_D$ (solvent)	Reference
Methyl 3-O-(2,3,4-tri-O-methyl-D-glucosyluronamide)-2,4,6-tri-O-methyl-D-galactopyranoside	156		309
Methyl 6-O-(4-O-methyl-β-D-glucosyluronamide)-α-D-galactopyranoside	267	+25 (W)	246,310
Methyl 6-O-(2,3,4-tri-O-methyl-β-D-glucosyluronamide)-2,3,4-tri-O-methyl-α-D-galactoside	160	+40.5 (W)	310
Methyl 6-O-[methyl-(2,3,4-tri-O-methyl-β-D-glucosyl)uronate]-2,3,4-tri-O-methyl-β-D-galactoside	94	−21 (W), −43 (C)	80,311
Methyl 6-O-(2,3,4-tri-O-methyl-β-D-glucosyluronamide)-2,3,4-tri-O-methyl-β-D-galactopyranoside	196	−18 (W)	311
4-O-Methyl-(D-glucosyl)uronate-D-glucose heptaacetate	250	+41.7 (C)	313
Methyl 4-O-(2,3,4-tri-O-methyl-β-D-glucosyluronic acid)-2,3,6-tri-O-methyl-β-D-glucoside	172	−32.6 (W)	312
Methyl 4-O-[methyl-(2,3,4-tri-O-methyl-β-D-glucosyl)uronate]-2,3,6-tri-O-methyl-β-D-glucoside	113–113.5	−32.2 (W)	312

(For the methyl derivatives of D-fructose see reference 314 and for the methyl ethers of lyxose and ribose see reference 315)

REFERENCES FOR APPENDIX II

1. Oldham, Mary A., and Honeyman, J., *J. Chem. Soc.*, 986 (1946).
2. Hirst, E. L., and Jones, J. K. N., *J. Chem. Soc.*, 1221 (1947).
3. Hirst, E. L., and Jones, J. K. N., *J. Chem. Soc.*, 2311 (1948).
4. Jones, J. K. N., Kent, P. W., and Stacey, M., *J. Chem. Soc.*, 1341 (1947).
5. Hirst, E. L., Jones, J. K. N., and Williams, (Miss) E., *J. Chem. Soc.*, 1062 (1947).
6. Smith, F., *J. Chem. Soc.*, 753 (1939).
7. White, E. V., *J. Am. Chem. Soc.*, **68**, 272 (1946).
8. Hirst, E. L., and Robertson, G. J., *J. Chem. Soc.*, **127**, 358 (1925).
9. Purdie, T., and Rose, R. E., *J. Chem. Soc.*, **89**, 1204 (1906).
10. Hirst, E. L., and Jones, J. K. N., *J. Chem. Soc.*, 1865 (1939).
11. Smith, F., *J. Chem. Soc.*, 744 (1939).
12. Smith, F., *J. Chem. Soc.*, 1035 (1940).
13. Jones, J. K. N., *J. Chem. Soc.*, 1055 (1947).
14. Cunneen, J. I., and Smith, F., *J. Chem. Soc.*, 1146 (1948).
15. Cunneen, J. I., and Smith, F., *J. Chem. Soc.*, 1141 (1948).
16. Avery, J., Haworth, W. N., and Hirst, E. L., *J. Chem. Soc.*, 2308 (1927).
17. Hirst, E. L., and Jones, J. K. N., *J. Chem. Soc.*, 506 (1946).
18. Robertson, G. J., and Speedie, T. H., *J. Chem. Soc.*, 824 (1934).
19. Percival, E. G. V., and Willox, I. C., *J. Chem. Soc.*, 1608 (1949).
20. Laidlaw, R. A., and Percival, E. G. V., *J. Chem. Soc.*, 528 (1950).
21. Levene, P. A., and Raymond, A. L., *J. Biol. Chem.*, **102**, 331 (1933).
22. Wintersteiner, O., and Klingsberg, Anna, *J. Am. Chem. Soc.*, **71**, 939 (1949).
23. Robertson, G. J., and Gall, D., *J. Chem. Soc.*, 1600 (1937).
24. Percival, E. G. V., and Chanda, S. K., *Nature*, **166**, 787 (1950).
25. Hampton, H. A., Haworth, W. N., and Hirst, E. L., *J. Chem. Soc.*, 1739 (1929).
26. Chanda, S. K., Percival, Elizabeth E., and Percival, E. G. V., *J. Chem. Soc.*, 260 (1952).
27. Barker, C. C., Hirst, E. L., and Jones, J. K. N., *J. Chem. Soc.*, 783 (1946).
28. James, Sybil P., and Smith, F., *J. Chem. Soc.*, 739, 746 (1945).
29. Hirst, E. L., and Jones, J. K. N., *J. Chem. Soc.*, 1482 (1939).
30. Phelps, F. P., and Purves, C. B., *J. Am. Chem. Soc.*, **51**, 2443 (1929).
31. Carruthers, A., and Hirst, E. L., *J. Chem. Soc.*, **121**, 2299 (1922).
32. Chanda, S. K., Hirst, E. L., and Percival, E. G. V., *J. Chem. Soc.*, 1240 (1951).
33. Bywater, R. A. S., Haworth, W. N., Hirst, E. L., and Peat, S., *J. Chem. Soc.*, 1983 (1937).
34. Chanda, S. K., Hirst, E. L., Jones, J. K. N., and Percival, E. G. V., *J. Chem. Soc.*, 1289 (1950).
35. Laidlaw, R. A., and Percival, E. G. V., *J. Chem. Soc.*, 1600 (1949).
36. Haworth, W. N., Hirst, E. L., and Oliver, Elsie, *J. Chem. Soc.*, 1917 (1934).
37. Mullan, J., and Percival, E. G. V., *J. Chem. Soc.*, 1501 (1940).
38. Haworth, W. N., and Long, C. W., *J. Chem. Soc.*, 345 (1929).
39. Schmidt, O. T., Mayer, W., and Distelmaier, A., *Ann.*, **555**, 26 (1943).
40. Conchie, J., and Percival, E. G. V., *J. Chem. Soc.*, 827 (1950).
41. Percival, Elizabeth E., and Percival, E. G. V., *J. Chem. Soc.*, 690 (1950).
42. Young, F. G., Jr., and Elderfield, R. C., *J. Org. Chem.*, **7**, 241 (1942).

43. MacPhillamy, H. B., and Elderfield, R. C., *J. Org. Chem.*, **4**, 150 (1939).
44. Schmidt, O. T., Plankenhorn, E., and Kübler, F., *Ber.*, **75**, 579 (1942).
45. Levene, P. A., and Compton, J., *J. Biol. Chem.*, **114**, 9 (1936).
46. Gill, R. E., Hirst, E. L., and Jones, J. K. N., *J. Chem. Soc.*, 1025 (1946).
47. Levene, P. A., and Muskat, I. E., *J. Biol. Chem.*, **105**, 431 (1934).
48. Tipson, R. S., Christman, C. C., and Levene, P. A., *J. Biol. Chem.*, **128**, 609 (1939).
49. Tipson, R. S., and Levene, P. A., *J. Biol. Chem.*, **130**, 235 (1939).
50. Haworth, W. N., Hirst, E. L., and Miller, E. J., *J. Chem. Soc.*, 2469 (1929).
51. Gill, R. E., Hirst, E. L., and Jones, J. K. N., *J. Chem. Soc.*, 1469 (1939).
52. Avery, J., and Hirst, E. L., *J. Chem. Soc.*, 2466 (1929).
53. Beaven, G. H., Hirst, E. L., and Jones, J. K. N., *J. Chem. Soc.*, 1865 (1939).
54. Oldham, J. W. H., and Bell, D. J., *J. Am. Chem. Soc.*, **60**, 323 (1938).
55. McCreath, D., and Smith, F., *J. Chem. Soc.*, 387 (1939).
56. Buchanan, J., Percival, Elizabeth E., and Percival, E. G. V., *J. Chem. Soc.*, 51 (1943).
57. Reber, F., and Reichstein, T., *Helv. Chim. Acta*, **28**, 1164 (1945).
58. Robertson, G. J., and Lamb, R. A., *J. Chem. Soc.*, 1321 (1934).
59. Pacsu, E., and Trister, S. M., *J. Am. Chem. Soc.*, **62**, 2301 (1940).
60. Smith, F., *J. Chem. Soc.*, 1724 (1939).
61. Percival, E. G. V., and Ritchie, G. G., *J. Chem. Soc.*, 1765 (1936).
62. Baldwin, E., and Bell, D. J., *J. Chem. Soc.*, 1461 (1938).
63. Freudenberg, K., and Smeykal, K., *Ber.*, **59**, 100 (1926).
64. Bell, D. J., and Greville, G. D., *J. Chem. Soc.*, 1136 (1955).
65. Dewar, E. T., and Percival, E. G. V., *Nature*, **156**, 633 (1945).
66. Bell, D. J., *J. Chem. Soc.*, 692 (1945).
67. Bell, D. J., and Baldwin, E., *J. Chem. Soc.*, 125 (1941).
68. Bacon, J. S. D., and Bell, D. J., *J. Chem. Soc.*, 1869 (1939).
69. Bacon, J. S. D., Bell, D. J., and Lorber, J., *J. Chem. Soc.*, 1147 (1940).
70. Percival, E. G. V., and Somerville, J. C., *J. Chem. Soc.*, 1615 (1937).
71. Bell, D. J., and Williamson, S., *J. Chem. Soc.*, 1196 (1938).
72. White, E. V., *J. Am. Chem. Soc.*, **69**, 622 (1947).
73. Haworth, W. N., Hirst, E. L., and Jones, D. I., *J. Chem. Soc.*, 2428 (1927).
74. Haworth, W. N., Loach, J. V., and Long, C. W., *J. Chem. Soc.*, 3146 (1927).
75. Schlubach, H. H., and Moog, K., *Ber.*, **56**, 1957 (1923).
76. Haworth, W. N., and Leitch, Grace, C., *J. Chem. Soc.*, **113**, 188 (1918).
77. Hirst, E. L., Jones, J. K. N., and Walder, Mrs. W. O., *J. Chem. Soc.*, 1443 (1947).
78. Smith, F., *J. Am. Chem. Soc.*, **70**, 3249 (1948).
79. Irvine, J. C., and McNicoll, D., *J. Chem. Soc.*, **97**, 1449 (1910).
80. Challinor, S. W., Haworth, W. N., and Hirst, E. L., *J. Chem Soc.*, 258 (1931).
81. Bell, D. J., *J. Chem. Soc.*, 1543 (1940).
82. Percival, E. G. V., and Thomson, T. G. H., *J. Chem. Soc.*, 750 (1942).
83. Luckett, Sybil, and Smith, F., *J. Chem. Soc.*, 1106, 1114 (1940).
84. Alexander, B. H., Dimler, R. J., and Mehltretter, C. L., *J. Am. Chem. Soc.*, **73**, 4658 (1951).
85. Haworth, W. N., Hirst, E. L., and Stacey, M., *J. Chem. Soc.*, 2481 (1932).
86. Haworth, W. N., Raistrick, H., and Stacey, M., *Biochem. J.* **31**, 640 (1937).

87. Haworth, W. N., Ruell, D. A., Westgarth, G. C., *J. Chem. Soc.*, **125**, 2468 (1924).
88. Pryde, J., Hirst, E. L., and Humphreys, R. W., *J. Chem. Soc.*, **127**, 348 (1925).
89. Levene, P. A., and Kreider, L. C., *J. Biol. Chem.*, **120**, 597 (1937).
90. Morell, S., and Link, K. P., *J. Biol. Chem.*, **100**, 385 (1933).
91. Jones, J. K. N., and Stacey, M., *J. Chem. Soc.*, 1340 (1947).
92. Edington, R. A., and Percival, Elizabeth E., *J. Chem. Soc.*, 2473 (1953).
93. Luckett, Sybil, and Smith, F., *J. Chem. Soc.*, 1506 (1940).
94. Tipson, R. S., *J. Biol. Chem.*, **125**, 341 (1938).
95. Hirst, E. L., Hough, L., and Jones, J. K. N., *J. Chem. Soc.*, 3145 (1949).
96. Smith, F., Stacey, M., and Wilson, P. I., *J. Chem. Soc.*, 131 (1944).
97. Levene, P. A., Tipson, R. S., and Kreider, L. C., *J. Biol. Chem.*, **122**, 199 (1937).
98. Levene, P. A., and Kreider, L. C., *J. Biol. Chem.*, **121**, 155 (1937).
99. Beavan, G. H., and Jones, J. K. N., *J. Chem. Soc.*, 1218 (1947).
100. Karrer, P., and Peyer, J., *Helv. Chim. Acta*, **5**, 577 (1922).
101. Haworth, W. N., Hirst, E. L., and Teece, Ethel G., *J. Chem. Soc.*, 2858 (1931).
102. Oldham, J. W. H., and Rutherford, Jean K., *J. Am. Chem. Soc.*, **54**, 1086 (1932).
103. Brigl, P., and Schinle, R., *Ber.*, **63**, 2884 (1930).
104. Schinle, R., *Ber.*, **64**, 2361 (1931).
105. Hickinbottom, W. J., *J. Chem. Soc.*, 3140 (1928).
106. Lieser, T., *Ann.*, **470**, 104 (1929).
107. Brigl, P., and Schinle, R., *Ber.*, **62**, 1716 (1929).
108. Oldham, J. W. H., *J. Am. Chem. Soc.*, **56**, 1360 (1934).
109. Irvine, J. C., and Hogg, T. P., *J. Chem. Soc.*, **105**, 1386 (1914).
110. Anderson, C. G., Charlton, W., and Haworth, W. N., *J. Chem. Soc.*, 1329 (1929).
111. Loder, D. J., and Lewis, W. L., *J. Am. Chem. Soc.*, **54**, 1040 (1932).
112. Vargha, v. L., *Ber.*, **67**, 1223 (1934).
113. Irvine, J. C., and Scott, J. P., *J. Chem. Soc.*, **103**, 564 (1913).
114. Bolliger, H. R., and Prins, D. A., *Helv. Chim. Acta*, **28**, 465 (1945).
115. Heddle, W. J., and Percival, E. G. V., *J. Chem. Soc.*, 249 (1939).
116. Helferich, B., and Lang, O., *J. prakt. Chem.*, **132**, 321 (1932).
117. Freudenberg, K., and Plankenhorn, E., *Ber.*, **73**, 621 (1940).
118. Mertzweiller, J. K., Carney, D. M., and Farley, F. F., *J. Am. Chem. Soc.*, **65**, 2367 (1943).
119. Schinle, R., *Ber.*, **65**, 315 (1932).
120. Munro, J., and Percival, E. G. V., *J. Chem. Soc.*, 873 (1935).
121. Vargha, L. v., *Ber.*, **69**, 2098 (1936).
122. Percival, Elizabeth E., and Percival, E. G. V., *J. Chem. Soc.*, 1398 (1935).
123. Levene, P. A., and Raymond, A. L., *J. Biol. Chem.*, **97**, 751 (1932).
124. Ohle, H., and Vargha, v. L., *Ber.*, **62**, 2435 (1929).
125. Bell, D. J., *J. Chem. Soc.*, 859 (1936).
126. Freudenberg, K., and Hüll, G., *Ber.*, **74**, 237 (1941).
127. Helferich, B., and Himmen, E., *Ber.*, **62**, 2136 (1929).
128. Ohle, H., and Vargha, L. v., *Ber.*, **62**, 2425 (1929).
129. Helferich, B., and Günther, E., *Ber.*, **64**, 1276 (1931).

130. Irvine, J. C., and Scott, J. P., *J. Chem. Soc.*, **103**, 575 (1913).
131. McCloskey, C. M., and Coleman, G. H., *J. Org. Chem.*, **10**, 184 (1945).
132. Schlüchterer, Elsa, and Stacey, M., *J. Chem. Soc.*, 776 (1945).
133. Freudenberg, K., and Boppel, H., *Ber.*, **73**, 609 (1940).
134. Brederick, H., *Ber.*, **68**, 777 (1935).
135. Mathers, D. S., and Robertson, G. J., *J. Chem. Soc.*, 696 (1933).
136. Bell, D. J., and Manners, D. J., *J. Chem. Soc.*, 1145 (1954).
137. Van Cleve, J. W., and Schaefer, W. C., *J. Am. Chem. Soc.*, **77**, 5341 (1955).
138. Adams, M. H., Reeves, R. E., and Goebel, W. F., *J. Biol. Chem.*, **140**, 653 (1941).
139. Reeves, R. E., and Goebel, W. F., *J. Biol. Chem.*, **139**, 511 (1941).
140. Reeves, R. E., Adams, M. H., and Goebel, W. F., *J. Am. Chem. Soc.*, **62**, 2881 (1940).
141. Dewar, J., and Fort, G., *J. Chem. Soc.*, 492 (1944).
142. Reeves, R. E., *J Am. Chem. Soc.*, **62**, 1616 (1940).
143. Haworth, W. N., Owen, L. N., and Smith, F., *J. Chem. Soc.*, 88 (1941).
144. Reeves, R. E., *J. Am. Chem. Soc.*, **70**, 259 (1948).
145. Bell, D. J., and Synge, R. L. M., *J. Chem. Soc.*, 833 (1938).
146. Dewar, J., and Fort, G., *J. Chem. Soc.*, 496 (1944).
147. Dewar, J., Fort, G., and McArthur, N., *J. Chem. Soc.*, 499 (1944).
148. McDonald, Emma J., and Jackson, R. F., *J. Res. Natl. Bur. Standards*, **24**, 181 (1940).
149. Bell, D. J., *J. Chem. Soc.*, 175 (1935).
150. Bell, D. J., *J. Chem. Soc.*, 1553 (1936).
151. Percival, E. G. V., and Duff, R. B., *Nature*, **158**, 29 (1946).
152. Haworth, W. N., and Sedgwick, W. G., *J. Chem. Soc.*, 2573 (1926).
153. Bell, D. J., and Synge, R. L. M., *J. Chem. Soc.*, 1711 (1937).
154. Bell, D. J., and Lorber, J., *J. Chem. Soc.*, 453 (1940).
155. Peat, S., and Wiggins, L. F., *J. Chem. Soc.*, 1810 (1938).
156. Salmon, M. R., and Powell, G., *J. Am. Chem. Soc.*, **61**, 3507 (1939).
157. Peat, S., Schluchterer, Elsa, and Stacey, M., *J. Chem. Soc.*, 581 (1939).
158. Coleman, G. H., Rees, D. E., Sundberg, R. L., and McGloskey, C. M., *J. Am. Chem. Soc.*, **67**, 381 (1945).
159. Irvine, J. C., and Oldham, J. W. H., *J. Chem. Soc.*, **119**, 1744 (1921).
160. Haworth, W. N., and Wylam, B., *J. Chem. Soc.*, **123**, 3120 (1923).
161. Haworth, W. N., Hirst, E. L., and Ruell, D A., *J. Chem. Soc.*, **123**, 3125 (1923).
162. Robertson, A., and Waters, R. B., *J. Chem. Soc.*, 1709 (1931).
163. Charlton, W., Haworth, W. N., and Herbert, R. W., *J. Chem. Soc.*, 2855 (1931).
164. Smith, F., *J. Chem. Soc.*, 571 (1944).
165. Dimler, R. J., Doris, H. A., and Hilbert, G. E., *J. Am. Chem. Soc.*, **68**, 1377 (1946).
166. Owen, L. N., Peat, S., and Jones, W. J. G., *J. Chem. Soc.*, 339 (1941).
167. Irvine, J. C., and Hirst, E. L., *J. Chem. Soc.*, **121**, 1213 (1922).
168. Irvine, J. C., and McGlynn, R. P., *J. Am. Chem. Soc.*, **54**, 356 (1932).
169. Carrington, H. C., Haworth, W. N., and Hirst, E. L., *J. Am. Chem. Soc.*, **55**, 1084 (1933).
170. Micheel, F., and Hess, K., *Ber.*, **60**, 1898 (1927).
171. Wolfrom, M. L., and Georges, L. W., *J. Am. Chem. Soc.*, **59**, 601 (1937).

172. Oldham, J. W. H., and Rutherford, Jean K., *J. Am. Chem. Soc.*, **54**, 366 (1932).
173. Peat, S., and Wiggins, L. F., *J. Chem. Soc.*, 1088 (1938).
174. Irvine, J. C., and Black, I. M. A., *J. Chem. Soc.*, 862 (1926).
175. Richtmyer, N. K., *J. Am. Chem. Soc.*, **61**, 1831 (1939).
176. Barker, C. C., Hirst, E. L., and Jones, J. K. N., *J. Chem. Soc.*, 1695 (1938).
177. Freudenberg, K., and Plankenhorn, E., *Ann.*, **526**, 257 (1938).
178. Zechmeister, L., and Tóth, G., *Biochem. Z.*, **270**, 309 (1934).
179. Granichstadten, H., and Percival, E. G. V., *J. Chem. Soc.*, 54 (1943).
180. Lake, W. H. G., and Peat, S., *J. Chem. Soc.*, 1417 (1938).
181. Bishop, C. T., and Schmorak, J., *Can. J. Chem.*, **34**, 845 (1956).
182. Sundberg, R. L., McCloskey, C. M., Rees, D. E., and Coleman, G. H., *J. Am. Chem. Soc.*, **67**, 1080 (1945).
183. Haworth, W. N., Hirst, E. L., and Panazzon, L., *J. Chem. Soc.*, 154 (1934).
184. Crammer, M., and Cox, E. H., *Helv. Chim. Acta*, **5**, 884 (1922).
185. Coles, H. W., Goodhue, L. D., and Hixon, R. M., *J. Am. Chem. Soc.*, **51**, 519 (1929).
186. Freudenberg, W., and Vajda, A. M., *J. Am. Chem. Soc.*, **59**, 1955 (1937).
187. Haworth, W. N., Peat, S., and Whetstone, J., *J. Chem. Soc.*, 1975 (1938).
188. Irvine, J. C., and Hynd, A., *J. Chem. Soc.*, **99**, 161 (1911).
189. Purdie, T., and Irvine, J. C., *J. Chem. Soc.*, **85**, 1049 (1904).
190. Irvine, J. C., and Moodie, Agnes M., *J. Chem. Soc.*, **89**, 1578 (1906).
191. Irvine, J. C., and Cameron, A., *J. Chem. Soc.*, **87**, 900 (1905).
192. Humphreys, R. W., Pryde, J., and Waters, E. T., *J. Chem. Soc.*, 1298 (1931).
193. Irvine, J. C., and Pryde, J., *J. Chem. Soc.*, **125**, 1045 (1924).
194. Charlton, W., Haworth, W. N., and Peat, S., *J. Chem. Soc.*, 89 (1926).
195. Haworth, W. N., Hirst, E. L., and Miller, E. J., *J. Chem. Soc.*, 2436 (1927).
196. Irvine, J. C., Fyfe, A. W., and Hogg, T. P., *J. Chem. Soc.*, **107**, 524 (1915).
197. Micheel, F., and Hess, K., *Ann.*, **450**, 21 (1926).
198. Schlubach, H. H., and Bomhard, H., *Ber.*, **59**, 845 (1926).
199. Haworth, W. N., Porter, C. R., and Waine, A. C., *J. Chem. Soc.*, 2254 (1932).
200. Drew, H. A. K., Goodyear, E. H., and Haworth, W. N., *J. Chem. Soc.*, 1237 (1927).
201. Pacsu, E., and Trister, S. M., *J. Am. Chem. Soc.*, **63**, 925 (1941).
202. Haskins, W. T., Hann, R. M., and Hudson, C. S., *J. Am. Chem. Soc.*, **65**, 70 (1943).
203. Schmidt, O. T., and Muller, Hertha, *Ber.*, **76**, 344 (1943).
204. Watters, A. J., Hockett, R. C., and Hudson, C. S., *J. Am. Chem. Soc.*, **61**, 1528 (1939).
205. Robertson, G. J., *J. Chem. Soc.*, 330 (1934).
206. Haworth, W. N., Hirst, E. L., and Isherwood, F. A., *J. Chem. Soc.*, 784 (1937).
207. Haworth, W. N., Heath, R. L., and Peat, S., *J. Chem. Soc.*, 833 (1941).
208. Ault, R. G., Haworth, W. N., and Hirst, E. L., *J. Chem. Soc.*, 1012 (1935).
209. Haworth, W. N., Hirst, E. L., Isherwood, F. A., and Jones, J. K. N., *J. Chem. Soc.*, 1878 (1939).
210. Zemplen, G., Gerecs, A., and Valatin, Theodora, *Ber.*, **73**, 575 (1940).

211. Haworth, W. N., Hirst, E. L., and Plant, Millicent M. T., *J. Chem. Soc.*, 1354 (1931).
212. Hirst, E. L., and Jones, J. K. N., *J. Chem. Soc.*, 1278 (1948).
213. Haworth, W. N., Hirst, E. L., and Streight, H. R. L., *J. Chem. Soc.*, 1349 (1931).
214. Hendricks, B. C., and Rundle, R. E., *J. Am. Chem. Soc.*, **60**, 2563 (1938).
215. Irvine, J. C., and Moodie, Agnes M., *J. Chem. Soc.*, **87**, 1462 (1905).
216. Bott, H. G., Haworth, W. N., Hirst, E. L., and Tipson, R. S., *J. Chem. Soc.*, 2653 (1930).
217. Haworth, W. N., Hirst, E. L., and Webb, J. I., *J. Chem. Soc.*, 651 (1930).
218. Schmidt, O. T., Weber-Molster, Catharina, C., and Hause, Helen, *Ber.*, **76**, 339 (1943).
219. Schmidt, O. T., and Heiss, H., *Ber.*, **82**, 7 (1949).
220. Rafique, C. M., and Smith, F., *J. Am. Chem. Soc.*, **72**, 4634 (1950).
221. Goodyear, E. H., and Haworth, W. N., *J. Chem. Soc.*, 3136 (1927).
222. Irvine, J. C., and Paterson, Bina, M., *J. Chem. Soc.*, **105**, 898 (1914).
223. Jones, J. K. N., *J. Chem. Soc.*, 3292 (1950).
224. Heslop, Doreen, and Smith, F., *J. Chem. Soc.*, 574 (1944).
225. Ahmed, Z. F., and Whistler, R. L., *J. Am. Chem. Soc.*, **72**, 2524 (1950).
226. Bott, H. G., Haworth, W. N., and Hirst, E. L., *J. Chem. Soc.*, 1395 (1930).
227. Hirst, E. L., and Jones, J. K. N., *J. Chem. Soc.*, 1174 (1938).
228. Levene, P. A., and Meyer, G. M., *J. Biol. Chem.*, **60**, 167 (1924).
229. Greene, R. D., and Lewis, W. L., *J. Am. Chem. Soc.*, **50**, 2813 (1928).
230. Lewis, W. L., and Greene, R. D., *Science*, **64**, 206 (1926).
231. Haworth, W. N., and Peat, S., *J. Chem. Soc.*, 350 (1929).
232. Levene, P. A., and Meyer, G. M., *J. Biol. Chem.*, **76**, 809 (1928).
233. Van Cleve, J. W., Schaeffer, W. C., and Rist, C. E., *J. Am. Chem. Soc.*, **78**, 4435 (1956).
234. Baker, S., and Haworth, W. N., *J. Chem. Soc.*, **127**, 365 (1925).
235. Pryde, J., and Humphreys, R. W., *J. Chem. Soc.*, 559 (1927).
236. Meek, E. G., *J. Chem. Soc.*, 219 (1956).
237. Kuhn, R., and Baer, H. H., *Ber.*, **88**, 1537 (1955).
238. Butler, K., Lloyd, P. F., and Stacey, M., *J. Chem. Soc.*, 1531 (1955).
239. Rebers, P. A., and Smith, F., *J. Am. Chem. Soc.*, **76**, 6097 (1954).
240. Hirst, E. L., Jones, J. K. N., and Jones, Winifred O., *J. Chem. Soc.*, 1880 (1939).
241. Ault, R. G., Haworth, W. N., and Hirst, E. L., *J. Chem. Soc.*, 517 (1935).
242. Marsh, C. A., *J. Chem. Soc.*, 1578 (1952).
243. Levene, P. A., and Meyer, G. M., *J. Biol. Chem.*, **60**, 173 (1924).
244. Hough, L., Jones, J. K. N., and Wadman, W. H., *J. Chem. Soc.*, 796 (1952).
245. Jones, J. K. N., and Wise, L. E., *J. Chem. Soc.*, 2750 (1952).
246. Smith, F., *J. Chem. Soc.*, 2646 (1951).
247. Pryde, J., and Williams, R. T., *Biochem. J.*, **27**, 1205 (1933).
248. Smith, F., *J. Chem. Soc.*, 584 (1944).
249. White, E. V., *J. Am. Chem. Soc.*, **75**, 257, 4692 (1953).
250. Lythgoe, B., and Trippett, S., *J. Chem. Soc.*, 1983 (1950).
251. Pryde, J., and Williams, R. T., *Biochem. J.*, **27**, 1197 (1933).
252. Dewar, E. T., and Percival, E. G. V., *J. Chem. Soc.*, 1622 (1947).
253. Hough, L., and Jones, J. K. N., *J. Chem. Soc.*, 1199 (1950).
254. Jeanloz, R. W., *J. Am. Chem. Soc.*, **76**, 5684 (1954).

255. Munro, J., and Percival, E. G. V., *J. Chem. Soc.*, 640 (1936).
256. Aspinall, G. O., Jamieson, R. S. P., and Wilkinson, J. F., *J. Chem. Soc.*, 3483 (1956).
257. Jones, J. K. N., *J. Chem. Soc.*, 3141 (1949).
258. Connell, J. J., Hainsworth, Ruth, M., Hirst, E. L., and Jones, J. K. N., *J. Chem. Soc.*, 1696 (1950).
259. Haworth, W. N., Raistrick, H., and Stacey, M., *Biochem. J.*, **29**, 2668 (1935).
260. Araki, C., *J. Chem. Soc. Japan*, **58**, 1362 (1937).
261. Andrews, P., Hough, L., and Jones, J. K. N., *J. Am. Chem. Soc.*, **77**, 125 (1955).
262. Hirst, E. L., and Dunstan, Sonia, *J. Chem. Soc.*, 2332 (1953).
263. Gorrod, A. R. N., and Jones, J. K. N., *J. Chem. Soc.*, 2522 (1954).
264. Brown, F., Hough, L., and Jones, J. K. N., *J. Chem. Soc.*, 1125 (1950).
265. Hirst, E. L., and Macbeth, A. K., *J. Chem. Soc.*, 22 (1926).
266. Purdie, T., and Young, C. R., *J. Chem. Soc.*, **89**, 1194 (1906).
267. Brading, Joyce W. E., Georg-Plant, M. M. T., and Hardy, Doreen M., *J. Chem. Soc.*, 319 (1954).
268. Andrews, P., Ball, D. H., and Jones, J. K. N., *J. Chem. Soc.*, 4090 (1953).
269. Jones, J. K. N., *J. Chem. Soc.*, 1672 (1953).
270. Honeyman, J., *J. Chem. Soc.*, 990 (1946).
271. Whistler, R. L., and McGilvray, D. I., *J. Am. Chem. Soc.*, **77**, 1884 (1955).
272. Fried, J., and Walz, Doris E., *J. Am. Chem. Soc.*, **74**, 5468 (1952).
273. Huffman, G. W., Lewis, B. A., Smith, F., and Spriestersbach, D. R., *J. Am. Chem. Soc.*, **77**, 4346 (1955).
274. Ehrenthal, I., Montgomery, R., and Smith, F., *J. Am. Chem. Soc.*, **76**, 5509 (1954).
275. Hough, L., and Jones, J. K. N., *J. Chem. Soc.*, 4349 (1952).
276. Aspinall, G. O., Hirst, E. L., and Mahomed, R. S., *J. Chem. Soc.*, 1734 (1954).
277. Ehrenthal, I., Rafique, M. C., and Smith, F., *J. Am. Chem. Soc.*, **74**, 1341 (1952).
278. Laidlaw, R. A., *J. Chem. Soc.*, 2941 (1952).
279. Whistler, R. L., Bachrach, J., and Tu, C. C., *J. Am. Chem. Soc.*, **74**, 3059 (1952).
280. Edington, R. A., Hirst, E. L., and Percival, Elizabeth E., *J. Chem. Soc.*, 2281 (1955).
281. Smith, F., unpublished.
282. Boissonnas, R. A., *Helv. Chim. Acta*, **30**, 1689 (1947).
283. Lindberg, B., and Wickberg, B., *Acta Chem. Scand.*, **8**, 821 (1954).
284. Tipson, R. S., and Levene, P. A., *J. Biol. Chem.*, **129**, 575 (1939).
285. Ohle, H., and Thiel, H., *Ber.*, **66**, 525 (1933).
286. Haworth, W. N., Jackson, J., and Smith, F., *J. Chem. Soc.*, 620 (1940).
287. Percival, E. G. V., Somerville, J. C., and Forbes, I. A., *Nature*, **142**, 797 (1938).
288. Forbes, I. A., and Percival, E. G. V., *J. Chem. Soc.*, 1844 (1939).
289. O'Neill, A. N., *J. Am. Chem. Soc.*, **77**, 2837 (1955).
290. Percival, Elizabeth E., *Chemistry and Industry*, 1487 (1954).
291. Percival, E. G. V., *J. Chem. Soc.*, 783 (1945).
292. O'Neill, A. N., *J. Am. Chem. Soc.*, **77**, 6324 (1955).

293. Valentin, F., *Collection Czechoslov. Chem. Commun.*, **4**, 364 (1932).
294. Rao, P. A., and Smith, F., *J. Chem. Soc.*, 229 (1944).
295. Duff, R. B., and Percival, E. G. V., *J. Chem. Soc.*, 830 (1941).
296. Araki, C., *J. Chem. Soc. Japan*, **65**, 725 (1944).
297. Araki, C., and Arai, K., *Bull. Chem. Soc. Japan*, **29**, 339 (1956); *Chem. Abstracts*, **51**, 3465 (1957).
298. Araki, C., and Hirase, S., *Bull. Chem. Soc. Japan*, **26**, 463 (1953); *Chem. Abstracts*, **49**, 9516 (1955).
299. Hands, J., and Peat, S., *Nature*, **142**, 797 (1938).
300. Araki, C., *J. Chem. Soc. Japan*, **61**, 503 (1940).
301. Jones, W. G. M., and Peat, S., *J. Chem. Soc.*, 225 (1942).
302. Araki, C., *J. Chem. Soc. Japan*, **65**, 533, 627 (1944).
303. Hirase, S., and Araki, C., *Bull. Chem. Soc. Japan*, **27**, 105 (1954).
304. Kuhn, R., Baer, H. H., and Gauhe, Adeline, *Ber.*, **89**, 2514 (1956).
305. Levene, P. A., and Kuna, M., *J. Biol. Chem.*, **127**, 49 (1939).
306. Montgomery, R., Smith, F., and Srivastava, H. C., *J. Am. Chem. Soc.*, **78**, 2837 (1956).
307. Montgomery, R., Smith, F., and Srivastava, H. C., *J. Am. Chem. Soc.*, **78**, 6169 (1956).
308. Dutton, G. G. S., and Smith, F., *J. Am. Chem. Soc.*, **78**, 3744 (1956).
309. White, E. V., *J. Am. Chem. Soc.*, **69**, 2264 (1947).
310. Abdel-Akher, M., Smith, F., and Spriestersbach, D. R., *J. Chem. Soc.*, 3637 (1952).
311. Jackson, J., and Smith, F., *J. Chem. Soc.*, 74 (1940).
312. Hotchkiss, R. D., and Goebel, W. F., *J. Biol. Chem.*, **121**, 195 (1937).
313. Goebel, W. F., *J. Biol. Chem.*, **110**, 391 (1935).
314. Barry, C. P., and Honeyman, J., *Advances in Carbohydrate Chem.*, **7**, 53 (1952).
315. Maher, G. G., *Advances in Carbohydrate Chem.*, **10**, 257 (1955).
316. Srivastava, H. C., Goldstein, I. J., and Smith, F., *J. Am. Chem. Soc.*, **79**, 982 (1957).
317. Kenner, J., and Richards, G. N., *J. Chem. Soc.*, 2921 (1956).
318. Clingman, A. L., Nunn, J. R., and Stephen, A. M., *J. Chem. Soc.*, 197 (1957).
319. Cadotte, J. E., Dutton, G. G. S., Goldstein, I. J., Lewis, B. A., Smith, F., and Van Cleve, J. W., *J. Am. Chem. Soc.*, **79**, 691 (1957).
320. Geerdes, J. D., Lewis, B. A., and Smith, F., *J. Am. Chem. Soc.*, **79**, 4209 (1957).
321. Bishop, C. T., *Can. J. Chem.*, **35**, 61 (1957).
322. Aspinall, G. O., and Carter, Mary E., *J. Chem. Soc.*, 3744 (1956).
323. Schmidt, O. T., and Kraft, H., *Ber.*, **74**, 33 (1941).
324. Aspinall, G. O., and Zweifel, G., *J. Chem. Soc.*, 2271 (1957).
325. Araki, C., and Hirase, S., *Bull. Chem. Soc. Japan*, **29**, 770 (1956).
326. McGilvray, D. I., *J. Chem. Soc.*, 3648 (1952).
327. Hayward, L. D., and Purves, C. B., *Can. J. Chem.*, **32**, 19 (1954).
328. Honeyman, J., Private Communication.
329. Levene, P. A., and Raymond, A. L., *J. Biol. Chem.*, **97**, 763 (1932); Munro, J., and Percival, E. G. V., *J. Chem. Soc.*, 873 (1935); Bell, D. J., and Synge, R. L. M., *ibid.*, 836 (1938).

330. Gardiner, J. G., and Percival, Elizabeth E., *J. Chem. Soc.*, 1414 (1958).

331. Goldstein, I. J., Lewis, B. A., and Smith, F., unpublished.

332. Timell, T. E., *Can. J. Chem.*, **37**, 827 (1959).

333. Myhre, D. V., and Smith, F., unpublished.

334. Whistler, R. L., Linke, E. G., and Kazeniac, S., *J. Am. Chem. Soc.*, **78**, 4704 (1956).

FORMULA INDEX

SUBJECT INDEX

Individual gums and mucilages are entered under their common name, e.g., Arabic, gum, and general references to gums and mucilages as a group are included under Polysaccharides. Although there is little scientific basis for the differentiation of gum or mucilage, these terms are retained where common usage is established.

The simple carbohydrates are named according to the accepted nomenclature rules (*Chemical and Engineering News*, **31**, 1776 (1953)), the entry being made in the case of disaccharides and oligosaccharides or their derivatives under the reducing residue or its equivalent, e.g., Fucibiitol is entered as L-Fucitol, 2-*O*-α-L-fucopyranosyl-,.

Wherever possible, cross references include the most relevant page as well as the entry in question, e.g., Alfalfa, see Lucerne, 324.

A

G

N

P

T

W

X

Y

Z